FRACTIONAL HORSEPOWER
ELECTRIC MOTORS

A few of the nameplates used on fractional horsepower electric motors.

FRACTIONAL HORSEPOWER ELECTRIC MOTORS

What Kinds Are Available—What Makes Them Run and What They Will Do—How to Repair, Rewind and Reconnect Them

BY

CYRIL G. VEINOTT, B.S. IN E.E., E.E.

Manager, Induction Motor Section, Small Motor Division, Westinghouse Electric Corporation; Member, American Institute of Electrical Engineers; Licensed Professional Engineer, State of Ohio

SECOND EDITION

SECOND IMPRESSION

McGRAW-HILL BOOK COMPANY, Inc.

NEW YORK : TORONTO : LONDON

1948

FRACTIONAL HORSEPOWER ELECTRIC MOTORS

WARNING

Many of the connections and constructions described and illustrated in this book are covered by letters patent or an application for letters patent. No attempt is made in this book to indicate whether any construction or connection is patented or is common property. Servicemen, of course, can repair a patented device or apparatus that was purchased from a duly authorized seller. Manufacturers, however, are warned to check the patent situation before incorporating into their own designs any of the types of construction or connections given in this book. Publication in this book does not imply that a device or system described herein is public property available to all who care to use it. Neither the publishers nor the author will assume any responsibility for damages arising out of patent litigation or suits involving any apparatus described in this book.

THE MAPLE PRESS COMPANY, YORK, PA.

To My Wife

DOROTHY BASSETT VEINOTT

WHOSE ASSISTANCE IN THE
PREPARATION OF THIS VOLUME
HAS BEEN INVALUABLE
THIS BOOK
IS
AFFECTIONATELY DEDICATED

PREFACE TO THE SECOND EDITION

Revision of this book was undertaken in a spirit of sincere appreciation for the widespread support given to the First Edition. It was also undertaken with a humble desire to serve old readers as well as new readers. Every effort has been made to preserve the original aims and objectives outlined in the Preface to the First Edition.

This edition is more than a simple revision. Eight chapters have been rewritten almost entirely, many old figures have been remade, and many new ones have been added. For the benefit of the motor repairman, nearly all the original material has been retained, though some rearrangements to serve his convenience have been made, and much new information has been added. The application engineer seeking guidance in the selection of the proper motor for his particular job has not been overlooked. Chapter XX was written particularly for him, and much information scattered throughout the book has been rewritten or rearranged for the express purpose of helping him. The author hopes that instructors and students who use this book as a text will find this Second Edition better arranged and better edited for their purposes; the expanded Table of Contents will help them find more quickly those portions of the text which best serve their interests. No effort has been spared to bring all chapters of the book up to date in conformity with the latest standards of the American Standards Association, the National Electrical Manufacturers' Association, the American Institute of Electrical Engineers, and latest practices of the industry in general.

Chapter I now includes the new Nema definition of "horsepower," along with minor changes. To Chap. III have been added a discussion of windings with dissimilar coils, hints on stripping windings, a discussion of insulating varnishes including dipping and baking procedures, a description of an electronic winding-insulation tester. In Chap. IV, the section on two-speed pole-changing motors has been completely rewritten and enlarged, a discussion of a motor system for a hermetic refrigerator has been added, and a section has been devoted to how to rewind a split-phase motor for a different number of poles. Chapter V has been almost entirely rewritten in order to bring it up to date and to achieve a better arrangement of material; important additions are the expanded discussion of electrolytic capacitors, the article on electrically reversible hoist motors, and the discussion of regeneration. The first eight articles of Chap. VIII are entirely new; they describe the phenomenally versatile all-purpose capacitor motor now used for unit-heater service. Chapter XII has been expanded slightly to include Nema dimensional standards for stator cores, notes on rewinding and reconnecting armature windings, and instructions for refinishing commutators. Chapter XIII has been entirely rewritten and expanded in order to improve the clarity of the presentation of the elementary theory of the shaded-pole motor and to give more information on the application and performance characteristics of shaded-pole motors, particularly in the miniature sizes. Chapter XIV has been revised to include instructions for laying out the coil grouping of fractional-slot windings, and an index of polyphase stator connection diagrams has been added. Chapter XV is almost entirely new; sections covering hysteresis motors and inductor motors are now included. Chapter XVI has been rewritten to describe types of self-synchronous machines and systems found useful in wartime combat equipment, as well as in many industrial applications. Chapter XVII has been rewritten and enlarged to provide a more convenient arrangement for all users of the book; additions include discussions of electrically reversible motors, of a novel two-speed motor, and of electric-truck motors. All sections of Chap. XVIII have been rewritten, enlarged, and brought up to date. Chapter XX is entirely new in content, as previously explained. Tables in the Appendix have been revised as required, and two new ones added. A new feature of this edition is the Glossary, which gives important definitions not found elsewhere in the book.

Grateful acknowledgment for assistance by supplying material for this Second Edition is hereby made to all those companies listed in the Preface to the First Edition, and also to the following additional companies not previously listed:

Alliance Mfg. Co., Alliance, Ohio
Barber-Colman Co., Rockford, Ill.
Delco Appliance Div., General Motors Corp., Rochester, N. Y.
Delco Products Div., General Motors Corp., Dayton, Ohio
Eastern Air Devices, Brooklyn, N. Y.
Lamb Electric Co., Kent, Ohio
Oster, John, Mfg. Co., Racine, Wis.
Redmond Co., Inc., Owosso, Mich.
Smith, F. A., Mfg. Co., Rochester, N. Y.
Trane Mfg. Co., La Crosse, Wis.
Victor Electric Products Co., Cincinnati, Ohio
Warren Telechron Co., Ashland, Mass.

Grateful acknowledgment is made to the National Electrical Manufacturers' Association for supplying prepublication copies of new Nema standards. Special thanks are given to T. E. M. Carville, who has contributed an unusually large number of helpful suggestions. Also, thanks for helpful comments and suggestions in the preparation of the manuscript are gratefully given to the following associates: M. W. Bartmess, F. C. Bradshaw, L. W. Buchanan, R. M. Davis, H. E. Ellis, R. W. Esarey, P. E. Fletcher, F. H. Gerlach, R. L. Irvin, E. B. Kaercher, W. E. Pakala, L. C. Schaefer, W. C. Spear, O. M. Swain, K. Y. Tang, J. O. Walz, and S. G. Yaney.

The author owes a debt of gratitude to his wife not only for the invaluable aid she has rendered in typing and retyping this manuscript many times and in checking it with infinite care, but also for the sacrifices she has made in order that this edition might be completed.

Likewise, the author is deeply grateful to readers who have sent in constructive suggestions, or pointed out errors; it is his hope that they will continue to do so.

Cyril G. Veinott

Lima, Ohio
January, 1948

PREFACE TO THE FIRST EDITION

Practically every electrified home today makes use of one or more fractional horsepower motors. This kind of motor may be used in a washing machine, refrigerator, vacuum cleaner, clock, oil burner, hair drier, room heater, sewing machine, razor, health machine, fan, air conditioner, stoker, ironer, floor waxer, or food mixer. In industrial use, the number of useful tasks performed by fractional horsepower motors is legion. In the United States alone, the value of fractional horsepower motors sold amounts to approximately $50,000,000 annually. In response to a long-felt need for general information on the subject, this volume was written.

The aim of this book is to tell the story of fractional horsepower motors, what types and kinds are available, what makes them run, what they will do, and how to repair them when necessary. It is believed that this story is of vital interest to everyone engaged in the manufacture, use, or servicing of fractional horsepower motors, regardless of how much or how little technical training he may have had.

The book is written so that it may be read or studied consecutively from the first to the last page. It is also written so that any single chapter can be read by itself in order that the reader who is interested merely in universal motors, for example, may read Chap. XII by itself without studying eleven chapters in which he is little interested. To accomplish this second purpose, a large number of cross references are given, more than would be necessary for a reader who studies the entire volume consecutively. Technical words and phrases are defined or informally explained in those places where such an explanation appears to be the most appropriate and most easily understood. Usually attention is called to the phrase being defined or explained by the use of **boldface type**; in other places where this phrase or word is used, **boldface type** is often used again to remind the reader that the word or phrase is defined elsewhere. (The page where the definition is to be found is given in the Index.)

This book is intended for all who have a vital interest in fractional horsepower electric motors, whether it be repair, maintenance, installation, application, inspection, selling, testing, manufacture, or design

xi

of such motors.   Primarily the book was written to serve the needs and interests of practical men engaged in installation, maintenance, or repair work.   However, the descriptions of the various types of motors and the nonmathematical explanations of the theory of these various types will, it is hoped, make the work valuable as a text for classroom use and instructive to others interested in general information on the subject.

The author gratefully acknowledges the cooperation and assistance of the following companies in supplying data, photographs, and drawings:

Advance Electric Co., St. Louis, Mo.
Baldor Electric Co., St. Louis, Mo.
Black & Decker Electric Co., Kent, Ohio.
Bodine Electric Co., Chicago, Ill.
Brown-Brockmeyer Co., Dayton, Ohio.
Carrier Corporation, Syracuse, N. Y.
Century Electric Co., St. Louis, Mo.
Crocker Wheeler Co., Ampere, N. J.
Diehl Manufacturing Co., Elizabethport, N. J.
Dumore Co., Racine, Wis.
Electric Motor Corporation, Racine, Wis.
Electric Specialty Co., Stamford, Conn.
Emerson Electric Mfg. Co., St. Louis, Mo.
Fedders Mfg. Co., Buffalo, N. Y.
Fidelity Electric Co., Lancaster, Pa.
Forbes & Myers Co., Worcester, Mass.
General Electric Co., Schenectady, N. Y., also Fort Wayne, Ind.
General Radio Co., Cambridge, Mass.
Holtzer-Cabot Electric Co., Boston, Mass.
Howell Electric Motors Co., Howell, Mich.
Imperial Electric Co., Akron, Ohio.
Janette Mfg. Co., Chicago, Ill.
Kingston-Conley Electric Co., North Plainfield, N. J.
Lee Engineering & Mfg. Co., Milwaukee, Wis.
Leland Electric Co., Dayton, Ohio.
Marathon Electric Mfg. Co., Wausau, Wis.
Master Electric Co., Dayton, Ohio.
Ohio Electric Mfg. Co., Cleveland, Ohio.
Peerless Electric Co., Warren, Ohio.
Reynolds Electric Co., Chicago, Ill.
Robbins & Myers, Inc., Springfield, Ohio.
Signal Electric Mfg. Co., Menominee, Mich.
Spencer Thermostat Co., Attleboro, Mass.
Sprague Specialties Co., North Adams, Mass.
Star Electric Motor Co., Bloomfield, N. J.
Sturtevant, B. F., Co., Boston, Mass.

Wagner Electric Corp., St. Louis, Mo.
Wesche, B. A., Electric Co., Cincinnati, Ohio.
Westinghouse Electric and Manufacturing Co., East Pittsburgh, Pa.; also Lima, Ohio.

Photographs or drawings supplied by these companies are specifically acknowledged as they appear.

Grateful acknowledgment is made for suggestions and constructive criticisms offered by the following associates: Messrs. M. W. Bartmess, E. M. Carville, Ralph Ehrenfeld, H. E. Ellis, H. D. Else, R. R. Miille, C. C. Shutt, J. O. Walz, and J. C. Winslow. Thanks are rendered to Mr. A. M. Dudley for permission to use some of his connection diagrams for polyphase motors. Also, the author wishes to express his sincere appreciation to the Westinghouse Electric and Manufacturing Co. for permission to reproduce many diagrams which are not specifically acknowledged as they are of too general a nature to be identified with the name of a single manufacturer.

CYRIL G. VEINOTT

LIMA, OHIO
December, 1938

CONTENTS

GENERAL-PURPOSE MOTORS

SPECIAL-PURPOSE MOTORS

MISCELLANEOUS

LIST OF TABLES

CHAPTER I

THE STORY BEHIND THE NAMEPLATE

When it becomes necessary to install or repair any electric motor, the first thing a serviceman does, or should do, is to look for the nameplate. The nameplate contains the principal information necessary to put a motor into service: it describes the motor briefly; it contains a remarkable wealth of information written in a language of its own. To some, little of the information contained thereon is intelligible; to others, most of it is intelligible; but only to the manufacturer is all of the information significant. The message is coded; part of the code is common to the trade, and part is the invention of the particular manufacturer to aid in completely identifying the motor, when it becomes necessary to do so.

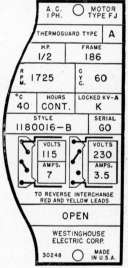

Fig. 1-1.—A motor nameplate.

If necessary to write the manufacturer for information or to order parts, the first and unalterable rule should always be: *Copy the entire nameplate reading.* It is essential to have the complete reading of the nameplate to assist the manufacturer in identifying the motor. Even if it is known positively that only a single number is complete identification, every bit of information on the nameplate should be recorded and reported; for it often happens that an error is made in recording or transmitting the important number and, if only a single number is transmitted, delays and confusion are caused.

By way of illustration, a typical nameplate, such as that pictured in Fig. 1-1, may be examined in detail to see what information it actually does contain. The remainder of this chapter is devoted to this examination.

1-1. Manufacturer.—The manufacturer's name and usually his address generally appear in a conspicuous place. The importance of

1

this item is obvious. Names and addresses of a number of leading manufacturers are given in Table I.

1-2. A.C.—A.C., of course, is the universal abbreviation for alternating current, as distinguished from direct current, or continuous current, as it is sometimes called. The letters A.C. signify that the motor is intended for use on a circuit of alternating current.

In an a-c circuit, the current repeatedly changes its direction of flow through the circuit many times every second. In any d-c circuit, the current flows in one direction continuously; while the *magnitude* of the current flowing into a d-c motor varies with the amount of the load imposed, *the direction of flow in the circuit does not change.* For this reason, the flow of direct current in a wire is usually likened to the flow of water in a pipe.

The nature of alternating current can be seen by referring to Fig. 1-2, which is a graph of instantaneous current flowing in an a-c

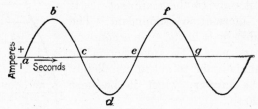

Fig. 1-2.—Current flow in an a-c circuit.

circuit, plotted against time. Points *a*, *c*, *e*, and *g* represent instants when the current is zero. From *a*, the current is seen to start at zero, increase to a maximum value at *b*, and decrease again to zero at *c*; the current then becomes negative, which signifies that it reverses its direction of flow in the circuit. Flowing in this opposite direction, the current again builds up to a maximum value at *d* and decreases to zero again at *e*; and one cycle is complete.

In other words, the current is reversing its direction of flow continually; hence the name **alternating current.** One reversal, as from *b* to *d*, is called an **alternation;** two alternations, as from *a* to *e*, make **one cycle.**

1-3. Type.—Fractional horsepower motors fall naturally into a number of different type classifications, such as **split-phase, capacitor-start, two-value capacitor, permanent-split capacitor, repulsion-induction, repulsion-start induction-run, universal, etc.** Each of these types of motors has its own particular characteristics, requiring certain parts inherent in the type; therefore, it is essential to recognize and identify these major types. One does not look for a commutator in a split-phase motor!

Manufacturers usually assign certain letters, or combinations of letters, to denote their major types. For example, on the nameplate of Fig. 1-1 the letters FJ stand for capacitor-start; it should be noted, however, that the letters FJ apply only to the motors of this one particular manufacturer. Each manufacturer has his own code or system of type-letter designations.

How to read and interpret the type-letter designations of principal manufacturers of fractional horsepower motors is shown in Table I.

1-4. "Thermoguard" Type.—Thermal protection of fractional horsepower electric motors has become much more general since 1938, although it was supplied by Westinghouse as early as 1928. In June, 1939, after conferring with electrical manufacturers making and using thermal protective devices, the Underwriters' Laboratories issued a standard for "inherent overheating protective devices"; this standard was incorporated as an appendix to the Underwriters' Standard for Industrial Control Equipment. Many motor manufacturers use thermal protection as a part of their motors and employ various ways of indicating this fact. At least four manufacturers use copyrighted trade-marks to indicate thermal protection. These are Delco Products of Dayton, Thermotron; General Electric, Thermotector; Leland, Thermomatic; Westinghouse, Thermoguard.

Delco Products use the following type-letter designations:

AD—Automatic reset, dual voltage
A—Automatic reset, single voltage
MD—Manual reset, dual voltage
M—Manual reset, single voltage
MO—Oil-burner Thermotron
CA—Automatic reset
CM—Manual reset

Westinghouse Thermoguard motors use these type-letter designations:

A—Automatic reset, approved by the Underwriters
D—Automatic reset, time-delay, approved by the Underwriters for oil-burner service
M—Manual reset, approved by the Underwriters
X—Automatic or manual reset. This letter indicates an application that was not submitted to Underwriters; it may or may not comply with Underwriters' requirements for inherent overheating protection

(*Continued on page* 15)

TABLE I.—Type-letter Designations
(**Boldface type** indicates current type-letter

Manufacturer's name and address	Alternating-current							
		Single-						
		Capacitor types				Repulsion		
	Split-phase	Capacitor-start	Permanent-split	Two-value	Adjustable varying-speed	Repulsion-	Repulsion start
Advance Electric Co. (See note 1)	....	....	....	....	....	RV	WS
Alliance Mfg. Co. Alliance, Ohio	....						
Baldor Electric Co. 4351–67 Duncan Ave. St. Louis 10, Mo.	**H, S**	**L, CI**	**C**	**CC**	**C**	....	**RB,RS,** R
Barber-Colman Co. Rockford, Ill.	....						
Black and Decker Electric Co. (See note 3)	**I,IW**	CAS	CA FCA	....	....	....	....
Bodine Electric Co. 2254 W. Ohio St., Chicago 12, Ill. (See note 4)	**NSI,** AE,SA	**NCS**	**NCI,** **KCI**	**NCS**	....	NRF	....
The Brown-Brockmeyer Co. 1000 S. Smithville Rd. Dayton 9, Ohio	**SH** (high-torq.) **SS** (gen. purp.)	CI	CC	CC	CC	**RM**	**RM**
Century Electric Co. 1806 Pine St. St. Louis 3, Mo. (See note 5)	**SP,** **SPM** SPC	**CSH,** **CSX**	C	**CPH,** **CPX**	**CPXM,** **CPHM** **CSXM**	BRS	**RS** (brush lifting)
Delco Appliance Div., General Motors Corp. Rochester, N.Y. (See note 6)	....						
Delco Products, Div. of Gen. Motors Corp. Dayton 1, Ohio (See note 7)	Note 2	Note 2	Note 2	Note 2	Note 2	....	Note 2
Diehl Mfg. Co. Finderne Plant Somerville, N.J. (See note 8)	FA,ZA, XA,GA	FT,ZT, XT	FB,ZB, XB	ZC	ZB	....	**ZIR,** **XIR,** **ZR** IR,R
Eastern Air Devices, Inc. 180 Flatbush Ave. Brooklyn 17, N.Y.	....	....	Note 2	....	....	....	....

(Numbered notes or refer

of FRACTIONAL HORSEPOWER MOTORS
designations; Roman type, inactive designations)

| | | motors | | | | A-c or d-c | | Direct current | | |
Repulsion-induction	Shaded-pole	Syn-chronous	Squirrel-cage	Wound-rotor	Un-compensated	Compensated	Governor-controlled	Shunt-wound	Compound-wound	Series-wound
WD	......	......	PC	PV						
......	A,M,K									
......	U*	CN	GM (glass-ins.) M, MM	......	......	......	......	D	D	D
......	Note 2									
......	SP	......	P	......	CS	CSC	......	S	C	
......	NSP, CA	NSY, NYC, KYC, NYP, (Note 4)	NPP, AE, SA	......	NSE,V, VCF, SM,C	......	NSEG, VCFG, CG	NSH, EB,SD	NCO, EB,SD	NSE, V,VCF, C,D, SM
......	......	......	PM	......	......	......	......	DM	DM	DM
BRC	S	YCP, YSC	SC, SCT, SCL	......	......	......	......	DM, DN	DM, DN	DM, DN
......	Note 2	......	......	......	Note 2	......	......	Note 2	......	Note 2
......	Note 2	......	Note 2	......	......	......	......	......	Note 2	
......	FS,ZS, GA	......	FP,NP, ZP,XP, GBT, GSP	ZW, FW	AU,BY, BU,BR, BZ,GL, H,R, RU	......	AU,FU, FD,BU, BR,RU	FD,ND, ZD, XD,L, G	FD,ND, ZD, XD,L, G	FD,ND, ZD, XD,L, G
......	Note 2	Note 2	Note 2							

ences will be found on pp. 12–14.)

TABLE I.—TYPE-LETTER DESIGNATIONS OF

Manufacturer's name and address	Alternating-current						
		Single-					
	Split-phase	Capacitor types				Repulsion	
		Capacitor-start	Permanent-split	Two-value	Adjustable varying-speed	Repulsion-	Repulsion start
Electric Motor Corp. 1215 State St. Racine, Wis.	. . . .	. . . .	. . . .	. . . .	. . . .	. . . .	. . . .
Electric Specialty Co. Stamford, Conn.	J,K,B	J,K,B, BL	J,K,B, BL	J,K,B, BL	. . . .	JD,KR, BR, BSR, BLR	BR, BLR, BSR
Emerson Electric Mfg. Co. 1824 Washington Ave. St. Louis 3, Mo.	S	KS	K	KK	KT	R	IR
Fidelity Electric Co. 331 N. Arch St. Lancaster, Pa.	AS,ASI	. . . .	ASC	. . . .	. . . .	RI,RIB
Forbes and Myers 172 Union St. Worcester, Mass. (See note 9)	. . . .	Note 2					
General Electric Co. Ft. Wayne, Ind. (See note 10)	KH, BKS, KS, KSA, SA	KC, RKS BKS	KCP, KC, KSC	KC, RKS, BKS	KC, RKS, BKS	. . . .	RSA
Holtzer-Cabot Electric Co. 125 Amory St. Boston, Mass. (See note 11)	RWS, RBS, CBS, CWS	RWE, RBE, CBE, CWE	RWC, RBC, CWC, CBC	RWH, RBH, CWH, CBH	RWC, RWH, RBC, RBH, CWC, CWH	RWR, RBR	RWR, RBR
Howell Electric Motors Co. Howell, Mich. (See note 12)	SP	CI	CRL	CRH	CIM	. . . .	RI

(Numbered notes or refer-

FRACTIONAL HORSEPOWER MOTORS.—(Continued)

	motors				A-c or d-c			Direct current		
phase	1, 2, 3, phase	Polyphase			Universal					
Repulsion-induction	Shaded-pole	Synchronous	Squirrel-cage	Wound-rotor	Uncompensated	Compensated	Governor-controlled	Shunt-wound	Compound-wound	Series-wound
....	Note 2	......	......	....	X,A	....	X,A	X,A	....	X,A
BR, BLR, BSR	....	J,K,B, BR (commutator type)	K,B, BL,BF, BH, BY,BP, BU	BR, BLR, BFR, BPR, BUR	JB,N	J,JS, BFR, BR, BLR	....	J,H,R, RL,L, LF,F, FB,Y, U	J,H,R, RL,L, LF,F, FB,Y, U	J,H,R, RL,L, LF
SR	F	SK (cap.-start), SN (split-phase), SP (poly-phase)	P	....	U	....	U	D	D	D
RV,RIK	......	......	AP, APB, APH	APW, APWB	SU	SCU	....	E,P, PB,EI	EC,PC, PCB	Note 2
SCA,SCR	KSP	SC, SM, SMY, SSA, SAS, SX	K, RKT, RKQ	M	P,PA, PD	PR, RSC	PG	BC, BN, SD, RSD	BC, SD, RSD	BA, PD, SDA
RWR, RBR	....	RWS, RBS, RWC, RBC	CRT, RWT, RBT, CWT, COT, CBT	CRT, RWT, RBT, CWT, COT, CBT	RWU, RBU	RWU, RBU	....	CWD, CBD, COD, CRD	CWD, CBD, COD, CRD	CWD, CBD, COD, CRD
......	......	......	SC, SCE	SR						

(ences will be found on pp. 12–14.)

TABLE I.—TYPE-LETTER DESIGNATIONS OF

Manufacturer's name and address	Alternating-current						
	Single-						
	Capacitor types					Repulsion	
	Split-phase	Capacitor-start	Permanent-split	Two-value	Adjustable varying-speed	Repulsion	Repulsion-start
Janette Mfg. Co. 556 W. Monroe St. Chicago 6, Ill.	SS	SAK, SSK, SCK	KC,KS, KA	KC	....	RS,RC	RS,RC
Kingston-Conley Electric Co. N. Plainfield, N.J.	SP (slv.-brg.) SB (ball-brg.)	KP (slv.-brg.) KB (ball-brg.)	CSR	....	....	....	....
Lamb Electric Co. (formerly the Black & Decker Electric Co.) Kent, Ohio (See note 13)	I,IW	CAS	CA,FCA	....	....		
Leland Electric Co. Dayton 1, Ohio (See note 14)	KS KT (2-speed) KS2 (2-speed)	KL KK (2-speed) KL2 (2-speed)	KV,KM	KV,K	KV, KM2, KM3, KM	....	RA,R
Marathon Electric Mfg. Co., Wausau, Wis.	SS,A, AA,N, NU	SCS	SC	SC	CF, C2F	....	SR,MR
Master Electric Co. Dayton 1, Ohio	....	CS	CL	CH	CL	RA	RA
Ohio Electric Mfg. Co. 5900 Maurice Ave. Cleveland 4, Ohio	SP	CS	CP	CSR	CP	....	....
Oster, John, Mfg. Co. 8 Main St. Racine, Wis.	ES,KS	....	EC,KC LC,PC	....	....	....	....
Redmond Co., Inc. 201–311 Monroe St. Owosso, Mich.	....					....	
Reynolds Electric Co. 2650 W. Congress St. Chicago 12, Ill. (See note 15)	SID,SIC SIB, SIA	CID, CIC, CIB	CID, CIC, CIB	CIB	CID, CIC, CIB	....	

(Numbered notes or refer-

FRACTIONAL HORSEPOWER MOTORS.—(*Continued*)

		motors			A-c or d-c			Direct current		
phase		1, 2, 3, phase	Polyphase		Universal					
types	Shaded-pole	Syn-chron-ous	Squir-rel-cage	Wound-rotor	Un-com-pen-sated	Com-pen-sated	Gover-nor-con-trolled	Shunt-wound	Com-pound-wound	Series-wound
Repul-sion-induc-tion										
....	....	KU,KA KS,KC	PA,PS PC,PD PE,PF	WPC, WPP, WPE, WPF	U	....	UG	DU, DA, DS, DC, DD, DE,DF	DU, DA, DS, DC, DD, DE,DF	DU, DA, DS, DC, DD, DE,DF
....	....	....	3P (slv.-brg.) 3B (ball-brg.)							
....	SP	....	P	....	CS	CSC	....	S	C	
RP	....	....	PA,P, P2,P3, PB, (2-speed), PC, (3-speed)	....	....	....	....	DM,D	DM,D	DM,D
....	....	....	TS,QS	....	U	....	....	DS	DP	DU
RE	....	SM	PA	SR	....	....	....	DM	DM	DM
....	SH	SN	P	....	....	....	....	D	D	D
....	....	ECY, ESY, LCY, PCY	....	....	AU,BU, CU, DU, EU	....	....	AH, BH, CH, DH, EH	AK, BK, CK, DK, EK	AU, BU, CU, DU, EU
....	T,L,U	....	....	....	F	....	....	H,D,F	....	H,D,F
....	PIB, PIC, PID, PIE	SSD, SSC, SSB	TID, TIC	....	....	....	....	SO, SP, SN	CO, CP, CN	EO,EN

ences will be found on pp. 12–.4.)

TABLE I.—TYPE-LETTER DESIGNATIONS OF

Manufacturer's name and address	Alternating-current							
	Single-							
		Capacitor types				Repulsion		
	Split-phase	Capacitor-start	Permanent-split	Two-value	Adjustable varying-speed	Repulsion	Repulsion-start
Robbins and Myers, Inc. 1345 Lagonda Ave., Springfield, Ohio (See note 16)	KS, (long-hour) KSX (short-hour) KST (torque mtr.)	KL, KLN (long-hour) KLX (short-hour)	KP KPT (torque mtr.)	KK, KKN	KPB (2-Sp.) KPV	R,RN RR, RNR, (revers.)	RA, RNA, RX, RNX
Signal Electric Mfg. Co. Menominee, Mich.	. . . .	. . . . . .					
Smith, F. A., Mfg. Co. Rochester 2, N.Y.	. . . .	. . . . . .					
Star Electric Motor Co. 200 Bloomfield Ave. Bloomfield, N.J. (See note 17)	S,SS	Q,KA	Q,K	Q,KQ, KY	KM	. . . .	. . . . .
Sturtevant, B. F., Co. Div. Westinghouse Elec. Hyde Park, Boston 36, Mass.	IS	IS	IS,ISP IMK	IS	IS,ISP, IMK		
Victor Electric Products 2950 Robertson Ave. Cincinnati 9, Ohio	. . . .	. . . . . .					
Wagner Electric Corp. 6400 Plymouth Ave. St. Louis 14, Mo. (See note 18)	RB,TB	RK,TK	RZ,TZ	RY,TY	. . . . . .	RH,TH	RA,TA
Wesche, B. A., Electric Co. 1622–28 Vine St. Cincinnati, Ohio (See note 19)	. . . . . .	NC, NBC	NC, NBC	NC, NBC	NC, NBC	. . . . . .	. . . . .
Westinghouse Electric Corp., Sm. Mtr. Div., Lima, Ohio	FH (gen.-purp.) FHT (high-torq.) CAH, CA,DA	FJ,CT	FL,CT	FT,CT	FL,CT	FV,RV, CV	FR,CR, AR

(Numbered notes or refer-

FRACTIONAL HORSEPOWER MOTORS.—(*Continued*)

	motors				A-c or d-c			Direct current		
phase	1, 2, 3, phase		Polyphase		Universal					
types										
Repulsion-induction	Shaded-pole	Synchronous	Squirrel-cage	Wound-rotor	Uncompensated	Compensated	Governor-controlled	Shunt-wound	Compound-wound	Series-wound
RK, RNK, RKR, RNKR (revers.)	K,KV	SL, SLN, SS,SK, SKN, SSK, SLD	L,LN	LV, LNV	B	B	....	D,DN, DW, DNW	D,DN, DW, DNW	BA,D, DN, DW, DNW
....	GS6, AS9, FF9B, BS5, QS5, JS3		....	CB2, GB3, BB5, GB5		....	LB3	GD6, AD9, FD9, BD5, QD5, JD3	....	CD2, GD3, BD5, GD5
....	Note 2									
R,AR, NR, ARH, **MRH**	....		N,NH, A,AH	S,AS	....	....		C,SB, SH, BS,HS	C,SB, SH, BS,HS	C,SB, SH, BS,HS
....	ISP	....	IS,ISP	....	UV	UV	....	O	O	O,UV
....	Note 2	....	....	....	Note 2	....	....	....	....	Note 2
RG,TG	RM, TM	RN,TN	RP,TP	RS,TS	....	....		RD, TD	RD, TD	RD, TD
....	....	....	N,NB	NR, NBR	....	....		H,HB	H,HB	H,HB
FU,CU, ARS	FE,CF	FBH, FBJ, FBL, FBT, FBS, CSS, (Note 20)	FS,CS, CSA	FW, CW	ADS	AD	ADS, AD	FK, SKL, CD, CDH	FK, SKL, CD	FK, FL,SF, SKL, CD

ences will be found on pp. 12–14.)

1. *Advance Electric Co.* This company discontinued business in 1939. Repair and service calls should be referred to *Acme Electric Company*, 922 North Broadway, St. Louis, Mo.

2. This type is built, but there is no specific type-letter designation for it.

3. *Black and Decker Electric Co.* The name of this company has been officially changed to *Lamb Electric Co.* (*q. v.*).

4. *Bodine Electric Co.* Latest motor is Model K; most popular is Model N. For Model N motors, the first digit of the frame number indicates the punching diameter; the second digit, the length of stack. A typical designation is NSI-54.

Other types not listed in the table are

> NLS—Reluctance-start (obsolete)
> NRF—Repulsion four-brush (obsolete)
> NRT—Repulsion three-brush (obsolete)

Synchronous-motor type letters are

> NSY—Split-phase
> NYC, KYC—Capacitor
> NYP—Three-phase

5. *Century Electric Co.*

> Type SPC has centrifugal clutch (now obsolete).
> Types CSH and CPH are high-torque motors.
> Types CSX and CPX are medium-torque motors.
> Type SCL is a torque motor.

6. *Delco Appliance.* A specialty is small permanent-magnet motors.

7. *Delco Products.* See Art. 1-4 for explanation of significance of marking of thermally protected (Thermotron) motors.

8. *Diehl Mfg. Co.*

> F, used as the first letter, indicates a subfractional rating.
> A, used as the first letter, indicates a flat-sided motor.
> N, used as the first letter, indicates a Navy motor.
> E, used as the last letter, indicates an enclosed motor.

9. *Forbes and Myers.* This company builds principally very special motors for unusual jobs.

10. *General Electric Co.* Type-letter designations are usually a part of the "Model No." Additional type-letter designations, either not listed or not fully explained in the table, are

AY, AZ, BY, KY, LY..	Motors or generators of special design
BBY..................	Permanent-magnet field motors
D.....................	Dynamotors
H....................	Synchronous converters
JA...................	Selsyn—without dampers—usually generators
JD...................	Selsyn—with dampers—special frames
JDA.................	Selsyn—with dampers—usually motors

KSA.................. Split-phase—wound rotor, squirrel-cage stator (obsolete)
KSC.................. Permanent-split capacitor—capacitor mounted on base —shaded-pole motor construction
KX................... Reactor split-phase motor
KY................... Special motor, dual-voltage
MJ................... Power-type selsyn unit
N.................... Hysteresis motors
NC.................. Hysteresis capacitor
NSP................. Shaded-pole hysteresis motor
PE.................. Tapped-series motors
PF.................. Shunted-series motors
PS.................. Split-series motors
PY.................. Special design, series motor
SC.................. Synchronous capacitor motor
SSA, SAS........... Synchronous split-phase wound rotor
SM, SMY............ Synchronous-inductor motor, slow-speed
SX................., Synchronous reactor-start motors
YA................. Induction disc and synchronous motors of similar construction

11. *Holtzer-Cabot Electric Co.* The first letter R indicates rolled-frame construction. C indicates a cast frame. The second letter indicates bearing construction:

W indicates wool-packed sleeve bearing.
B indicates ball bearings.
O indicates oil-ring sleeve bearings.

The third letter indicates the electrical type. Some older and less specific designations are

Single-phase....................... AL, ST, QS, HAS, AS, BD
Polyphase.......................... AL, QP, AT
Direct-current..................... K, QD, C, HD, AD, BD
Repulsion type of any kind.......... HRI, AR, BRI
Anything very special............... SP

A fourth letter K is added to the motor-type designation when a Klixon motor-protection thermostat is incorporated into the motor.

12. *Howell Electric Motors Co.* This company's principal products are integral-horsepower polyphase induction motors. A small number of single-phase fractional horsepower motors are made to supplement the polyphase line.

Type T denotes totally enclosed motors, any winding.

Type K denotes totally enclosed, fan-cooled motors, any winding.

Type EK denotes explosion-proof motors approved by Underwriters under Class I, Group D requirements.

13. *Lamb Electric Co.* All motors are identified by means of an instruction-sheet number. The "I. S." number is stamped on the nameplate or, when parts only are furnished, it is stamped on the armature core or on the stator core. No other information is needed to identify the unit, since the I. S. number covers only one specific mechanical and electrical design.

14. *Leland Electric Co.*   The complete identification of a motor consists of (1) motor type, (2) motor frame, and (3) motor form.   Minor modifications are covered by the *specification number,* which is unique for each rating and mechanical design.

The nameplate serial number consists of

The *specification number* of five digits.
The *date of manufacture,* coded in two letters.
The *serial number* of four or five digits.

15. *Reynolds Electric Co.*   The type letters are followed by five numerals used by the manufacturer to identify the winding.

16. *Robbins and Myers, Inc.*   Additional type-letter designations either omitted from Table I, or not wholly explained, are

SL, SLN........ Reluctance synchronous, polyphase winding
SS............. Reluctance synchronous, split-phase winding
SK, SKN, SSK.. Reluctance synchronous, capacitor-type winding
SLD............ Synchronous motor, polyphase winding, d-c excitation
KR............. Permanent-split reactance motor
KVR........... Permanent-split reactance motor, variable-speed
KSB............ Two-speed, two-winding, split-phase motor
KLB, KLNB.... Two-speed, two-winding, capacitor-start motor
RKR, RKNR... Electrically reversible repulsion-induction motor
RR, RNR....... Electrically reversible repulsion motor

"Form" designations are used to describe the basic mechanical features of the motor.

17. *Star Electric Motor Co.*   Newest design d-c motors, laminated poles, interpoles, are

BS—General-purpose motor
HS—Heavy-duty motor for hoists and cranes

Older types of d-c motors are

SB—General-purpose motor
SH—Heavy-duty motor for hoists and cranes

18. *Wagner Electric Corporation.*   R, used as the first of the two type letters denotes an open motor.   T, similarly used, denotes a totally enclosed motor.

19. *B. A. Wesche Electric Co.*   Type-letter designations appear as a prefix to the frame number.   The letter V added to any type indicates vertical mounting. The letter A added to any type designation indicates flange mounting.

20. *Westinghouse Electric Corp.*   Type-letter designations appear by themselves on the nameplate; they are not combined with any other number.   The letter F used as the first type letter indicates rolled-steel frame construction. Type-letter designations for synchronous motors are as follows:

FBH—Split-phase
FBJ—Capacitor-start
FBL—Permanent-split capacitor
FBT—Two-value capacitor
FBS—Polyphase

(*Continued from page 3*)

For a complete listing of all thermally protected motors examined and approved by the Underwriters, reference may be had to their Bulletin of Inspected Electrical Equipment which is issued annually, with bimonthly and semiannual supplements.

Nema standards were changed in June, 1946, to require that the words "thermal protection" be shown on the nameplates—or on a separate decalcomania—of motors equipped with inherent overheating protection.

1-5. H.P. (Horsepower).—Electric motors, like any other motors, are usually rated in horsepower. By definition, a motor is said to be "developing" 1 hp when it is doing work at the rate of 33,000 ft-lb per min. This figure is said to have been arrived at by determining the average rate at which London dray horses could do work over an 8-hr period. Power is the rate of doing work, and the horsepower is merely one unit for measuring it. One horsepower is also equivalent to 550 ft-lb per sec. The watt is also a unit of power, and 1 hp is equivalent to 745.7 watts. Other units of power are given in Table XXX, together with the numerical factors to be used to convert from one unit of power to another.

The horsepower figure stamped on the nameplate is the horsepower the motor is rated to develop when connected to a circuit of the voltage, frequency, and number of phases specified on the motor nameplate. Some motors will develop their rated horsepower continuously, and others are designed for use on intermittent service and are rated to develop their horsepower for only a limited period. This length of time is stamped on the nameplate in some fashion or other and signifies the time the motor will carry its rated load without exceeding the temperature rating, also stamped on the nameplate. This time may be indicated by "Cont." for continuous or by a definite time interval, such as "½ hr."

Until recently, the horsepower rating implied only the load-carrying ability of the motor, and torques were separately specified, as in Tables IV, VI, VIII, and Art. 14-2. Nema now defines the term "horsepower" primarily on the basis of the breakdown torque of the motor; this definition eliminates the separate torque specifications. Values of breakdown torque for the purpose of defining horsepower rating are given in Table II, reproduced from Nema.

1-6. R.P.M.—It hardly needs saying that R.P.M., also written rpm, stands for revolutions per minute. This figure represents the approximate speed at which the motor will run when properly connected and delivering its rated output. In the case of synchronous motors, this figure is exact.

TABLE II.—BASIS OF RATING SINGLE-PHASE MOTORS

3600 3450	3000 2850	1800 1725	1500 1425	1200 1140	900 850	Syn. rpm F-L rpm
			Breakdown torque in oz-ft			Brake hp rating
2.0–3.7	2.4–4.4	4.0–7.1	4.8–8.5	6.0–10.4	8.0–13.5	$\frac{1}{20}$
3.7–6.0	4.4–7.2	7.1–11.5	8.5–13.8	10.4–16.5	13.5–21.5	$\frac{1}{12}$
6.0–8.7	7.2–10.5	11.5–16.5	13.8–19.8	16.5–24.1	21.5–31.5	$\frac{1}{8}$
8.7–11.5	10.5–13.8	16.5–21.5	19.8–25.8	24.1–31.5	31.5–40.5	$\frac{1}{6}$
11.5–16.5	13.8–19.8	21.5–31.5	25.8–37.8	31.5–44.0	40.5–58.0	$\frac{1}{4}$
16.5–21.5	19.8–25.8	31.5–40.5	37.8–48.5	44.0–58.0	58.0–77.0	$\frac{1}{3}$
21.5–31.5	25.8–37.8	40.5–58.0	48.5–69.5	58.0–82.5	....	$\frac{1}{2}$
31.5–44.0	37.8–53.0	58.0–82.5	69.5–99	....	....	$\frac{3}{4}$
44.0–58.0	53.0–69.5	....	....	....	....	1

NOTES: Breakdown torque range includes the higher figure, down to, but not including the lower figure.

For the purpose of defining horsepower rating, the breakdown torque shall be the minimum for that particular design. For example, if a group of 1800-rpm motors of a particular design have an average torque of 7.5 oz-ft and a minimum torque for any particular motor of 6.9 oz-ft, they would be rated $\frac{1}{20}$ hp, since 6.9 falls within this band; or if another group of 1800-rpm motors having an average torque of 4.4 oz-ft and a minimum torque of 4.1 oz-ft, they would also be rated $\frac{1}{20}$ hp since 4.1 falls within this band.—Nema rule MG8-89, adopted June 11, 1946.

The full-load speed of a normal *induction* motor is determined by the frequency and **number of poles.*** Approximate speeds are given in Table III. This tabulation lists the normal rated speeds of induc-

TABLE III.—APPROXIMATE SPEEDS OF FRACTIONAL HORSEPOWER INDUCTION MOTORS

Poles	Frequency				
	25	30	40	50	60
2	1425	1725	2300	2850	3450
4	710	850	1140	1425	1725
6	....	565	765	960	1140
8	....	....	565	710	850
10	....	....	....	565	680
12	....	....	....	....	565

* For the significance of the term "number of poles," see Art. 2-15.

tion motors and, conversely, may be used to determine the number of poles for which a motor is wound.

Occasionally, two or more speeds are stamped on the nameplate. If the speeds are close together, as 1725/1425 rpm, the motor is probably a dual-frequency motor; but this point can be checked definitely by referring to the frequency stamping. Such a motor is, however, a single-speed motor. Dual-frequency stamping is more common in the case of polyphase motors than it is in the case of single-phase motors. If the two speeds are in the ratio of approximately 3:2 or 2:1, the motor is probably a **multi-speed motor.** The change in speeds may be effected by changing the number of poles in the winding, in which case definite speeds are obtained that are substantially independent of the load; or the change in speed may be effected by changing the slip of the motor, in which case the speed, particularly on the low-speed connection, depends to a large extent upon the load. Pole-changing motors are discussed in Arts. 4-29 to 4-31, and 5-29; slip-changing motors are treated in Chaps. VIII and IX.

Constant-speed shunt or compound-wound d-c motors ordinarily are rated to operate at one of the 60-cycle motor speeds in Table III, but the speed bears no relation to the number of poles. Direct-current series motors may operate at almost any speed.

Universal motors, or motors of the straight repulsion type (Art. 11-1), may operate at almost any speed independent of the number of poles or frequency.

1-7. Cycles.—As we have seen in Art. 1-2, a **cycle** consists of two reversals or two alternations. **Frequency** refers to the rate of these reversals in a given period of time. It is usually expressed in cycles per second, though the words "per second" are usually dropped. Hence, "60 cycles" actually means 60 cycles per second. At one time, frequency was commonly expressed in alternations per minute, *i.e.*, in the number of reversals per minute. Sixty cycles corresponds to 7,200 **alternations per minute.** Kilocycles and megacycles are two common terms in radio work. One kilocycle equals 1,000 cycles per second, and one megacycle equals 1,000,000 cycles per second. Standard frequencies for power circuits are 60, 50, and 25 cycles.

The number of cycles stamped on the nameplate specifies the frequency of the circuit to which the motor is intended to be connected. Frequently, polyphase motors are stamped "50/60 cycles" to signify that they will operate on a circuit of either frequency or on a circuit of any intermediate frequency, *i.e.*, between 50 cycles (per second) and 60 cycles (per second).

1-8. Frame Sizes.—It is customary for each manufacturer to adopt a system of **frame numbers,** each one of which indicates—to him at least—a certain definite physical size of motor and fixed mounting dimensions. In integral horsepower sizes, Nema has developed a standard system of frame numbering and standardized dimensions for these frame sizes, but no standard frame designations for fractional horsepower motors are yet, at this writing, in effect. Consequently, each manufacturer has his own standard dimensions and uses his own system of nomenclature.

Some manufacturers add the motor type letters as a prefix to the frame designation. Others use letters as prefixes or suffixes to indicate certain features about the motor. For example, on the Westinghouse nameplate shown, there is no prefix to the frame number, but the following prefixes are commonly used when applicable:

B—Motor ½ in. longer than standard for plain frame (*i.e.*, the B-145 frame is
    ½ in. longer than the 145 frame)
D—Motor 1 in. longer than standard for plain frame
F—Motor 1½ in. longer than standard for plain frame
X—Special mechanical construction

Increases in length indicated by the prefix refer only to the over-all length of the motor and not to the mounting feet. An F-186 frame motor, for example, is interchangeable with a 186-frame motor so far as mounting dimensions are concerned.

In general, the frame number is of little significance to the serviceman, *unless he wishes to write the manufacturer about the motor* or unless he happens to have dimension leaflets listing that particular frame size and type.

1-9. Volts.—The **volt** is the unit of electrical pressure. Just as hydraulic pressure is necessary in order to force water or any other fluid through pipes, so is it necessary to have electrical pressure to drive current through a circuit, and this electrical pressure is measured in terms of volts. A corresponding unit of water pressure would be *pounds per square inch.*

The voltage figure given on the motor nameplate refers to the voltage of the supply circuit to which the motor should be connected.

Sometimes two voltage figures are given, as "115/230." In this case, the motor is intended for use on either a 115- or 230-volt circuit, and special instructions are furnished as to how to connect the motor for each of the different voltages. These instructions are indelibly etched on the nameplate of Fig. 1-1. Often this is not the case, and the correct connections must be found elsewhere—perhaps on an instruction tag or perhaps on a second nameplate located elsewhere on the motor. *The proper connection must always be used.*

Standard voltage ratings were changed in 1941. According to Nema they now are

115 and 230 volts for universal and all other single-phase motors
110 and 220 volts for polyphase general-purpose motors (also 208 volts for 60-cycle circuits only)
32, 115, and 230 volts for d-c motors

The discussion in Arts. 1-2 and 1-10 as to the nature of an alternating current applies equally well to an a-c voltage. Thus, the relationship between **effective volts** and **peak volts** is the same as the relationship between effective amperes and peak amperes, which is explained in Art. 1-10. In practice, unless otherwise specified, "115 volts" means "115 volts effective."

1-10. Amperes.—The **ampere** is the unit of measurement of rate of current flow. The unit of quantity of electricity is the **coulomb,** which corresponds to *gallons*. The rate of flow of water could be expressed in *gallons per second*, and the rate of flow of electric current could be expressed in coulombs per second. Instead, the shorter term ampere is applied. (One d-c ampere is actually 1 coulomb per second.)

The amperes figure given on the motor nameplate represents the approximate current drawn by the motor when developing rated horsepower on a circuit of the voltage and frequency specified on the nameplate. (Approximate values of the full-load currents of various ratings of induction motors are given in Tables XXVI and XXVII.) In Fig. 1-1 the motor is a dual-voltage motor, and two figures of amperes are given, 7.0 and 3.5; the larger figure corresponds to the lower of the two voltages and the smaller figure to the higher voltage, as clearly shown on the nameplate itself. On **adjustable varyingspeed** fan motors (Chap. VIII), it is customary to give only the current at the top speed. Dual-frequency, 50/60-cycle motors usually have two stampings of full-load amperes; the 50-cycle current is approximately 10 to 15 per cent higher than the 60-cycle current.

The nature of alternating current was shown in Art. 1-2 and illustrated in Fig. 1-2. (Figure 1-2 describes the pulsating nature of an *a-c voltage* equally well.) In a d-c circuit, the current is flowing continuously in one direction and, expressed in amperes, is the total rate of flow of electricity in coulombs per second. In an a-c circuit, the direction of current flow periodically reverses many times per second, so that the total flow, as measured in coulombs per second, is zero. In direct current, the ampere is easy to define: it is simply a current flow of 1 coulomb per second. What is an a-c ampere? *The a-c ampere is defined as that amount of alternating current which will produce the same heating effect in an ohmic resistance that one ampere of direct current would produce if it were flowing through the same ohmic resistance.* Since the heating effect is proportional to the square of the current, the **effective value** of an alternating current is the square root of the average (mean value) of the squares of the instantaneous currents, these instantaneous currents being taken at a large number of uniform time intervals throughout 1 cycle. Often the effective value is referred to as the **root-mean-square** value, because of the manner in which it is found. The **maximum** or **peak** value is the current at the instant *b*, *d*, or *f* in Fig. 1-2. If the wave is a sine wave, as is usually the case, the following relationship holds:

Effective value = rms value = 0.7071 × (maximum or peak value)

In practice, the a-c ampere is always taken as the effective or rms value, or the equivalent value of d-c current necessary to produce the same heating effect. One a-c volt impressed across a noninductive resistance of 1 ohm will produce a current of 1 a-c amp.

1-11. Phases.—In the upper left-hand corner of the nameplate of Fig. 1-1 is found the inscription "1PH." Alternating-current

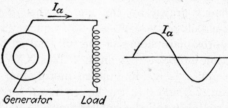

Fig. 1-3.—A simple, single-phase, a-c system.

systems may have one, two, three, or any number of phases. Single-phase and three-phase systems are the most common.

a. Single-phase Systems.—The single-phase system is the simplest form of a-c system. A typical system is shown in Fig. 1-3. The single-phase system corresponds to a simple d-c system and might be said to be its a-c counterpart. Residences, and most other places where fractional horsepower motors are used, usually are wired only for single-phase alternating current. For this reason, nearly all fractional horsepower a-c motors are designed for operation on a single-phase system.

b. Two-phase Systems.—A two-phase system is shown in Fig. 1-4. It can be thought of as two electrically distinct single-phase systems, as illustrated. There, the two a-c generators are shown mechanically coupled, and the loads are electrically distinct, one from another. The currents in both phases alternate through their respective cycles, as shown in Fig. 1-4b, but they do not reverse simultaneously. The current in phase B reaches its maximum value one-quarter cycle behind the current in phase A; in fact, the current in phase B always reaches any particular point in its own cycle 90 deg or one-quarter cycle behind the time when the current in phase A reaches the same

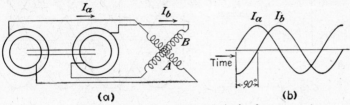

(a)   (b)

FIG. 1-4.—A two-phase system with two single-phase generators.

point in its cycle; hence the two-phase system is sometimes designated as a **quarter-phase** system.

Actually, however, only a single a-c generator is used, instead of the two shown in Fig. 1-4. This single machine has two electrically distinct windings, or phases, which are displaced 90 electrical degrees in space so that the voltages induced in them are 90 deg out of time phase. There are two common two-phase systems in use, *viz.*, the

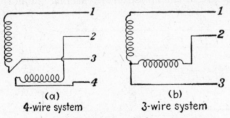

(a)   (b)
4-wire system   3-wire system

FIG. 1-5.—Practical two-phase systems.

four-wire and the three-wire, shown in Fig. 1-5. The three-wire system is the same as the four-wire system except that lines 3 and 4 are combined into a single line. With the three-wire system, the phases are no longer electrically distinct, but a voltage of 1.414 × phase voltage exists between lines 1 and 2. ("Phase voltage" is the voltage between lines 1 and 3 or between lines 2 and 3; these two voltages are equal in a balanced system.) Also, if a balanced two-phase load is being supplied, the current in line 3 is 41.4 per cent greater than the current in either line 1 or line 2.   Currents in lines 1 and 2 are equal for balanced loads.

c. Three-phase Systems.—For simplicity's sake, it may be well to think of a three-phase system as three electrically distinct single-phase systems with three distinct sources of voltage, and two wires for each

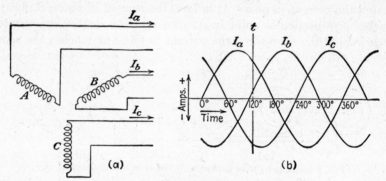

(a)   (b)

Fig. 1-6.—A three-phase six-wire system.

phase, making six wires in all, as shown in Fig. 1-6*a*.   In this figure, each source of voltage is represented by a single coil as *A*, *B*, and *C*. This system is arranged so that the currents in the respective three phases reach their maximum value in time at three different instants, differing by $\frac{1}{3}$ cycle, *i.e.*, by 120 deg, as shown in Fig. 1-6*b*.   In practice, however, the three phases are not usually electrically distinct as they generally are in the two-phase systems.   The reason, of course,

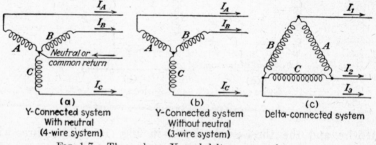

(a)   (b)   (c)
Y-Connected system   Y-Connected system   Delta-connected system
With neutral   Without neutral
(4-wire system)   (3-wire system)

Fig. 1-7.—Three-phase, Y- and delta-connected systems.

is the unnecessary complication and expense of using six wires, and resort is had to other systems described in the following paragraphs.

Figure 1-7*a* represents the system shown in Fig. 1-6, except that a common return wire has been used for all three phases.   (The three phases are now no longer electrically distinct, for they are using a common return wire.)   This type of system is often used in practice. Sometimes the common return, or neutral, is grounded; sometimes the earth itself is made to act as the common return circuit. If the load is balanced, the current in this return wire is zero at all instants; and since the wire carries no current, it can be omitted, as shown in Fig. 1-7b. The reader may check this point by drawing any vertical line, as *t*, in Fig. 1-6b, and adding up the instantaneous values of the three currents; he will find that the sum of the three currents is zero. In like manner, if the line *t* is drawn at any other point, it will also be found that the sum of the three currents is zero. Therefore, the fourth wire is unnecessary in a balanced three-phase system and often is omitted. Both of these connections are **Y-connections,** also called **wye connections** or **star connections.** The line-to-line voltage = $\sqrt{3}$ × line-to-neutral voltage, and line-to-neutral voltage = 0.577 × line-to-line voltage. Windings of three-phase fractional horsepower induction motors are usually star-connected.

Another form of connection is the **delta connection,** shown in Fig. 1-7c. This connection undoubtedly derives its name from its similarity of appearance to the Greek capital delta. With this connection and a balanced three-phase load, the line currents are all equal to $\sqrt{3}$ × the current in the individual phases or coils.

All connections and systems described on the preceding pages are applicable to motors as well as to generators.

1-12. °C—Rated Rise.—A figure of 40°C stamped on the nameplate means that the manufacturer guarantees that the temperature rise of the motor at rated load will not exceed 40°C, if the following conditions obtain:

1. The motor is connected to a circuit of the specified voltage and frequency (no tolerance allowed).

2. The motor load is not more than the specified horsepower rating.

3. There is no obstruction to a free flow of air to and from the motor.

4. The motor is not exposed to unusual conditions, as outlined in Art. 20-6.

5. The temperature rise is measured by *thermometer* on the hottest accessible part of the winding.

6. The altitude does not exceed 1,000 meters (3,300 ft).

7. The ambient temperature is not more than 40°C.

Open general-purpose motors generally are rated at 40°C rise, though sometimes at 50°C rise. Enclosed motors usually are rated at 55°C rise. Enclosed fan duty motors may have the words "air over" on the nameplate following °C, if the motor must be in the air stream to meet its temperature rating.

1-13. Hours.—The term "Cont. Hours" is used to indicate that the motor will develop continuously the rated horsepower at the rated voltage and frequency without exceeding the rated rise stamped on the nameplate.

1-14. Locked Kva.—The addition of a code letter indicating the locked-rotor kva to the motor nameplate is required in the 1940 National Electrical Code, a standard of the National Board of Fire Underwriters for Electric Wiring and Apparatus. This code letter is required to be marked on the nameplate of all a-c motors rated $\frac{1}{2}$ hp or larger, except polyphase wound-rotor motors. In June, 1946, Nema standards were changed to require this code letter for motors rated $\frac{1}{20}$ hp and larger. This code letter is to be used for determining the branch-circuit overcurrent protection as provided in the National Electrical Code. These code letters indicate locked-rotor kva per horsepower in accordance with the following table taken from the Code:

A	0 –3.14	J	7.1– 7.99
B	3.15–3.54	K	8 – 8.99
C	3.55–3.99	L	9 – 9.99
D	4 –4.49	M	10 –11.19
E	4.5 –4.99	N	11.2–12.49
F	5 –5 59	P	12.5–13.99
G	5.6 –6.29	R	14 –and up
H	6.3 –7.09		

Approximate locked-rotor amperes can, therefore, be computed from the above table for any motor when the horsepower, voltage, number of phases, and code-letter marking are known. For the reader's convenience, the author has computed a table from which the locked-rotor current limits corresponding to the code letters in the accompanying table can be read directly for standard ratings of fractional horsepower motors. (See Table XXIX, Locked-rotor Amperes from Code-letter Markings.) For example, code letter K appears on the nameplate of Fig. 1-1 which applies to a $\frac{1}{2}$-hp 115-volt single-phase motor; Table XXIX shows that the locked-rotor current is from 34.78 to 39.13 amp.

1-15. Style.—The style number shown on the nameplate of Fig. 1-1 is a special designation used by Westinghouse to identify this particular design. It is of no particular significance to the repairman but does enable the manufacturer to identify the motor. If the number is followed by a subletter, such as A or B, this letter must always be given. With other manufacturers, the style number may have an entirely different meaning.   Style numbers for Master Motors, for example, indicate the mechanical construction; these are not stamped on the nameplate, however.

1-16. Serial.—The serial number appearing on a motor nameplate may be an actual serial number used on only one motor manufactured by that company; it may indicate the serial number of a motor built on a particular order for some customer; or it may be coded with numbers or letters to indicate merely the date of manufacture; or it may have a deeper significance.   Holtzer-Cabot report that they file all test records by motor serial number.   (For Leland motors, see Note 14, Table I.)

1-17. Open.—The word "open" appearing on the motor nameplate refers to the housing of the motor; *i.e.*, there are openings in the motor housing which permit free passage of cooling air through the motor.   An internal fan is usually employed to induce this circulation. A **totally enclosed** machine is enclosed so as to prevent any flow of air through the motor, though the latter is not airtight.

1-18. Other Information on the Nameplate.—Sometimes it is necessary to use auxiliary apparatus with a motor; in this case, the nameplate usually so indicates.   For example, it may be stamped "use capacitor number ———" or "use controller number ———"; and some distinguishing style number or model number is given to refer to the capacitor or controller which is to be used with this motor. Even if the capacitor is mounted on the motor, its distinguishing number may be carried on the motor nameplate; a reason for this is that, in the service shop, the capacitors may get separated from their respective motors and it may be difficult to determine just which capacitor is the proper one to be reassembled on the motor.   Since about 1940, General Electric has made a practice of stamping the instruction tag number, a GEJ-number, on the nameplate whenever practicable.

1-19. Fan-duty Motor.—Sometimes the words "Fan Duty Motor" appear on the nameplate.   This term usually signifies that the motor is designed to have sufficient thrust capacity to withstand the thrust of any normal propeller-type fan that might be mounted directly on the motor shaft.   Such a motor is often rated on the basis of air being drawn over the motor, and many of them are enclosed because of the hazard of getting dirt inside the motor if the motor is in the air stream.   As mentioned in Art. 1-12, if the motor rating is based on air over the motor, the words "air over" may appear on the nameplate following the temperature rating.

1-20. Service Factor.—Sometimes a service factor appears on a motor nameplate. **Service factor** is defined by the American Standards Association as follows:

The service factor of an electric machine is a multiplier which, applied to the rated output, indicates a permissible loading which may be carried continuously under the conditions specified for that service factor.

—ASA C42—1941.   10.50.080.

In other words, the service factor specifies the amount of overload that can be safely carried by the motor under favorable conditions. Unless marked on the nameplate, service factors should be obtained from the motor manufacturer. They may range as high as 1.4 for motors up to $\frac{1}{8}$ hp, 1.35 for motors from $\frac{1}{6}$ to $\frac{1}{3}$ hp, and 1.25 for larger fractional horsepower motors.

1-21. What Is a Fractional Horsepower Motor?

A **fractional horsepower motor** is a motor built in a frame smaller than that having a continuous rating of 1 hp, open type, at 1700 to 1800 rpm.

—ASA C42—1941.   10.10.240.

This does not mean that the horsepower rating is less than one, for a 1-hp 3450-rpm 60-cycle motor is a *fractional* rating, and $\frac{3}{4}$ hp 1140 rpm is an *integral* rating. Following are the maximum horsepower ratings of 60-cycle motors of any given speed which are recognized generally as fractional horsepower ratings:

Rpm	Open motors	Enclosed motors
3450	1	$\frac{3}{4}$
1725	$\frac{3}{4}$	$\frac{1}{2}$
1140	$\frac{1}{2}$	$\frac{1}{3}$
850	$\frac{1}{3}$	$\frac{1}{4}$

Enclosed fan-duty motors operated in the air stream usually are built on the same frames as open motors.

Ratings smaller than these are, of course, fractional ratings. For a list of standard horsepower and speed ratings, see Table XXIII. Nema refers to fractional horsepower motors as "small power motors."

CHAPTER II

WHAT MAKES AN INDUCTION MOTOR RUN?

Of all the various types of a-c motors, the induction-type motor is the most popular, whether for use on single-phase or on polyphase circuits. This statement is equally true for fractional horsepower motors, the majority of which are operated on single-phase circuits. The enormous popularity of the induction motor is principally because it is simple in construction, it is rugged and reliable, and it has constant-speed characteristics; *i.e.*, the speed is substantially independent of the load within the normal working range. Constant-speed motors are required for the majority of applications. The polyphase induction motor is the essence of simplicity. Current is conducted into the **primary** windings (usually on the stator) but *induced* in the **secondary** windings (usually on the rotor) by electromagnetic action; hence the name **induction motor.** The secondary windings are short-circuited upon themselves, either directly or through an external resistance, and are not connected to the power supply.

2-1. Single-phase and Polyphase Motors.—Because the secondary current is entirely an induced current, the secondary winding usually is put on the rotating member; for, with this arrangement, no brushes, collector rings, or commutator is required. In the **squirrel-cage** form of construction of secondary windings, the "winding" consists of individual copper conductors placed in the slots (brass or aluminum is sometimes used), one in each slot. These conductors are all mutually short-circuited at each end of the rotor by **end rings,** or **resistance rings** (see Fig. 5-2*g*). This type of rotor is known as a squirrel-cage rotor because of the resemblance of the current-carrying conductors and end rings to the cylindrical cages originally made to exercise pet squirrels.

The squirrel cage is by far the most popular but not the only form of secondary winding used in induction motors. Polyphase induction motors may have a secondary winding generally resembling the primary winding, in which case, collector rings and brushes are necessary. Such motors are known as **wound-rotor induction motors** and may be used, with external resistors, for applications requiring adjustable varying-speed motors. Single-phase repulsion-start induc-

27

tion motors use a secondary winding that is similar to the armature winding of a d-c motor.

Single-phase induction motors have no inherent locked-rotor torque and must be started by other means. There are a number of different methods employed for starting single-phase induction motors, giving rise to a number of different types of motors, each type being named after the starting method.

Full and complete treatment of the theory of polyphase and single-phase induction motors would fill a book in itself. However, for those who wish a short explanation of the basic principles of induction motors, a brief discussion is given here. It is believed that this short explanation will help the reader to understand and remember some of the simpler facts about induction motors such as why they run at all; why collector rings and brushes are seldom necessary; why polyphase motors are inherently self-starting whereas single-phase motors require some special starting arrangement. To the serviceman, such an understanding of the principles of what actually makes the motor run is of almost invaluable assistance in diagnosing and remedying faults in motors given him to repair. To the student, it may well serve as an introduction to the study of fractional horsepower motors, a study that may be pursued further in the references given at the end of this chapter.

In the fractional horsepower sizes, as previously mentioned, the single-phase induction motor is far more commonly used than the polyphase induction motor. However, the principle of the operation of the polyphase induction motor is a little easier to grasp, and this understanding materially helps in understanding single-phase induction motors. Therefore, we shall be concerned first with the polyphase induction motor.

2-2. Rotation of a Copper Disc Produced by a Rotating Magnet. The basic principle of induction-motor action is illustrated by the horseshoe magnet and the copper disc shown in Fig. 2-1. Here the magnet is being rotated by hand, causing the disc to rotate likewise, though at a slower speed. This disc follows the magnet, not because of any magnetic attraction between the two, for the former is of copper, a nonmagnetic material, but because of the action which is due to the eddy currents induced in the disc and to their reaction against the revolving magnetic field. As the magnet and its lines of force are caused to revolve, the lines of force cut the disc, which is a metallic conductor of low resistance. Eddy currents are, therefore, induced in the disc. The flow of these currents is in such a direction as to tend to oppose the motion of the magnetic field, *i.e.*, to try to stop the magnet from rotating. (It is a fundamental principle of electricity and magnetism that the current flow in an electric circuit induced by a change of magnetic flux linking the circuit is always in a direction tending to oppose the change of flux.) The result is a retarding drag on the magnet; but, since action is always equal to reaction, there is an equal and opposite force exerted on the disc, which, if free to turn, will revolve.

The disc can never rotate as fast as the magnet (assuming that the magnet is being rotated at a uniform speed). For, if the disc

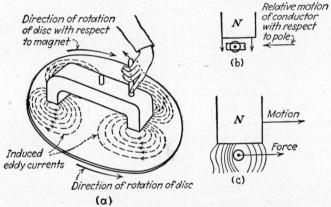

Fig. 2-1.—Rotation of a copper disc produced by the rotation of a permanent magnet. (*Courtesy of Dawes, Elec. Eng., vol. 2.*)

were to rotate at the same speed as the magnet, there would be no cutting of lines of force by the conductor; hence no voltage induced; hence no current set up to produce torque. If no torque were produced, the disc would slow down until sufficient current were induced to develop enough torque to rotate the disc. Therefore, the disc must rotate more slowly than the magnet.

Here is illustrated the principle of the induction motor. In induction motors, a rotating field is set up by the stator, and the rotor can never revolve as fast as this field. The difference between the speed of the rotating magnetic field and the speed of the disc, or the rotor, is called the **slip.** The speed of the rotating field is known as the **synchronous speed.**

But the device shown in Fig. 2-1 does not resemble a commercial induction motor very closely in actual appearance. That it does represent the *principle* is developed in the following paragraphs.

2-3. Rotation of a Squirrel-cage Rotor Produced by a Rotating Field Magnet.—A d-c motor has a field structure generally resembling the one shown in Fig. 2-2. Here the pole pieces and the yoke are shown as a single piece, and only the cross section of the field coils is shown. The rotating member is an ordinary cage rotor. A squirrel-cage rotor, as previously discussed in part, consists of steel punchings to carry the magnetic flux and to support the individual rotor conductors, which are perpendicular, or approximately perpendicular, to the plane of the paper; all of these conductors are mutually short-circuited at each end by means of a resistance ring.

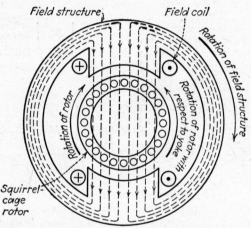

F<small>IG</small>. 2-2.—Rotation of a squirrel-cage rotor produced by a rotating field magnet.

Suppose that the field coils were excited with direct current. Flux lines would be set up as shown by the dotted lines. Assume now that the field structure is arranged so that it can be rotated (collector rings, of course, would be necessary to introduce the direct current into the field coils) and that it is revolved mechanically. This rotation of the magnetic field structure causes the flux to revolve with it. As this flux revolves, it will tend to make the rotor follow its rotation for the same reasons that the magnet of Fig. 2-1 makes the metal disc follow it. To repeat, flux lines that emanate from the field structure are caused to revolve around the rotor by the mechanical rotation of the field structure, thereby cutting the conductors in the squirrel-cage rotor and inducing currents in them. These induced currents react with the revolving magnetic field, tending to make the squirrel-cage rotor follow this field, but at a speed slightly less than that of the field structure.

The structure shown in Fig. 2-2 is a rather hypothetical motor, and it is doubtful if any practical motors were ever built like this, although electric clutches have been made embodying the principle. It does, however, resemble an induction motor in appearance more than does the structure of Fig. 2-1. The rotor is of the familiar squirrel-cage construction actually used in induction motors; the stator member, however, differs from the primary member of an induction motor in two respects: (1) The primary field structure revolves mechanically, whereas the stator structure of an induction motor is stationary. (2) The stator windings of an induction motor are energized with alternating current instead of with direct current.

It will be the purpose of the subsequent paragraphs to show that the alternating currents flowing in the windings of the stationary member of a two-phase induction motor actually do set up a rotating field which has the same effect on the rotor that the revolving field magnet shown in Fig. 2-2 has on its rotor.

PRODUCTION OF A ROTATING FIELD IN A TWO-PHASE STATOR

2-4. A Simple-Two-phase Motor and Generator System.—It is rather interesting and curious to note that, though the polyphase

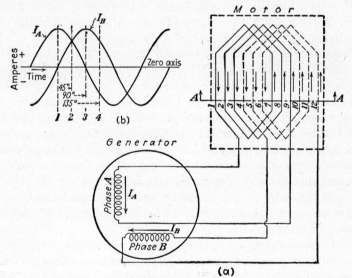

Fig. 2-3.—A two-phase motor and generator system.

motor (in fractional horsepower sizes) is used less than the single-phase motor, it is being discussed first because it is the simpler to understand. It is further curious to note that the two-phase motor is simpler to explain than the three-phase motor. For these reasons the two-phase motor has been chosen for purposes of illustration, and not because it is more important commercially. It was selected for explanation for the further reason that a discussion of the single-phase motor follows more directly from it than from a discussion of the three-phase motor.

A two-phase generator and motor are represented in Fig. 2-3a. Here the generator is shown diagrammatically as having two electrically distinct circuits or phases, designated as phase A and phase B. These phases are electrically distinct circuits, and in them are generated voltages which are equal in magnitude and 90 deg out of phase. If a balanced two-phase load is connected to the generator, the currents in the two phases will be balanced also; these are represented in Fig. 2-3b. Here the instantaneous values of currents I_A and I_B are shown. In both the generator and motor diagrams of Fig. 2-3a, arrows are shown to indicate the directions of the currents I_A and I_B. These directions of current correspond to positive values of current, i.e., to values of current indicated above the zero axis in Fig. 2-3b. Negative currents in Fig. 2-3b, i.e., currents represented below the zero axis, flow in a direction opposite to the arrows shown in Fig. 2-3a.

2-5. Windings of a Two-phase Motor.—The motor winding represented in Fig. 2-3 is a simple type of single-layer diamond-coil winding. In this figure, the motor is represented as though the stator had been rolled out flat. The windings in the circuit of phase A, including the active conductors (that portion of the conductors embedded in the stator iron) and end windings, are shown with a solid black line. The windings comprising the circuit of phase B are shown in dotted lines. The directions of the currents through the active conductors are represented by arrows drawn parallel to the latter. As in the case of the generator, these arrows represent the positive directions of current, i.e., the actual direction of current flow at instants when the latter is positive in Fig. 2-3b; at the instants when the current is negative, the actual direction of current flow in the active conductors is opposite to that shown by the arrows.

Now, assume the motor to be rolled back into its normal cylindrical form. Further, assume an imaginary plane parallel to the punchings (i.e., perpendicular to the shaft) as shown at A-A in Fig. 2-3a. Four cross-sectional views of the motor taken at this plane are given in Fig. 2-4.

2-6. How the Rotating Field Is Set Up.—The four views shown in Fig. 2-4 are drawn to represent the instantaneous currents in the various conductors and the corresponding instantaneous fields set up in the motor at each of four different instants of time; the instantaneous fields are set up by the currents flowing in both windings *at that par-*

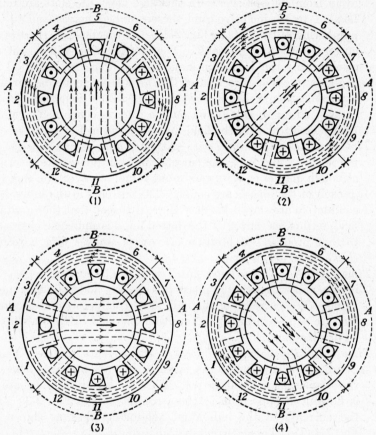

Fig. 2-4.—The rotating field set up by a two-phase stator.

ticular instant. Each of the views (1), (2), (3), and (4) corresponds to the current and flux conditions in the motor at the instants. 1, 2, 3, and 4 in Fig. 2-3*b*, respectively. These instants of time will be discussed separately.

Time 1.—At this instant, the current in phase *A* is at its maximum value *in a positive direction*, which means that the currents are flowing through the conductors of phase A in the directions shown by the arrows in Fig. 2-3a. In Fig. 2-4 (1), a single dot, or point, represents the head of an arrow and indicates that current is flowing directly toward the observer; a cross represents the tail of an arrow and indicates that the current is flowing directly away from the observer. In this first view, the slots are numbered 1 to 12, inclusive, and these numbers correspond to the numbering of the slots in Fig. 2-3a. At this instant, there is no current flowing in phase B. Therefore, a field will be set up as shown by the dotted lines and in the directions indicated by the arrows. The direction of this field flux can be determined by application of the *right-hand rule.** The field flux set up, at least so far as any action on the rotor is concerned, is practically identical with the field flux as shown in Fig. 2-2.

Time 2, 45 Deg Later in Time.—At this time, as can be seen by reference to Fig. 2-3b, the currents in both phases are positive, although neither is at its maximum value; however, the currents in each of the phases are equal. The currents in the individual conductors are shown in (2). Here, it is seen that the resultant field, or flux, as shown by the dotted lines, is similar in character to that produced at position (1), *except that the field is rotated clockwise 45 deg in space.*

Time 3, 90 Deg in Time Later than Time 1.—The current in phase A is zero, and the current in phase B is positive and at its maximum value. The currents in the individual conductors and the field flux are as shown in (3). Note that the field has again shifted 45 deg in space.

Time 4, 135 Deg Later than Time 1.—The currents in phases A and B are again equal; but the latter current is positive, whereas the former current is negative. That is, the current in phase A is flowing in opposition to the arrows shown in Fig. 2-3a, and the currents in the individual conductors flow as shown in Fig. 2-4 (4). These currents set up a stator field as shown in (4). Note that this field again has moved 45 deg in space from position (3), or 135 deg in space from position (1).

It seems unnecessary to prolong the discussion further to show

---

* The *right-hand rule* is used to determine the direction of the magnetic flux which is produced by current flowing in a coil of wire. It is stated as follows: *If an electromagnet be taken in the right hand with the fingers coiling in the direction of the flow of current, the thumb, extending along the magnet away from the hand, will point in the direction of flow of magnetic flux, i.e., to the north pole of the magnet.*

that the field will make one complete revolution in 1 cycle of current, since the field has been shown to revolve 45 deg in space for each 45 deg of lapsed time. It will be observed that there is set up an air-gap flux, or field, that actually rotates in space, just as the field of Fig. 2-2 was caused to rotate in space by actual rotation of the field-magnet structure; in the case of Fig. 2-4, however, there was no actual rotation of the field structure itself, although the magnetic field set up by the stationary field structure did itself rotate in space.

Thus it has been shown how alternating current, flowing in the windings of a *stationary* primary member of a two-phase induction motor, can actually set up a *rotating* field that is practically the same, so far as any action on the rotor is concerned, as the rotating field that is set up by a mechanically revolving field magnet similar to the one represented in Fig. 2-2.

2-7. Conditions Necessary to Set Up a Rotating Field in a Two-phase Motor.—The two conditions necessary to set up a rotating field in a motor excited from a two-phase source are, as we have seen:

1. Two separate phase windings in the motor located 90 deg apart in space. (The windings should be separated by 90 **electrical degrees** and not necessarily by 90 mechanical degrees. A distinction between electrical and mechanical degrees is made in Art. 2-16.)

2. Two phases, or sources of a-c voltages, equal in magnitude and displaced by 90 deg in time phase.

In the two-phase motor, there are, in effect, two distinct magnetic fields, 90 deg apart in time and 90 electrical degrees apart in space. One of these fields is set up by the winding of phase *A*, and the second is set up by phase *B*. Actually, both fields do not exist simultaneously in the motor; at any particular instant, only the resultant exists. This resultant is a uniformly rotating magnetic field, practically constant in magnitude, as shown by the four pictures in Fig. 2-4.

It can be shown that, in three-phase induction motors, a rotating field is produced in a somewhat similar manner.

PRODUCTION OF A ROTATING FIELD
IN A SINGLE-PHASE INDUCTION MOTOR

2-8. The Single-phase Motor a Special Case of the Two-phase Motor.—Suppose the winding of phase *B* in the two-phase motor just discussed is omitted; we would then have a single-phase induction motor such as is represented in Fig. 2-5a. In the two-phase motor, as just learned, there are two component *stationary* fields which combine to form a single resultant field which *rotates*. One of these component

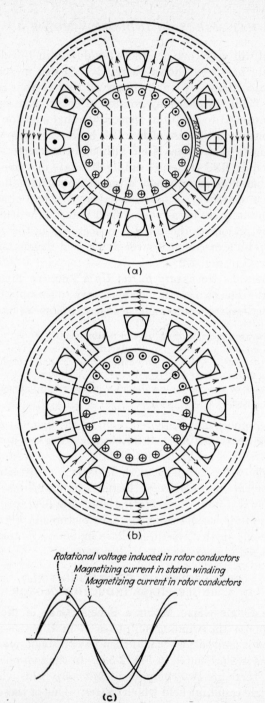

Rotational voltage induced in rotor conductors
Magnetizing current in stator winding
Magnetizing current in rotor conductors

(c)

Fig. 2-5.—The fields of a single-phase induction motor. (a) The stator field and the rotational voltages induced in the rotor by it. (b) Magnetic field set up by the currents flowing in the rotor bars (cross field). (c) Instantaneous values of stator current, rotor axis, and voltage in the cross field.

fields is set up by one phase, and the other component field by the second phase, *but both components of the rotating field are set up by stator windings.* However, in the single-phase motor, there is only one winding on the stator, and this one winding can set up only one of the two components required to produce a rotating field. How a second component is actually set up by the rotor when the latter is turning is developed in Art. 2-10. But first it is necessary to examine the field set up by the stator winding.

2-9. Field Set Up by Stator Winding Alone.—Assume that the stator winding of the motor in Fig. 2-5a is excited with alternating current. At any particular instant when the current is positive, *i.e.*, flowing in the directions indicated by the dots and crosses in the stator slots, a magnetic field will be set up as shown. Neglecting the effect of the rotor, this field will be stationary in space but will pulsate in magnitude; it will be at a maximum value when the current is maximum and zero when the current is zero—the significant point, however, being that the field is stationary in space and does not revolve, as in the case of the two-phase motor.

Since the field set up by the stator winding does not revolve, there is no tendency for the rotor to turn; hence, there is no inherent locked-rotor torque. Once the motor is started and running, the single-phase motor will develop torque because of the action of the cross field set up by the rotor. How this field is set up is the subject of the following article.

2-10. Field Set Up by the Rotor.—Assume that the squirrel-cage rotor is revolving, having been started by some means or other, for it was not inherently self-starting. Voltages will be induced in each of the individual conductors in the squirrel cage because they are cutting magnetic lines of force. By applying Fleming's right-hand rule,* it can be ascertained that all the currents above the center of the rotor would tend to flow toward the observer and all the currents below

* Fleming's right-hand rule can be applied as follows: Extend the thumb and the first and second fingers of the right hand so that all three are mutually perpendicular and in the most natural and comfortable position; this position is with the thumb and index finger both lying in the plane of the hand with the second finger perpendicular to the plane of the hand. With the hand held in this position, the thumb points in the direction of motion of the conductor, the first finger in the direction of the field, and the second finger in the direction of induced voltage. If this rule is applied in the case at hand, it will be seen that the currents and voltages in the rotor bars will be in the directions shown in Fig. 2-5a. As an aid to remembering this rule, some students memorize the expression "My fine clothes" to stand for motion, field, current, as being represented by the thumb, first finger, and second finger, respectively.

the center of the rotor would tend to flow away from the observer. This fact is indicated by the use of dots and crosses in the rotor bars.

It should be noted that the *rotational voltages induced in the rotor conductors* are in phase with the stator field and stator magnetizing current, as shown in Fig. 2-5c. Now, since voltages are induced in the rotor conductors, currents will be caused to flow. The impedance to the currents in the rotor bars is almost entirely reactive, so that these currents will lag the voltage by nearly 90 deg, as shown in Fig. 2-5c. (For a discussion on the phase relation between the voltage and current in an a-c circuit containing principally inductance, the reader is referred to any elementary text on alternating currents.)

These rotor currents will set up a magnetic field, known as the **cross field,** as shown in Fig. 2-5b. This field is displaced 90 deg in space from the field shown in Fig. 2-5a, *i.e.,* 90 deg in space from the field set up by the stator winding. Moreover, this field set up by the rotor is not only displaced 90 deg in space from the stator field, but it also lags the latter by approximately 90 deg in time. In other words, the effect of the magnetizing current flowing in the rotor is somewhat similar to the effect of the current flowing in phase *B* in Fig. 2-4 (3).

2-11. Rotating Field.—We have just seen that the stator will set up a pulsating field and that the rotor, *if revolving*, will set up a second pulsating field 90 deg behind the stator field in time and in space. If the rotor is revolving at synchronous speed, this field set up by the rotor will be substantially equal in magnitude to the stator field. Therefore, a rotating field will be set up in the single-phase motor just as it was in the two-phase motor; in general, this field will be similar in character to the rotating field set up in Fig. 2-2, except as noted in the following paragraphs.

COMPARISONS BETWEEN SINGLE-PHASE INDUCTION MOTORS AND POLYPHASE INDUCTION MOTORS

2-12. Differences in the Rotating Field.—In the well-designed polyphase induction motor, the strength of the rotating magnetic field does not vary appreciably as it rotates. This condition can be described by the use of a vector, as shown in Fig. 2-6a; the angular position of the field is represented by the angular position θ of the vector, and the strength of the field is represented by the length of the vector. In the case of the polyphase motor, the locus (the imaginary line that is traced by the extremity of the arrow) of this field vector is a circle. In the case of the single-phase motor, the locus of this field vector is an ellipse, as shown in Fig. 2-6b. It is due to this method of representation of the field that one sometimes hears the expression: A polyphase motor has a circular field, whereas a single-phase motor has an elliptical field. The words **circular** and **elliptical** refer to the shape of the locus of the vector describing the field, and not to any characteristic of the field itself.

Why is the locus of the field vector of a single-phase motor an ellipse? The strength of the cross field depends upon the speed of the motor, for the rotational voltage induced in the rotor conductors must depend upon the speed. Therefore, if the strength of the field in the cross-field axis decreases with a reduction in speed, the shape

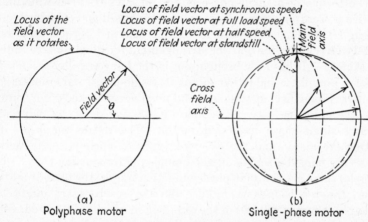

(a)
Polyphase motor

(b)
Single-phase motor

FIG. 2-6.—Rotating fields of single-phase and polyphase induction motors compared. *(a)* Polyphase motor. *(b)* Single-phase motor.

of the ellipse must change with speed. At synchronous speed, the cross field is practically equal to the main field, and the field locus is a circle, as in a polyphase motor. As the speed decreases, the ellipse becomes flatter and flatter in shape, until finally, at standstill, it collapses to a straight line; *i.e.*, when the rotor is at rest, the field pulsates in value along the stator axis but does not rotate.

2-13. Losses, Breakdown Torque, and Torque Pulsations.—The rotor of a polyphase motor carries no magnetizing current, unless the supply voltages are unbalanced, and the rotor I^2R losses at no load are negligible. However, the rotor of a single-phase motor carries the magnetizing current to set up the cross field; hence, there are appreciable rotor I^2R losses even at no load.

It is quite commonly known that the breakdown torque of a polyphase induction motor is not affected by the rotor resistance. However, such is not the case with a single-phase induction motor, because rotor resistance limits, to some extent, the amount of current that will flow in the rotor conductors to set up the cross field; hence, increasing the rotor resistance means weakening the cross field and thereby reducing the maximum torque that can be developed. Thus, if the rotor resistance rings of a single-phase motor are machined to a smaller cross section, the rotor resistance is increased and the breakdown torque decreased. Further, it is an interesting fact that the breakdown torque of a single-phase motor always occurs at some speed above two-thirds synchronous, whereas the breakdown torque of a polyphase motor can occur at any speed, even including negative speeds.

The torque of a single-phase motor pulsates between wide limits at twice power frequency. This point is discussed and explained more fully in Art. 18-11. Polyphase motors have no such torque pulsations.

2-14. Necessity for Starting Arrangement for Single-phase Induction Motors.—It has been brought out in the foregoing discussion that, unlike a polyphase induction motor, a single-phase induction motor has no revolving field at standstill and no inherent locked-rotor torque. It is, therefore, necessary to employ a starting device of some sort for any single-phase induction motor. The means employed for starting are many, and the different types of single-phase induction motors are named after the method employed for starting them. For example, there are the split-phase induction motor, the capacitor-start motor, the repulsion-start motor, and the reactor-start motor. A single-phase motor will run in the direction in which it is started, without any change in main winding connections.

MISCELLANEOUS

2-15. Number of Poles.—In d-c motors, there are definite pole pieces which can be seen and counted, so that there is no doubt as to the number of poles. In an induction motor, there are no such salient poles, but the windings are arranged so that a revolving magnetic field is set up just as though it were produced by a rotating d-c field structure, as has been explained previously. A motor is said to be wound for four poles if the winding sets up a magnetic field with four poles.

2-16. Electrical Degrees.—The term **electrical degrees** was used in the preceding articles and is frequently heard in connection with motors. It is defined as follows:

Electrical degrees = (mechanical degrees) $\times$ (number of pairs of poles)

Why is the term electrical degrees used? It was shown in Art. 2-6 that the magnetic field of the induction motor of Fig. 2-4 moved

45 deg in space for each 45 deg of lapsed time. In 360 deg of time, the field moves a distance of two poles. If there are only two poles, as in Fig. 2-4, this distance is a complete revolution. If the machine is wound for four poles, 720 deg of time is necessary for a complete revolution. In other words, one pair of poles always represents 360 electrical degrees, regardless of the total number of poles. Thus it happens that 1 mechanical degree represents as many electrical degrees as there are pairs of poles. In dealing with electric motors, the meaning of the term *electrical degrees* should be borne in mind continuously, because this term is usually far more significant than *mechanical degrees.*

2-17. Synchronous Speed.—The speed of the rotating field of an induction motor is known as the **synchronous speed.** The synchronous speed can always be figured from the line frequency and the number of poles for which the motor is wound. Since the field moves one pair of poles per cycle,

$$\text{Synchronous rpm} = \frac{60 \text{ (sec per min)} \times \text{cycles (per sec)}}{\text{pairs of poles}}$$

or

$$\text{Synchronous rpm} = \frac{120 \times \text{frequency}}{\text{number of poles}} \qquad (2\text{-}1)$$

The actual operating speed, under full-load conditions, is about 5 per cent less than synchronous speed, as can be seen by referring to Table III.

2-18. References for Further Study of Induction-motor Theory.— It was pointed out in the first part of this chapter that full treatment of the theory of induction motors was beyond the scope of this book. For the eager student who wishes to pursue this fascinating subject further, the literature is full of help. Every elementary textbook on a-c machinery carries an explanation of the theory of operation of the polyphase induction motor. A classic, nonmathematical, and comprehensive explanation of polyphase motor theory has been given by Lamme.[1] A procedure for calculating the running performance of polyphase induction motors from constants of the motor, suitable for routine design calculations, is given by the author.[2] Fortunately, polyphase motors are uniformly treated from the viewpoint of a single theory: the revolving-field theory. Not so fortunate is the single-phase motor, which is explained by two theories: the cross-field theory and the revolving-field theory, each of which has its stanch advocates.

[1] For numbered references, see Bibliography at end of this chapter.

For purposes of explanation, the cross-field theory was used in this chapter. This theory was used by Branson in his classic paper in 1912 wherein he developed a circle diagram for the single-phase motor.[3] This theory has found its way into some textbooks[4,5] and was used by H. R. West[6] to develop mathematical equations for calculating the performance of single-phase induction motors; these equations form the basis of a modified calculating method developed by the author for routine design calculations on single-phase induction motors.[2] More recently, Robin Beach has published a comprehensive nonmathematical exposition of the cross-field theory, which presents a clear interpretation of how the stator and rotor fluxes and currents mutually interact to develop torque and maintain rotation; his treatise is recommended as an introduction to the mathematical treatments.[7]

The second point of view is quite different from the cross-field theory and is known as the revolving-field theory. This theory essentially holds that the resultant field in a single-phase induction motor is made up of two component *revolving* fields rotating in opposite directions. This point of view is explained very fully and exceptionally clearly in a nonmathematical manner by Lamme.[8] It is used by Morrill to develop a calculation procedure for single-phase motors[9] as well as for his classic paper on capacitor-motor theory.[10] It is explained in some textbooks[4,5] and has been used in a number of A.I.E.E. papers.

That the two theories give the same results has been shown by a number of writers, among the most recent of whom are Kimball and Alger[11] and Button.[12]

Bibliography

1. LAMME, B. G.: "Electrical Engineering Papers," pp. 5–39, *Westinghouse Technical Night School Press.*
2. VEINOTT, C. G.: Performance Calculations on Induction Motors, *A.I.E.E. Trans.,* vol. 51, 1932, pp. 743–754.
3. BRANSON, W. J.: Single-phase Induction Motors, *A.I.E.E. Trans.,* June, 1912, p. 1749.
4. LAWRENCE, R. R.: "Principles of Alternating-current Machinery," 3d ed., McGraw-Hill Book Company, Inc., New York, 1940.
5. PUCHSTEIN, A. F., and LLOYD, T. C.: "Alternating-current Machines," John Wiley & Sons, Inc., New York.
6. WEST, H. R.: The Cross-field Theory of AC Machines, *A.I.E.E. Trans.,* February, 1926, p. 369.
7. BEACH, ROBIN: A Physical Conception of Single-phase Motor Operation, *Elec. Eng.,* July, 1944, pp. 254–263.
8. LAMME, B. G.: A Physical Conception of the Operation of the Single-phase Induction Motor, *A.I.E.E. Trans.,* April, 1918, p. 627.

9. MORRILL, W. J.: The Apparent-impedance Method of Calculating Single-phase Motor Performance, *A.I.E.E. Trans.*, vol. 60, 1941, pp. 1037–1041.
10. ———: The Revolving-field Theory of the Capacitor Motor, *A.I.E.E. Trans.*, vol. 48, 1929, pp. 614–629.
11. KIMBALL, A. L., and ALGER, P. L.: Single-phase Motor Torque Pulsations, *A.I.E.E. Trans.*, June, 1924, p. 730.
12. BUTTON, C. T.: Single-phase Motor Theory—Correlation of Cross-field and Revolving-field Theory, *A.I.E.E. Trans.*, vol. 60, 1941, pp. 664–665.

CHAPTER III

SINGLE-PHASE INDUCTION MOTOR WINDINGS AND CONNECTIONS

Before proceeding to a description and a discussion of specific types of single-phase induction motors, it seems advisable to give a general description of the more common types of windings used. To illustrate the different classifications, a simple winding is presented in four different common forms (see Figs. 3-1, 3-2, 3-10, and 3-11).

Also, in this chapter the various types of diagrams that are used later in this book are described and defined, together with an explanation of how to interpret these diagrams. It is not intended, however, to cover all phases of repair-shop technique; information of this sort can be found, if desired, in books on the subject and in current magazines.*

3-1. Concentric Winding.—Single-phase induction motors are generally wound with concentric coils. For this reason, it may be well to give a rather general description of the concentric winding, comparing it with the more familiar diamond-coil lap winding such as is used both in d-c armatures and in polyphase motors. A diamond-coil lap winding was used in Fig. 2-3 to explain the production of a rotating field by

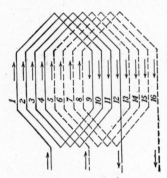

FIG. 3-1.—A two-phase, progressive, lap winding with diamond coils, eight slots per pole. This winding is shown here merely to illustrate one of various types of windings and should not be considered as a recommended winding arrangement for two-phase motors because it is a single-layer winding. A two-layer winding is normally used for polyphase motors.

polyphase alternating current. Another form of this winding, but with eight slots per pole instead of six, is shown in Fig. 3-1. An *exactly equivalent* concentric type of winding is shown in Fig. 3-2. To understand why the windings of Figs. 3-1 and 3-2 are exactly equivalent, compare the two winding arrangements: in both, slots 1, 2, 3, and 4 carry *A* phase current upward; slots 5, 6, 7, and 8 carry *B* phase

* See Bibliography at end of this chapter for specific references.

44

current upward; slots 9, 10, 11, and 12 carry *A* phase current downward; and slots 13, 14, 15, and 16 carry *B* phase current downward. In other words, the direction of current flow through the active conductors of every slot of the winding of Fig. 3-2 is identical with the direction of current flow in every slot of the winding of Fig. 3-1; the difference between these two winding arrangements is only in the end connections. The strength, location, and distribution of the useful magnetic fields in the motor depend wholly upon the total number and arrangement of ampere-conductors in the slots; in no respect do these factors depend upon how the end connections are made between these conductors. Therefore, one winding is said to be **exactly equivalent** to a second winding if, with the same current flowing in the external leads of either winding, there are exactly the same number of **ampere-conductors** in every slot of the first winding as in every slot of the second winding. (The number of ampere-conductors in a slot is the product of the number of conductors multiplied by the amperes flowing in each conductor.)

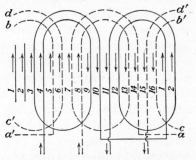

FIG. 3-2.—A two-phase, concentric winding. This winding is exactly equivalent to the winding of Fig. 3-1. It is often used in single-phase motors, seldom in polyphase motors.

It is always possible to find a concentric winding that is exactly equivalent to a progressive, or diamond-coil, winding, as has just been done. The reverse of this statement, however, is not always true; for a concentric winding is the more flexible arrangement. Concentric windings are used in single-phase induction motors because of this greater flexibility. With this type of winding, it is possible and practicable to use more copper in the main winding than in the auxiliary or starting winding; and, moreover, the number of turns does not have to be the same in both windings. In most single-phase induction motors, it is desirable to use more copper in the main winding than in the auxiliary winding and to employ a different number of turns. Split-phase motors, in particular, start on the principle that the resistance in the starting winding, as compared with the reactance of the starting winding, is higher than the resistance of the main winding compared with the reactance of the main winding.

In the diamond-coil or polyphase type of winding, all the coils have the same pitch or "throw," and the center of each coil is dis-

placed—usually by one slot—from the center of the neighboring coil.
In the concentric type of winding, every coil in any given pole group
has a different throw. But the centers of all the coils in a single pole
group coincide; *i.e.*, the coils are concentric with one another.

3-2. Necessity for Different Types of Connection Diagrams.—
The complete specification of all the details of a winding could be
shown on a single drawing. Such a drawing would indicate size of
wire; number of turns or conductors in each and every slot; end connections of all coils to form the groups; connections of the coil groups
to one another to form both the main and auxiliary windings, respectively; and the connections of the main and auxiliary windings to the
line and to the starting switch, capacitor, reactor, or any other piece
of apparatus essential to the operation of the motor. All of this
information is absolutely necessary in order to wind and connect a
motor. Yet if it were all on a single drawing, it would be necessary
to have such a drawing for every type, design, and rating; the number
of diagrams would be literally without limit; and fundamental principles would be lost in a hopeless multiplicity of diagrams. By breaking this information down into a few different *kinds* of diagrams, the
total number necessary can be reduced to a practical number, so that
fundamental principles are not overlooked.

There are at least three different independent operations incident
to the winding and connecting of a motor:

1. Winding and connecting the stator coils in groups.
2. Connection of these groups.
3. Assembly of the motor which involves connection of the windings to the
switch or capacitor, if either is used, and to the external or line leads.

For each of these operations, there is a specific type of diagram.
For connecting the motor to the line or to auxiliary apparatus, such
as a controller or capacitor, a fourth type of diagram is essential.
What these diagrams are and how to interpret them is the basis of the
following articles.

3-3. Distribution Chart.—A distribution chart gives the number
of turns or conductors in each slot for all the windings. The winding

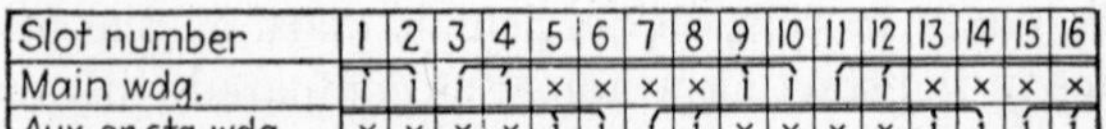

Slot number	1	2	3	4	5	6	7	8	9	10	11	12	13	14	15	16
Main wdg.	ʃ	ʃ	ʃ	ʃ	×	×	×	×	ʃ	ʃ	ʃ	ʃ	×	×	×	×
Aux. or stg. wdg.	×	×	×	×	ʃ	ʃ	ʃ	ʃ	×	×	×	×	ʃ	ʃ	ʃ	ʃ

Fig. 3-3.—A winding distribution chart for Fig. 3-2.

distribution chart for Fig. 3-2 is Fig. 3-3. Since Fig. 3-2 is a very
simple winding, consisting of only one strand of wire throughout, the

corresponding distribution chart is simple. A typical winding distribution chart may take the form of Fig. 3-4, which specifies the size of wire used in each winding, the insulation covering on the wire, the number of strands per conductor, the total number of strands in each and every slot, and the end connections of the coils in a group. In short, the distribution chart of Fig. 3-4 gives all the information necessary for *winding the stator coils* and connecting them in groups, except for the coil perimeters and the winding method. The winding method is more or less optional but can be given on this chart if desired.

Slot number		1	2	3	4	5	6	7	8	9	10	11	12	13	14	15	16	Wire size (gage)	Insulation	Strands per cond.
Main wdg.	Strands	72	72	72	72	×	×	×	×	72	72	72	72					21	S.C.C.En.	2
Aux.or stg.wdg.		×	×	×	×	43	43	43	43	×	×	×	×	43	43	43	43	19	S.C.C.En.	1

Fig. 3-4.—A more detailed winding distribution chart.

3-4. A Stator (or Rotor) Connection Diagram.

—After the stator coil groups are wound, the next step is to connect the groups together. A **group** is simply the combination of all the coils in a given winding or phase under one pole. For example, in Fig. 3-4, both windings have two coils per group; each main-winding group consists of two coils of 36 turns (72 strands) each. One of these coils has a throw of 4 and 9, the other a throw of 3 and 10.

How to connect the groups together is shown in Fig. 3-5. In this diagram, each group is represented by a single, solid, black, elongated

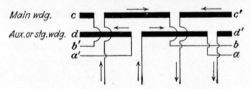

FIG. 3-5.—Group connections for Fig. 3-3.

rectangle. The connections of the ends of these groups are shown. In the diagram of Fig. 3-5, it will be noted that two of the rectangles representing a group have to be drawn in two sections; in the figure, *c* should be joined to *c'* and *d* to *d'*. To avoid this difficulty, such diagrams are usually drawn in the form of a circle; a diagram of this kind is a **stator connection diagram.** A number of stator connection diagrams drawn in circular form are given throughout the book; the one that corresponds to the connection diagram just discussed is Fig. 4-8.

A diagram such as that discussed in the preceding paragraph would be a **rotor connection diagram** if it were used to connect a rotor winding.

Thus, we have shown how a winding, such as that represented in Fig. 3-2, is represented by two diagrams, such as Figs. 3-3 and 4-8. It is more convenient to use two diagrams than one, for one stator connection diagram can be used with a large number of distribution charts.

3-5. Wiring Diagram.—A **wiring diagram** shows the internal connections of the various windings to one·another and to any auxiliary devices such as a starting switch, capacitor, reactor, or thermal protective device.   Examples of this type of diagram are Figs. 4-24a, 5-6a, and 5-40.   A wiring diagram may or may not be necessary to supplement the stator connection diagram.   If no leads other than those shown on the stator connection diagram are necessary, a wiring diagram is not needed.   For example, if the stator connection diagram is Fig. 4-21, a wiring diagram is unnecessary because there are only two line leads.

3-6. Line Connection Diagram.—A **line connection diagram** shows the permissible connections of the motor leads to the line.   Representative examples are Figs. 4-24b, 5-6b, and 6-10.   If there are but two line leads, as in Fig. 4-21, a line connection diagram is not necessary.

3-7. Magnetic Polarity.—It would be impossible in any book of this size to give all the possible connection diagrams.   Some knowledge of how to check the correctness of diagrams, and also of how to make new ones, is absolutely essential to one who has to rewind or reconnect motors.

It is a fundamental principle of winding that adjacent poles must be wound to give opposite **magnetic polarity** (except in the case of consequent-pole windings); *i.e.*, if one pole is wound in a clockwise direction, the next adjacent pole must be wound in a counterclockwise direction, as has been done in Fig. 3-2.   This statement does not mean that the coils actually have to be wound in this direction before being put into the stator; but it does mean that the winding must be connected so that, if the current proceeds through one pole in a clockwise direction, it must proceed through the next pole in a counterclockwise direction.

This principle—*viz.*, that the magnetic polarity must alternate from pole to pole as we progress about the winding—is made use of to determine the correctness of connection diagrams.   It is essential to understand this principle in order to check these diagrams, or the winding itself, particularly if it is necessary to draw up new connection diagrams. Taking a representative diagram, say Fig. 4-10, and tracing through the main winding, we find that we go from pole to pole, but we go through one pole in one direction and through the next adjacent pole in the opposite direction; *i.e.*, if we enter at lead $T1$, we proceed clockwise around the diagram through the first group and counterclockwise around the diagram through the second group, and so on through the rest of the groups until we come out at $T4(T3)$. This tells us that all adjacent poles are of opposite magnetic polarity, as they should be.

3-8. Hand or Gun Winding.—Coils can be wound directly in the stator punchings by hand alone, or by means of a gun, one turn at a time. For example, assume that a motor is to have the winding of Fig. 3-2 put in it by hand or gun method. The operator starts with a single wire and winds the inner coil (4 and 9) until this coil is completed, then progresses to the next coil, which is wound in the two adjacent outside slots (3 and 10), and so on, if there are more coils in the group, until all the coils in a pole group are wound, each coil being wound in the same direction. The operator then carries the wire over to slot 1 and winds, in the opposite direction, all the turns in the coil spanning slots 1 and 12 and then winds the last coil from 2 to 11, still continuing in the same direction as the 1-to-12 coil and bringing out the finish lead from slot 11. Usually the turns are counted mentally.

Since the sharp edges of the slot openings may cut or scrape the insulation off the wire, it is the usual factory practice to employ winding guides. These guides are arranged so as to cover up the sharp edges of the slots to protect the wire so that it can be wound into the slots more rapidly. Also, rods are provided to insert in the slots to keep the wires from "climbing the core," *i.e.*, to keep the end connections from covering up the unwound slots, in order to provide room for the coils which are later to be wound.

Inasmuch as the wire tends to cut and chafe the operator's hand, a "gun" is provided to facilitate insertion of the wire in the slots. Gun winding, if the proper guides and guns are provided, is a cheap and fast method, and end extensions are cut down to a minimum. It is not used generally if the wire size is larger than No. 16 or if there are more than 50 turns per slot. Hand winding can be used in repair shops but is apt to be rather slow; for the proper guides are practically never available, and the cost of making them to wind only a few motors would be prohibitive, since they have to be very carefully and accurately machined.   In production, gun winding is not so popular as formerly.

Of importance to service departments is the fact that this method of winding gives a very short wire connecting adjacent pole groups and this wire is usually tight against the iron, so that it may be very difficult to reconnect such a winding in parallel.

Fig. 3-6.—Winding a concentric coil group on a tapered concentric mold.   The taper gives a different perimeter to each individual turn—a feature that greatly simplifies insertion of the coils in the slots.   For a close-up of this mold, see Fig. 3-7.   (Courtesy of Westinghouse Electric Corporation.)

3-9. Mold Windings—Concentric Coils.—Concentric coils are wound on a stepped block, or mold, provided with as many steps as there are parts to the coil.   If these steps are tapered, as shown in Figs. 3-6 and 3-7, a considerable advantage is gained because each individual turn has a different perimeter, and the turns do not interfere with one another when the coil is being inserted in the slots. With this method, all the coils for a single group are wound in succes-

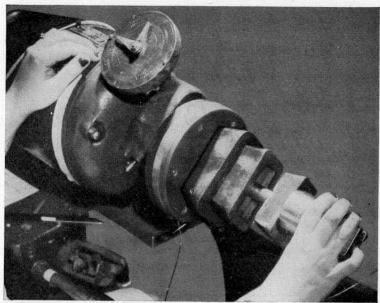

Fig. 3-7.—A tapered mold for concentric coils, partly dismantled. Dismantling is necessary to remove the coils after winding. (*Courtesy of Westinghouse Electric Corporation.*)

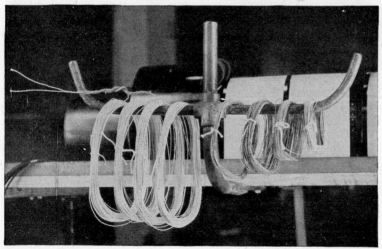

Fig. 3-8.—Typical mold-wound coils. The coils at the right comprise one pole group for a concentric winding; they were not wound on tapered molds. The four coils at the left each have the same perimeter and can be used either for a single-phase progressive winding or for a polyphase winding. (*Courtesy of Westinghouse Electric Corporation.*)

sion with a single strand of wire, or with two strands of wire, if there are two strands per conductor.

For repair shops, a few simple adjustable molds can be made out of wood for permanent shop equipment. These molds should be arranged so that they can be padded on any or all of the sections; however, tapered-section molds are not so convenient to pad as straight-sided molds. If only a few jobs of this type are done, wire finish nails can be driven into the bench, and the coils wound around

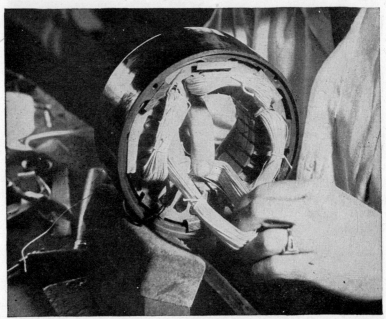

FIG. 3-9.—Mold- or form-wound coils being inserted by hand. (*Courtesy of Emerson Electric Manufacturing Company.*)

these finish nails. The perimeter of the molds probably is best determined by a trial with a single strand of wire looped around the stator in the same position that the finished coil is to occupy. With this type of winding, the length of the mean turn will usually be larger than for hand winding, and the end extensions will be greater.

Mold winding has the further advantage over hand or gun winding in that the insulation on the wire is less likely to become damaged during the winding process.

3-10. Mold Windings—Progressive Coils.—In the concentric winding, as mentioned in Art. 3-1, there are a number of coils in each pole group; each of these coils has a different throw, but all the coils have a common axis or center, which is the center of the pole. In the progressive type of winding, illustrated in Fig. 3-10, all the coils in a pole group have the same throw (but not necessarily the same number of turns), but the center of each coil is displaced from the center of the preceding coil. These coils are, therefore, a little simpler to wind on an external mold because all the coils have the same perimeter. They can, in fact, be wound on regular polyphase molds, such as illustrated in Figs. 14-2 and 14-3. The progressive winding of Fig. 3-10 is exactly equivalent to the windings of Figs. 3-1 and 3-2.

It should be noted that the progressive winding for single-phase motors is similar to a polyphase winding, but there are important differences. These differences can be seen, in principle, by comparing the winding of Fig. 3-10 with the winding of Fig. 3-1. In the polyphase winding, the throw of the coils is eight slots, or 1 to 9; in the single-phase winding, the throw of the coils is six slots, or 1 to 7. In the polyphase winding, four coils are connected in series to make one pole group; in the single-phase winding, only two coils are connected in series for each pole group, but there are two pole groups in each winding so that the

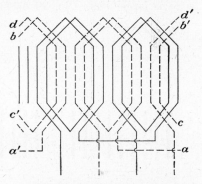

Fig. 3-10.—A single-phase, progressive winding, diamond coils, eight slots per pole. This winding is an exact equivalent of Fig. 3-2.

total number of series conductors is the same in either case. (In the polyphase winding of Fig. 3-1, there are only two groups, whereas a two-pole two-phase polyphase motor normally has four groups. Figure 3-1 has only two groups because there is only one coil side per slot, whereas a polyphase motor normally has at least two coil sides per slot.)

The single-phase progressive winding is a more flexible arrangement than the polyphase type of winding. The latter is primarily suited to polyphase windings wherein the number of turns, wire size, and copper weight are identical for the two phases. With the single-phase progressive winding, any proportion of the winding space, within limits, can be used for the main winding. Furthermore, it is not necessary to wind the auxiliary winding by the same method as the main winding, for the latter can be hand- or skein-wound, if desired.

Certain distributions of windings can be wound in a progressive fashion, and others cannot. As a rule, it is advantageous, when possible, to use the progressive type of winding, as compared with the concentric mold winding.   The end extensions of a progressive winding, however, are apt to be slightly larger; and this point should be taken into consideration if there is limited room for end extensions in the motor being rewound.

3-11. Skein Windings.—Skein winding is a popular method of winding, although it is probably somewhat less popular than formerly, at least for main windings.   It is now used principally for starting or auxiliary windings; most split-phase starting windings are wound by this method.   This method of winding is somewhat difficult to handle if the weight of wire is more than 2 or 3 oz per skein, or if the wire is larger than No. 20 or 21.   Of the various winding methods

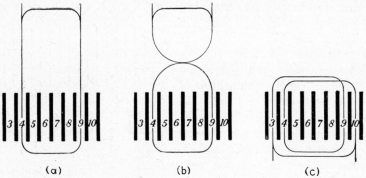

(a)   (b)   (c)

Fig. 3-11.—Procedure for winding a skein winding which is an exact equivalent of the concentric winding of Fig. 3-2.

just discussed, this one is probably the most complicated and most difficult to explain, although it is not at all difficult of execution, once it is understood and mastered.   It is not particularly flexible from a design standpoint, for the choice of possible distributions is limited.

Successive steps required to produce a skein winding which is exactly equivalent to the concentric winding shown in Fig. 3-2 are given in Fig. 3-11.   The operation consists of three steps as shown. No set rules or general explanations as to how to wind all types of skein windings can be given here, for each distribution is an individual problem which must be worked out by itself.   The number of possible variations are too numerous to discuss here.   Braymer and Roe go into this subject slightly more in detail.[2]   A partly completed skein winding is shown in Fig. 3-12.

When the procedure of Fig. 3-11 is followed, it is necessary to pass the skein through the bore twice.   When this principle is extended

[2] For numbered references, see Bibliography at end of this chapter.

to more complicated distributions, it is often necessary to pass the skein back and forth through the bore several times. If a slightly different procedure is followed, it is not necessary to pass the skein through the bore at all. This procedure is easier to execute than to explain. The principle of this method is to pass one side of the skein through the slot and then back through another slot; the other side of the skein is passed through and back in a similar fashion. To illustrate, using Fig. 3-11c: leave the entire skein on the bottom side (of this figure); pass one side of the skein up through slot 4 and around and back through slot 10; then pick up the side of the skein now in slot 4 and pass it up through slot 9 and around and down through slot 3; this winding is then complete.

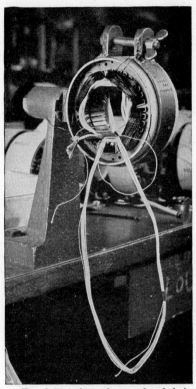

The best way to determine the length of the skein is to try first a single wire, looping it in the same manner that the final skein will be looped. Then, a trial skein can be made up and tried out. Sometimes, the trial skein will be too long or too short, and the other skeins should be adjusted in length accordingly.

FIG. 3-12.—A partly completed skein winding. The main winding coils and three of the auxiliary winding coils are in place; the fourth auxiliary coil has been started. Note the use of friction tape to hold the strands of the skein together and to keep the ends from unwinding. (*Courtesy of Westinghouse Electric Corporation.*)

3-12. Windings with Dissimilar Coils, and Consequent-pole Windings.—Windings with dissimilar coils on adjacent poles are often used in single-phase motors to avoid the use of split coils. Figure 3-13a shows a conventional balanced-coil arrangement requiring two coil sides in slots 1, 7, 13, and 19. However, by the use of unequal coils, as shown in (b), the split coils can be avoided. A logical extension of this same idea is the arrangement in (c) which uses only one coil per pair of poles, and which connects all coils for the same magnetic polarity; this is a consequent-pole winding. All three of these arrangements are exactly equivalent, within the scope of the definition of that term given in Art. 3-1, but there are differences to be noted. Use of identical coils on all poles is the best arrangement from an engineering point of view; end extensions are uniform around the stator; greatest flexibility is permitted in parallel connections because any pole can be paralleled with any other. Dissimilar coils are perhaps easier to wind because there are no split coils, which are usually tighter in the slots owing to the additional insulation required; however, care must be taken in parallel connections that a small coil is never paralleled with a large coil; for example, if large and small coils alternate, the parallel

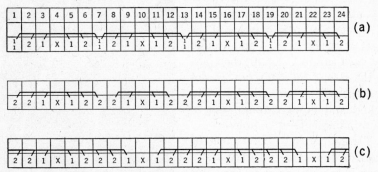

Fig. 3-13.—Comparison of different winding arrangements. All three arrangements are exactly equivalent—within the scope of the definition in Art. 3-1—but all three are not equally desirable. (a) Conventional winding, identical coils on all poles, adjacent poles connected for opposite magnetic polarities. (b) Dissimilar coils on adjacent poles, no split coils, adjacent poles connected for opposite magnetic polarities. (c) Consequent-pole winding, one coil per pair of poles, all coils connected for *same* magnetic polarity.

diagram of Fig. 4-12 can be used, but the diagram of Fig. 4-13 cannot. Consequent-pole windings, such as shown in Fig. 3-13c generally have little to recommend them: they result in bulky and nonuniform end extensions and, if used in split-phase motors, are likely to result in somewhat less torque because of slightly higher reactance. The distribution factor is the same for all three arrangements shown in Fig. 3-13.

3-13. Some Practical Hints on Winding.—Detailed instructions on the technique of winding and the tools and equipment necessary for rewinding small motors are given in other books, but it may be well to summarize a few of the more important points here.

For 115- and 230-volt motors, the slots should each be insulated carefully with a U-shaped rag-paper cell, approximately 0.015 in. thick. If the line voltage is more than 250 volts, a combination cell, consisting of fish paper and varnished cambric, about 0.020 in. thick, should be used. These cells should be about ⅜ in. longer than the width of the core. When winding and shaping the coils, care should be taken not to split the slot cells, allowing the wire to scrape on the iron core. The coils should be started in the proper place so that the finished coils will avoid any through bolts or end-shield screws. Usually the main winding has the greater amount of copper in it and is the bulkier. Therefore, it is advisable to wind the centers of the main poles halfway between the through-bolt holes. In the case of motors having a commutator and brushes, special attention must be given to the location of the stator winding, as this is very important, particularly if the brushes are not on an adjustable rocker ring. Barriers should be placed in the slots to insulate the starting winding from the main winding; these barriers should also insulate the end connections of one winding from the end connections of the other. The soldered or welded connections of the coils and external leads should be free from sharp points which might cut through the insulation; these connections should be carefully wrapped with tape. The leads and windings should be tied or sewed down with a good grade of machine thread.

Care should be taken to wind the coils uniformly and neatly in such a manner as to require a minimum amount of pounding and shaping of the final coil. The bore of the completed winding should be larger than the bore of the stator core so that the rotor can be inserted readily. The winding must be shaped back enough so that the ventilating fan or switch cannot chafe the coils.

3-14. Points to Note before Stripping a Winding.—Some important steps to take before and during the stripping of a motor that is to be rewound are the following:

1. Make a complete record of the nameplate reading of the motor. (The importance of the complete nameplate reading is discussed more fully in Chap. I.)

2. The recorded data must be *complete* and *clear* so that anyone could rewind the motor without ever having seen the original winding.

3. Note how the windings are connected to one another, to the starting switch, to any external device such as capacitor, reactor, or resistor, and to the lines. This information can be recorded in the form of a **wiring diagram** and a **line connection diagram** as defined in Arts. 3-5 and 3-6. A figure number from this book may be sufficient for a record, or it may be necessary to sketch the diagrams.

4. It is desirable to note and determine, if possible, the original method of winding of each of the various windings of the motor,

whether they were mold-wound, hand-wound, or skein-wound. If mold-wound, note whether a concentric or a progressive coil was used. If skein-wound, note the number of turns in the skein, also how many times the skein was passed through the slots; try to determine the perimeter of the skein.

5. The connections of the various pole groups forming a single winding should be noted: *i.e.*, whether the pole groups are connected in series or parallel; and if they are in parallel, whether or not they are cross-connected, and how. This information can be recorded in the form of a **stator connection diagram.** If possible, find the corresponding stator connection diagram in this book, and record the number; otherwise it may be necessary to draw the diagram.

6. If only one or two coils are short-circuited, it may be possible to measure the resistance of the coils that are not defective and to record these values for reference.

7. The distribution of the winding, *i.e.*, the number of conductors in each slot, and the throw of all the coils should be noted and recorded in some form of **distribution chart** as illustrated in Fig. 3-4. Whether or not there are one, two, or more strands per conductor should also be noted. The wire gauge and type of insulation covering on each of the strands should be noted carefully, for the two strands in parallel may not necessarily be of the same size wire. The wire can be measured with a micrometer or with a wire gauge; the measurement may be taken over the enamel, if a suitable allowance is made for its thickness, or the enamel can be burned off in a gas flame, care being taken not to burn away too much copper. For a wire table, refer to Table XXXII. *The number of strands should be counted on the side opposite the connections, for otherwise an error in counting may result.*

8. The mean length of turn should be determined when measuring one of the wires removed; and, if a skein winding, the length of the skein should be determined. In the case of split-phase motors which depend for their starting upon the correct value of resistance in the starting winding, it is especially important to duplicate the resistance and number of turns of the starting winding.

9. The thickness and kind of insulation in the slots and between the end windings should also be noted and recorded.

3-15. Stripping a Winding.—Before stripping, the winding should be preheated either in an oven or by passing a current through the winding, in order to soften the varnish. End connections, preferably at the lead end, are then cut and the coils withdrawn through the slots by means of pliers or screw driver. If the preheating is done in

FIG. 3-14.—First step in stripping a winding. Stator is set up in a machine lathe, and the end windings on one end are turned off practically to the laminations. (*Courtesy of Westinghouse Electric Corporation.*)

FIG. 3-15.—Second step in stripping a winding. Stator is placed in an oven over a gas flame and covered with a motor end shield to retain the heat. All the insulation is burned away, making subsequent removal of the winding easy. (*Courtesy of Westinghouse Electric Corporation.*)

an oven, the coil ends can be cut before putting the wound part in the oven.

A somewhat faster method of stripping a stator winding, which has proved very satisfactory in a factory repair shop, is illustrated in Figs. 3-14 and 3-15. The windings are first turned off from one end of the motor in a lathe, and the stator, covered by an old end shield, is placed over a gas flame, as shown in Fig. 3-15. After the insulation has been burned off, the windings are very easily removed by means of a screw driver. Some special tools are required, however. Use of a special faceplate can be noted in Fig. 3-14; also, in Fig. 3-15, both the oven and the handling tool in the operator's hand are special. Where there are a large number of stators to be stripped, the few special tools required more than pay for themselves. Care must be taken not to oxidize or burn the punchings excessively.

3-16. Varnish Impregnation—General.—Electric motors are usually varnish-impregnated for one or more of the following reasons:

1. Bonding of the windings into a rigid mass to prevent chafing, and, in the case of rotating members, to prevent loss of balance.

2. Removal of moisture from the insulation and addition of a permanent barrier against reentry of moisture, abrasive dirt, and dust.

3. Reduction of the temperature rise.

4. Lengthening the life of the insulation by reducing the rate of oxidation, thermal decomposition, and dehydration.

5. Increasing the dielectric and mechanical strength of the insulation, as well as its resistance to certain chemicals.

Almost invariably, moisture resistance and dielectric strength of a film of baked insulating varnish are proportional to the film thickness. For good bonding and good heat dissipation, the varnish must penetrate the windings thoroughly during the dipping process. Some further penetration occurs as the varnish thins during the initial stages of baking. Penetration can be improved greatly by lowering the viscosity and percentage of solids in the varnish by addition of solvents (see Art. 3-17g), but the film produced is thin, and numerous dips and bakes are required to build up an adequate film. A solids content of 30 to 50 per cent is common for open dip-tank varnishes, and 60 per cent or better for vacuum-and-pressure impregnation. There are so many kinds of varnishes and impregnation procedures that it is practicable to cover these only in a brief fashion.

3-17. Kinds of Insulating Varnishes.—Selection of the insulating varnish for any particular motor in general is based upon a compromise between tensile strength and heat life of the film. Highest strength varnishes tend to be inherently brittle and are, therefore, subject to cracking by vibration or by repeated expansions and contractions due to temperature changes. Air-drying varnishes, particularly those with a shellac spirit base, can be used in emergencies when time does not permit use of a baked varnish, but baked varnishes are invariably better. Of the baking varnishes available today, the thermosetting kinds are superior to oleoresinous varnishes. For very high temperature applications, silicone varnishes with Class B insulation (glass, mica, asbestos, etc.) are best.

a. Air-drying Varnishes.—By comparison with baking varnishes, air-drying varnishes have low strength and high porosity because their films do not flow well enough to seal up the voids left by the drying out of the solvent. Furthermore, they tend to deteriorate rather rapidly in the dip tank, and even on the shelf. Fastest drying of these have a shellac spirit base and may be either clear or black; these can be used for emergency repair jobs or for touch-up work. Black, asphalt-base varnishes are available, but these have only fair resistance to oil. A number of oleoresinous varnishes, both black and clear, are available; these dry by loss of solvent and by oxidation and are more oil-resistant than asphalt-base varnishes. Synthetic-base air-drying varnishes are also used to some extent.

b. Baking Varnishes—Oleoresinous.—Varnishes of this type were more widely used before thermosetting varnishes were developed. They dry partly by polymerization and partly by oxidation, dependent upon the drying oils they contain. Linseed-oil varnishes dry almost entirely by oxidation; tung-oil varnishes by both oxidation and polymerization. Drying by oxidation causes a hard surface to form while the varnish is still wet underneath. This is a disadvantage of this type of varnish, particularly in deep coils.

Oleoresinous black varnishes are either dyed or modified with a black asphalt called *gilsonite*. The latter is cheap, a good insulator, and readily soluble in ordinary varnish solvents; however, the oil resistance of the varnish is lowered by the addition of gilsonite.

Oleoresinous varnishes deteriorate and become more brittle through a continuation of the same oxidation and polymerization reactions by which they dry. Thus, quick-drying oleoresinous varnishes can be expected to lose toughness at elevated temperatures more rapidly than the slow-drying oleoresinous varnishes. Synthetic resins are often added to oleoresinous varnishes to prolong their life at elevated temperatures, or to improve their resistance to some specific chemical.

c. Thermosetting Varnishes.—These are heat-hardening, clear, synthetic varnishes which represent a vast improvement over ordinary baking varnishes, which depend upon oxidation for hardening. These materials are suitable for use either with Class B or Class A insulation. Compared with conventional oleoresinous varnishes, they have considerably more flexibility after proper baking and will retain their flexibility longer at higher temperatures. Moreover, they are generally superior in dielectric strength and have almost unsurpassed resistance to oil, acid, alkali, and moisture. For the most part, they consist of thermosetting resins of the phenolaldehyde (bakelite) or alkyd types. These types may even be mixed together and modified by the addition of other synthetic or natural resins so that almost any desired property may be obtained in the varnish film. Good thermosetting varnishes will not corrode copper and have little effect on wire with synthetic coatings, provided the apparatus is not immersed in the varnish more than 6 hr before baking.

d. *Silicone Varnishes.*—These varnishes represent one of the most spectacular and outstanding developments in their field. The Dow-Corning Company, and the General Electric Company have developed a series of these varnishes for apparatus that has to operate continuously at temperatures of 130 to 175°C with occasional peaks of 250°C. Although present silicone varnishes do not have high strength at these elevated temperatures, they do retain their flexibility, adhesion, and continuity of film, and hence make very suitable impregnants for stationary electrical components.

Constant development of new and better silicone products is going on. The following descriptions of existing silicone varnishes should be considered as only illustrative of the varnishes known at the time these words are being written.

1. *Dow-Corning* 993 *varnish.* This varnish has a solids content of 50 per cent; it is soluble in toluene and must be baked at 225 to 250°C. It is used principally in making flexible treated glass cloth and is semitacky at operating temperatures.

2. *Dow-Corning* 996 *varnish.* This varnish has a solids content of 50 per cent and should be thinned with V. M. and P. naphtha. Undercoats must be baked at 80°C, and the top coat at 150°C to prevent lifting. This varnish is thermosetting and is stronger than 993 at operating temperatures. Its relatively low baking temperature permits it to be cured in ovens now used for baking organic varnishes

3. *Dow-Corning* 2103 *varnish.* This varnish has a solids content of 50 per cent and is soluble in toluene, naphtha, and alcohols. It air-dries to give a resin with a definite melting point of 70°C; however, for best results, it should be cured at 250°C. Its principal use is in making glass silicone laminates.

Before the application of a silicone varnish, apparatus insulated with Class B insulation should be thoroughly baked at 250°C in order to remove all gas-forming binders. It is preferable to use silicone-bonded or -sized mica, glass, and asbestos products as the insulating materials, so that prebaking the apparatus before impregnation is not a necessity.

e. Fungus-proofing.—Complete fungus-proofing of electrical apparatus is, in itself, a complicated subject. Chlorinated phenols, organic mercury compounds, salicylanilide, and other fungicides are often added to selected insulating vanishes and lacquers to prevent fungus and bacterial attack on synthetic as well as on cellulose insulating materials. For temperatures up to 70°C, a 2 per cent addition of Dowicide No. 4 and a 3 per cent addition of Dowicide No. 7 are recommended; these compounds are chlorinated phenols. Phenyl mercury stearate, added to varnish at a strength of 1 per cent, is still active even after exposure to temperatures as high as 135°C for a period of not more than 6 hr. Like all mercury fungicides, its fumes will damage selenium rectifiers. Also, proper precautions should be taken to safeguard the health of those handling fungicides. Attacks on insulation by termites can usually be prevented by coatings of varnish containing chlorinated naphthalene known by the trade name of Halowax.

f. Solventless Varnishes.—Recent developments indicate that in a few years satisfactory solventless varnishes (100 per cent solids) may be commercially available; and these will be free from the poor shelf-life characteristics and tank deterioration of present solventless varnishes. However, until freedom from shrinking and cracking is also attained with these varnishes, they will probably enjoy little usage. Service shops are cautioned that solventless varnishes have been known to set up overnight in a dip tank!

g. Varnish Thinners.—Thinners are used to adjust the viscosity and solids content of varnish to the desired amount. Addition of thinners should be done slowly, accompanied with rapid agitation of the varnish to obtain thorough mixing. Any livering, curding, or precipitation in the varnish is an indication that an incorrect solvent is being used and that one of higher solvency powers is required to redissolve the precipitated resins. A localized cloudy appearance indicates that the solvent being used can be only partly tolerated by the varnish resins, and that further additions of solvent must be made in small quantities, accompanied by more thorough mixing; in such a case, it is often better to switch to a more powerful solvent. So-called V. M. and P. naphtha, a cheap hydrogenated petroleum solvent of moderate solvency powers, is suitable for thinning many varnishes. Lower viscosity—for the same percentage of solids—is possible if more powerful solvents, such as toluol and xylol, are used. Toluol is probably the best general-purpose solvent for obtaining rapid drying of the varnish and dissolving resins, but the inflammable and toxic nature of its vapors require caution in its use. Specific recommendations for particular types of varnish should be obtained from the varnish manufacturer.

3-18. Dipping Procedures.—Dipping in an open tank is usually the easiest way for a service shop to apply the necessary varnish. The apparatus is submerged, individually or collectively on racks, until all bubbling of the varnish ceases, when the part or parts are removed and allowed to drain. Wound armatures should be held with the shaft vertical during drainage, with the commutator end up after the first dip, and down after the second dip. This procedure is to avoid accumulation of varnish, which will unbalance the armature. If the piece has been wet-ground, it must be thoroughly dried before dipping.

Recent experience has shown that dipping times can be decreased and quality improved by dipping the parts while they are hot. Preheating parts before dipping increases the hazards due to fire and toxic vapors and also makes the varnish somewhat more difficult to control. However, when properly done, preheating offers many advantages; it ensures elimination of moisture, reduces the dipping time to 30 to 40 sec, and the draining time to 40 to 90 sec. The preheating should bring the work as rapidly as possible to 160 to 170°C. A good way is with infrared lamps. Dipping must be done immediately because Class A insulation will deteriorate rapidly if held at that temperature. Hot dipping should be done with the minimum amount of varnish because of the fire hazard incident to the introduction of work at a temperature above the flash point of the varnish solvent. An advantage of dipping the part while hot is that the part then heats the varnish rapidly upon contact, thus reducing its viscosity and giving it more penetrating power. Moreover, the cooling effect of the varnish decreases the volume of the air in the voids of the winding, thereby sucking some varnish into them. When hot dipping is used, it is necessary to provide means for cooling the varnish in the tank, either by means of a water jacket, or by cooling coils in the varnish itself. By withdrawing the work from the varnish after 30 to 40 sec, when the penetration is complete, numerous advantages are gained: the amount of heat imparted to the varnish in the tank is minimized; the draining time is kept to a minimum; the varnish immediately begins to bake and eliminate the solvent from the inside out; the baking can be most rapidly and efficiently accomplished; and the maximum film thickness is obtained.   After the first bake, further hot dips may be made immediately, while the part is still hot from the baking operation.

Pressure impregnation requires special apparatus but produces superior results.   To obtain full benefit from this process, varnish with a solids content of more than 60 per cent is necessary.   The stator (or armature) is placed in an impregnating tank, which is then sealed and evacuated to an absolute pressure of 2 or 3 in. of mercury.   Varnish is then admitted from the bottom of the varnish tank until the apparatus is immersed to the desired level.   After 10 to 30 min, an inert gas, such as carbon dioxide or nitrogen, is pumped into the impregnating tank at a pressure of from 75 to 100 lb per sq in., and this pressure is maintained for 10 min or more.   The varnish is then pumped back into its own reservoir, and the treated part is allowed to drain.   Use of an inert gas eliminates the hazard of explosion that exists if air is admitted to the closed tank of varnish.   Even better results will be obtained if the varnish tank is itself evacuated down to 1 or 2 in. of mercury for a period of 10 min or more before the varnish is pumped into the impregnating tank, in order to allow the vacuum to withdraw the air dissolved in the varnish and thereby forestall bubbling of the latter when it is introduced into the pressure-impregnating tank.

3-19. Baking Windings.—After the motor winding has been properly dipped in varnish and drained, it should be baked until the surface at least is firm, hard, and free of all tackiness.   The proper baking time and temperature should both be obtained from the varnish supplier.   Baking time will vary with type of varnish, size of apparatus, and type of oven; it can be shortened by increasing the baking temperature.   Baking times and temperatures are of the orders indicated below:

Oleoresinous, black, baking varnishes..... 4–12 hr at 110–120°C
Oleoresinous, clear, baking varnishes...... 6–12 hr at 110–120°C
Thermosetting varnishes................ 2–12 hr at 140°C
Silicone varnishes..................... Undercoats: air-dry 6 hr, bake 15 hr at 80°C.   Top coat: air-dry 6 hr, bake 1–3 hr at 150°C

Baking is usually done in an oven.   However, it can be done in open air by passing through the winding an electric current of sufficient strength to heat the winding and maintain it at the desired temperature long enough to obtain a good baking job.   When this method is used, it is desirable to measure the temperature of the winding during all the baking process either by thermometer, by thermocouple, or by resistance (see Art. 19-10). Infrared heat can be used to accelerate baking, but the application of this process requires selection of varnishes and solvents formulated especially for this purpose, and careful heating to avoid varnish "frothing" and charring of insulation.

3-20. Varnish Stripping.—After a part has been dipped and baked, it is often necessary to remove excess varnish from such places as air-gap surfaces or end-shield fits, since there are no practical means for preventing the varnish from accumulating there. A rag saturated with the correct solvent for the varnish to be removed can be used to wipe off excess accumulations of wet varnish. Baked varnish coatings can readily be stripped from metallic surfaces if these surfaces are treated with a suitable masking compound—such as Westinghouse No. 8574-3—before dipping. This compound is thinned with acetone to a sirupy state for spraying, or is maintained at a heavy molasses-like consistency if it is to be applied by dipping or by brushing. After this coating has been dried for a half hour, the apparatus may be given the normal varnish impregnation and baked. After baking, the masking compound will strip cleanly from the bare metal merely by inserting a knife or fingernail under it at one point. Both varnish and masking compound can be removed as a single intact film.

3-21. Points to Check after Rewinding.—Before assembly in the motor, a rewound stator should be carefully checked for short circuits, grounds, open circuits, or wrong connections.

Minor short circuits may not be easy to detect without assembling and testing the motor. However, if a portable internal growler is available and if this growler is passed around the inside of the stator bore, a short-circuited coil may be indicated by either (1) heat in the short-circuited coil, (2) increased current flowing in the growler primary, or (3) attraction of iron to the short-circuited coil.

A simpler and usually effective way to check for a short-circuited coil is to excite the stator winding with alternating current, preferably of 200 cycles or more. Touch a knife or any convenient piece of iron or steel to the inside of the stator bore in the center of one of the excited coils. Pull away the knife or piece of iron. Repeat for each coil. If the pull of one pole is substantially weaker than the other poles, the coil is short-circuited.

The winding should be tested for grounds by applying 900 volts alternating current between each winding and ground and between windings not electrically connected to one another.

Open-circuited coils can be tested by using a "lighting-out light." When testing for open circuits, a **wiring diagram** is most helpful, for the tester can determine readily between what leads there should be a circuit and between what leads there should not be any circuit.

Reversed coils can be checked by passing a small value of direct current through each winding separately and passing a compass around the inner periphery of the stator bore. A small premagnetized paper clip suspended on a string may serve the same purpose as the compass.

3-22. Electronic Winding Insulation Tester.—Recently, an electronic tester has been developed that detects faults in motor windings

FIG. 3-16.—Electronic winding-insulation tester, which applies repeated surges to the winding for detecting many types of faults. (*Courtesy of the General Electric Company.*)

such as turn-to-turn, coil-to-coil, and winding-to-ground faults. Such an instrument is illustrated in Fig. 3-16. The tester consists of a repeating-type surge-voltage generator, cathode-ray oscilloscope, and synchronous switching equipment. The generator produces a rapid succession of voltage surges (60 per second when used with 60-cycle power) of very steep wave front and of only a few microseconds duration for each surge. These surges are alternately applied to two coils or to two windings, and the picture of each surge appears on the screen of the oscilloscope. These appear together because of persistence of vision. The tester thus compares two windings, as illustrated in Fig. 3-17. Because of the steepness of the wave front, a high turn-to-turn voltage stress can be imposed upon the windings to test the insulation, as well as to check for winding faults.

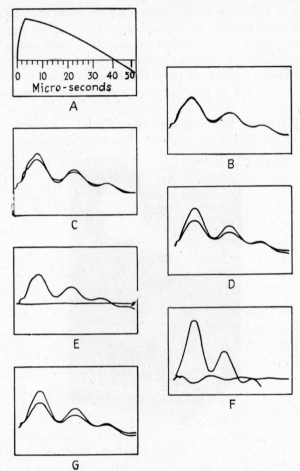

FIG. 3-17.—Typical oscillograms from surge tester of Fig. 3-16. (*Courtesy of the General Electric Company.*) (*A*) Wave shape of voltage applied to winding being tested. Note steepness of front and short duration of wave. (*B*) No faults. (*C*) One turn short-circuited. (*D*) One coil short-circuited. (*E*) Ground. (*F*) Reversed phase. (*G*) Reversed coil.

Bibliography

1. WEBER, C. A. M.: Winding and Connecting Small Motors, *Elec. J.*, August, 1924, pp. 377–382.
2. BRAYMER, DANIEL H., and ROE, A. C.: "Rewinding Small Motors," 2d ed., McGraw-Hill Book Company, Inc., New York, 1932.
3. SMITH, A. G.: "Care and Repair of Fractional Horsepower Motors," International Textbook Company, Scranton, Pa., 1936.
4. LANOY, HENRY: "Les petites machines électriques," vols. I, II, and III, Giradot et Cie, Paris, France, 1938–1941.

CHAPTER IV

SPLIT-PHASE INDUCTION MOTORS

The split-phase motor is one of the oldest types of single-phase motors ever built for commercial use.[1] Even today, it is one of the most important and most widely used of all the types of single-phase motors. It is used for such applications as washing machines, oil burners, blowers, centrifugal pumps, woodworking tools, business machines, bottle washers, churns, automatic musical instruments, buffing machines, grinders, machine tools, and a host of other applications. It is most widely used in the ratings from $\frac{1}{20}$ to $\frac{1}{3}$ hp.

4-1. Split-phase Motor Defined.—The American Standards Association[4] formally defines a split-phase motor as follows:

A split-phase motor is a single-phase induction motor equipped with an auxiliary winding, displaced in magnetic position from, and connected in parallel with, the main winding.

Note: Unless otherwise specified, the auxiliary circuit is assumed to be opened when the motor has attained a predetermined speed. The term split-phase motor, used without qualification, describes a motor to be used without impedance, other than that offered by the motor windings themselves, other types being separately defined.—ASA C42—1941. 10.10.360.

The split-phase motor is defined and described in somewhat less formal language in the following article.

4-2. Essential Parts of a Split-phase Motor.—The essential parts of a split-phase motor are represented diagrammatically in Fig. 4-1. There are two separate and distinct windings on the stator: a main, or running, winding; and an auxiliary, or starting, winding.

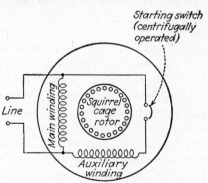

FIG. 4-1.—The split-phase motor.

Each winding is a complete circuit in itself, consisting of as many sections or pole groups as there are poles (except in

---

[1] For numbered references, see Bibliography at end of this chapter.

consequent-pole windings).   Ordinarily the two windings are spaced 90 electrical degrees apart; *i.e.*, the center of each pole group of the auxiliary winding is spaced halfway between the centers of two pole groups of the main winding.   The two windings are drawn 90 deg apart in Fig. 4-1 to represent this space displacement of the windings.   The rotor is usually of the squirrel-cage construction.

For starting purposes, both main and auxiliary windings are connected in parallel across the line.   (The sections or pole groups of either winding may be connected in series or in any number of parallel circuits, but the windings as a whole are connected in parallel with each other.)   In series with the auxiliary winding is a starting switch which opens at approximately 75 to 80 per cent of synchronous speed. (In a clutch motor, the switch operates at a lower speed.   See Art. 4-25.)   This switch is usually and preferably operated by centrifugal means; for detailed information on switches, refer to Arts. 18-5 to 18-9. Constructional details of a typical split-phase motor are illustrated in the cutaway view in Fig. 5-2, except that no capacitor is used on a split-phase motor.

4-3. Split-phase Starting Principle.—Like the two-phase motor, the split-phase induction motor has two primary (or stator) windings or phases displaced by 90 electrical degrees.   An idea of how locked-rotor torque is developed may be gained by comparing these two types of motors.   The two windings of a two-phase motor are connected to two different phases of the supply circuit which differ 90 deg in time phase.   Therefore, the respective currents produced by these two voltages are necessarily 90 deg apart in *time* phase, and they flow through two windings displaced 90 deg apart in *space* phase. In Chap. II it was shown how, under such conditions, a rotating field is produced, causing the rotor to develop torque.   The motor starts and runs—if the load is not too great—because the rotor tries to follow the revolving magnetic field.

If the two windings of a two-phase induction motor were both connected to the same single-phase voltage, the currents in the two stator windings would then be in phase, and no torque would be produced.*   If, however, an external resistor is connected in series with one winding, *it will decrease the current in that phase, but it will bring this decreased current more nearly in phase with the voltage.*   If,

---

* The truth of this point may perhaps be better understood when it is realized that, if the currents in the two windings were in time phase, the two windings would, in effect, be equivalent to a single winding and only a pulsating field could be set up, as explained in Art. 2-9.

then, one phase is connected directly across the line and the other across the line in series with a resistance, a phase displacement will be obtained between the two currents. This phase displacement is seldom large, being of the order of 20 to 30 deg in time. A vector diagram of the locked-rotor currents of a typical split-phase motor is given in Fig. 4-2.

Split-phase motors do not use two-phase windings because the best results are generally obtained with a different size of wire and a different number of turns in the two windings, whereas, in a true two-phase winding, both windings are identical. Rather than use an external resistor, it is more economical to obtain the additional resistance required in the auxiliary phase by using either a small size of copper wire, or wire of a material having a specific resistance higher than copper. Either arrangement, particularly the former, which is the more common, results in a starting winding of light weight, requiring *less* than half the total slot space. Thus, *more* than half the total slot space can be used for the main winding, thereby permitting use of a larger size of wire for it than use of a two-phase winding would allow; the larger wire, of course, means lower resistance, better efficiency, and somewhat more breakdown torque.

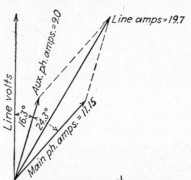

Fig. 4-2.—A vector diagram of the locked-rotor currents in a general-purpose split-phase motor rated ⅙ hp, 115 volts, 60 cycles, 1725 rpm.

Hence, in split-phase motors the main winding is usually of heavier wire, is distributed in more slots, and is bulkier than the auxiliary winding. In addition, the main winding usually consists of more turns than the auxiliary winding and is wound almost invariably in the bottoms of the slots; *i.e.*, it is wound first, and then the auxiliary winding is placed on top of it as can be seen in Fig..3-12.

4-4. Purpose of the Starting Switch.—At standstill, both windings must be in the circuit to develop torque, as explained previously. But after the motor has come up to approximately 75 or 80 per cent of synchronous speed, the main winding alone can develop nearly as much torque as the combined windings; this point is shown in Figs. 4-3 and 4-4. At a higher speed, between 80 and 90 per cent of synchronous speed, the combined-winding torque curve crosses the main-winding torque curve, so that, at speeds above this point, the motor develops less torque, for any given slip, with the auxiliary winding in the circuit than with it out. Consequently, it would be advantageous, purely

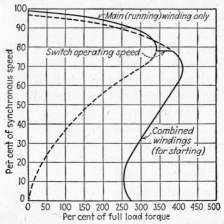

Fig. 4-3.—Speed-torque curve of a high-torque split-phase motor.

from a torque standpoint, to cut the auxiliary winding out of circuit exactly at the "crossover" point of the speed-torque curves. How-

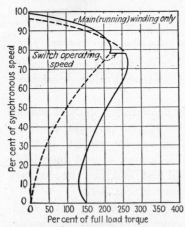

Fig. 4-4.—Speed-torque curve of a general-purpose split-phase motor.

ever, this point does not always occur at the same speed, even in individual motors of the same design, and varies in motors of different designs; moreover, switches vary in operating speeds, so that the usual practice is to make the average switch operate at a speed slightly below the average crossover point.

There is a second reason why the starting switch is important; *viz.*, it prevents the motor from drawing excessive watts from the line and burning up the starting winding when operating at normal running speeds, as it would do if the auxiliary winding were left in circuit continuously.

Split-phase motors of low horsepower ratings, however, can be built for continuous operation with the auxiliary winding in circuit; they formerly were popular for small fans but are seldom used now.

The usual starting switch is a centrifugally operated mechanical device. (For more details on starting switches, see Arts. 18-5 to 18-9.) Magnetically operated switches are used in hermetically sealed refrigerators, where a switch inside the refrigerant would not be permissible (see Art. 4-33).

4-5. General-purpose and High-torque Motors.—Applications for split-phase motors fall into two broad general classes:

1. Those which require frequent starting and a relatively large total running time per year; e.g., oil-burner and domestic refrigerator applications.
2. Those requiring infrequent starting and a relatively small total running time per year; e.g., washing machines and cellar-drainer pumps.

General-purpose motors (formerly called **long-hour motors** by Nema) are built in a wide variety of horsepower and speed ratings for the first class of applications. These are used for the great majority of applications where split-phase motors are used. **High-torque motors** (formerly called by Nema by the rather confusing name of **short-hour motors**) are used for the second class of applications, of which there are relatively few. Compared with general-purpose motors, high-torque motors have higher torques, substantially lower efficiencies, and much higher locked-rotor currents. Because they are built in high-volume production *and in few models* for such applications as washing machines, they are generally lower in first cost. However, their very high locked-rotor current precludes their general use on lighting circuits for applications requiring frequent starting because of the light flicker that they tend to produce. Moreover, the

TABLE IV.—MINIMUM TORQUES OF SPLIT-PHASE MOTORS*

Horsepower rating	Locked-rotor torque†	Pull-up torque†	Breakdown torque†
60 cycles—1725 rpm			
⅛	150	150	200
⅙	150	150	200
¼	90	90	185
60 cycles—1140 rpm			
⅛	125	125	175
⅙	125	125	175
¼	75	75	175

These torques are expressed in percentage of full-load torque.
* These torques were Nema requirements until June, 1946.
† For definitions of these terms, refer to Glossary.

fact that they are commercially available in but a few ratings still further limits their range of usefulness.

4-6. Torque Characteristics of Split-phase Motors.—The minimum torque requirements established by Nema for general-purpose split-phase motors are shown in Table IV. This table of torques was rescinded in June, 1946, by Nema and replaced with the torques given in Table II (see Art. 1-5).

Maximum permissible values of locked-rotor currents for general-purpose motors, according to Nema, are given in Table XXVI. High-torque split-phase washing-machine motors have much more locked-rotor current.

CONNECTION DIAGRAMS FOR SPLIT-PHASE MOTOR WINDINGS

4-7. Motor Connections and Terminal Markings.   *a. Motors with Leads.*—Terminal markings for a 4-lead, externally reversible, split-

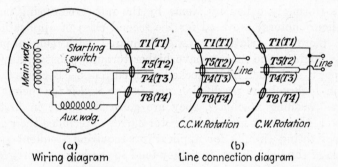

(a)
Wiring diagram

(b)
Line connection diagram

Fig. 4-5.—Wiring and line connection diagrams for a reversible split-phase motor with four lead lines tagged per A.S.A. standards. Terminal markings in parentheses were A.S.A. standard until 1938 and were used in the first edition of this book.

phase motor are given in Fig. 4-5. Two systems are shown there, and both are at present widely used. Needless to say, many other systems of tagging the leads have been used, some of which are tabulated below together with the standard systems:

	Main winding		Auxiliary winding	
A.S.A. Standard, 1938 to date....	$T1$	$T4$	$T5$	$T8$
A.S.A. Standard, before 1938....	$T1$	$T3$	$T2$	$T4$
Ohio Electric Motors............	Black	Black	Brown	Brown
Robbins and Myers..............	(1)gray	(4)green	(5)blue	(8)black
Westinghouse:				
Before 1930..................	$M1$	$M2$	$S1$	$S2$
Present unit-heater motors.....	($T1$)red	($T4$)yellow	($T5$)blue	($T8$)black

b. Motors with Cast Conduit Box and Built-in Terminal Board.— Many manufacturers now supply split-phase motors that have the conduit box cast as an integral part of the front end shield; usually such motors are provided with a built-in terminal board (see also Art. 5-22). This practice is now quite common. Typical wiring and line connection diagrams for motors of this construction are given in Figs. 4-6 and 4-7. Basic methods of connection are essentially as shown, though many variations may be encountered. One typical variation is to mount the stationary member of the starting switch directly on the terminal board; such an arrangement is shown in Fig. 4-27. In Figs. 4-6 and 4-7, it will be observed that the motor can be connected for either direction of rotation simply by interchanging two leads connected to the outside of the terminal board, and it is not necessary to dismantle the motor to do this.

Before a serviceman dismantles a motor, he should determine how the windings are connected to each other and to the line. These connections can best be recorded in the form of a **wiring diagram** similar to Fig. 4-5a, showing plainly the tagging or coloring of the leads and their connections. (It is desirable to make a record of line connections such as those shown in Fig. 4-5b if they are given on instruction cards; or the repairman may have to determine these connections for himself.) In order to make such a diagram, it is necessary to know how to tell the windings apart and how to identify the leads.

4-8. How to Tell the Windings Apart and How to Identify the Leads.—If the motor is assembled and the lead markings are indistinguishable or not understood, and if there are four leads, the main winding usually can be differentiated from the auxiliary winding, in one of two ways:

1. By measuring the ohmic resistance of each winding with a Wheatstone or Kelvin bridge or by the voltmeter-ammeter method.[*] For motors rated $\frac{1}{12}$ hp or more, the resistance of the auxiliary winding is almost invariably—but not necessarily—greater than the resistance of the main winding; for $\frac{1}{20}$-hp motors, the main winding is likely to have the higher resistance.

2. By measuring the locked power factors of the two windings separately, at rated voltage and frequency with the rotor in place. The power factor of the auxiliary winding is invariably and necessarily higher than that of the main winding. The power factor is best measured with a voltmeter, ammeter, and wattmeter, in preference to a power-factor meter. For further details, see Art. 19-16b.

[*] See Art. 19-9.

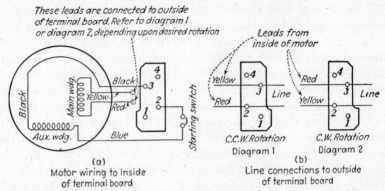

Fig. 4-6.—Wiring and line connection diagrams for a reversible split-phase motor with cast conduit box and 4-hole built-in terminal board. (*Courtesy of Westinghouse Electric Corporation.*)

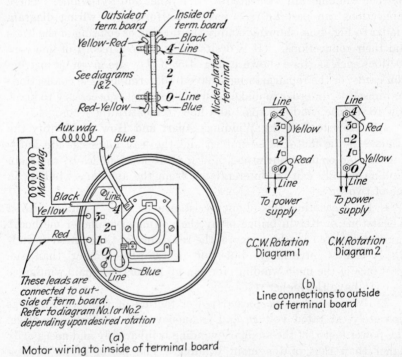

Fig. 4-7.—Wiring and line connection diagrams for an externally reversible split-phase motor with cast conduit box and 5-hole terminal board. (For Westinghouse motors with style numbers above 1,177,000.)

If the end shields are removed, permitting an inspection of the windings, identification of the leads is simpler:

3. One lead from the auxiliary winding goes to the switch (this identification is not necessarily positive; see Fig. 4-22).

4. The auxiliary winding usually is wound on top of the main winding.

5. The auxiliary winding has less weight of copper and, usually, fewer turns and is generally of a smaller size of wire than the main winding.

The connections of the windings as a whole to the switch and to the line being known, it is important next to determine and record the internal connections of the pole groups or coils comprising the windings. These connections can be recorded in the form of a **stator connection diagram,** illustrative examples of which are Figs. 4-8 to 4-17, inclusive.

THE MORE COMMON WINDING CONNECTIONS

The more common forms of winding connections will be discussed first before proceeding with some of the unusual or special connections.

4-9. Both Windings Series-connected.—Split-phase motors are wound usually as two-layer concentric windings (except for two-speed motors). **Stator connection diagrams** for two-, four-, six-, and eight-pole windings are given in Figs. 4-8, 4-9, 4-10, 4-11, respectively. (It is a simple matter to make up, if necessary, a similar diagram for a ten- or twelve-pole motor.) In these four diagrams, both the main and the auxiliary windings are separately connected in series. These diagrams all show the lead $T5(T2)$ which goes to the starting switch tied into the winding as a "dummy" lead. A motor connected by any of these diagrams will have terminals marked in accordance with Fig. 4-5, which will then apply. Both old and new A.S.A taggings are given for these diagrams.

If a motor has a built-in conduit box and terminal board and if it is desired to follow the color scheme of lead identification followed in Figs. 4-6 and 4-7, the stator connection diagrams (Figs. 4-8 to 4-11) still apply, provided that the leads are colored as follows, instead of being tagged:

The $T1$ lead is to be made red.
The $T5(T2)$ lead is omitted, and the other "switch lead" is to be made blue.
The $T4(T3)$ lead is to be made yellow.
The $T8(T4)$ lead is to be made black.

The direction of rotation specified in Fig. 4-5 applies only if the leads are tagged in accordance with the connection diagrams given

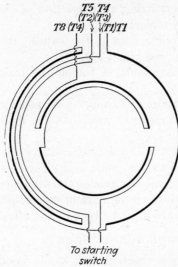

FIG. 4-8.—Stator connection diagram; two poles, one phase, both windings series, four line leads, externally reversible.

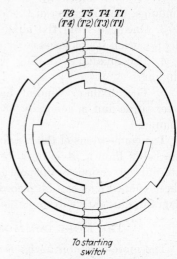

FIG. 4-9.—Stator connection diagram; four poles, one phase, both windings series, four line leads, externally reversible.

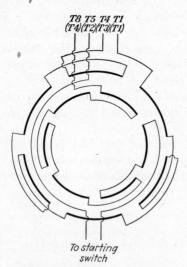

FIG. 4-10.—Stator connection diagram; six poles, one phase, both windings series, four line leads, externally reversible.

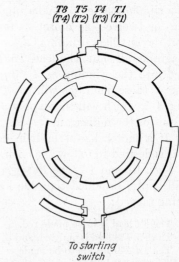

FIG. 4-11.—Stator connection diagram; eight poles, one phase, both windings series, four line leads, externally reversible.

and if the direction of rotation is specified from the *connection end.* Connections are usually made in the **front end** of the motor, which is defined as the *end opposite the shaft extension.* Nema specifies direction of rotation when looking at the end opposite the shaft extension, but this procedure is not necessarily followed by all manufacturers. Unless otherwise stated, direction of rotation in this book is always specified from the front end.

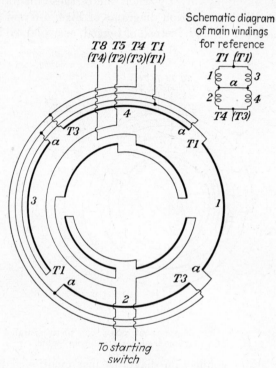

FIG. 4-12.—Stator connection diagram; four poles, one phase, parallel main, series auxiliary, four line leads, externally reversible.

4-10. Parallel-connected Main Winding, Series-connected Auxiliary Winding.—The main, or running, winding of a split-phase motor is often connected in two or more parallel circuits for the sake of quietness. This practice is more common in six- or eight-pole motors than it is in two- or four-pole motors. There is less necessity for connecting the auxiliary winding in parallel, for the latter is in the circuit only during the starting period; moreover, the auxiliary winding usually is wound with a rather small size of wire—to obtain the necessary resistance—and the size might be inconveniently small if a parallel winding were used.

A set of diagrams for parallel-connected motors is given in Figs. 4-12, 4-13, 4-14, and 4-15 for four-, six-, eight-, and ten-pole motors, respectively. Like Figs. 4-8 to 4-11, inclusive, these diagrams all show the lead $T5(T2)$, which goes to the starting switch, tied into the windings as a dummy lead; also, the **wiring and line connection diagrams** of Fig. 4-5 apply directly when one of these diagrams is used. The wiring and line connection diagrams of Figs. 4-6 and 4-7 can be used if the leads are colored, instead of tagged, as explained in Art. 4-9.

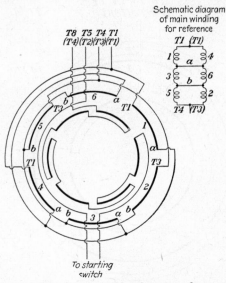

Fig. 4-13.—Stator connection diagram; six poles, one phase, parallel main, series auxiliary, four line leads, externally reversible.

The four stator connection diagrams just mentioned have cross, or equalizing, connections so that each pole is connected directly in parallel with the pole diametrically opposite it. This arrangement is best shown in the schematic diagram accompanying each figure; in these schematic diagrams, each numbered coil represents the corresponding numbered pole group. The letters a, b, etc., are used to identify the cross or equalizing connections. These schematic diagrams show how the diametrically opposite poles are paralleled and cross-connected; they are of invaluable assistance in checking these diagrams. The correctness of any of them can be checked by following the schematic diagram, remembering that the magnetic polarity

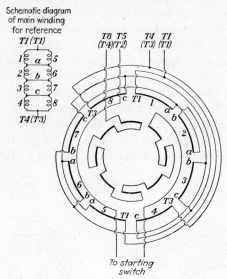

Fig. 4-14.—Stator connection diagram; eight poles, one phase, parallel main, series auxiliary, four line leads, externally reversible.

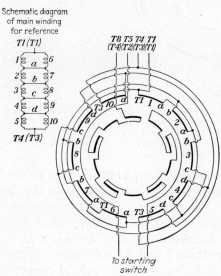

Fig. 4-15.—Stator connection diagram; ten poles, one phase, parallel main, series auxiliary, four line leads, externally reversible.

alternates from pole to pole around the circumference. The repairman, following these principles, could construct a similar diagram for a motor having more than 10 poles.

The purpose of connecting diametrically opposite poles in parallel is to equalize the flux in these poles as much as possible to minimize any unbalanced magnetic pull and consequent vibration and noise.

4-11. Both Windings Parallel, Cross-connected.—If both windings are to be connected in parallel, the diagrams shown in Figs. 4-12 to 4-15, or similar diagrams, can be used, except that the auxiliary winding must be connected in the same fashion as the main winding.

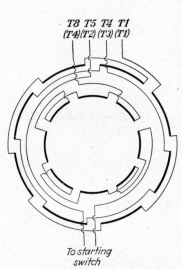

T8 T5 T4 T1
(T4)(T2) (T3) (T1)

To starting
switch

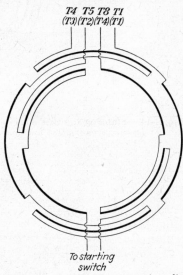

T4 T5 T8 T1
(T3)(T2)(T4)(T1)

To starting
switch

FIG. 4-16.—Stator connection diagram; eight poles, one phase, main winding long throw, auxiliary winding short throw, both windings series, four line leads, externally reversible.

FIG. 4-17.—Stator connection diagram; four poles, one phase, both windings series, switch in center of auxiliary winding.

Care must be taken, however, to provide the switch leads, and also to tag the leads properly if it is desired to know the direction of rotation before the motor is assembled. Or, if it is more convenient, the stator connection diagrams (Figs. 8-11 to 8-13) can be used, except that the switch must be inserted in the $T5(T2)$ lead, or in the $T8(T4)$ lead.

4-12. "Short-throw" and "Long-throw" Connections.—Consider Fig. 4-11. In this diagram, each pole is connected directly to an adjacent one. This is the most usual form of connection and, especially with hand or gun winding, is the easiest and most logical way to connect the coils. When this type of connection, known as a **short-**

throw connection, is used, each pole group is connected to an adjacent pole group. In the **long-throw** connection, illustrated in Fig. 4-16, the connections are between alternate pole groups. (Short-throw and long-throw connections for polyphase motors are discussed in Art. 14-6.) Electrically, it is not important which connection is used in a simple series winding such as those shown in Figs. 4-8 to 4-11. However, if the repairman should encounter such a connection as is shown in Fig. 4-16 in a motor he is rewinding, it is a safer general rule to duplicate the connections *exactly* rather than to attempt to modify

Fig. 4-18.—High-torque washing-machine motor with a direction-connection plug. (*Courtesy of Westinghouse Electric Corporation.*)

them, even though such a modification may appear to give identical results.

4-13. Switch in Center of Auxiliary Winding.—In Figs. 4-8 to 4-16, the switch was connected at one end of the auxiliary winding; *i.e.*, one of the switch leads came from the winding directly, and the other from the line. Sometimes the switch is connected in the center of the auxiliary winding; such a connection, for a four-pole motor, is shown in Fig. 4-17, which is otherwise the same as Fig. 4-9. This connection is identical in performance with Fig. 4-9, and generally it is not important which one of the two is used. It seems superfluous to show similar diagrams for other numbers of poles.

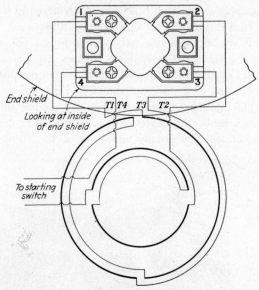

Fig. 4-19.—Stator connection diagram for motor with direction-connection plug, two poles, both windings series.

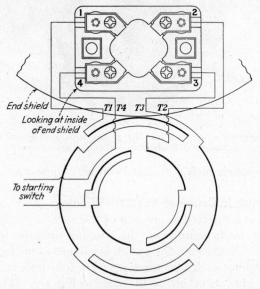

Fig. 4-20.—Stator connection diagram for motor with direction-connection plug, four poles, both windings series.

4-14. Motors with Direction-connection Plug.—One manufacturer formerly supplied high-torque split-phase motors with a direction-connection plug, as illustrated in Fig. 4-18. A square plug, attached to a rubber cord, can be plugged into a square receptacle in either one of two 90-deg positions (actually there are four positions). Two white arrows on the black (or male) plug point to two embossed arrows on an escutcheon plate, and the latter two arrows indicate the direction of rotation. The plug must be inserted correctly the first time to give the desired direction of rotation; for the escutcheon plate locks the male portion in place, and the latter can be removed only after removing the escutcheon plate.

Connection diagrams for the windings of this motor are given in Figs. 4-19 and 4-20 for two- and four-pole motors, respectively.

4-15. Connecting Motor Windings for a Definite Direction of Rotation. Split-phase motors with four line leads, as shown in Fig. 4-5, can be connected to the power line for either direction of rotation. If the external line connections shown in Fig. 4-5 or their equivalent are made inside the motor and only two line leads brought out, the motor becomes nonreversible. Before connecting a motor for a definite direction of rotation, it is advisable to make certain that the direction of rotation is unmistakably specified by the customer.

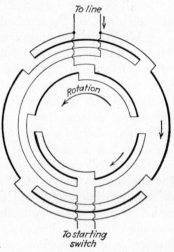

FIG. 4-21.—Stator connection diagram; four poles, one phase, both windings series, two line leads, CCW rotation.

Ordinarily, direction of rotation is specified from the **front end.** (As stated in Art. 4-9, the front end is the end opposite the shaft extension.) The *standard* direction of rotation is counterclockwise, viewed from the front end. (This is standard for both the A. S. A. and Nema.)

The **stator connection diagram** of a four-pole series-connected winding with two leads, connected for counterclockwise rotation, is given in Fig. 4-21. This diagram was derived from Fig. 4-9 by connecting together leads $T1$ and $T5(T2)$ and bringing out a single lead and also by bringing out $T4(T3)$ and $T8(T4)$ as a single lead. In like fashion, diagrams for counterclockwise rotation can be derived from any of the four-lead diagrams (Figs. 4-8 to 4-17). Similarly, if clockwise rotation is desired, any of Figs. 4-8 to 4-17 can be converted to a two-lead diagram by connecting $T1$ and $T8(T4)$ inside the winding and bringing out a single lead and also by connecting $T5(T2)$ and $T4(T3)$ together to make the second line lead.

Direction of rotation, as used in the preceding paragraph, refers to *the end of the motor where the connections are made* and not necessarily to the front end. Usually the switch is at the front end, and connections are made there. In these cases, the rotation on the diagram is the rotation of the motor. Sometimes motors are connected on the shaft-extension end—in this case, if Figs. 4-8 to 4-17 are used and if rotation of the motor is to agree with the line connection diagram (Fig. 4-5), it will be necessary to interchange the tags $T1$ and $T4(T3)$.

In all of these diagrams, the outer winding is the main winding and the inner one the auxiliary.

4-16. Predetermining Direction of Rotation.—The direction in which a split-phase motor will run for a given connection of line leads can be determined by actual test on the connected windings or by inspection of the connection diagram. The one principle which must be remembered is that rotation *is always from an auxiliary winding pole toward the nearest main winding pole of the same magnetic polarity.* Why this principle is true and how it can be applied will be shown in the following paragraphs.

The current in the auxiliary winding is more nearly in phase with the line voltage than is the current in the main winding because of the resistance deliberately built into the auxiliary winding (see Fig. 4-2 and Art. 4-3). Hence, the auxiliary-winding current leads the main-winding current in time phase. Therefore, it follows that the stator flux set up by the auxiliary phase will lead the main-phase flux in time phase. As a result, the stator flux of the auxiliary winding reaches its maximum or crest value ahead (in time) of the main-winding stator flux; when the flux is building up under the main poles, it is decaying under the auxiliary poles. The resultant flux, therefore, shifts in the direction from the auxiliary pole to the main pole of the *same magnetic polarity*, and the motor starts and runs in the same direction as the motion of the flux.

This principle can be applied in the following ways to predetermine direction of rotation:

a. By Testing the Connected Windings.—Connect one end of the auxiliary winding to one end of the main winding, leaving the other ends of the two windings apart. Pass a small value of direct current through the auxiliary winding, and locate and mark a north pole on the stator core by a figure 1. Now, open the auxiliary winding; leaving unchanged the lead of the d-c supply that is on the common connection, connect the other d-c lead to the open end of the main winding, and locate and mark the nearest adjacent north pole on the core with a figure 2 (this distance should be 90 electrical degrees). Care must be taken not to reverse the magnetism in the compass needle by restraining its free motion, by allowing it to get too near the stator core, or by using too much current. The assembled motor will rotate in the direction from 1 to 2 when the main- and auxiliary-winding leads are connected as they were for the test. If desired, a premagnetized paper clip or short length of soft iron wire suspended by a fine thread can be substituted for the compass.

If there are only two line leads (as in Fig. 4-21), join the two switch leads together, and apply the direct current to the two line leads, thus exciting both windings. Place the compass inside the stator core, and allow it to come to rest; then open the starting-switch leads. When this is done, the compass needle will move in the direction that the rotor will turn when the motor is assembled.

A third method, which most repair shops are apt to find more practical than either of the two methods just mentioned, is as follows: Join the main and auxiliary windings, short-circuiting the two switch leads, and excite the two line leads with alternating current of any frequency available. Suspend a soft iron wire, about 1 to 1½ in. long, on the end of a thread in the stator bore, but not touching the stator iron. *Now open the starting switch leads, and the wire will move in the direction of rotation.* If 60 cycles is used for this test, not more than half voltage should be applied; but if the frequency is 120 cycles or higher, rated voltage may be applied. If the current is too strong, it is better not to lower the wire all the way into the stator core, but merely into the end windings.

b. By Inspection of the Stator Connection Diagram.—How to predetermine the direction of rotation by inspection of the stator connection diagram is illustrated in Fig. 4-21. Assume current to be entering the line lead at the right, as indicated by the arrow. The current divides, and a portion of it flows through the first main-winding coil in a clockwise direction on the diagram, as shown by a curved arrow; now, following the other portion of the current through the starting switch to the first coil of the auxiliary winding, a second curved arrow is drawn as shown. Now the two poles indicated are both of the same magnetic polarity, since the imaginary current traverses both poles in the same direction on the diagram. Therefore, the direction of rotation will be counterclockwise, *i.e.*, from the auxiliary coil to the nearest main coil of the same magnetic polarity.

4-17. Nonreversible Motor with One Line Lead on the Starting Switch.—Figure 4-22 is an interesting variation of Fig. 4-21. It shows a connection employed by at least one manufacturer to eliminate one soldered or welded joint and thereby reduce cost of manufacture. There is only one soldered connection, *viz.*, where one side of the line connects to the common point of the main and auxiliary windings. The free or open ends of the main and auxiliary windings are connected to the two separate terminals of the starting switch. The remaining line lead is connected to the same switch terminal as is the main winding.

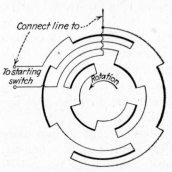

FIG. 4-22.—Stator connection diagram for a motor with a line lead on the starting switch, four poles, series.

This method of connection will give the same results as the more conventional diagram of Fig. 4-21, but it is given here to illustrate one of the many various types of connections that may be encountered; it is also given to warn the serviceman that a switch lead is not necessarily a lead from the auxiliary winding. The example chosen for illustration was a four-pole series-connected motor, but this same type of connection might equally well be used in place of any of the stator connection diagrams, Figs. 4-8 to 4-16.

This type of connection is often employed where a two-conductor rubber cable is used for the line leads. One strand of the cable is provided with an eyelet for connecting to the starting-switch terminal, and the other strand is merely skinned for soldering to the common point of the winding. This soldered connection and the connection to the starting-switch terminal must be made before the motor is assembled.

4-18. Motor with Cord and Plug and Built-in Line Switch.—Split-phase motors are often supplied with a built-in line switch and cord and plug. Connections of one such motor are illustrated in Fig. 4-23. In this motor, the line switch is a toggle switch affixed to the front end shield of the motor with the operating lever coming out perpendicular to the shaft. The terminal board is retained, and the motor can be connected for either direction of rotation by changing the yellow and red leads connected to the outside of the terminal board. Thermal protection can be added to this motor simply by connecting the thermostat in series with the line. Motors of this type are very popular for home workshops and similar applications.

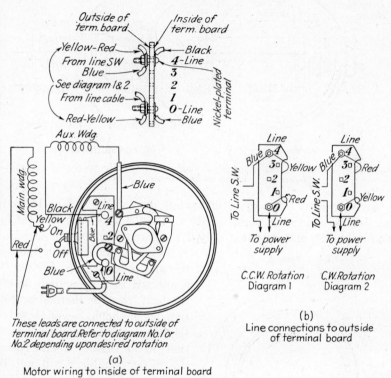

(a)
Motor wiring to inside of terminal board

(b)
Line connections to outside of terminal board

FIG. 4-23.—Wiring and line connection diagrams for an externally reversible split-phase motor equipped with built-in line switch and cord-and-plug connections. (*Courtesy of Westinghouse Electric Corporation.*)

THERMALLY PROTECTED MOTORS

A general description of thermal protective devices and how they function is given in Arts. 18-14 to 18-16. How they are used in split-phase motors is the subject of the following paragraphs.

4-19. Reversible—Five or Six Line Leads.—Figure 4-24 shows wiring and line connection diagrams of a split-phase motor equipped with a thermal protective device which is mounted on or in the motor, becoming an integral part of the latter. The connections are the same as for the typical split-phase motor of Fig. 4-5 except that the thermal protective device is connected in series with the line. The stator winding connections can, of course, be the same as those of any split-phase motor not equipped with thermal protection.

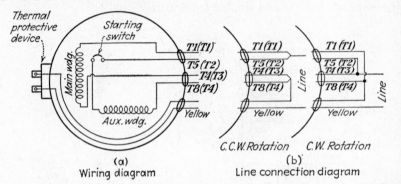

(a)
Wiring diagram

(b)
Line connection diagram

FIG. 4-24.—Wiring and line connection diagrams; thermally protected, split-phase motor with six line leads, externally reversible.

Five external leads are sufficient if one of the yellow leads in Fig. 4-24 is connected permanently to the $T8(T4)$ lead; this can be done inside the motor so that only five external leads are required.

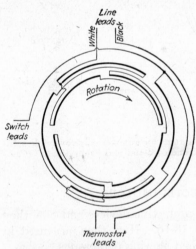

FIG. 4-25.—Stator connection diagram for a nonreversible, thermally protected, split-phase motor, four poles, series-connected.

When a motor with built-in thermal overload protection is connected to a grounded circuit, the lead from the thermal protective device should be connected to the ungrounded side of the line so that, if the thermal device opens, the motor windings will not be "hot." In Fig. 4-24, the $T1(T1)$ lead should be connected to the grounded side of the line, and the yellow lead to the ungrounded side. Most manufacturers state on the instruction tag furnished with the motor which lead is to be connected to the ungrounded side of the line.

4-20. Nonreversible—Two Line Leads.—A nonreversible motor, even if thermally protected, requires only two line leads, as does any other split-phase motor. The **stator connection diagram** of a representative four-pole series-connected motor is given in Fig. 4-25. One lead is colored white to denote that this should be the lead connected to the grounded side of the line on a grounded circuit in order that the protective device be on the "hot" side of the circuit. Some manufacturers, however, use a distinctive marking to indicate the thermostat lead; Robbins and Myers, for example, use a black lead with red tracer to denote the thermostat lead. The serviceman should take care to determine which is the proper lead to connect to the grounded side of the line, and act accordingly. Another **stator connection diagram** is given in Fig. 4-26; in this diagram, one line lead is connected directly to one terminal of the starting switch, just as was done in Fig. 4-22.

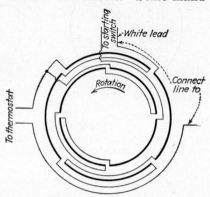

Fig. 4-26.—Stator connection diagram for a nonreversible, thermally protected, split-phase motor, four poles, series-connected, with a line lead on the starting switch.

4-21. Motors with Terminal Board.—Thermally protected split-phase motors equipped with a terminal board may be wired as shown

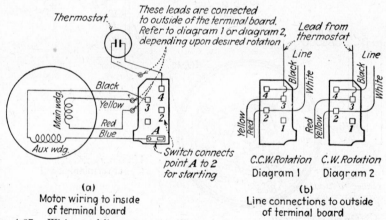

Fig. 4-27.—Wiring and line connection diagrams for a thermally protected, externally reversible, split-phase motor with conduit box and 4-hole terminal board.

in Fig. 4-27, which is similar to Fig. 4-6 except for the addition of a third terminal, and Fig. 4-29, which is likewise similar to Fig. 4-7. These motors are both externally reversible. CAUTION: *Post 3 must*

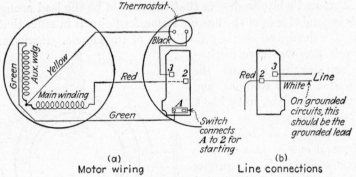

(a)
Motor wiring

(b)
Line connections

FIG. 4-28.—Wiring and line connection diagrams for a thermally protected, nonreversible split-phase motor with conduit box and 4-hole terminal board.

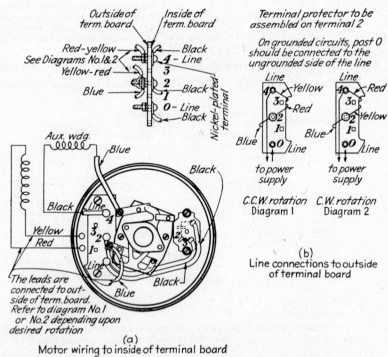

(a)
Motor wiring to inside of terminal board

(b)
Line connections to outside of terminal board

FIG. 4-29.—Wiring and line connection diagrams for a thermally protected, externally reversible, split-phase motor with cast conduit box and 5-hole terminal board. (For Westinghouse Type FHT motors with style numbers above 1,117,000.)

on no account be connected to either side of the line. The same **stator connection diagrams** as for Fig. 4-6 apply.

A similar connection, except for a nonreversible motor, is shown in Fig. 4-28. This motor requires only two terminals. A representative **stator connection diagram** which applies exactly is Fig. 8-14.

4-22. Heating Coil of Protective Device in Auxiliary Phase Only.— Built-in thermal protective devices usually are provided with a heating coil, or its equivalent, so that the device is influenced both by temperature and by current passing through the heater coil. In the motors just discussed, line current passes through the heater coil. If a third terminal is added to the protective device, the latter can be connected so that only the current of the auxiliary phase passes through the heater, although the contacts open the line circuit. This arrangement is shown in Fig. 4-30.

4-23. Oil-burner Motor with Automatic-reset Thermal Overload Protection.—The new Nema standard oil-burner motor (Art. 20-16) is equipped with manual-reset thermal overload protection. Before these oil-burner motor standards were adopted in June, 1946, automatic-reset protection was used to a limited extent.

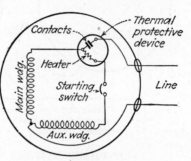

Wiring diagram

Fig. 4-30.—Wiring and line connection diagram of a thermally protected split-phase motor with the heater coil in the auxiliary phase only.

Automatic resetting of the thermal overload device is a difficult problem when inherent overheating protection is added to a motor used on an oil burner provided with intermittent ignition; this is because of a requirement of the Underwriters' Laboratories that the device never reset in less than 3 min when the motor is in an ambient of 15°C (59°F). Most overload devices would not reset in that time if they were tripped from a running overload, but are certain to reset in less time than that if tripped by locked-rotor conditions, unless some special provision is made. In Fig. 4-31, a successful arrangement that has been used for obtaining this 3-min reset time is shown. A heat-storage coil of copper wire is placed in the thermostat cavity in close proximity to the disc of the thermostat; this coil is connected in series with the auxiliary winding only. In addition, the thermostat is a special one with lower than normal resetting temperature, but with a normal opening temperature. Under stalled-rotor conditions, current flows through the heat-storage coil, thereby generating heat in it, which is stored up and used to delay the resetting of the disc. Since this heat-storage coil is not in series with the main winding, it does not affect the operation of the thermal overload on running loads.

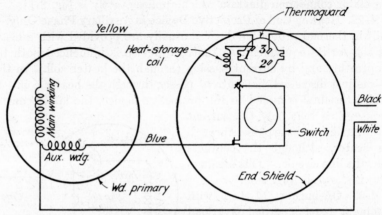

Fig. 4-31.—Wiring and line connection diagram for a split-phase oil-burner motor with automatic-reset inherent-overheating protection; single-voltage, nonreversible, Type D Thermoguard. (*Courtesy of Westinghouse Electric Corporation.*)

SPLIT-PHASE MOTORS WITH A MECHANICAL CLUTCH

Clutch-type motors, as described in the following paragraphs, are no longer commercially available; but their description is retained in this edition because there are still a large number of them in service.

4-24. Construction.—In a motor with built-in clutch, the rotor core is free to revolve on the shaft, without turning the latter, until the former has reached a certain predetermined speed, when a centrifugally operated clutch allows the motor to pick up its load.

One form of clutch construction is illustrated in Fig. 4-32. The rotor core is provided with three weights, to the outer surface of each of which is firmly riveted a section of molded brake lining made of the material used for automobile brakes. The three weights are restrained by means of a garter spring, shown in the photograph. The inside of the rotor core has a bronze bearing which allows the rotor core to turn freely on the shaft. When the rotor core comes up to speed, centrifugal action causes the weights to fly out, bringing the friction surfaces into contact with the clutch bell shown at the right of the photograph. Each weight pivots individually about the steel pin provided for that purpose, making the clutch partially self-energizing. The pivoting about the pin and the partial self-energizing

FIG. 4-32.—The rotor of a clutch motor.   (*Courtesy of Westinghouse Electric Corporation.*)

a. Rotor core.
b. Clutch weight
c. Brake shoe.
d. Garter spring.

e. Clutch bell.
f. Cast fan blades.
g. Journal about which rotor core turns.
h. Shaft extension.

action are due, at first, to the inertia of the weight itself and, later, to the friction torque developed when the clutch is in engagement.

4-25. Characteristics.—When the shaft of this motor is locked, the rotor core comes up to approximately two-thirds of the full-load speed and remains there, the clutch slipping the while. Under such conditions, the current drawn from the line is approximately 13 amp (for a $\frac{1}{4}$-hp 110-volt 60-cycle 1725-rpm motor). The average locked-shaft torque of this motor is approximately 260 per cent, and the breakdown torque approximately 280 per cent of full-load torque. The effective locked-shaft torque, on many applications, is far in excess of the average locked-shaft torque of 260 per cent owing to the

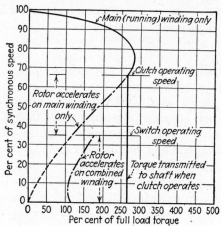

FIG. 4-33.—The speed-torque curve of a split-phase clutch motor.

unusual nature of the starting of the clutch-type motor. Under a locked-shaft condition, this clutch motor delivers hammer blows and often will start a load that would require a very much higher steady value of starting torque. It is particularly useful for hammering loose tight bearings, such as are apt to occur on outdoor pumps or compressors in cold weather. A representative speed-torque curve is given in Fig. 4-33.

It should be noted that the switch operating speed is only 35 per cent of synchronous speed instead of 70 to 80 per cent as in the case of the conventional split-phase motor. This point is very important and must be borne in mind when the switch operating speed is checked or when the switch is replaced.

4-26. Windings and Connections—Single-voltage Motors.—The windings and connections of the single-voltage clutch motor are similar to those of the conventional split-phase motors described in this chapter.

4-27. Windings and Connections—Dual-voltage Motors.—The windings of a clutch motor may be arranged for dual voltage. In this

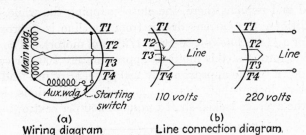

(a)
Wiring diagram

(b)
Line connection diagram.

Fig. 4-34.—Wiring and line connection diagrams for a dual-voltage split-phase clutch motor.

case, the main winding is connected in two sections, one section comprising half the stator coils in series, the second section comprising the remainder of the stator coils. This arrangement, so far as the main winding is concerned, is exactly the same as for that of a dual-voltage repulsion-start motor. For a four-pole motor, the **stator connection diagram** *for the main winding only* is Fig. 10-8; the **stator connection diagram** *for the starting winding only* is Fig. 4-9. The corresponding wiring and line connection diagrams are given in Fig. 4-34. The main winding is connected in series for 220 volts and in parallel for 110 volts. The auxiliary phase is connected across the line in either case; it is necessarily a 220-volt winding. This arrangement gives only half as much starting torque on 110 as on 220 volts; but since it is necessary to bring the rotor core only up to speed, the torque is ample in either case. However, the torque available to start the load is the same on either voltage because the auxiliary winding is not in the circuit when the clutch picks up the external load.

This same winding arrangement is used sometimes for dual-voltage split-phase motors made for fan or blower applications. (Such motors have no clutch.)

OTHER SPECIAL CONSTRUCTIONS

4-28. Split-phase Motor with Revolving Primary.—This construction was formerly used by General Electric for washing-machine motors, but has been obsolete for a long time. A brief description of it is retained in this edition partly because there are still a large number of them in service, and partly because it illustrates an interesting engineering principle. In all the motors so far discussed in this chapter, the primary windings have been on the stator member. The **primary windings,** let it be remembered, are those windings which set up the rotating field; they are always connected to the line or source of power. Although the primary windings ordinarily are on the stator, there is no fundamental reason why they should be. A large number of split-phase motors have been built with a squirrel-cage stator and a wound rotor; in these motors, the rotor is the primary. In principle, these windings are no different from the primary windings ordinarily found on the stator; and a connection diagram such as Fig. 4-22 is applicable, except that the actual direction of rotation of the rotor will be opposite to that indicated by the arrow.

The reason why the rotor will revolve against the arrow in Fig. 4-22 may be explained briefly: This arrow indicates the direction of rotation of the magnetic field. The magnetic field tries to carry the squirrel cage with it, as explained in Chap. II, and actually exerts a torque on the stator; an equal and opposite torque must also be exerted upon the primary, or rotor. Since the stator is not free to revolve, but the rotor is, the latter will revolve *against* the magnetic field. At synchronous speed, the field would be stationary in space.

To reverse the direction of rotation, it is necessary to remove the front (collector) end shield. There are two leads from each winding, making four in all, and these four leads are connected to three terminals. The direction of rotation will be reversed if the two main-winding leads are interchanged, or if the two auxiliary-winding leads are interchanged. To assist in locating which two leads to interchange, one design has copper clips on the proper two leads; in another design, the two leads to be interchanged have brass terminals.

4-29. Two-speed, Pole-changing Motors.—Split-phase motors can be wound with pole-changing windings to give two different normal speeds of operation, either of which can be selected by making changes in the external connections. Regardless of the speed selected, the motor will operate at a substantially constant speed within the range of its rating. The number of combinations of windings is legion and only a few of the basic ones can be given here. For purposes of this discussion, pole-changing windings are broken down into two broad general classes: four-winding arrangements and three-winding arrangements.

4-30. Two-speed, Pole-changing Motors with Four Windings.—With this arrangement, there are two main windings and two auxiliary

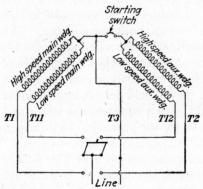

FIG. 4-35.—Wiring and line connection diagram of a two-speed, pole-changing, split-phase motor with four windings.

windings, one of each for each of the two speeds. A schematic wiring and line connection diagram is given in Fig. 4-35, which shows the use of a double-pole double-throw switch to select the desired speed; a three-pole switch would be required to deenergize the motor completely. It will be noted that the connections are so arranged as to require but one starting switch. *This starting switch must operate at 75 to 80 per cent of the synchronous speed of the low-speed winding.* To some extent, this requirement limits the switching torque on the high-speed connection.

The motor of Fig. 4-35 is not reversible, but it could be made so by bringing out the other ends of both main windings, at the expense of bringing out two more leads. It is also interesting to note that this motor could be arranged to operate in one direction on one speed, and in the other direction on the other speed; the same is not true of the three-winding arrangements discussed in Art. 4-31.

Because of the fact that four windings are used, considerable winding space is required in the motor. For this reason, the physical dimensions of a two-speed pole-changing split-phase motor are necessarily greater than those of a single-speed motor of the same horsepower

and speed rating.   To facilitate winding, the low-speed windings often
use a consequent-pole connection.

Briefly, a **consequent-pole winding** has only half as many pole
groups as there are poles, and all of these groups are connected for the
same magnetic polarity.   (In Art. 3-7, it was stated that adjacent
poles should always be connected for opposite magnetic polarities,

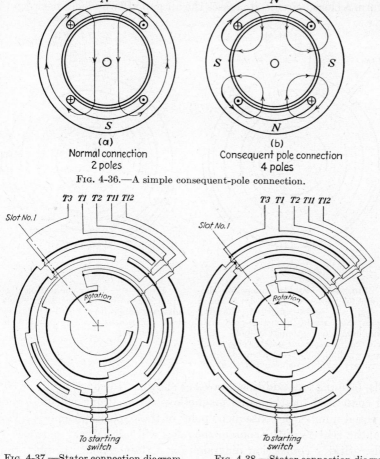

(a)
Normal connection
2 poles

(b)
Consequent pole connection
4 poles

Fig. 4-36.—A simple consequent-pole connection.

Fig. 4-37.—Stator connection diagram
for motor of Fig. 4-35; 4 and 6 poles, all
series-connected.   Both   main   windings
are conventional; 4-pole auxiliary is consequent-pole, and 6-pole auxiliary (extreme
inner winding) has only two coils as shown.

Fig. 4-38.—Stator connection diagram
for motor of Fig. 4-35; 4 and 8 poles, all
series-connected.   Reading from the outside inward: 4-pole main winding, conventional; 8-pole main winding, consequent-pole; 4-pole auxiliary winding,
consequent-pole; 8-pole auxiliary winding, consequent-pole.

except for consequent-pole windings.) Why the magnetic field has twice as many poles as there are coils was explained by C. W. Kincaid[5] by the use of a figure very similar to Fig. 4-36. In this figure, there are two coil groups; and when these are connected for opposite magnetic polarities, as in (*a*), the magnetic field has two poles. When these two coil groups are connected to have the *same* magnetic polarity, the two coils "buck" one another; but since the flux has to return to form a closed circuit, it crosses the air gap at two places between the

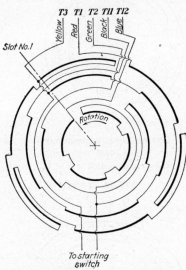

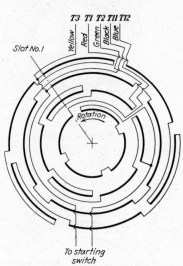

FIG. 4-39.—Stator connection diagram for motor of Fig. 4-35; 6 and 8 poles, all series-connected. Reading from the outside inward: 6-pole main winding, conventional; 8-pole main winding, consequent-pole; 6-pole auxiliary winding, only two coils used; 8-pole auxiliary winding, consequent-pole.

FIG. 4-40.—Stator connection diagram for motor of Fig. 4-35. This diagram differs from Fig. 4-39 only in that the 6-pole auxiliary winding is conventional.

coils, forming two additional poles as shown. In short, if all the coils are connected for the same magnetic polarity, there will be formed an equal number of consequent poles of the opposite magnetic polarities; the centers of the consequent poles will fall halfway between the coils. Stator connection diagrams for certain popular combinations are given in Figs. 4-37 to 4-40.

Figure 4-41 is a **line connection diagram** showing a two-speed split-phase motor being controlled by means of a snap switch. The lead tagging on this diagram corresponds to the lead tagging of all four stator connection diagrams given.

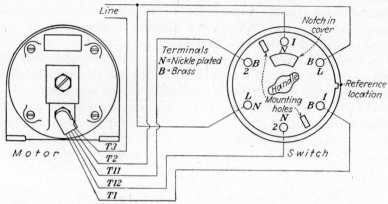

FIG. 4-41.—Line connection diagram for two-speed split-phase motor using a snap switch. The arrangement of the switch terminals shown is for a Bryant switch, Cat. #2613.

4-31. Two-speed, Pole-changing Motors with Three Windings.—

Three-winding arrangements were developed for pole-changing single-phase motors to simplify the winding process by omitting one auxiliary winding entirely. Many such arrangements and modifications of this kind have been made. Generally speaking, they are easier to wind and require fewer changes in external connections to change speed than do four-winding arrangements. By starting always on the same speed connection, the necessity for two starting windings is eliminated, at the expense of more complicated automatic internal switching. Two basic variations may be recognized: semiautomatic starting and full-automatic starting, depending upon whether the motor will start on one, or on both, positions of the external speed-selector switch.

a. Semiautomatic Starting.—A wiring and line connection diagram

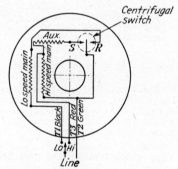

FIG. 4-42.—Wiring and line connection diagram for a two-speed, pole-changing, split-phase motor with semiautomatic starting. Motor will start only when external switch is in the "high" position, but will run in either position. (*Courtesy of General Electric Company.*)

is given in Fig. 4-42. This motor will start from rest only if the external switch is set for high-speed operation; however, after the motor is part way up to speed, the external switch can be changed to the low-speed position, and the motor will then continue to operate. But if, because of power failure or for any other reason, the motor stops while the external switch is set for low speed, the motor will not restart automatically. This motor requires a single-pole double-throw centrifugal switch such as used in two-value capacitor motors. Although this motor was designed for automatic starting on only the high-speed connection, it is obvious that the same arrangement could be used to obtain a motor that starts only on the low-speed connection.

b. Full-automatic Starting.—Figure 4-43 shows the wiring and line connection diagram of a motor that automatically starts on the high-speed connection, regardless of whether it is connected externally for high or for low speed. If connected for low speed, it starts on the

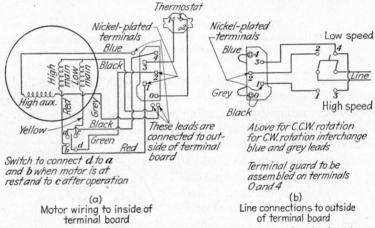

(a)
Motor wiring to inside of
terminal board

(b)
Line connections to outside
of terminal board

Fig. 4-43.—Wiring and line connection diagram of a two-speed, pole-changing, split-phase motor. Motor always starts on the high-speed connection; if connected externally for low speed, it automatically starts on the high-speed connection and then transfers to the low-speed connection at a predetermined speed. (*Courtesy of Westinghouse Electric Corporation.*)

high-speed connection and transfers automatically to the low-speed connection at a predetermined speed. Only a single-pole double-throw switch is actually necessary for speed control, but a double-pole switch is shown as it provides complete deenergization of the motor. The direction of rotation can be changed simply by interchanging two leads on the outside of the terminal board. This motor has a special starting switch, which makes two contacts on the starting position. It also has a thermal overload device to protect the motor on the high-speed connection, which affords locked-rotor protection regardless of whether the motor is connected for high or for low speed. Figure 4-44 shows the wiring and line connection diagram for a similar motor, except that it starts on the low-speed connection; it, too, has a special centrifugal transfer switch which makes two contacts in the starting position, and one in the running position.

Full-automatic starting is also achieved in two-speed three-winding motors by using two centrifugal switches, one at either end of the motor. A single-pole double-throw transfer switch in the front end of the motor is used to transfer the line voltage from the main winding used for starting, to the other main winding; a single-pole single-throw switch in the rear end of the motor automatically opens the auxiliary winding. *The switch that opens the auxiliary winding must be set to operate at a lower speed than the switch that transfers the main winding.*

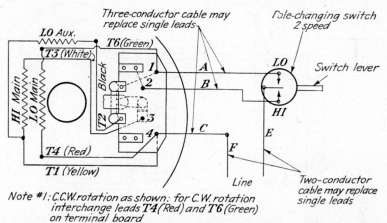

Fig. 4-44.—Wiring and line connection diagram of a two-speed, pole-changing, split-phase motor. Motor always starts on the low-speed connection; if connected externally for high speed, it automatically starts on the low-speed windings and transfers to the high-speed connection at a predetermined speed. (*Courtesy of General Electric Company.*)

If a single special switch is used, as in Fig. 4-43, and if the motor starts on the high-speed connection, the switch-operating speed may be set by the manufacturer either above or below the full-load speed of the low-speed connection; if the motor is started on the low-speed connection, the switch must operate at approximately 75 to 80 per cent of the synchronous speed of the low-speed winding.

4-32. Dual-voltage Split-phase Motors.—Dual-voltage split-phase motors are offered by some manufacturers. These may use either the arrangement described for dual-voltage clutch motors (see Art. 4-27, and Fig. 4-34) or the arrangement used for dual-voltage capacitor-start motors (see Art. 5-15, and Fig. 5-10), except that the capacitor, of course, is omitted. The former arrangement is simpler from the standpoint of winding, but it gives only half as much locked-rotor torque on 115 as on 230 volts; for fan or blower service, this may be ample. With the second arrangement, the torque is substantially the same on either voltage.

4-33. Motor System for a Hermetic Refrigerator.—Figure 4-45 shows an interesting system used for the main (compressor) and fan motors of a hermetic refrigerator. A magnetic relay is connected in series with the main winding of the main motor. This relay is normally open but, when power is applied, the locked-rotor current of the main winding picks up the relay, causing the contacts to close,

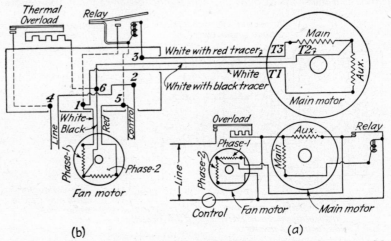

Fig. 4-45.—Wiring and line connection diagram of a hermetic refrigerator. Main motor uses external thermal overload relay and magnetic starting switch. Fan motor obtains two-phase power by utilizing the main motor as a phase converter. (a) Schematic diagram. (b) Detailed wiring diagram. (*Courtesy of General Electric Company.*)

thereby energizing the starting winding. As the motor accelerates, the current in the main-winding circuit decreases until, at a predetermined value, the relay again drops out, opening its contacts and the starting-winding circuit.* A thermal overload device, connected in series with the line, provides both overload and locked-rotor protection. When the main motor is energized, line voltage is simultaneously applied to both phases of the two-phase fan motor, which does not start because the same voltage is applied to both phases. However, after the main motor is up to speed and after the magnetic switch has opened, a voltage appears across the terminals of the starting winding of the main motor; this voltage is approximately in quadrature with the voltage impressed on the main winding. (It will be recalled that,

* A further discussion of these relays will be found in Art. 5-28a.

in Art. 2-10, it was explained that the rotor of a single-phase squirrel-cage motor running light sets up a field which is displaced approximately 90 deg in both time and space from the field set up by the main winding. This cross field induces a voltage in the starting winding of a split-phase motor by transformer action. Another way to understand this phenomenon is to recall that there is a rotating field in a single-phase induction motor when the motor is running light; this point is developed in Art. 2-12. The revolving field induces a voltage in the starting winding.) Ordinarily, the voltage induced in the starting winding serves no useful purpose, but it does no harm since the starting-winding circuit is open. However, in the motor system of Fig. 4-45, phase No. 1 of the fan motor is connected across the starting winding of the main motor, receiving therefrom a voltage in quadrature with the voltage applied to the main phase. Since the magnitudes of the two phase voltages impressed are not equal, the two phases do not have the same number of turns. Strictly speaking, therefore, the fan motor is not a true two-phase motor. In effect, the main motor is a **phase converter** converting the single-phase line power to two-phase power for the two-phase fan motor. The principle involved is the same as that employed in large phase converters such as are used on railroads; these phase converters convert the single-phase power collected from the overhead wire to three-phase power for operating the traction motors.

4-34. Resistance-start Split-phase Motors.

A resistance-start motor is a form of split-phase motor having a resistance connected in series with the auxiliary winding. The auxiliary circuit is opened when the motor has attained a predetermined speed.—ASA C42—1941. 10.10.370.

4-35. Reactor-start Motors.

A reactor-start motor is a form of split-phase motor designed for starting with a reactor in series with the main winding. The reactor is short-circuited or otherwise made ineffective and the auxiliary circuit is opened when the motor has attained a predetermined speed.—ASA C42—1941. 10.10.380.

The arrangement just mentioned is shown in Fig. 4-46. The effect of the reactor is to reduce the locked-rotor current in the main winding, at the same time increasing the angle of lag of the main-winding current behind the voltage. This increase in the angle of lag compensates approximately for the reduction in main-winding current so that substantially the same locked-rotor torque is obtained, but with appreciably less locked-rotor current than would be obtained without the reactor. The starting switch has to be single-pole and double-throw, like the transfer switch used in the two-value capacitor motor shown in Fig. 6-1. Equations for calculating the reactor required for this type of motor have been developed by the author.[6]

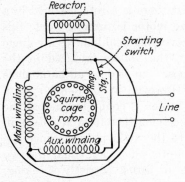

FIG. 4-46.—The reactor-start motor.

MISCELLANEOUS SERVICE PROBLEMS

4-36. How to Reverse the Various Types of Motors.—The fundamental principle involved in reversing split-phase motors is that the direction of current in the auxiliary phase, with respect to the current in the main phase, must be reversed. How to accomplish this change, in the case of four-lead motors, is shown in Fig. 4-5.

How to connect the motor for a definite direction of rotation and how to predetermine this direction of rotation is fully covered in Arts. 4-15 and 4-16. It should be pointed out that, if the line leads of Fig. 4-5 are connected to a snap switch for reversing, the motor cannot be **plugged;** it is necessary to wait at least until the rotor has slowed down sufficiently for the starting switch to close the auxiliary-phase circuit, and sometimes until the motor comes to rest, before the motor can be reversed.

4-37. Rewinding or Reconnecting Motor for a Different Voltage and the Same Performance.—If a split-phase motor is series-connected in both windings, it can be reconnected for half voltage by connecting in parallel; but both windings must be so connected. Sometimes it may be difficult in practice to reconnect the motor, particularly if the coils were originally hand- or gun-wound, because the connections between coils are very short and may be of heavy wire, leaving only a very short connection to which a lead can be soldered. Aside from this practical difficulty, there is no reason why the motor cannot be so reconnected.

If it is desired to make a 230-volt motor out of a 115-volt motor and if both windings are series-connected, it will be necessary to rewind both main and auxiliary windings, using twice as many turns and wire three sizes smaller in each. If the motor is a 230-volt motor, it is inadvisable to attempt to rewind it for 440 volts, because of starting-switch limitations. If the main winding is parallel-connected but the auxiliary winding is series-connected and it is desired to change from 115 to 230 volts, the main winding can be reconnected in series and the auxiliary winding rewound with twice as many turns and wire three sizes smaller.

If the change in voltage is not to double the voltage or to halve it, as mentioned in the two preceding paragraphs, the same general principles used for rewinding polyphase motors for a different voltage can be employed. For example, if it is desired to wind the motor for 25 per cent higher voltage, increase the turns in both main and auxiliary windings by 25 per cent, and use wire one size smaller. In general, the change in turns should be proportional to the change in voltage of the supply circuit for which the motor is being rewound; and the wire used in the main winding should be of as large a size as will go into the slots without omitting any turns. For example, if the motor is rewound for 10 per cent more voltage, the number of turns should be increased by 10 per cent and the same-sized wire used, if possible. In the auxiliary winding, it is desirable to change the turns in direct ratio with the voltage; but it is definitely *not advisable* to use wire of the largest size possible. In general, it will be a fairly safe rule to keep the difference in wire sizes between auxiliary and main windings the same in the rewound motor as it was in the original motor. For example, suppose the motor were wound originally with No. 18 wire in the main and No. 27 in the auxiliary winding, and suppose it were rewound with No. 20 wire in the main winding, then No. 29 should be used in the auxiliary winding.

4-38. Rewinding for Different Torques at the Same Voltage.— Probably it is not often that the service shop will be called upon to rewind a motor to obtain a different torque, but some general hints may be of help for those occasions when such a thing is to be done. At a given voltage and frequency, the breakdown torque will vary approximately inversely as the square of the number of turns in the main winding. Therefore, to increase the breakdown torque, decrease the turns in the main winding.

A word of caution must be given here. Before rewinding for a different torque, some careful check tests should be made on the motor that is to be rewound. Determine experimentally how high the voltage must be increased to obtain the desired breakdown torque. Measure the watts input at normal voltage and at the increased voltage. If the input is appreciably higher, a temperature run should then be taken at the operating load at this increased voltage to see if the motor is capable of dissipating the increased losses. Measure the air temperature, and the temperature of the windings on the hottest accessible place. Run the motor until the winding temperature becomes constant (3 to 6 hr will usually be necessary), and shut down. Note the maximum temperature attained after shutdown, and subtract the air temperature from this figure to obtain the "degrees rise." If the motor is open, the degrees rise should not be over 40°C; if the motor is enclosed, it should not be over 55°C. For further details at to test procedure, refer to Chap. XIX. Also, listen carefully to the motor while it is operating at the higher voltage, also while operating at normal voltage, to make sure that with the increased torque the "magnetic noise" will not become objectionable. If the temperature run indicates that the torque of the motor can be safely increased by as much as the ratio of, say 110:120 volts [the torque increase will be $(^{120}/_{110})^2$, or 19 per cent], the turns in the main winding can be decreased in the ratio of 110:120. For such a small change in turns, it will be unnecessary to change the auxiliary winding. If the main winding turns are decreased, it is desirable, if possible, to use a larger size of wire when rewinding.

If the motor is to be rewound for less torque, it is also important to check the input at reduced voltage; for the full-load losses may be either increased or decreased by a change in applied voltage in either direction. If any change in torque is desired, it is recommended that a "full-load saturation" be taken. For details as to this test, refer to Art. 19-16*h*.

4-39. Rewinding for a Different Frequency.—The general rules for rewinding a polyphase induction motor for a different frequency can be applied to split-phase induction motors, provided that the changes are made in both windings. It is necessary, however, to obtain a starting switch that operates at a different speed. If the change in frequency is very great, the rewound motor may not be entirely satisfactory in operation; for example, if a 25-cycle motor is rewound for 120 cycles, the performance may be generally unsatisfactory. If the change in frequency is small, say from 50 to 60 cycles, ordinarily it will not be necessary to make any change in the windings of general-purpose motors unless the motor is severely overloaded. If the change is from 60 to 50 cycles, no winding change is apt to be necessary. If the motor is a high-torque motor, it may be necessary to increase the turns of a 60-cycle motor 10 per cent to obtain satisfactory operation on 50 cycles without overheating. When changing either a general-purpose or a high-torque motor from 60 to 50 cycles, the rotating member of the starting switch should be changed, for the switching torque is adversely affected. Should the change be from 50 to 60 cycles and should the torque requirements be not too severe, it may be unnecessary to change either the winding or the switch.

4-40. Use of a Capacitor in the Auxiliary Phase to Raise Locked-rotor Torque or to Reduce Locked-rotor Current.—The question is frequently raised as to the possibility and practicability of increasing

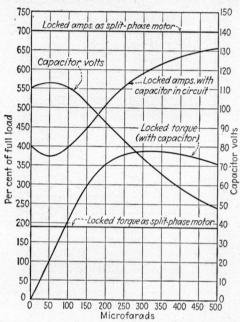

Fig. 4-47.—Effect of inserting an electrolytic capacitor in series with the auxiliary winding of a $\frac{1}{6}$-hp, 115-volt, 60-cycle, 1725-rpm, general-purpose, split-phase motor.

the locked-rotor torque or of reducing the locked-rotor current of a split-phase motor by the use of an electrolytic capacitor in series with the auxiliary phase. In Fig. 4-47 is shown the effect of inserting different values of capacitance in series with the auxiliary winding of a general-purpose $\frac{1}{6}$-hp 115-volt 60-cycle four-pole split-phase motor. It will be noted that with 90 mfd,* the torque is the same as with a split-phase motor, but the locked-rotor current is reduced from 700 to 390 per cent, or a total reduction of 44 per cent. The use of a

* Abbreviation for microfarads.

smaller number of microfarads reduces the locked current only slightly, but, within this range, the locked-rotor torque will be proportional to the number of microfarads used. It will be noted that, by use of 250 mfd, it is possible to double the locked-rotor torque with less locked-rotor current than is drawn as a split-phase motor. The conclusion may be drawn that use of a capacitor is both feasible and practical. If an electrolytic capacitor is available, it is suggested that an actual test be made to indicate whether an important gain is effected or not. It would be well to check the locked capacitor volts to see that the

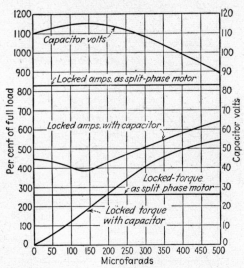

Fig. 4-48.—The effect of inserting an electrolytic capacitor in series with the auxiliary winding of a ¼-hp, 110-volt, 60-cycle, 1725-rpm, high-torque, split-phase, washing-machine motor.

voltage is not more than 20 per cent higher than the rated voltage of the capacitor. (Commercial capacitors for 115-volt motors are built to withstand 135 volts for starting service.)

In Fig. 4-48 are shown corresponding curves for the use of a capacitor in series with the starting winding of a ¼-hp high-torque split-phase washing-machine motor. It will be noted that it is necessary to use more actual microfarads to obtain a gain in locked-rotor torque than is the case with a general-purpose ⅙-hp motor.

It is difficult to estimate the exact value of capacitance necessary to use with a complete line of motors, but the two curves just mentioned give some indication of what may be expected.

REWINDING FOR A DIFFERENT NUMBER OF POLES

Of all the types of winding changes, this one is, perhaps, the most difficult and the one least likely to be encountered; usually it will not be economically justifiable tó attempt such a change. However, as servicemen do occasionally attack this problem by choice or by necessity, the following paragraphs are devoted to this subject. One prerequisite to such a change, of course, is a new starting switch that operates at the correct speed for the new winding. The first step is to determine the distribution factor and number of effective conductors in the old winding.

4-41. Distribution Factor and Effective Conductors.—For a single-phase winding, the **distribution factor** may be defined as the ratio

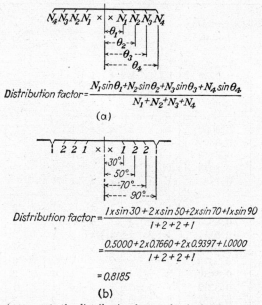

$$Distribution\ factor = \frac{N_1 \sin\theta_1 + N_2 \sin\theta_2 + N_3 \sin\theta_3 + N_4 \sin\theta_4}{N_1 + N_2 + N_3 + N_4}$$

(a)

$$Distribution\ factor = \frac{1 \times \sin 30 + 2 \times \sin 50 + 2 \times \sin 70 + 1 \times \sin 90}{1 + 2 + 2 + 1}$$

$$= \frac{0.5000 + 2 \times 0.7660 + 2 \times 0.9397 + 1.0000}{1 + 2 + 2 + 1}$$

$$= 0.8185$$

(b)

Fig. 4-49.—How to compute the distribution factor of a single-phase concentric winding.

of the actual voltage generated in a distributed concentric winding to the voltage that would be generated if all the turns in the distributed winding were wound full-pitch. For a better understanding of the meaning of the distribution factor, refer to Fig. 3-2. Less voltage is induced in the inner coil lying in slots 4 and 9 than in the outer coil lying in slots 3 and 10 because the latter coil embraces more flux. Hence the smaller coils in a concentric winding are less effective than the larger ones. If a given winding has, say, 100 turns, and if the distribution factor is 0.8500, the total number of effective turns is 85. In other words:

Effective conductors = actual conductors × distribution factor   (4-1)

where

$$\text{Actual conductors} = \frac{\text{total main-winding conductors}}{\text{no. of circuits in main winding}} \quad (4\text{-}2)$$

For winding calculations, the number of effective conductors is always more significant than the number of actual conductors, except when figuring the resistance.

Distribution factors for a number of different single-phase windings are given in Table V.

TABLE V.—DISTRIBUTION FACTORS FOR SINGLE-PHASE CONCENTRIC WINDINGS

No.	Slots per pole	Distribution factor	Distribution												
			1	2	3	4	5	6	7	8	9	10	11	12	13
1	4	0.8536	1	1	x	1	1								
2	4	0.8047	1	2	x	2	1								
3	4	1.0000	1	x	x	x	1								
4	6	0.9659	1	x	x	x	x	1							
5	6	0.8365	1	1	x	x	1	1							
6	6	0.6440	1	1	1	1	1	1							
7	6	0.8080	1	2	1	x	1	2	1						
8	6	0.7887	1	1	1	x	1	1	1						
9	9	0.8186	1	2	2	1	x	x	1	2	2	1			
10	9	0.8823	1	2	2	x	x	x	x	2	2	1			
11	9	0.9114	1	2	1	x	x	x	x	1	2	1			
12	9	0.9254	1	1	x	x	x	x	x	1	1				
13	9	0.9373	3	2	x	x	x	x	x	2	3				
14	9	0.8689	2	2	1	x	x	x	1	2	2				
15	9	0.8312	1	1	1	x	x	x	1	1	1				
16	9	0.8557	3	3	2	x	x	x	2	3	3				
17	9	0.8581	8	8	5	x	x	x	5	8	8				
18	12	0.9250	2	1	1	x	x	x	x	x	x	1	1	2	
19	12	0.8721	2	2	1	1	x	x	x	x	1	1	2	2	
20	12	0.8294	1	1	1	1	x	x	x	x	1	1	1	1	
21	12	0.7400	1	1	1	1	1	x	x	1	1	1	1	1	
22	12	0.7763	3	3	2	2	2	x	x	2	2	2	3	3	
23	12	0.8387	1	2	2	1	1	x	x	x	1	1	2	2	1
24	12	0.9010	1	2	1	1	x	x	x	x	x	1	1	2	1
25	12	0.8223	1	2	2	2	1	x	x	x	1	2	2	2	1
26	12	0.9495	1	2	1	x	x	x	x	x	x	x	1	2	1

A method for computing the distribution factor for any single-phase winding with a whole number of slots per pole is given in Fig. 4-49.

4-42. Determination of the Main Winding.—First, the number of effective conductors in the *old* main winding must be determined. Next, the number of effective conductors for the *new* main winding is determined, either by following the method outlined in Art. 14-20 and making use of Table XV or, more accurately, by following the method outlined in Arts. 14-21 and 14-22. [NOTE: Volts per phase for Eq. (14-8) is simply line volts.] Once the number of effective conductors required for the new main winding has been determined, a new distribution is chosen, and the number of turns is proportioned so as to give the required number of effective conductors.

To illustrate: Suppose that it has been determined by following the procedure outlined above that the new winding, a four-pole winding, requires 433 effective conductors and must be wound in a 36-slot stator. Then there are nine slots per pole. Suppose that distribution No. 9 in Table V is selected; it has a distribution factor of 0.8186. Then, from Eq. (4-1),

$$\text{Actual conductors} = \frac{433}{0.8186} = 530$$

Now, note that the bundle of conductors represented by N_1 in Fig. 4-49 is repeated 12 times in the winding for a single pole, so that it is repeated 48 times in the complete winding of four poles. Therefore, if we divide 530 by 48 we obtain 11, which is the required number of turns in N_1. Similarly, the number of turns in coils N_2 and N_3 is 22. Hence the new main winding is distributed thus:

$$11 \quad 22 \quad 22 \quad 11 \quad x \quad x \quad 11 \quad 22 \quad 22 \quad 11$$

This is the winding required if all four poles are to be connected in series. It is to be wound with the largest diameter of wire that can be put into the slots without undue abuse of the wire.

4-43. Determination of the Starting Winding.—For motors rated ⅛ hp and above, a simple rule for the starting winding is to wind it with about 60 per cent of the number of effective conductors used for the main winding, using wire five sizes smaller in diameter. (For example, if the main winding uses No. 18 wire, the starting winding should use No. 23.) For motors rated ¹⁄₁₂ or ¹⁄₂₀ hp, the starting-winding turns may be made 30 per cent of the main-winding turns; wire size should be smaller by three or four gauge numbers. In general, it is desirable to distribute the starting winding as much as the main winding permits; if distribution No. 9 (Table V) is used for the main winding, either No. 12 or No. 13 could be used for the starting winding, though No. 14 would be better than either.

Following the simple rules given above usually results in a satisfactory winding but, in certain special cases, it may be found that the starting winding thus determined is unsatisfactory in one or more of the following respects:

1. Locked-rotor torque, or pull-up torque, or both, too low.
2. Locked-rotor amperes too high.
3. Starting winding gets too hot or burns out.

To increase the locked-rotor torque and current, decrease the number of effective conductors in the starting winding; conversely, to decrease the locked-rotor torque and current, increase the number of effective conductors in the starting winding. If the starting winding gets too hot, measure the locked-rotor current in the starting winding only and divide this value into the number of circular mils in the wire used in the starting winding (see Table XXXII for the number of circular mils); if the value of circular mils per ampere is 30 or more, the starting winding should not overheat unless the motor takes a long time to come up to operating speed. If there are less than 30 circ. mils per amp, it may be advisable to use larger wire in the starting winding. If the number of conductors in the starting winding is varied much from the recommended value of 60 per cent of the number of main-winding conductors, it will be preferable to use a different size of wire in the starting winding. A simple and useful rule is

$$\text{Starting-winding gauge No.} = \text{main-winding gauge No.} + 2 + 5K \tag{4-3}$$

where

$$K = \frac{\text{effective conductors in starting winding}}{\text{effective conductors in main winding}} \tag{4-4}$$

In applying Eq. (4-3), the main-winding gauge number must be taken as the gauge number of a main winding that has the same number of parallel circuits as the starting winding. For example, if the main winding uses gauge No. 16 and has two parallel circuits, but the starting winding is to have but one circuit, the main-winding gauge number must be taken as No. 13, not No. 16. Equation (4-3) is valid for values of K up to 1.0, but not so valid for higher values of K.

More information on the design of starting windings can be found in the A.I.E.E. Transactions.[6,9]

Bibliography

1. VEINOTT, C. G.: An Old Tesla Motor, Grandfather of Modern Split-phase Motors, *Elec. J.*, March, 1931, p. 187.
2. HANSSEN, I. E.: Calculations of the Starting Torque of Single-phase Induction Motors with Phase-splitting Devices, *A.I.E.E. Trans.*, May, 1908, p. 373.
3. BOOTHY, C. R.: Discussion on Capacitor Motor Papers, *A.I.E.E. Trans.*, April, 1929, p. 629.
4. "American Standard Definitions of Electrical Terms," A.S.A. Standard C42—1941, published by American Institute of Electrical Engineers, New York.
5. KINCAID, C. W.: Change-speed Induction Motors, *Elec. J.*, August, 1924, pp. 357–363.
6. VEINOTT, C. G.: Starting Windings for Single-phase Induction Motors, *A.I.E.E. Trans.*, vol. 63, 1944, pp. 288–294.
7. "Nema Motor and Generator Standards," Nema Publication, No. 45–102, National Electrical Manufacturers' Association, New York, 1946.
8. "American Standard Terminal Markings for Electrical Apparatus," A.S.A. Standard C6.1—1944, published by National Electrical Manufacturers' Association, New York.
9. LLOYD, T. C., and KARR, J. H.: Design of Starting Windings for Split-phase Motors, *A.I.E.E. Trans.*, vol. 63, 1944, pp. 9–13.

CHAPTER V

CAPACITOR-START MOTORS

For general-purpose heavy-duty applications requiring high locked-rotor and running torques, the capacitor-start motor is now the most popular type of single-phase motor. This popularity was made possible by the development of inexpensive and reliable electrolytic capacitors. This type of motor is built in all fractional horsepower sizes from ⅛ hp up.

5-1. Capacitor Motor Defined.—A definition of the capacitor-start motor is included in the following definition of capacitor motor, published by Nema, May 1, 1946:

A capacitor motor is a single-phase induction motor with a main winding arranged for direct connection to a source of power and an auxiliary winding connected in series with a capacitor.

There are three types of capacitor motors:

1. Capacitor-start motor.
   A capacitor-start motor is a capacitor motor in which the capacitor phase is in the circuit only during the starting period.
2. Permanent-split capacitor motor.
   A permanent-split capacitor motor is a capacitor motor having the same value of capacitance for both starting and running conditions.
3. Two-value capacitor motor.
   A two-value capacitor motor is a capacitor motor using different values of effective capacitance for the starting and running connections.

Capacitor-start motors formerly were not recognized as capacitor motors, either by Nema or by the A.S.A., until the above definition was published, although they have long been recognized as such by the trade. Since there are now three recognized types of capacitor motors, the term "capacitor motor" should never be used by itself in specifying a motor because the characteristics of the three different types are so different from one another. When a prospective motor user writes to a manufacturer to make inquiries about a "capacitor" motor, he should be very explicit as to what kind of capacitor motor he wants. It is best to state the application together with approximate torque requirements and reasons why a capacitor motor is desired.

5-2. Essential Parts of a Capacitor-start Motor.—We saw, in Art. 4-40, that a split-phase motor could be made into a capacitor-start motor simply by inserting a capacitor in series with the auxiliary winding. This arrangement is represented schematically in Fig. 5-1, which resembles Fig. 4-1—the similar sketch for a split-phase motor—except for the addition of the capacitor in the auxiliary phase. This does not mean that commercial capacitor-start motors are merely split-phase motors with a capacitor added, for the windings have to be specially designed and proportioned. Moreover, the torques of capacitor-start motors are generally higher than the corresponding torques of general-purpose split-phase motors.

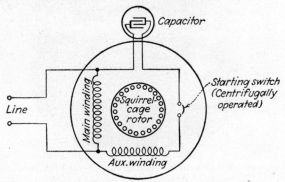

Fig. 5-1.—The capacitor-start motor.

Both types of motors have two electrically distinct windings, generally located 90 electrical degrees apart. As in the case of the split-phase motor, the main winding is the bulkier of the two. It is usually wound with a larger size of wire and with fewer turns than the auxiliary winding. The auxiliary winding of a capacitor-start motor, however, generally contains more copper than the starting winding of a split-phase motor of the same rating. Articles 4-8, 4-15, and 4-16 on how to identify windings and how to predetermine rotation are equally applicable to capacitor-start motors.

There are, therefore, two electrical circuits, or phases. The main phase consists of only the main winding connected across the line. The auxiliary phase—also called "capacitor phase"—comprises an auxiliary winding, a capacitor, and a centrifugal switch which opens at approximately 75 to 80 per cent of synchronous speed; all three are connected in series, the whole being connected across the line in parallel with the main winding. On the higher-voltage connection, dual-voltage capacitor-start motors usually have the auxiliary-phase circuit connected across only half of the main phase, instead of across the line.   These motors are discussed in Arts. 5-14 to 5-16.

A cutaway view of a capacitor-start motor is shown in Fig. 5-2.

Fig. 5-2.—Cutaway view of a sleeve-bearing rubber-mounted capacitor-start motor.
(*Courtesy of Westinghouse Electric Corporation.*)

a. Electrolytic starting capacitor.   One terminal in cross section.
b. Clamp for holding capacitor assembly to motor.
c. Stator laminations (punchings).
d. End windings.   Sections of both main and auxiliary windings can be seen.
e. Rotor laminations (punchings).
f. Rotor conductors.   Parts of three conductors are visible because the rotor is skewed and the rotor was cut parallel to shaft.
g. Resistance rings (end rings).   Every conductor is brazed at each end to a resistance ring.
h. Ventilating duct through the rotor.
i. Fan that draws air in through openings in the front end shield, through rotor vents, and out through the rear end shield.
j. Motor frame, of rolled steel.
k. Rear end shield.
l Front end shield.
m. Shaft.   Knurled to prevent punchings, fan, and switch from turning on the shaft.
n. Bearing.   Steel-backed, babbitt-lined; visible is the rectangular window-like opening through which oil is fed by wool wicking held against the shaft by the coil spring.   Wicking extends down into oil reservoir in bearing housing.
o. Oil cup.
p. Section of annular rubber cushion mounting, which is bonded to the two metallic rings visible. The inner ring is pressed onto the nose of the end shield and the outer ring is clamped in the cradle base by clamps q.
r. Rotating member of starting switch.
s. Lead from stationary member of starting switch to capacitor.
t. Thermoguard element.   The mounting cup, heater, and bimetallic disc are plainly visible.
u. Cradle base.
v. Terminal post for line connections to motor.   Refer to Fig. 5-18 for a view of terminal board.

5-3. Capacitor-starting Principle.

—Like the split-phase motor, the capacitor-start motor generally resembles the two-phase motor in that there are two stator windings, displaced 90 electrical degrees. In order to obtain the rotating field necessary to develop locked-rotor torque, it is necessary that the currents in these two windings be displaced in time phase. In the case of the polyphase motor, as has been pointed out (Art. 4-3), this phase displacement is obtained by connecting the two electrically similar windings to two voltages differing in phase. In both the split-phase and capacitor-start motors, the two circuits are connected to the same voltage; and the phase displacement of currents is obtained by a dissimilarity of the electrical constants of the two circuits.

In the split-phase motor, resistance is deliberately built into the auxiliary winding to bring the current more nearly in phase with the line voltage than is the main-winding current, as shown in Fig. 4-2. In a capacitor-start motor, the capacitor causes the auxiliary-phase current to *lead* the main-phase voltage, obtaining a large angle of displacement between the currents in the two windings. A vector diagram of the locked-rotor currents of a typical capacitor-start motor is given in Fig. 5-3. The line current of this motor is only two-thirds the line current of the corresponding split-phase motor shown in Fig. 4-2; yet this motor develops more than twice the locked-rotor torque of the split-phase motor. Thus a capacitor is seen to be a much more effective starting device than is a resistor.

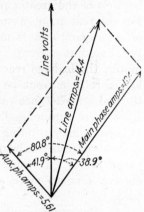

Fig. 5-3.—A vector diagram of the locked-rotor currents in a general-purpose, capacitor-start motor rated at $\frac{1}{6}$ hp, four poles, 60 cycles, 115 volts, 1725 rpm.

5-4. Capacitor Starting Compared with Split-phase Starting.—A capacitor-start motor develops considerably more locked-rotor torque per ampere of line current than the split-phase motor for a number of reasons. The locked-rotor torque of a single-phase induction motor with two windings displaced 90 deg is proportional among other things, to the product of these three factors:[1]

1. The sine of the angle of phase displacement between the currents in the two windings.
2. The product of the main-winding current multiplied by the auxiliary-winding current.
3. The number of turns in the auxiliary winding.

Each of these three factors is more favorable in the capacitor-start motor. (1) Using the figures from the typical examples chosen, the

[1] For a technical explanation, see Ref. 1 of the Bibliography at end of chapter.

phase displacement between the currents is 24.3 deg in the split-phase motor and 80.8 deg in the capacitor-start motor. The sines of these two angles (from Table XXXIII) are 0.4115 and 0.987, respectively; *i.e.*, because of this factor alone, the locked-rotor torque of the capacitor-start motor would be $0.987/0.4115 = 2.4$ times as much as for the split-phase motor. (2) It will be noted that, in the split-phase motor, the line current is nearly equal to the numerical sum of the currents in the main and auxiliary windings; whereas, in the capacitor-start motor, the line current is considerably less than the numerical sum because of the greater phase displacement between the two currents. For this reason, more current can be allowed in either or both windings of the capacitor-start motor, obtaining more locked-rotor torque for the same line current. (3) In the auxiliary winding of a split-phase motor, the leakage reactance has to be kept small in order that the locked-rotor current be nearly in phase with the voltage. Because the leakage reactance varies as the square of the number of turns, only a few turns can be used. In the capacitor-start motor, the reactance of the auxiliary winding is more than neutralized by the capacitor, so that more turns can be used than in the auxiliary winding of the split-phase motor. If the auxiliary winding has more turns, the same current sets up more ampere-turns and hence more flux and more torque.

Another explanation for the greater effectiveness of starting is the fact that the flux conditions in a capacitor-start motor at standstill are similar to the flux conditions of a two-phase motor.

The main winding is usually of heavier wire, is distributed in more slots, and is bulkier than the auxiliary winding, although the latter frequently has more turns than the main winding. As in the case of split-phase motors, the main winding is usually wound into the slots first.

5-5. Purpose of the Starting Switch.—It was explained in Art. 4-4 that a starting switch was necessary in split-phase motors to improve the torque characteristics at full-load speed, to keep down the watts input, and to prevent burnouts at normal operating speeds. All of these considerations apply with equal force to capacitor-start motors; but there is an even more important reason, *viz.*, to prevent burnout or breakdown of the capacitor. In Fig. 5-4 are shown the speed-torque characteristics of a typical capacitor-start motor. In general, the torque characteristics are similar to those of the split-phase motor, except that the torques are much higher. *Capacitor volts vs. rpm* is also plotted on this curve. Observe that the capacitor volts increase

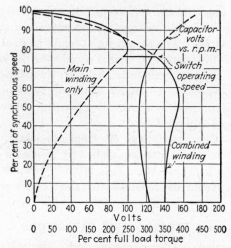

FIG. 5-4.—Speed-torque curve of a capacitor-start motor.

rapidly above switch-operating speed. The switch must function at the proper speed; if it fails to operate and if the motor comes up to speed and is operated in this condition for an appreciable length of time, injury to the capacitor is certain.

TABLE VI.—MINIMUM TORQUES OF CAPACITOR-START MOTORS*

Horsepower rating	Locked-rotor torque	Pull-up torque	Breakdown torque
60 cycles—1725 rpm			
⅛	350	200	200
⅙	350	200	200
¼	350	200	200
⅓	325	200	200
½	300	200	200
¾	275	200	200
60 cycles—1140 rpm			
⅛	300	185	185
⅙	300	185	185
¼	300	185	185
⅓	300	185	185
½	300	185	185

These torques are expressed in percentage of full-load torque.. Maximum permissible values of locked-rotor currents are given in Table XXVI.

* These torques were Nema requirements until June, 1946.

The switch must, moreover, be positive in action; it must not flutter. As high as double voltage can be impressed on the capacitor by a fluttering switch. The reason for this will be explained: Suppose that the switch is fluttering and that it interrupts the circuit at such a time as to leave the capacitor fully charged; then suppose the switch happens to close when the voltage is of the opposite polarity—double voltage will be impressed momentarily upon the capacitor. *Switches must not be allowed to flutter!*

5-6. Torque Characteristics of Capacitor-start Motors.—The minimum torque requirements established by Nema for capacitor-start motors are shown in Table VI. This table of torques was rescinded in June, 1946, by Nema and replaced with the torques given in Table II (see Art. 1-5).

A-C ELECTROLYTIC CAPACITORS

5-7. Construction.—Alternating-current electrolytic capacitors were used for motor-starting service as far back as 1892, but it is only since 1930 that capacitor-start motors have attained commercial importance. It is interesting to note that, in 1896, the repulsion-start motor wiped the capacitor-start motor out of existence. Now, 50 years later, the capacitor-start motor is making the repulsion-start motor obsolete for most applications.

The modern dry-type electrolytic capacitor is formed by winding two sheets of aluminum foil into a cylindrical shape. The two sheets of aluminum foil are separated by a suitable insulator which may be of gauze, two layers of thin paper, or a combination of gauze and paper. The insulator is impregnated with an electrolyte, usually ethylene glycol or a derivative. Capacitors with paper spacing are slightly smaller than those with gauze spacing. On each of the two layers of foil, an anodic film is produced by electrochemical means. The capacitor is then provided with suitable terminals and the whole sealed into an aluminum case—aluminum is used to prevent corrosion. A safety vent usually is provided to prevent explosion.

Ordinarily this aluminum can is not alive or "hot," for the element is insulated inside the can; but good practice requires that the aluminum case be insulated from the motor frame and ground and also from any live part. Capacitors are made in round and oblong cans and in many other shapes. They have been made even in the shape of a doughnut to fit inside a motor. A typical construction of a round capacitor is shown in Fig. 5-5.

In modern electrolytic capacitors, the aluminum plates are etched and the effective surface area for a given size of plate thereby increased, so that 2 to 2½ times as much capacitance can be obtained in a given volume as could be obtained with plain plates.

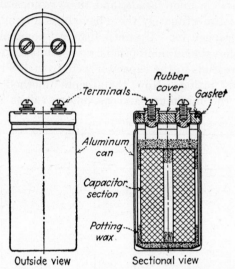

Outside view   Sectional view

Fig. 5-5.—An a-c dry electrolytic capacitor. Soldering-lug terminals are now more common. (*Courtesy of Sprague Specialties Company.*)

5-8. Characteristics of Motor-starting Capacitors.—These capacitors are designed for use on alternating current and for intermittent service only. They must not be confused with the d-c electrolytic capacitors used in radios and other electronic devices. For the same voltage and microfarad rating, a-c capacitors are larger and bulkier, and the terminals do not bear any polarity markings. Present commercially available a-c electrolytic capacitors have characteristics as follows:

a. Voltage Rating.—The voltage rating is usually stamped on the capacitor itself. This may or may not be the same as the voltage rating of the motor itself. Both 115-volt and 115/230-volt capacitor-start motors commonly use 110-volt capacitors. Also, 230-volt motors often use 110-volt capacitors when the windings are suitably arranged (see Arts. 5-20 and 5-21). Sometimes the capacitor carries a higher voltage rating than the motor; for example, 125-volt capacitors may be used on 115-volt motors. The proper voltage rating is determined more by the design and arrangement of the windings than by the voltage rating of the motor. Good electrolytic capacitors will withstand, within the limits of the prescribed duty cycle, 125 to 130 per cent of the rated voltage.　An increase in operating voltage increases the power factor and slightly increases the capacitance.

b. Capacitance Rating.—Capacitance ratings of electrolytic capacitors are expressed in microfarads, and these ratings are stamped on the capacitors.　Unfortunately there have been a number of methods used for rating capacitors.　Up until 1936, a "nominal" rating, consisting of a single value of microfarads, was stamped on the capacitor; the actual microfarads in the capacitor were from 108 to 120 per cent of the "nominal" rating.　Now, the accepted method is to mark the capacitor with the minimum and maximum values of microfarads

TABLE VII.—RATINGS AND TEST LIMITS FOR A-C ELECTROLYTIC CAPACITORS

Capacity rating, microfarads			110-volt ratings		125-volt ratings		220-volt ratings	
Nominal	Limits	Ave.	Amps. at rated voltage, 60 cycles	Approx. max. watts	Amps. at rated voltage, 60 cycles	Approx. max. watts	Amps. at rated voltage, 60 cycles	Approx. max. watts
	25–30	27.5	1.04– 1.24	10.9	1.18– 1.41	14.1	2.07–2.49	43.8
	32–36	34	1.33– 1.49	13.1	1.51– 1.70	17	2.65–2.99	52.6
	38–42	40	1.56– 1.74	15.3	1.79– 1.98	19.8	3.15–3.48	61.2
	43–48	45.5	1.78– 1.99	17.5	2.03– 2.26	22.6	3.57–3.98	70
50	53–60	56.5	2.20– 2.49	21.9	2.50– 2.83	28.3	4.40–4.98	87.6
60	64–72	68	2.65– 2.99	26.3	3.02– 3.39	33.9	5.31–5.97	118.2
65	70–78	74	2.90– 3.23	28.4	3.30– 3.68	36.8	5.81–6.47	128.1
70	75–84	79.5	3.11– 3.48	30.6	3.53– 3.96	39.6	6.22–6.97	138
80	86–96	91	3.57– 3.98	35	4.05– 4.52	45.2	7.13–7.96	157.6
90	97–107	102	4.02– 4.44	39.1	4.57– 5.04	50.4	8.05–8.87	175.6
100	108–120	114	4.48– 4.98	43.8	5.09– 5.65	56.5	8.96–9.95	197
115	124–138	131	5.14– 5.72	50.3	5.84– 6.50	65		
135	145–162	154	6.01– 6.72	62.8	6.83– 7.63	85.8		
150	161–180	170	6.68– 7.46	69.8	7.59– 8.48	95.4		
175	189–210	200	7.84– 8.71	81.4	8.91– 9.90	111.4		
180	194–216	205	8.05– 8.96	83.8	9.14–10.18	114.5		
200	216–240	228	8.96– 9.95	93	10.18–11.31	127.2		
215	233–260	247	9.66–10.78	106.7	10.98–12.25	145.5		
225	243–270	257	10.08–11.20	110.9	11.45–12.72	151		
250	270–300	285	11.20–12.44	123.2	12.72–14.14	167.9		
300	324–360	342	13.44–14.93	147.8	15.27–16.96	201.4		
315	340–380	360	14.10–15.76	156				
350	378–420	399	15.68–17.42	172.5				
400	430–480	455	17.83–19.91	197.1				

for which the capacitor was designed.　Standard ratings are given for both of these systems in Table VII.　In lieu of these the minimum, or even average, value of microfarads may be stamped on the capacitor.

c. Temperature Rating.—Electrical characteristics of capacitors are normally tested at 25°C, but they are rated to operate at 65°C (150°F) and will function successfully up to 80°C (176°F). However, their life is shorter at elevated temperatures. Operation at very low temperatures does not harm the capacitor, but at temperatures lower than 0°C the capacitance falls off, and may drop as low as 50 per cent of normal at −50°C. However, at these reduced temperatures, the power factor becomes quite high so that the capacitors draw more watts from the line and warm up quickly.

d. Duty Cycle.—Motor-starting capacitors are rated on the basis of 20 three-second periods per hour, or an equivalent duty cycle; 60 one-second periods per hour would be one equivalent duty cycle.

e. Power Factor.—At normal room temperatures, the power factor of electrolytic capacitors is of the order of 5 to 6 per cent, but it may be as high as 8 per cent for small units, and 9.5 per cent for large ones. Watt limits given in Table VII are based on these maximum figures.

5-9. When Replacing Electrolytic Capacitors.—*When a defective capacitor is replaced, it is imperative that the new capacitor be of the same voltage and microfarad rating.* A 124–138-mfd capacitor may sometimes be substituted for the 161–180-mfd size without apparently impairing the ability of the motor to start its load, particularly if the machine is broken in and requires less power to drive than it did when new. However, reducing the microfarads of the capacitor in any given motor normally increases the voltage across the capacitor, incurring danger of an early breakdown. (It is perfectly possible to get 150 volts across the capacitor with only 110 volts on the motor. The inductance of the motor winding is in series with the capacitor; and as the capacitance is reduced, series resonance* is approached, increasing the capacitor voltage.) Using a capacitor that is too large generally will not harm the capacitor, but the switching torque of the motor may be adversely affected. Therefore, the serviceman should use the same value of capacitance that the motor manufacturer did.

Capacitor testing boxes are sold for testing motors to determine, by means of a test on the motor, the size of capacitor to use. The locked-rotor torque is determined with different values of microfarads in series with the auxiliary winding, and the serviceman has often been advised to use that value of capacitance which gives the maximum locked-rotor torque. However, the author recommends always using less microfarads than required for maximum locked-rotor torque; 80 per cent of this value is probably a safer figure to use than 100 per cent.

* See any elementary textbook for an explanation of the phenomenon of series resonance.

A much safer procedure is to obtain the required *voltage and micro-farad* rating from the motor manufacturer.

5-10. Testing Electrolytic Capacitors.—When an electrolytic capacitor is suspected of being defective, it should be tested for

1. Short circuits
2. Open circuits
3. Capacitance in microfarads
4. Power factor
5. Grounds

Connect the capacitor in series with a suitable fuse across a 115-volt 60-cycle line.   (1) If the capacitor is *short-circuited*, the fuse will blow. (A lighting-out lamp cannot be used, for a capacitor will pass enough current to light an ordinary light bulb.)   If the capacitor is not short-circuited, connect meters in the circuit as shown in Fig. 19-3.   Adjust the voltage across the capacitor to the rated voltage of the capacitor. Take a reading of watts and amperes input and also applied voltage, as explained in Art. 19-12, making sure to correct for meter losses. (2) If no current can be measured, the capacitor is *open-circuited*.   (3) If a readable value of current input is obtained, the *capacitance in microfarads* can be determined by comparing the reading with the currents given in Table VII.   The tested value of microfarads should be checked against the rating marked on the can.   Or the microfarads and power factor can be computed from the following formulas (the formula for microfarads is valid only if the applied frequency is 60 cycles):

$$\text{Microfarads} = \frac{2,650 \times \text{amperes}}{\text{applied voltage}} \qquad (5\text{-}1)$$

$$\text{Power factor} = \frac{\text{watts}}{\text{volts} \times \text{amperes}} \qquad (5\text{-}2)$$

(4) As a check on the *power factor*, the watts may be checked against Table VII.   If desired, the power factor may be computed; 5 or 6 per cent is normal, and a maximum of 10 per cent is permissible.   (5) To check for a grounded capacitor, take all meters out of the circuit, and apply rated voltage between either terminal and the metal container in series with a 10-amp fuse.   A grounded capacitor will blow the fuse.   Ordinarily, since the case is insulated from the motor frame, a grounded terminal will do no harm unless the other terminal is also grounded.

These readings should be taken as quickly as possible, for electrolytic capacitors are intermittently rated.

GENERAL-PURPOSE SINGLE-VOLTAGE MOTORS—
WITHOUT TERMINAL BOARD

5-11. Capacitor Mounted—without Thermal Protection.—These motors may have two, three, or four external leads.

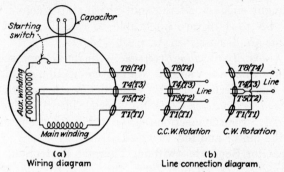

(a)
Wiring diagram

(b)
Line connection diagram

Fig. 5-6.—Wiring and line connection diagrams for an externally reversible, capacitor-start motor, with four line leads tagged per A.S.A. standards. Terminal markings in parentheses were A.S.A. standard until 1938, and were used in the first edition of this book.

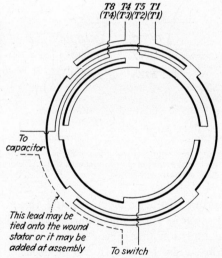

Fig. 5-7.—Stator connection diagram for a capacitor-start motor, four poles, both windings series, externally reversible, four line leads.

a. Four Leads, Externally Reversible.—Terminal markings according to old and new A.S.A. standards are given in Fig. 5-6. External connections to the line are the same as for the corresponding split-phase motor of Art. 4-7. A stator connection diagram for a four-pole series-connected winding is given in Fig. 5-7.   This stator connection diagram is very nearly identical with Fig. 4-9, the corresponding diagram for a split-phase motor, except that the auxiliary-phase connections are slightly altered to permit insertion of the capacitor in the circuit.   With slight changes, such as a comparison between these two figures might suggest, all the split-phase stator connection diagrams, Figs. 4-8 to 4-16, are applicable to capacitor-start motors. These diagrams are discussed in Arts. 4-9 to 4-12.

   b. Three Leads, Externally Reversible.—Single-voltage motors for 230-volt service often use a special winding connection requiring only three leads.   For a discussion of these motors, see Art. 5-20.

   c. Two Leads, Nonreversible.—No special identification of the leads is required.   Line connections shown in Fig. 5-6 are permanently made inside the motor and but two leads are brought out.

   5-12. Capacitor Separate—without Thermal Protection.   *a. Four Leads, Externally Reversible.*—When the capacitor is separately

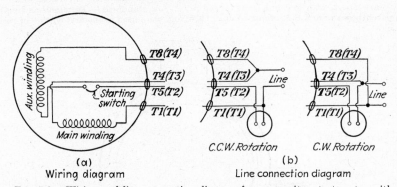

(a)
Wiring diagram

(b)
Line connection diagram

FIG. 5-8.—Wiring and line connection diagram for a capacitor-start motor with a separate capacitor.   Terminal markings in parentheses were A.S.A. standard until 1938, and were used in the first edition of this book.

mounted, the internal wiring connections and the stator connection diagrams are the same as for a split-phase motor.   Figure 5-8 shows wiring and line connection diagrams for such a motor.   For stator connection diagrams, Figs. 4-8 to 4-16 can be used.

   b. Three Leads, Nonreversible.—A three-lead nonreversible motor can be made from Fig. 5-8 by connecting the $T8(T4)$ lead internally to the $T4(T3)$ lead.   This connection can be made in the winding itself, as shown in Fig. 6-13.

   5-13. Thermally Protected Motors.—Motors with mounted capacitor may have from two to six line leads.

a. Six Leads, Externally Reversible.—Wiring and line connection diagrams are given in Fig. 5-9.   Applicable stator connection diagrams are Figs. 4-8 to 4-16, except that provision must be made for the connection of the capacitor in the auxiliary-winding circuit.   If one side of the line circuit is grounded, the yellow lead should be connected to the "hot" or ungrounded side, so that, if the thermostat opens, there will be no potential between the windings and ground.

b. Five Leads, Externally Reversible.—From inspection of Fig. 5-9*b* it is apparent that one of the yellow thermostat leads is always connected to the *T*1 lead, for either rotation.   Obviously then, this

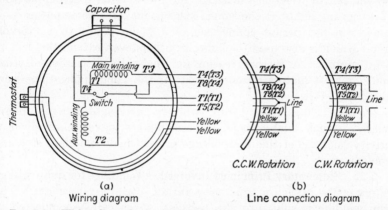

(a)
Wiring diagram

(b)
Line connection diagram

Fig. 5-9.—Wiring diagram of a thermally protected, capacitor-start motor; motor is externally reversible and capacitor is attached.   Terminal markings in parentheses were A.S.A. standard until 1938, and were used in the first edition of this book.

lead could be connected internally to the *T*1 lead, so that only five external leads would be required.   The thermostat lead in General Electric motors of this type is often tagged *L*.   Robbins and Myers use either a black lead with a tracer, or one tagged *T*.   However marked, the lead from the thermostat should be connected to the ungrounded side of the line on a grounded circuit.

c. Four Leads, Externally Reversible.—Motors for 230-volt service often use the swing connection, which requires but four leads.   For a description of this connection, refer to Art. 5-21 and to Fig. 5-17.

d. Two Leads, Nonreversible.—All the connections made in Fig. 5-9*a* and *b* are made internally and only two line leads are brought out; one of these leads comes from the windings and the other from the thermostat.   On grounded circuits, the thermostat lead should always be connected to the ungrounded, or live, side of the line.   Westinghouse motors usually use a white lead to mark the winding or ground lead. General Electric often mark the leads $L1$ and $L2$; $L1$ is the thermostat lead, which goes to the ungrounded line. Robbins and Myers indicate the thermostat lead by means of a tag T or a black lead with a tracer; it should be connected to the ungrounded side of the line.

DUAL-VOLTAGE MOTORS—GENERAL

5-14. Reasons for Dual-voltage Windings.—Capacitor-start motors rated $\frac{1}{3}$ hp and above are usually wound dual-voltage so that they can be operated on either 115- or 230-volt circuits. If a choice exists, it is generally preferable to connect a motor of this size to a 230-volt line in preference to a 115-volt line, in order to avoid possibility of causing lights on the same feeder to flicker. Some power companies will not permit connection of a $\frac{3}{4}$-hp motor to a 115-volt circuit which is also used for lighting; others even extend this ban to $\frac{1}{2}$-hp motors. A further reason for dual-voltage windings is that repulsion-start motors formerly used for the same applications were wound dual-voltage.

Even in ratings below $\frac{1}{3}$ hp, two-, six-, and eight-pole motors are usually wound dual-voltage. These motors have relatively low activity, and use of the dual-voltage arrangement simplifies stocking problems.

5-15. Elementary Principles Involved.—Windings for dual-voltage motors of the capacitor type use a rather special arrangement. The main winding is split into two sections, which can be connected in series or in parallel, as might be supposed. These two sections are both wound on the same magnetic axes; *i.e.*, the windings are in space phase with each other. However, the auxiliary winding is in but one section, which is displaced 90 electrical degrees from the main winding. This arrangement is shown schematically in Fig. 5-10. In series with the auxiliary winding is the customary centrifugal switch, and a single capacitor.

For a 115-volt circuit, the two sections of the main winding, and the auxiliary phase (auxiliary phase consists of winding, switch, and capacitor) are connected in parallel. Principles of operation are the same as for the single-voltage motor of Fig. 5-1.

On 230 volts, the principle of operation is somewhat different when the motor is operating on the starting connection. By reference to Fig. 5-10*b*, it can be seen that the auxiliary phase is connected in parallel with one of the sections of the main winding, instead of across the line. Since the two main-winding sections are in series, each section, as well as the auxiliary phase, has 115 volts across it. Thus, the main winding has to perform a dual function: it serves as a 230-volt main winding and, in addition, acts as a 2-to-1 autotransformer so that the auxiliary phase is operated on 115 volts when the motor as a whole is connected to a 230-volt circuit. Since the main winding is also an autotransformer, both sections of it have to carry auxiliary phase current as well as the normal main-winding current. Because of this autotransformer requirement, the series-parallel winding for a motor of this type is somewhat special, as described in the following article.

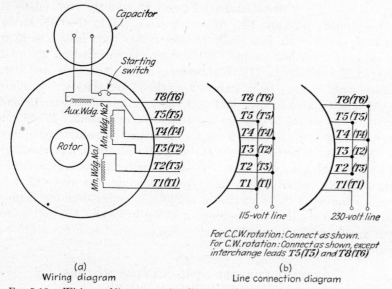

(a)
Wiring diagram

(b)
Line connection diagram

Fig. 5-10.—Wiring and line connection diagrams of a six-lead, dual-voltage, externally reversible, capacitor-start motor. Terminal markings are in agreement with A.S.A. standards. Terminal markings in parentheses show an alternate system that has been widely used.

5-16. Winding Dual-voltage Motors.—Stator windings for repulsion-type motors are usually divided into two sections by connecting half the poles in one section, and the other half in the second section. This arrangement generally does not work so well when the main winding has to be used as an autotransformer because of the relatively high magnetic leakage between the two sections. A much better arrangement is to wind each section on all the poles. There are two ways of accomplishing this. One method is to wind section 1 in the bottom of the slots, one coil for every pole, just as if this section were a complete winding, bringing out the two leads $T1$ and $T2$; section 1 is covered with suitable insulation barriers, section 2 is then wound into the same slots as the first winding, and leads $T3$ and $T4$ are brought out.   Section 2 is wound with exactly the same number of turns in each slot, and the distribution is exactly the same as that of section 1, but the wire sizes of the two sections may or may not be identical.   This method of winding results in a **three-layer winding** (the auxiliary winding is the third layer.)

A second method is to wind two strands in parallel, using two spools of wire; one strand is utilized for section 1, the other for section 2; the two ends of one strand are $T1$ and $T2$, and the two ends of the other strand are $T3$ and $T4$.   When wound by this method, the strands of both sections are in a single bundle, rather than in two as in the previously described method; if the motor is operated on 230 volts, there will normally be 115 volts between adjacent strands, and sometimes even more.   It is imperative, therefore, that well-insulated good quality wire be used and that the wire be handled particularly carefully so as not to damage or weaken the insulation.   When complete, the winding appears to be a conventional two-layer winding.

So far as the performance of the motor is concerned, it is immaterial which of the two methods is used, though the second method is theoretically better.   With this type of winding, the wire size of the main winding is the wire size of a 230-volt motor, but the turns in each section are the same in number as the turns of a 115-volt motor; the auxiliary winding and capacitor are designed as if for a 115-volt motor.

GENERAL-PURPOSE DUAL-VOLTAGE MOTORS— WITHOUT TERMINAL BOARD

5-17. Capacitor Mounted—without Thermal Protection.—These motors may have four or six leads.

a. Six Leads, Externally Reversible.—Wiring and line connection diagrams are given in Fig. 5-10.   Terminal markings given are in accordance with principles implied in present A.S.A. standards. Terminal markings in ( ) follow a system that has been widely used. Robbins and Myers sometimes use colored leads which correspond to the tagged leads in Fig. 5-10 as follows:

$T1$—gray	$T3$—yellow	$T5$—blue
$T2$—red	$T4$—green	$T8$—black

For stator connection diagrams, Figs. 5-13 to 5-15 may be used with the following changes, which apply equally to all three diagrams:

1. Omit the red lead.

2. Omit the black lead connected to T4 and brought out at the top of the diagram.

3. Bring the blue lead out as an external lead and tag it T5.

4. Connect black lead from auxiliary winding internally to one terminal of the capacitor.

5. Connect other terminal of capacitor to one terminal of the starting switch.

6. Bring out an external lead from the other terminal of the starting switch and tag it T8.

If the above changes are correctly followed, the motor will be wired in accordance with Fig. 5-10, which then will show the correct external connections.

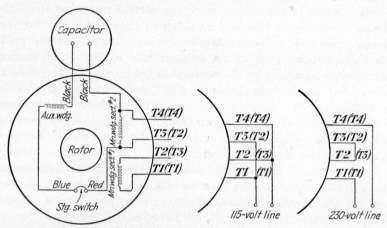

Internal connections are for C.C.W. rotation. For C.W. rotation, interchange either black and blue from aux. wdg., or black and red from main wdg.

(a)   (b)
Wiring diagram   Line connection diagram

Fig. 5-11.—Wiring and line connection diagrams of a four-lead, dual-voltage, capacitor-start motor. Terminal markings conform in principle to present A.S.A. standards. Markings in parentheses show a widely used alternate system.

b. Four Leads, Nonreversible.—Wiring and line connection diagrams are given in Fig. 5-11, which is somewhat similar to Fig. 5-10. Stator connection diagrams are Figs. 5-13 to 5-15, which apply directly. Although this motor is nominally nonreversible, it can be connected for the opposite direction of rotation by dismantling it and making the connection change indicated in Fig. 5-11a, which reverses the auxiliary phase with respect to the main. For some motors it is necessary to remove an end shield to make this connection change;

on other motors these connections are made accessible through a window in the front end shield which is covered by a suitable cover, or by a thermal protective device.

5-18. Capacitor Separate—without Thermal Protection.—This motor is similar to Fig. 5-10 except that the capacitor is connected externally in series with either the $T8$ or the $T5$ lead. Such a motor, if externally reversible, requires six external leads. A nonreversible motor would require five external leads.

5-19. Thermally Protected Motors. *a. Elementary Principles Involved.*—Dual-voltage windings pose rather special problems for inherent-overheating protective devices, which operate upon current as well as upon temperature,* since the current drawn on the high-voltage connection is but half as much as that drawn on the low-voltage connection. Thermostats for such motors are usually made with three terminals, as shown schematically in Fig. 5-12*a*, so that the current interrupted by the contacts is not necessarily the same as that through the heating element. Usual arrangement is to connect the heating element in series with one of the two halves of the main winding, and the contacts in series with both sections in parallel. On the running connection, the current divides about equally between the two sections of the main winding, so that the current flowing through the heater is about the same on either voltage connection. However, the contacts, being in series with the line, open both sections when the thermostat operates. Thus, *running protection* of a dual-voltage winding is not so difficult, but *locked-rotor protection* introduces still another element.

By reference to Fig. 5-11, it will be observed that there are three windings carrying current when the rotor is locked. Current in the $T1$ line is less than half the total current, and current in the $T3$ line is more than half, because of the current in the auxiliary phase. Therefore, if the heater is connected in the $T3$ line, the thermostat will operate faster on 115 volts than on 230. However, if the heater is connected in the $T1$ lead, it will operate slower on 115 volts. At least, that would be the tendency, but there is another factor yet to be considered. In the disc-type thermostat, which is widely used for this purpose, the current that flows through the contacts also has to flow through the disc. Since the disc has a certain amount of resistance, heat is generated in the disc and at the contacts, as well as in the heater. On the 115-volt connection, twice as much current flows

---

* See Arts. 18-14 to 18-16 for a more complete discussion of inherent-overheating protection.

through the contacts and disc as on the 230-volt connection. This consideration tends to make the disc open faster on 115 than on 230 volts *for the same current in the heater*; conversely, for the same tripping time on both voltages, the current through the heater must be less for the 115- than for the 230-volt connection.

The above considerations suggest putting the heater in the $T1$ rather than in the $T3$ lead of Fig. 5-11, and this appears to be the common practice. However, it is not possible to make any general statement as to whether the thermostat will trip faster on the high-

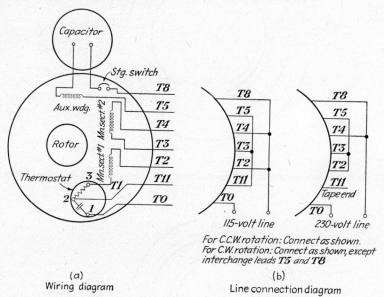

(a)
Wiring diagram

(b)
Line connection diagram

For C.C.W. rotation: Connect as shown.
For C.W. rotation: Connect as shown, except interchange leads *T5* and *T8*

Fɪɢ. 5-12.—Wiring and line connection diagrams for a seven-lead, thermally protected, dual-voltage, capacitor-start motor, externally reversible.

or on the low-voltage connection. If the resistance of the disc and contacts is negligible, it may be desirable to connect the heater in the $T3$ lead. (In some ratings of the disc-type thermostat, the heater effect of the disc is negligible.)

To summarize: the contacts are always connected to open the line circuit; on the high-voltage connection, the heater, too, carries line current; on the low-voltage connection, the heater carries the current of one section of the main winding and may or may not carry the current in the auxiliary winding in addition. Seven leads are required if the motor is to be externally reversible, and five if it is not.

b. Seven Leads, Externally Reversible.—Wiring and line connection diagrams are given in Fig. 5-12. Tagging of the five leads from the winding are in accordance with principles implied in A.S.A. standards,

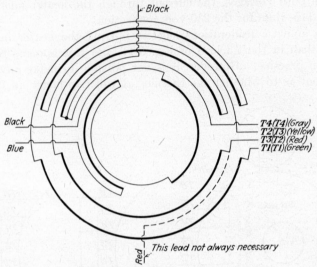

Fig. 5-13.—Stator connection diagram for a two-pole, dual-voltage, capacitor-start motor.

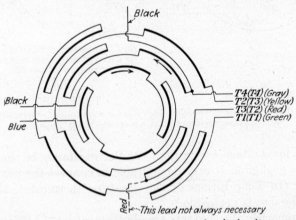

Fig. 5-14.—Stator connection diagram for a four-pole, dual-voltage, capacitor-start motor.

but there are no standard markings for the two leads from the thermostat, which have been arbitrarily tagged as shown. Robbins and Myers motors are tagged substantially as shown unless the leads are colored, in which case the $T0$ lead is black with a tracer, the $T11$ lead is brown, and remaining leads use the coding given in Art. 5-17*a*. Stator connection diagrams are the same as for Art. 5-17*a*.

c. Five Leads, Nonreversible.—Figure 5-12 applies except that the *T*8 lead is internally connected to the *T*4 lead, and the *T*5 lead is internally connected to the *T*3 lead. External leads *T*5 and *T*8 are omitted. One Westinghouse motor with internal capacitor uses this arrangement except that the leads are colored as follows:

*T*0 —Black	*T*3-*T*5—Red
*T*11—Gray	*T*4-*T*8—White
*T*2 —Green	

Internal connections are identical with Fig. 5-12 except that the auxiliary winding is between the capacitor and the switch.

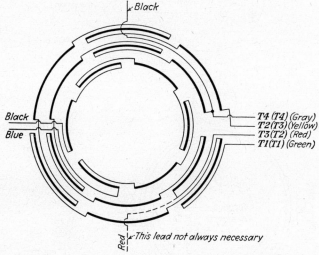

Fig. 5-15.—Stator connection diagram for a six-pole, dual-voltage, capacitor-start motor.

THE SWING CONNECTION—WITHOUT TERMINAL BOARD

5-20. "Swing" Connection (Three Leads—Reversible).—The **swing connection** makes it possible to build a single-voltage externally reversible capacitor-start motor that uses only three line leads instead of the customary four leads of Fig. 5-6. Such a motor is shown in Fig. 5-16. Like the dual-voltage motor of Art. 5-15, the main winding is arranged in two sections, but, unlike this dual-voltage motor, these two sections are always connected in series. One end of the auxiliary phase is permanently connected to the mid-point of the main winding. For one direction of rotation, the auxiliary phase is shunted across one section of the main winding; for the opposite direction of rotation, across the other section. This connection is used mainly for 230-volt motors.

In the swing connection, the main winding serves not only as a main winding, but also as an autotransformer to reduce the line voltage 50 per cent for the capacitor phase. The principle of operation

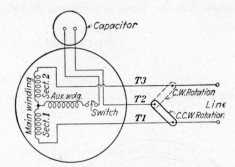

Fig. 5-16.—The swing connection.

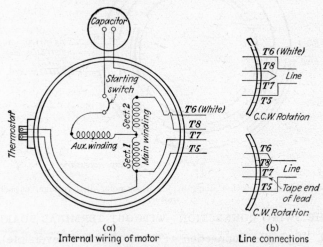

(a)
Internal wiring of motor

(b)
Line connections

Fig. 5-17.—Wiring and line connection diagram of a thermally protected, swing-connected motor. (*Courtesy of Westinghouse Electric Corporation.*)

is analogous to that of the dual-voltage motor shown in Fig. 5-11 when the latter is connected for the higher of the two voltages. However, when the swing connection is used, the auxiliary phase may be paralleled with either section of the main winding, depending upon the desired direction of rotation. (Swinging the link from $T1$ to $T3$ reverses the direction of current flow in the auxiliary winding with respect to the main winding, thereby connecting the motor for the opposite direction of rotation.)

From the standpoint of the serviceman, the swing connection has the advantage that it permits rewinding a 115-volt motor for 230 volts, using the same capacitor. This point is discussed further in Art. 5-32.

5-21. Swing-connected Motor with Thermal Protection.—A swing-connected motor can be equipped with built-in thermal protection as shown in Fig. 5-17. The protective device can be connected in either line, but the auxiliary-phase lead must be connected on the motor side of the protective device and not on the line side. The white lead indicates that it is the one to be connected to the ground side of a grounded circuit.

GENERAL-PURPOSE MOTORS—WITH TERMINAL BOARD

5-22. Generalities.—Terminal posts have long been common on all types and kinds of electrical apparatus, including fractional horse-

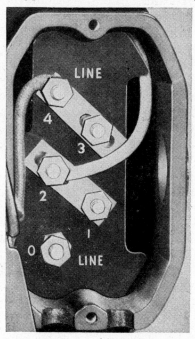 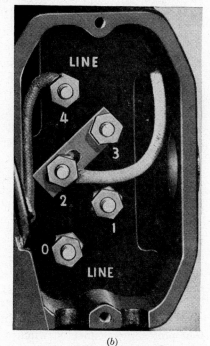

(a)   (b)

Fig. 5-18.—Cast conduit box and built-in terminal board. Leads shown are used to reverse direction of rotation. Note large hole for conduit connection, and two small slots for rubber-covered cord or cable. (a) Links arranged for 115 volts. (b) Links arranged for 230 volts. (*Courtesy of Westinghouse Electric Corporation.*)

power motors.   Within the past 10 years, it has become the usual thing for manufacturers to furnish capacitor-start motors with a conduit box cast as an integral part of the front end shield, with a terminal board inside.   A typical arrangement is shown in Fig. 5-18.

Cast-integral conduit boxes have the important advantage over attached steel boxes that they cannot possibly rattle.   Moreover, the cast conduit box is usually provided with one hole large enough to accommodate a conduit connection, and with two or more small slots suitable for the use of rubber-covered cable.   Two such slots are shown in the figure: one for the line leads, and one for control leads. Built-in terminal boards tend to minimize, but do not eliminate, the chances of wrong connections.   Some manufacturers mark the two line posts in a distinctive manner, as shown in Fig. 5-18, but this does not preclude the possibilities of connecting the links or leads incorrectly.

No uniform practice exists for the number, marking, and arrangement of terminals for built-in terminal boards.   A.S.A. standards covering this situation do not now exist, and each manufacturer follows his own preferences.   Sometimes the stator member of the starting switch is combined with, or mounted on, the terminal board.   Even the marking of the terminals varies considerably.   Terminals may be numbered from top to bottom, or vice versa, and the numbering may not be consecutive; numbers, letters, or combinations of the two are used to mark individual terminals.   In the following paragraphs, a series of diagrams is given to illustrate the principles involved.   Space does not permit inclusion of all variations; even diagrams for separate capacitor have been omitted.

5-23. Single-voltage   Motors—without   Thermal Protection.— These motors are usually made externally reversible and may employ either the conventional or the swing connection.

a. Conventional Arrangement (115-*volt Motors*).—Wiring and line connection diagrams for one arrangement are given in Fig. 5-19.   The starting switch is shown combined with the terminal board.   Capacitor-phase leads are connected to the inside of the terminal board, and main-phase leads, provided with eyelets, are connected to the outside. This arrangement provides a reversible motor with only two binding posts required.   The corresponding **stator connection diagram** for a four-pole series-connected winding is Fig. 5-20.   Diagrams for other numbers of poles, or for a parallel connection, can be made up by slight alterations in the fundamental stator connection diagrams used for split-phase motors.   A study of the differences between Figs. 5-20 and 4-9 will show how to convert any of the split-phase diagrams (Figs. 4-8 to 4-16) into a similar diagram for the motor of Fig. 5-19.

Figure 5-21 shows wiring and line connections for a similar motor except that the line terminals are definitely marked "Line." This is

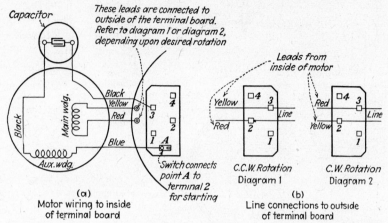

(a)
Motor wiring to inside of terminal board

(b)
Line connections to outside of terminal board

Fig. 5-19.—Wiring and line connection diagram of a single-speed, single-voltage, externally reversible, capacitor-start motor with built-in conduit box. Starting switch is combined with the terminal board. (*Courtesy of Westinghouse Electric Corporation.*)

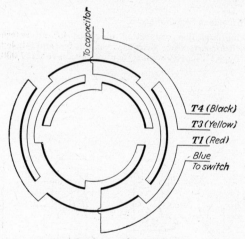

Fig. 5-20.—Stator connection diagram for a four-pole, capacitor-start motor using built-in terminal board.

a more recent arrangement, the reasons for which are explained in Art. 5-24a. Stator connection diagrams are the same as for the motor of the preceding paragraph.

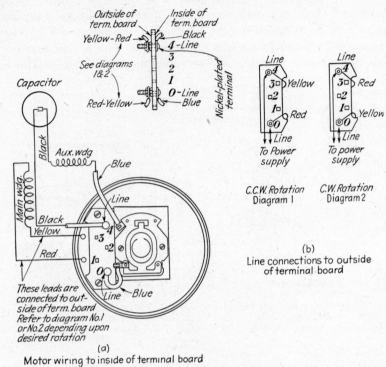

(b)
Line connections to outside
of terminal board

(a)
Motor wiring to inside of terminal board

Fig. 5-21.—Wiring and line connection diagrams for an externally reversible, single-voltage, capacitor-start motor with cast conduit box and 5-hole terminal board. (For Westinghouse Type FJ motors with style numbers above 1,177,000.)

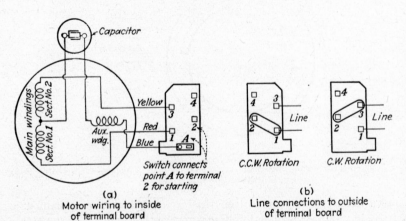

(a)
Motor wiring to inside
of terminal board

(b)
Line connections to outside
of terminal board

Fig. 5-22.—Wiring and line connection diagrams for a swing-connected motor with built-in conduit box.

b. Swing Connection, or Half-voltage Starting Windings (230-volt Motors).—Most 230-volt motors use an arrangement of windings which gives, on the starting connection, half voltage on the capacitor phase. There are at least three methods for obtaining reversibility. Wiring and line connection diagrams for one method are shown in Fig. 5-22. Note that this is essentially the same motor as Fig. 5-16, except for a minor difference in the capacitor-phase circuit. Either direction of rotation can be obtained merely by changing the position of the one link as shown. Stator connection diagrams are shown in

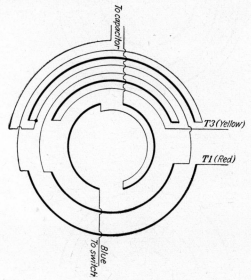

Fig. 5-23.—Stator connection diagram for the swing connection, two poles.

Figs. 5-23 to 5-25. With this winding arrangement—known as the "swing" connection—reversal of rotation is effected by moving one end of the capacitor phase from one line to the other.

A second method of changing the direction of rotation of a motor with a half-voltage starting winding consists of interchanging the two ends of the main winding, leaving the capacitor-phase lead connected to the same line. For example, the motor of Fig. 5-22 could be reversed by leaving the blue lead permanently connected to one side of the line, while the yellow and red leads were interchanged; this would cause the capacitor phase to be paralleled with the one or the other section of the main winding, thus effecting reversal of rotation. In a practical motor, this method would be embodied by connecting the red and yellow leads to the outside of the terminal board, to posts

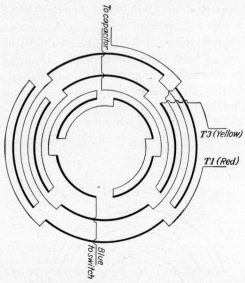

FIG. 5-24.—Stator connection diagram for the swing connection, four poles.

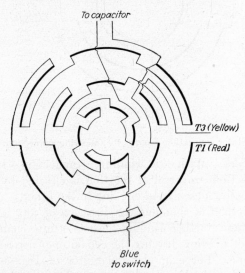

FIG. 5-25.—Stator connection diagram for the swing connection, six poles.

2 and 3, respectively; with this change, the line connection diagram for Fig. 5-22 would become identical with Fig. 5-19b. This arrangement is followed in principle on many motors.

Still a different method of obtaining reverse rotation is to interchange the two ends of the capacitor phase; this method is illustrated in the wiring and line connection diagram of Fig. 5-26. In this motor the mid-point of the main winding is brought out to the terminal board (post 2), and both ends of the capacitor phase are connected to the outside of the terminal board; reversal of the direction of rotation is effected by interchanging the position of the two capacitor-phase leads (marked yellow and red) on the outside of the terminal board. This arrangement keeps the capacitor phase always in parallel

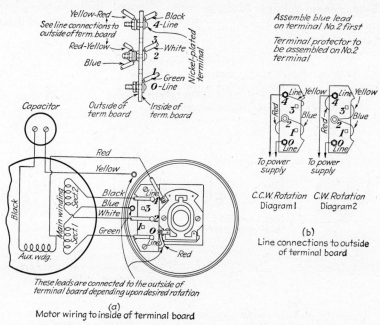

Fig. 5-26.—Wiring and line connection diagrams for an externally reversible, capacitor-start motor with a half-voltage starting winding. Motor has cast conduit box and 5-hole terminal board. (For Westinghouse Type FJ motors with style numbers above 1,177,000.)

with the same section of the main winding, but the method of changing the direction of rotation is essentially the same as for the motor of Fig. 5-21. In Fig. 5-26 it will be noted that the blue lead is connected to the outside of post 2 rather than to the inside. There is a very practical reason for this: terminal studs are made with a square head—like a carriage bolt—to prevent them from turning when an external nut is tightened; if two leads with eyelets are put over this square head, the latter will not engage with the square hole in the terminal board, and the stud is likely to turn when a nut is tightened on the outside. Stator connection diagrams applicable to Fig. 5-26 are the dual-voltage diagrams of Figs. 5-13 to 5-15, except for the following changes which apply to all three:

1. Omit the *red* and *black* leads connected to the main winding.
2. Change *blue* auxiliary-phase lead to *red*.
3. Change *red* main-winding lead to *white*.
4. Change *yellow* main-winding lead to *blue*.
5. Change *gray* main-winding lead to *black*.

5-24. Single-voltage Motors—with Thermal Protection.—These motors are similar to the motors of Art. 5-23 except for the addition of thermal protection.

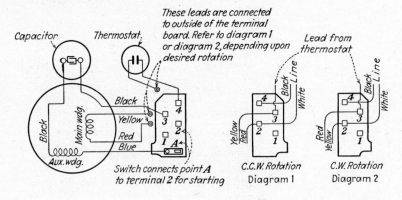

(a)
Motor wiring to inside
of terminal board

(b)
Line connections to outside
of terminal board

FIG. 5-27.—Wiring and line connection diagram for an externally reversible, thermally protected, capacitor-start motor with built-in conduit box.

a. Conventional Arrangement (115-*volt Motors*).—Wiring and line connection diagrams for one arrangement are given in Fig. 5-27, which corresponds to the motor of Fig. 5-19. It will be noted that three terminal posts are required for the thermally protected motor. The line is shown connected to posts 2 and 4. However, if the line is incorrectly connected to posts 2 and 3, the motor will operate in a perfectly normal manner, but the thermal protective device will not be in the circuit and will be useless. Or, if the line is inadvertently connected to posts 3 and 4, the thermal device will be burned out like a fuse. *Post 3 must on no account be connected to either side of the line.*

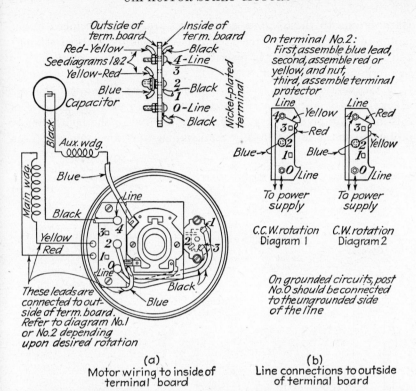

(a)
Motor wiring to inside of
terminal board

(b)
Line connections to outside
of terminal board

FIG. 5-28.—Wiring and line connection diagrams for a thermally protected, externally reversible, single-voltage, capacitor-start motor with cast conduit box and 5-hole terminal board. (For Westinghouse Type FJ motors with style numbers above 1,177,000.)

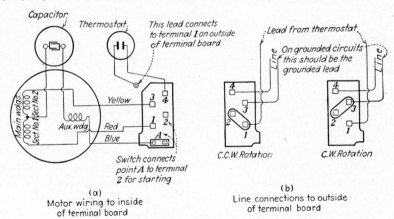

(a)
Motor wiring to inside
of terminal board

(b)
Line connections to outside
of terminal board

FIG. 5-29.—Wiring and line connection diagrams for a thermally protected motor using the swing connection—cast conduit box.

Hazards due to these wrong connections are greatly reduced in the motor of Fig. 5-28; the line terminals are plainly marked "Line," and a terminal protector is placed over post 2. Thus, only the two *line* terminals are exposed.

b. Swing Connection, or Half-voltage Starting Windings (230-*volt Motors*).—Motor wiring and line connection diagrams for one form of this motor are given in Fig. 5-29, corresponding to the nonthermally protected motor of Fig. 5-22. Similar diagrams for a more modern

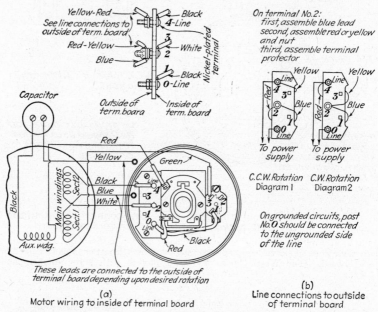

Fig. 5-30.—Wiring and line connection diagrams for a thermally protected, externally reversible, capacitor-start motor with a half-voltage starting winding, cast conduit box, and 5-hole terminal board. (For Westinghouse Type FJ motors with style numbers above 1,177,000.)

and foolproof motor are given in Fig. 5-30, corresponding to the nonthermally protected motor of Fig. 5-26.

5-25. Dual-voltage Motors—without Thermal Protection.—Figure 5-31 shows motor wiring and line connections for a typical nonreversible motor. The motor can be reversed, however, by dismantling and making the changes in connections indicated. However, when the starting switch is separate from the terminal board, it is possible to make a dual-voltage externally reversible motor with but four terminal posts. Such a motor is shown in Fig. 5-32. Stator connection diagram, Figs. 5-13 to 5-15, all apply directly to the motor of Fig. 5-31; they also apply to the motor of Fig. 5-32 except that the black capacitor lead is brought to the outside of the terminal board instead of being connected internally to the *T*4 (gray) lead.

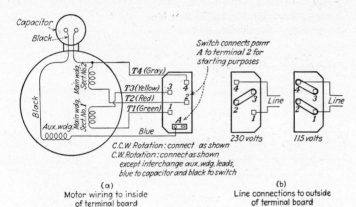

(a)
Motor wiring to inside
of terminal board

(b)
Line connections to outside
of terminal board

FIG. 5-31.—Wiring and line connection diagrams for a dual-voltage, capacitor-start motor. The starting switch is a part of the terminal board.

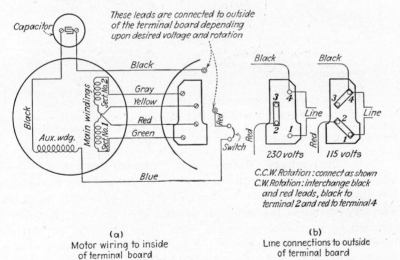

(a)
Motor wiring to inside
of terminal board

(b)
Line connections to outside
of terminal board

FIG. 5-32.—Wiring and line connection diagrams of a dual-voltage, externally reversible, capacitor-start motor.

Wiring and line connection diagrams for a more modern motor with a five-hole terminal board are given in Fig. 5-33. This motor is externally reversible. Applicable stator connection diagrams are given in Figs. 5-13 to 5-15, except for the following changes which apply to all three:

1. Omit the *red* and *black* leads connected to the main winding.
2. Change *blue* auxiliary-phase lead to *red*.
3. Change *red* main-winding lead to *white*.
4. Change *yellow* main-winding lead to *blue*.
5. Change *gray* main-winding lead to *black*.

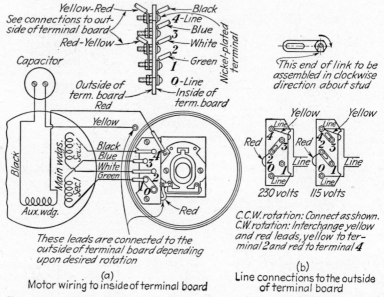

Fig. 5-33.—Wiring and line connection diagrams of a dual-voltage, externally reversible, capacitor-start motor with cast conduit box and 5-hole terminal board. (For Westinghouse Type FJ motors with style numbers above 1,177,000.)

5-26. Dual-voltage Motors—with Thermal Protection.—Motor and line connections are shown in Fig. 5-34 for a motor having four terminals and a loose lead. This motor is not externally reversible. The three-terminal thermostat is so connected that, on the 115-volt connection, it carries somewhat more than half the line current, because it carries the current in section 2 of the main winding plus the auxiliary-phase current. (See Art. 5-19*a* for an explanation of thermal protection of dual-voltage motors.) Stator connection diagrams are given in Figs. 5-13 to 5-15.

Wiring and line connection diagrams for a more modern motor with five-hole terminal board are given in Fig. 5-35. This motor is externally reversible. On the 115-volt connection, the heater in the

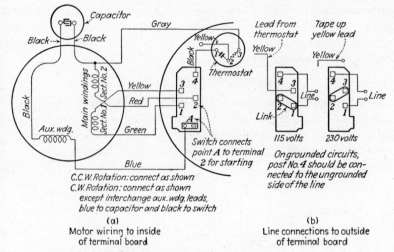

(a)
Motor wiring to inside
of terminal board

(b)
Line connections to outside
of terminal board

FIG. 5-34.—Wiring and line connection diagrams for a thermally protected, dual-voltage, capacitor-start motor, not externally reversible.

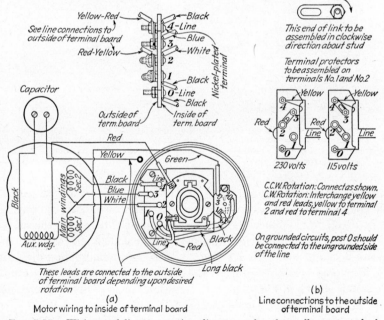

(a)
Motor wiring to inside of terminal board

(b)
Line connections to the outside of terminal board

FIG. 5-35.—Wiring and line connection diagrams of a thermally protected, dual-voltage, externally reversible, capacitor-start motor with cast conduit box and 5-hole terminal board. (For Westinghouse Type FJ motors with style numbers above 1,177,000.)

thermostat carries slightly less than half the line current, because it carries no auxiliary-phase current. Applicable stator connection diagrams are given in Figs. 5-13 to 5-15, except for the five changes noted in the preceding article.

SPECIAL-PURPOSE MOTORS

5-27. Motors with a Terminal Board in the Mounted Capacitor.— Some motors, formerly supplied for refrigeration service, are provided with a terminal board inside the capacitor box. Two such arrangements are shown in Figs. 5-36 and 5-37. Both motors have three terminals, marked *T*, *TL*, and *L*. *TL* is simply a dummy terminal not

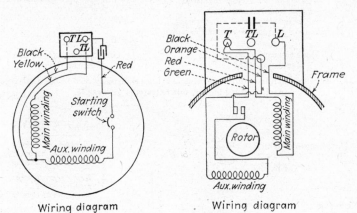

Wiring diagram

Fig. 5-36.—Wiring diagram of a capacitor-start refrigerator motor with a terminal board in the capacitor. This motor is not externally reversible. (*Courtesy of Westinghouse Electric Corporation.*)

Wiring diagram

Fig. 5-37.—Wiring diagram of a capacitor-start motor with terminal board in the capacitor. These connections are for CCW rotation; for CW rotation, interchange the red and black leads on the terminal board. (*Courtesy of Wagner Electric Corporation.*)

connected to the windings. The line is connected across *TL* and *L*. The cold control, or any other external line switch, is connected across *T* and *TL*. When *T* and *TL* are connected together, the motor will operate. If no external line switch or cold control is used, the line can be connected across *T* and *L*. The **stator connection diagram** of a four-pole series-connected motor using the wiring diagram of Fig. 5-36 is shown in Fig. 6-13. Recent practice is to put the terminal board in the motor end shield (see Art. 20-11).

5-28. Motors with Magnetically Operated Switch.—Motors for hermetic refrigeration service commonly employ an external relay, or switch, located outside the sealed unit, because the presence of a switch inside the unit—necessary for a centrifugal switch—cannot be tolerated. Magnetic relays may be either current-operated or voltage-operated.

a. Current-operated relays make use of the fact that the current in the main winding decreases sharply as the motor approaches normal operating speed. A typical arrangement is shown in Fig. 5-38a. The magnet coil is connected in series with the main winding, and the switch contacts in series with the auxiliary winding. When there is no current in the relay coil, the contacts remain in the open position. When the motor is thrown on the line, the current drawn by the main winding under locked-rotor conditions is sufficient to close the contacts, thereby energizing the capacitor phase. As the motor comes up

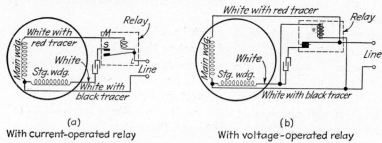

(a)
With current-operated relay

(b)
With voltage-operated relay

Fig. 5-38.—Schematic diagrams of a capacitor-start motor with separate capacitor and magnetic relay, for hermetic refrigerator applications. Motor lead markings are Nema standard.

to speed, the main-winding current decreases; the relay is set so that when the current has fallen below a predetermined value, the relay drops out, opening the capacitor phase and allowing the motor to run as a single-phase induction motor.

Many relays used for this purpose are not adjustable. If the relay does permit of adjustment, it must be set so that it will always close under locked-rotor conditions with low voltage impressed. (By low voltage is meant the lowest circuit voltage likely to be encountered at the motor terminals.) It must also be set to drop out as the motor comes up to speed, even when driving its heaviest load, at any voltage, from the lowest to the highest, likely to be encountered at the motor terminals. If there is an appreciable difference between these two adjustments, the proper setting becomes largely a matter of judgment; some intermediate setting can be used.

b. Voltage-operated relays make use of the increase in auxiliary-winding voltage as the motor nears normal operating speed. A typical arrangement is shown in Fig. 5-38b. The operating coil of the relay is connected in parallel with the auxiliary winding (not including the capacitor), and the contacts in series with the capacitor phase. When not energized, the relay contacts are normally closed. When the motor is thrown on the line with the rotor at standstill, the voltage across the auxiliary winding is not sufficient to open the relay contacts; as the motor comes up to speed, the voltage across the auxiliary winding steadily increases and, finally, as the motor nears normal operating speed, the voltage becomes great enough to open the relay contacts, thereby deenergizing the auxiliary phase. It might be supposed that the voltage on the auxiliary winding would disappear and that the relay contacts would again close. However, when the motor is up to speed and energized, there is a voltage induced in the auxiliary winding,* and this voltage is sufficient to maintain the relay contacts open.

These relays may or may not be adjustable. If the relay does permit of adjustment, it must be set so that (1) it will never pick up with rotor at standstill and with maximum voltage impressed; (2) it will always pick up as the motor comes up to speed while driving its heaviest load, with minimum voltage impressed; (3) once it has opened, it will not reclose with minimum voltage impressed. If all three of these conditions cannot be met simultaneously, a compromise setting has to be made.

5-29. Two-speed, Pole-changing Motors.—These motors are basically similar to their split-phase counterparts (see Arts. 4-29 to 4-31). If a four-winding arrangement is used, either one or two capacitors may be used; with a three-winding arrangement, only one capacitor is required. These motors are generally used in preference to the split-phase type for the larger ratings, *viz.*, for ⅓ hp and larger.

5-30. Electrically Reversible Motor for Hoist Service.—Hoist motors must reverse instantly when either the "down" or the "up" cord is pulled. Capacitor-start motors have the high torques necessary for hoist service and will operate equally well in either direction of rotation, but the conventional motor of Fig. 5-6 is not electrically reversible.† Direction of rotation is determined by the way in which the capacitor phase, is connected with respect to the main winding. When the motor is up to speed, the starting switch is open so that the capacitor phase is not in the circuit. Consequently, if the capacitor-phase connections are suddenly changed while the motor of Fig. 5-6 is operating at any speed above switch-operating speed, the motor *will*

---

* For an explanation, see Art. 4-33.

† For definition of "electrically reversible," see Glossary.

not reverse but will continue to operate on the main winding only in the same direction. On a hoist application, this might well be disastrous!

This inherent limitation is overcome in the hoist motor shown in Fig. 5-39, which uses a special two-contact centrifugal starting switch,

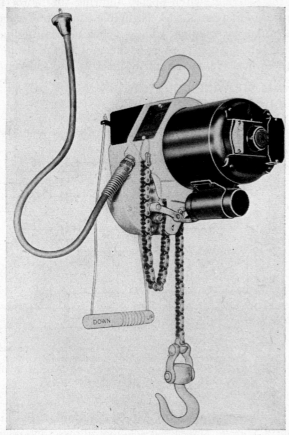

FIG. 5-39.—Electrically reversible (plug-reversing), capacitor-start motor mounted on a hoist. A relay mounted on the motor automatically short-circuits the starting switch when the motor is plugged. This short circuit persists for only the first part of the plugging cycle, until the starting switch has reclosed. (*Courtesy of Westinghouse Electric Corporation.*)

a voltage relay, and a resistor. Manual control of the motor is effected by the three-position three-pole drum controller operated by the down and the up cords and handle. Figure 5-40 shows the schematic arrangement of connections. The motor is started in the desired direction of rotation by closing the drum switch, which simultaneously energizes the main winding, capacitor and auxiliary winding, and the solenoid relay, which immediately picks up on line voltage and seals itself across the line through its own upper contact.   Meanwhile, since the motor is energized in a normal manner, it comes up to speed and the starting switch opens, allowing the motor to operate on the main winding only.   (A negligible amount of current flows through the auxiliary winding, which is then across the line in series with the resistor.)   To plug-reverse the motor, the drum switch is moved to the other side, momentarily interrupting the voltage to the

DIAGRAM SHOWING CONNECTIONS
WITH H-37 DRUM CONTROLLER

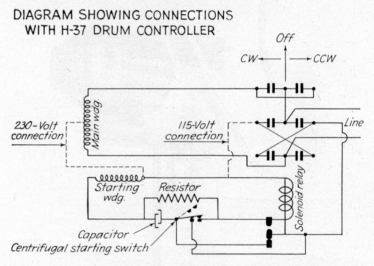

When handle is in CW position, right hand terminals are connected to respective center terminals. When handle is in CCW position, left hand terminals are connected to respective center terminals.

Fig. 5-40.—Schematic wiring diagram for the motor of Fig. 5-39.

motor during the inevitable in-between position.   This momentary interruption of voltage across the solenoid allows that relay to drop to the lower position where it short-circuits the starting switch.   When the drum switch restores power to the motor, the capacitor-phase connections are made for the opposite rotation but, since the centrifugal switch is now short-circuited by the relay, full power is applied to both windings and the motor starts to decelerate rapidly.   As soon as the speed has dropped to the point where the centrifugal switch recloses, the solenoid relay again picks up and seals itself in the up position through its own upper contact.   Meanwhile, the motor continues to decelerate and then comes up to speed in the opposite direction until the starting switch again opens and the motor again operates normally, but in the opposite direction.

An important feature of this circuit is the resistor bridged across the capacitor and starting switch. Its function is to prevent the solenoid from connecting the starting winding and capacitor across the line if there is a momentary interruption of line voltage, or if the operator opens the line switch momentarily and then recloses it for the same direction of rotation; under such conditions the winding or the capacitor would surely burn up. This consideration merits further discussion. If, while the motor is running, power is interrupted momentarily, the solenoid relay immediately drops down to the lower position, short-circuiting the starting-switch contacts which are, of course, open. Now, when power is restored, both main and capacitor phases are energized on the starting connection, and the coil of the solenoid relay is connected across the starting winding in series with the resistor. The magnitude of the voltage across the starting winding depends very much upon whether the connections are (1) for the same direction of rotation or (2) for the opposite direction of rotation. In the first case, the auxiliary-winding voltage is high—appreciably above line voltage; in the second case, it is much less than line voltage. In the first case, the voltage is high enough to cause the solenoid relay to pick up in spite of the resistance introduced by the resistor; this opens the starting phase, and the motor continues to operate normally on the main winding only in the same direction of rotation. In the second case, the auxiliary-winding voltage is not enough to operate the solenoid relay with the resistor in series, so that the motor decelerates rapidly until the speed is reduced enough for the starting switch to reclose, impressing full line voltage across the solenoid coil, which immediately picks up and seals itself in across the line, allowing the motor to complete its reversal.

It should be noted in passing that the capacitor phase is connected across the line for 115-volt motors, and across half of the main winding for 230-volt motors.

Service Instructions.—The solenoid relay is not adjustable and should be replaced by a new one if it does not function properly. It should pick up immediately (1) if voltage is applied to the motor at rest; (2) if power is interrupted momentarily and restored before the motor has slowed down enough for the starting switch to reclose. If the relay will pick up when the motor is at rest, but will not after a momentary interruption of power, the trouble is likely to be in either the resistor or its connections. When the motor is energized, the solenoid relay should remain in the lower position only for the very start of a plug reversal—until the motor speed has dropped enough to cause the starting switch to reclose.

5-31. Miscellaneous Special Arrangements.—There are so many special arrangements used that only a few can be mentioned.

Three terminal posts suffice for the dual-voltage, externally reversible motor of Fig. 5-41, which is used for refrigerator applications. On the low-voltage connection, only two of these posts are used. The third post is used as a dummy for tying together the starting winding and the two ends of the main winding that form the half-voltage point.

Some dual-voltage reversible motors furnished for washing-machine applications by General Electric use two line leads and a four-post

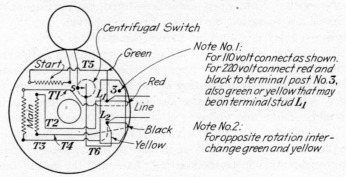

Fig. 5-41.—Wiring and line connection diagram for a dual-voltage, externally reversible, capacitor-start motor with only three terminals. Used for refrigerator applications. (*Courtesy of General Electric Company.*)

built-in terminal board. The arrangement is generally similar to Fig. 5-32 with line leads soldered to posts 1 and 4. Voltage connections are changed by the links, and direction of rotation by the two leads connected to the outside of the terminal board.

Certain Westinghouse motors used on Kolmaster stokers were equipped with a reversing switch in a conduit box mounted on the motor frame. This switch was used to reverse the direction of rotation of the motors in the event that the feed screw jammed, in order to back out the obstruction, and was intended to be used only when the motor was at rest.

Line switches are often built into the motor, particularly when it is for a home workshop application.

Use of a choke coil in series with the capacitor phase is reported by the Ohio Electric Manufacturing Company to retard the rush of current at the moment of opening the capacitor-phase circuits. This choke is an air-core reactor consisting of 50 to 150 turns of wire larger than the auxiliary-phase winding by about three gauge sizes; it is usually a part of the capacitor assembly.

MISCELLANEOUS SERVICE PROBLEMS

5-32. Rewinding or Reconnecting Motor for a Different Voltage and Same Performance. *a. Changing from* 115 *to* 230 *Volts.*—(1) One way to do this is to double the number of turns in each winding, using wire three sizes smaller in each; it is then necessary to use a 220-volt capacitor having one-fourth the microfarad rating of the capacitor used with the 115-volt motor. (2) Another way is to rewind the motor for dual voltage or for the swing connection (see Arts. 5-14 to 5-21): in this case, the same capacitor and the same auxiliary winding are used; but each section of the main winding should use wire three sizes smaller and each section must have the same number of turns as the 115-volt main winding, as discussed in Art. 5-16. (3) If the main and auxiliary windings are both parallel-connected, it may be possible to reconnect them in series and use a 220-volt capacitor of one-fourth the microfarad rating. If the main winding is wound in two parallel-connected sections, each section containing only half the total number of poles (*i.e.*, using the diagram of Fig. 10-8), it is not recommended that such a winding be split in two sections to use for a swing connection or for a dual-voltage connection. (4) If the main winding is wound of two strands of wire in parallel and if it is possible to separate these strands, test between strands at 500 volts; if the winding stands this test, it is safe and simple to reconnect the motor for 230 volts, using the proper swing connection diagram.

b. Changing from 230 *to* 115 *Volts.*—(1) If the motor is swing-connected, it is a simple matter to reconnect the two main-winding sections in parallel (if due care as to magnetic polarity is exercised), leaving the auxiliary winding and capacitor undisturbed. (2) If the stator connections are conventional (like those shown in Fig. 5-7), a 110-volt capacitor of four times the microfarad rating of the 220-volt capacitor must be used, and the windings can be either reconnected in parallel or rewound. If they are to be reconnected, each winding can be split into two sections, each section including every alternate pole. (Care must be taken to preserve proper magnetic polarities!) In Fig. 5-42 is shown a motor reconnected in this manner; this motor was originally connected according to the diagram of Fig. 5-7. (3) If the windings are rewound, half as many turns and wire three sizes larger should be used in each winding.

c. Changing from 230 *to* 440 *Volts.*—The problem of changing a 230-volt motor to a 440-volt motor, if the motor has conventional connections (like those shown in Fig. 5-7), is similar to the problem of changing from 115 to 230 volts, which is discussed in the first paragraph of this article, except that, because of switch and capacitor limitations, only the swing or dual-voltage connection is recommended.

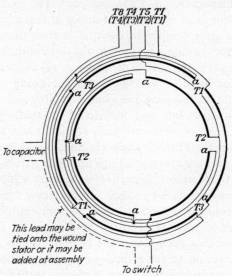

Fig. 5-42.—Stator connection diagram for reconnecting a 230-volt motor for 115 volts.

d. Other Voltage Changes.—In general, changes for voltages other than those just described are not to be recommended, for a capacitor of the proper voltage and microfarad rating is seldom available. The rules for such a change would be as follows:

If $\qquad$ V_r = rated voltage

$\qquad\qquad$ V_d = desired circuit voltage

the number of turns of both main and auxiliary windings is

$$\frac{V_d}{V_r} \times \text{turns in old windings}$$

and the cross-sectional area of the copper wire should be

$$\frac{V_r}{V_d} \times \text{area of copper wire in present winding}$$

or as near as possible to this value. The capacitor should be rated for V_d volts, and the microfarad rating should be

$$\left(\frac{V_r}{V_d}\right)^2 \times \text{the microfarad rating of the present capacitor}$$

5-33. Rewinding for Different Torques.—In general, it is not wise for a repair shop to attempt to rewind for a different torque by changing the wire size or number of turns, as discussed for split-phase motors in Art. 4-38. The serviceman may rewind a capacitor-start motor, actually obtaining more torque, but in so doing he may subject the capacitor to higher voltages, a fact that may not show up in his test but that will eventually show up in reduced life of the capacitor.

5-34. Rewinding for a Different Frequency.—The redesign of a winding of a capacitor-start motor to operate on a different frequency is a problem for a design engineer, and no simple rules can be laid down that the serviceman can follow with safety. Such a rewinding job is, therefore, not to be recommended unless the winding specification can be obtained from the manufacturer.

5-35. Changing a Capacitor-start to a Split-phase Motor.—It was brought out in Art. 4-40 that a split-phase motor could be converted to a capacitor-start motor by the addition of a capacitor in series with the auxiliary winding. By use of the capacitor it was possible to increase the locked-rotor torque and decrease the locked-rotor amperes. Likewise, it is usually possible to operate a capacitor-start motor as a split-phase motor by substituting an external resistance for the capacitor. Some capacitor-start motors will start under no-load conditions as split-phase motors, and others will not; even if a particular motor will start as a split-phase motor, a resistor in series with the auxiliary winding will usually improve the locked-rotor torque and reduce the locked-rotor current. For any given motor, there is a definite value of resistance that will give a maximum locked-rotor torque. This "best value" of resistance to give the most locked-rotor torque will probably be from one to two times the ohmic resistance of the auxiliary winding; different values of resistance in this range may be tried to determine the best value to use.

A rough idea of what might be expected is given in the example as shown on page 162 which is based on a ⅓-hp 4-pole 60-cycle 115-volt capacitor-start motor.

This example illustrates the point that an external resistance boosts the locked-rotor torque and cuts the line current, but with the best value of external resistance (which in this case happened to be 133 per cent of the auxiliary winding resistance) the locked-rotor torque is very small compared with that of a capacitor-start motor. This torque is sufficient to start a fan or blower but would not start a compressor. The running performance, of course, is the same whether the motor starts as a resistance-start split-phase motor or as a capacitor-start motor.

CAPACITOR-START MOTOR USED AS A SPLIT-PHASE MOTOR

	As a normal capacitor-start motor	As a split-phase motor, no external resistance	As a split-phase motor, 6.7 ohms external resistance
Locked amperes:			
Main winding.................	22.5	22.5	22.5
Auxiliary winding..............	8.05	9.71	6.38
Line.........................	24.5	32.1	28.4
Locked-rotor torque, oz-ft.........	65.0	12.5	19.2
Full-load torque, oz-ft...........	16.0	16.0	16.0

5-36. Regeneration in Capacitor-start Motors.—Regeneration is an effect that can occur with a capacitor-start motor, particularly if the motor is driving a high-inertia load such as a fan or blower. The effect may be noticed in either of two ways:

1. While the motor is slowly coasting to a stop, the starting switch closes; immediately the motor vibrates and becomes noisy and decelerates rapidly, as if it were being suddenly braked electrically; which, in fact, it is.

2. In an oil-burner application, a solenoid-operated oil valve is sometimes connected across the motor so that the valve is open only when the motor is energized. If regeneration occurs while the motor is coasting to a stop, a voltage appears at the motor terminals and may cause false opening or fluttering of the oil valve, or any other relay connected across the motor.

a. Causes of Regeneration.—It is a well-known fact that an induction motor can be made to act as an induction generator and supply power to the line to which it is connected, merely by driving it above synchronous speed. It is also well known that the power output of an induction generator must always have a leading power factor, never unity or lagging power factor; *i.e.*, the current output of the generator must always have a leading component in order to provide the excitation to set up the magnetic field required in the generator. It has been shown that an induction motor can be made to act as an induction generator by connecting shunt capacitors of proper value across the output terminals; these capacitors draw the leading current necessary for the machine to build up as a self-excited generator, without the necessity for its being connected to an external supply line.[7] Suppose that the starting switch of the motor of Fig. 5-1 is closed, and further suppose that the motor is being driven mechanically at full-load speed with no external voltage applied to the terminals. There will always be a little residual flux in the rotor, which will cut the stator windings and induce a small voltage in them. Referring to Fig. 5-1, it is seen that there is a voltage impressed across the capacitor which is equal to the sum of the two voltages induced in the main and auxiliary windings; this voltage causes a small leading current to flow through the capacitor. The leading current increases the field excitation in the motor, increasing the output voltage, increasing the leading current, and so on, until quite an appreciable output voltage is reached; the magnitude of this voltage is limited only by saturation of the magnetic circuit of the machine. This effect is so marked that it is probable that almost any general-purpose capacitor-start motor would burn out in a short time if it were driven at synchronous speed with the starting switch closed—so great is the regenerative effect under these conditions. This effect has been discussed more completely by the author, and some of the more important conclusions are merely summarized below without proof:[8]

1. For any given motor driven always at the same speed, there is a critical value of capacitance, below which the machine will not build up at all. The more this capacitance is exceeded, the greater will be the voltage, current, and dynamic-braking torque.

2. For any given machine with a fixed value of capacitance, there is a critical speed below which the machine will not build up at all. The more the speed exceeds this critical value, the greater will be the current, voltage, and dynamic-braking torque.

3. For any given machine, the critical value of capacitance is inversely proportional to the square of the speed; the converse of this is likewise true.

4. If the capacitor is charged at the instant that the starting switch closes, build-up is much more likely to occur, but build-up can occur with no initial charge in the capacitor.

5. If a resistor is connected in parallel with the capacitor, the tendency of the machine to build up is reduced, partly because the resistor bleeds off the capacitor charge, and partly because the resistor acts as a load on the generator—just as a load across a shunt generator decreases the critical field resistance above which the machine will not build up.

b. Remedies.—Probably the easiest remedy for a serviceman is to install a small resistor—of the type found in a radio supply store—in the capacitor assembly, connecting it across the capacitor terminals. If it is observed that the regenerative build-up occurs only if the motor is stopped within a few seconds after starting, but does not occur if the motor has been running for some time, then a fairly high resistance, say, 1000 ohms, can be tried.   If this does not cure the difficulty, a smaller value of resistance should be tried.   This process can be repeated until a value of resistance is found that cures the trouble. This resistor should have the maximum resistance that can be used and still be effective.   Care should also be exercised to use a resistor of a high enough watt rating so that it does not overheat during a starting or stopping period.   Use of a resistor tends to increase the locked-rotor current.

Lowering the reclosing speed of the starting switch enough will eliminate the difficulty.   Ordinarily a serviceman can do this only by using a switch with a lower opening as well as lower reclosing speed, and this would generally affect the pull-up switching torques adversely. With a current-operated magnetic switch, regeneration difficulties cannot occur because the starting circuit never closes after the motor is deenergized.   With a voltage relay, regeneration is almost certain to occur because the starting switch closes instantly after the power is shut off; however, these relays are used mostly for hermetic refrigerators, which stop very quickly so that there is little danger of serious trouble on this account.

Bibliography

1. BOOTHBY, C. R.: Discussion on Capacitor Motor Papers, *A.I.E.E. Trans.*, April, 1929, p. 629.
2. SPECHT, H. C.: Fundamental Theory of the Capacitor Motor, *A.I.E.E. Trans.*, April, 1929, p. 607.
3. BAILEY, BENJAMIN F.: The Condenser Motor, *A.I.E.E. Trans.*, April, 1929, p. 596.
4. MORRILL, WAYNE J.: The Revolving Field Theory of the Capacitor Motor, *A.I.E.E. Trans.*, April, 1929, p. 614.
5. TRICKEY, P. H.: Design of Capacitor Motors for Balanced Operation, *A.I.E.E. Trans.*, September, 1932, p. 780.
6. VEINOTT, C. G.: Starting Windings for Single-phase Induction Motors, *A.I.E.E. Trans.*, vol. 63, 1944, pp. 288–294.
7. BASSETT, E. D., and POTTER, E. M.: Capacitive Excitation for Induction Generators, *A.I.E.E. Trans.*, 1935, pp. 540–545.
8. VEINOTT, C. G.: Discussion of Bassett and Potter Paper, *A.I.E.E. Trans.*, 1935, p. 1106.
9. DEELY, PAUL McKNIGHT: "Electrolytic Capacitors," Cornell-Dubilier Electric Corp., South Plainfield, N. J., 1938.
10. GEORGIEV, ALEXANDER M.: "The Electrolytic Capacitor," Murray Hill Books, Inc., Technical Division, New York.

CHAPTER VI

TWO-VALUE CAPACITOR MOTORS

The two-value capacitor motor gained great commercial importance in the early 1930's for applications requiring high locked-rotor torque, such as refrigerators, compressors, and stokers. It has since been replaced largely by the capacitor-start motor.

6-1. Two-value Capacitor Motor Defined.—A **two-value capacitor motor** is a form of capacitor motor that starts with one value of capacitance in series with the auxiliary winding and runs with a different value. This change in value of capacitance is automatic and may be effected either by the use of an autotransformer or by the use of two separate capacitors. This motor is formally defined in Art. 5-1. The two-value motor has high starting and running torques.

6-2. Essential Parts of the Two-value Motor.—There are two major types of two-value capacitor motors: one uses a capacitor-

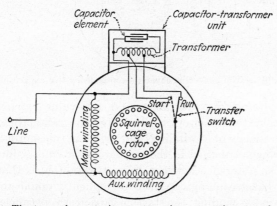

Fig. 6-1.—The two-value capacitor motor using a capacitor-transformer unit.

transformer unit, and the other uses two capacitors. These two types will be discussed in order:

a. Motor Using a Capacitor-transformer Unit.—A two-value motor using a capacitor-transformer unit is represented diagrammatically in Fig. 6-1. To all intents and purposes, the windings are the same as for the capacitor-start motor that was discussed in Art. 5-2, and the

165

rotor is of squirrel-cage construction. A difference in the starting switch will be noted, however, for this motor uses a "transfer switch" which is equivalent to a single-pole double-throw switch. (The split-phase and capacitor-start motors use a switch which is equivalent only to a single-pole single-throw switch, as can be seen by referring to Figs. 4-1 and 5-1.) By means of this transfer switch, a high voltage (approximately 600 to 800 volts) is impressed for starting purposes across the capacitor element; this voltage is then reduced to approximately 330 volts for continuous running. This change in voltage is effected by changing taps on the primary side of the autotransformer and corresponds to changing the effective microfarads in series with the auxiliary winding. Delco Products refer to these as **transformer condenser motors.**

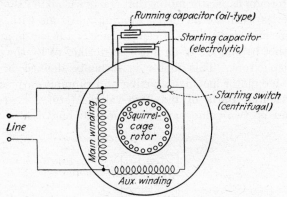

Fig. 6-2.—The two-value capacitor motor using two capacitors.

b. Motor Using Two Capacitors.—A two-value capacitor motor using two separate capacitors is illustrated diagrammatically in Fig. 6-2. The arrangement of windings and switch in this motor is identical with the arrangement used in the capacitor-start motor illustrated in Fig. 5-1. The difference between these two motors is that the two-value motor has a running capacitor permanently connected in series with the auxiliary winding; the starting capacitor is paralleled with the running capacitor only during the starting period. The running capacitor is usually of the paper-spaced oil-filled type, rated at 330 volts alternating current, continuous operation. Castor oil, mineral oil, Dykanol, Inerteen, Insulatum, and Pyranol are variously used as the impregnating medium. The capacities range from 3 to 16 mfd. The electrolytic capacitors for 115-volt 60-cycle motors range in size from 85 mfd or less to 300 mfd or more. A motor of this type is illustrated in Fig. 6-3. The two capacitor units may be contained in a case as shown there, or both units may be separately mounted on the motor, or contained one within the other, as in Fig. 6-21.

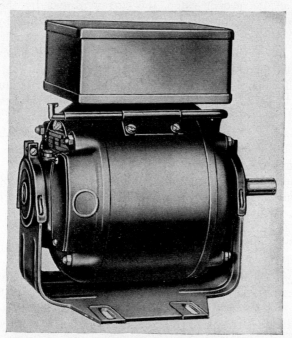

Fig. 6-3.—A two-value capacitor motor with capacitor unit mounted on the motor. (*Courtesy of Century Electric Company.*)

6-3. Effect of the Running Capacitor.—It was pointed out in the preceding paragraph that the motor of Fig. 6-2 is merely the capacitor-start motor of Fig. 5-1 with a "running capacitor" permanently connected in the circuit. Considering any given motor, the effect of adding this capacitor is to

1. Increase the breakdown torque from 5 to 30 per cent.
2. Improve the full-load efficiency and power factor.
3. Reduce the noise under full-load operating conditions.
4. Increase the locked-rotor torque 5 to 20 per cent.

Why does the running capacitor improve performance? The reader is referred to Chap. II, Arts. 2-8 to 2-11, wherein it is pointed out that the rotating field of a single-phase induction motor may be considered as comprised of two component pulsating fields, a main field and a cross field spaced 90 electrical degrees apart and differing in time phase by 90 deg; the main-field component is set up directly by the main winding and the cross field by the rotor. When the auxiliary winding is connected across the line in series with a running capacitor of the proper value, the current drawn by the auxiliary winding leads the current drawn by the main winding by approximately 90 deg. The net result is that the auxiliary winding sets up a part or all of the cross field, thereby reducing or eliminating the magnetizing currents in the rotor and the accompanying copper losses.

The effect of the addition of a running capacitor is illustrated in Fig. 19-8, lines 38 to 47. The first column is an analysis of the full-load losses of a $\frac{1}{4}$-hp motor operating without a capacitor, and the second column is a similar analysis of the same motor operating with a running capacitor in the circuit. The reduction in losses and improvement in performance are marked.

Another effect of the running capacitor is to give 5 to 30 per cent more breakdown torque. Still another effect is the reduction of the double-frequency torque pulsations normally inherent in single-phase motors. (For a discussion of this phenomenon, see Art. 18-11.) This effect is noticeable at or near full load and may not be noticed at no load.

In short, the effect of the running capacitor is to make the motor perform more nearly like a two-phase motor, particularly at one value of load. It is not possible to duplicate two-phase motor performance at all load values with a single value of capacitance, however, because a different value of capacitance would be required for each different load. Trickey[1,7] shows how to proportion a winding and capacitor to obtain two-phase motor performance at any one desired load point. Morrill,[2,6] Trickey,[7] and others show how to calculate the performance of a capacitor motor at any load.

6-4. Purpose of the Starting Switch.—The starting or transfer switch serves the same purpose as the starting switch of a capacitor-start motor, discussed in Art. 5-1. A representative speed-torque curve of a two-value motor is illustrated in Fig. 6-4. The curve of *capacitor volts vs. rpm* indicates, in the case of a motor such as that illustrated in Fig. 6-1, the voltage across the primary of the transformer; the actual voltage across the capacitor element is approximately five to seven times the voltage across the primary, or up to 800 volts. In the case of the motor of Fig. 6-2, the capacitor volts curve represents the actual voltage across the two capacitor elements when the motor is operating *on the starting connection*.

[1] For numbered references, see Bibliography at end of this chapter.

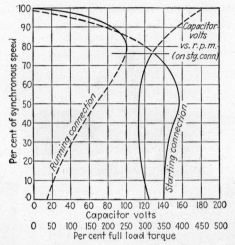

Fig. 6-4.—The speed-torque curve of a two-value capacitor motor.

6-5. Torques of Two-value Capacitor Motors.—By comparing Fig. 6-4 with Fig. 5-4, it will be noted that the capacitor-start motor has substantially the same torques as the two-value motor. The reason for this is simply that the main winding of the capacitor-start motor is designed for more torque, so that the torques of the two types of motors are practically identical. The two-value motor, however, will start a light load on the running connection, whereas the capacitor-start motor will not. The torques given in Table VI apply also to two-value motors, as do the locked-rotor current requirements in Table XXVI.

CAPACITOR-TRANSFORMER UNITS

6-6. Construction of the Capacitor-transformer Unit.—A **capacitor-transformer unit** is illustrated in Fig. 6-5; it consists essentially of

1. An autotransformer.
2. A capacitor element.
3. A metal case to enclose these two parts.
4. Sometimes, a terminal block as discussed in Art. 5-27, or a conduit box.

Wiring diagrams of capacitor-transformer units are shown in Fig. 6-6; Fig. 6-6a indicates an arrangement used with 110-volt motors, and Fig. 6-6b an arrangement used with 220-volt motors. Designs of transformers vary considerably, but the voltage figures given indicate roughly what voltages might be expected across the various taps. These figures also indicate the approximate voltages in the unit when the motor is operating on the *starting connection;* when the motor is operating on the *running connection,* the voltages are somewhat less than half the values shown.   The autotransformer

FIG. 6-5.—A capacitor-transformer unit with the cover removed.   (*Courtesy of Westinghouse Electric Corporation.*)

a. Laminations of the autotransformer.
b. The transformer coil.
c. The capacitor element.

d. Metal enclosing case.
e. Wood spacing blocks.

consists essentially of a coil of wire surrounded by a closed magnetic circuit of laminations.*   This coil of wire is divided into three sections

* For those tho do not understand the principle of an autotransformer, the following may be helpful.   Assume the capacitor element of Fig. 6-6a is removed from the circuit and 110 volts is impressed across the *common* and *starting* leads. Current will flow through *this section only* and will set up an alternating magnetic flux in the surrounding laminations of such a value that substantially 110 volts is induced as a counter emf in the section 110 to oppose the line voltage.   The difference between the line voltage and the counter emf causes a small current to flow to set up the flux.   This small current is known as the **magnetizing current.**   As pointed out before, the alternating magnetic flux induces a voltage in the turns of

by the two taps, and each section may use wire of a different size, or all sections may use wire of the same size.

The autotransformer of Fig. 6-6*a* is a step-up transformer on both the starting and running connections, but the transformer of Fig. 6-6*b* is a step-up transformer on the starting connection and a step-

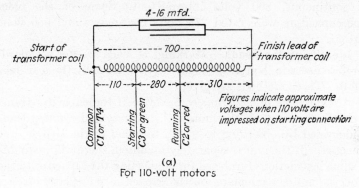

(a)
For 110-volt motors

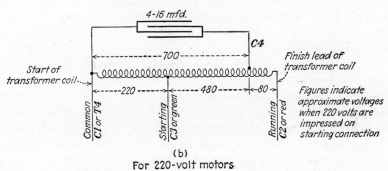

(b)
For 220-volt motors
Fig. 6-6.—Wiring diagrams of a capacitor-transformer unit.

down transformer on the running connection. Sometimes, on 220-volt motors, the *C*4-lead is made common with the running lead so that the coil does not function as an autotransformer but merely floats across the capacitor when the motor is operating on the running connection.

section 110; but this flux also links all the other turns and induces the same volts per turn in all the other parts of the winding. If we know the number of turns in section 110, we can then compute the volts per turn. Knowing the volts per turn, we can then compute the voltage across any other section if we know the turns; or if we know the measured voltage, we can compute the number of turns. In the illustration, the turns are proportioned so that the line voltage of 110 is stepped up to 700 volts. The capacitor is connected across the 700 volts and becomes the load on the transformer.

The capacitor element is constructed of layers of foil separated by paper. It is usually designated by the type of medium used to impregnate the paper, which may be wax, castor oil, mineral oil, Dykanol, Inerteen, Insulatum, or Pyranol. The unit is hermetically sealed in a tin can. A usual rating of this type of unit is 330 volts alternating current continuous, 800 volts intermittent. Some of the older wax-type capacitors were rated 275 volts continuous and 660 volts intermittent.

6-7. Identifying the Leads.—Markings of leads are not standard; it is therefore not safe to attempt to identify the leads by the markings of Fig. 6-6. Three methods are given:

a. By Connections to the Transfer Switch.—If the capacitor-transformer unit is mounted on the motor, the *starting* and *running* leads can be identified by observing to which terminal of the switch they are connected. If the unit is separately mounted, there will undoubtedly be some instructions furnished for connecting the capacitor to the motor, on the motor nameplate, on the capacitor nameplate, or on a separate tag; examination of the motor will reveal which two motor leads are from the *starting* and *running* contacts of the switch, and these will identify the *starting* and *running* leads of the capacitor-transformer unit.

b. By External Resistance Measurements.—Suppose there are three leads to identify. First, measure the three resistances; when the highest resistance is being measured, the open lead necessarily is the center lead, which must be the *starting* lead (see Fig. 6-6a or 6-6b). The resistance between the *starting* and *common* leads is almost invariably less than the resistance from the *starting* tap to the *running* tap; this fact permits almost positive identification of the leads.

c. By Inspection of the Autotransformer.—To inspect the autotransformer, it will be necessary to open the capacitor case and, in a few cases, remove some sealing compound. The *common* lead is almost invariably the beginning of the transformer coil, *i.e.*, a tap from the bottom of the coil. As the coil is wound, the next tap to be brought out is the *starting* tap; the next tap may be either the *running* tap or the capacitor lead, as illustrated in Fig. 6-6.

6-8. Testing Capacitor-transformer Units.—Capacitor-transformer units should be tested on a circuit of the voltage and frequency shown on the nameplate of the motor with which they are designed to be used; otherwise, the test procedure is substantially the same as for testing electrolytic capacitor elements described in Art. 5-10. If rated voltage and frequency are applied, and watts input (corrected for meter losses) and amperes are read,

$$\text{Effective microfarads} = \frac{159,200}{\text{test frequency}} \times \frac{\text{amperes}}{\text{applied voltage}} \quad (6\text{-}1)$$

or, for 60-cycle circuits only,

$$\text{Effective microfarads} = 2,650 \times \frac{\text{amperes}}{\text{applied voltage}} \quad (6\text{-}2)$$

$$\text{Power factor} = \frac{\text{watts}}{\text{volts} \times \text{amperes}} \quad (6\text{-}3)$$

The effective microfarads on the starting connection, for commercial 60-cycle 110-volt fractional horsepower motors may range from 100 to 400.* The power factor may range from 10 to 20 per cent. These readings should give a good indication as to whether or not a unit is defective.

If desired, similar readings can be taken on the running connection. A fair value for 60-cycle 110-volt motors is from 10 to 50 effective microfarads. The total watts input may be approximately 5 to 20 watts.

6-9. Defective Capacitor-transformer Units.—If a capacitor-transformer unit is found to be defective, the first step should be to determine whether the defect is in the transformer or in the capacitor element, for the trouble is not likely to be in both. Disconnect the capacitor element from the transformer, and test the former for short circuits, open circuits, capacity in microfarads, and grounds. The method described in Art. 5-10 for checking electrolytic capacitors may be used here—except that the power factor is entirely too low to be read with commercial meters unless the unit is defective.

Check the transformer for open circuits, short circuits, and grounds. If no defect is found, apply 110 volts to the starting connection, and measure the other voltages as shown in Fig. 6-6. (The figures given will help select a voltmeter of the proper scale, but it should not be expected to check these values too closely.) If suitable voltmeters are not available, 110 volts may be applied to the running connection, and the voltages will be proportionately less; in the two cases illustrated, the voltages will be about 40 per cent of the values given. With the capacitor disconnected, the amperes input to the starting connection should be very low—hardly enough to deflect the needle of a 5-amp ammeter—and the watts input should be less than 10.

* The actual microfarads of the capacitor element by itself may be only 3 to 16 mfd, but the autotransformer effectively increases this value. If the step-up ratio is 6:1, the effective capacitance is increased $6 \times 6 = 36$ times.

If the capacitor only is defective, it can be replaced by a new capacitor element of the *same voltage and microfarad rating and designed for this type of service.*

If the transformer winding is defective, it is usually better to obtain a complete new unit from the manufacturer rather than attempt to rewind the coil. One attempt to rewind a transformer with wire of the same size and with the same number of turns between all taps and to reassemble this transformer using all of the laminations originally supplied usually will convince a serviceman of the wisdom of this recommendation. The serviceman should not attempt to simplify matters by using smaller wire or by leaving out turns of wire or punchings, if he does rewind the transformer.

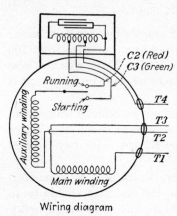

Wiring diagram

Fig. 6-7.—Wiring diagram of a two-value capacitor motor, four line leads, externally reversible. The line connections for this motor are Fig. 4-5b. (*Courtesy of Westinghouse Electric Corporation.*)

SINGLE-VOLTAGE MOTORS

6-10. Capacitor Mounted on Motor, Four Leads, Reversible.—The wiring diagram of a two-value capacitor motor with attached capacitor-transformer unit is given in Fig. 6-7. The line connection diagram is found in Fig. 4-5b. The wiring diagram of another similar motor is given in Fig. 6-8.

The **stator connection diagram** for a four-pole series-connected motor wired according to the diagram of Fig. 6-7 is shown in Fig. 6-9. Note that this diagram is the same as the corresponding diagram for a capacitor-start motor (Fig. 5-7), except that the dummy leads to the capacitor are omitted.

In general, the **stator connection diagrams** for two-value motors are the same as those used for corresponding split-phase motors, except for minor modifications of external wiring. The split-phase stator connection diagram corresponding to that of Fig. 6-9 is given in Fig. 4-9. A comparative study of these two diagrams will show how to use any of the other split-phase diagrams (Figs. 4-8 to 4-15) for two-value capacitor motors.

6-11. Separately Mounted Capacitor-transformer Unit.—The motor wiring and line connection diagrams of a two-value capacitor

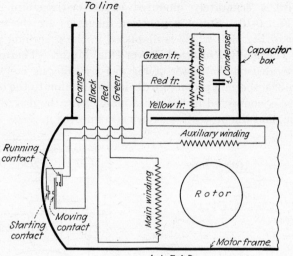

FIG. 6-8.—Wiring diagram of a two-value capacitor motor, four line leads, externally reversible.   To operate motor, connect black and orange leads to one line and the red and green leads to the other line.   To reverse direction of rotation, interchange orange and green leads.   (*Courtesy of Wagner Electric Corporation.*)

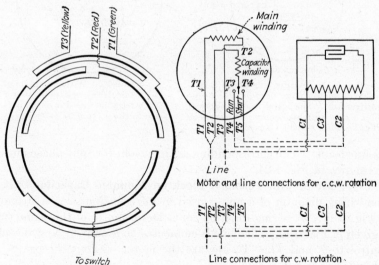

FIG. 6-9.—Stator connection diagram for a two-value capacitor motor.   This diagram is for a four-pole, series-connected stator.

FIG. 6-10.—Wiring and line connection diagrams of a two-value capacitor motor with separate capacitor-transformer unit.

motor with a separately mounted capacitor-transformer unit are given in Fig. 6-10. Stator connection diagrams are the same as for the motor of Fig. 6-7, which is discussed in the preceding paragraph.

6-12. Thermally Protected Reversible Motor.—Thermal protection is provided on the motor of Fig. 6-7 by bringing out two yellow leads from the thermal protective device in addition to the other leads. The motor is connected in the usual manner for the desired direction of rotation, and the protective device is connected in series with one of

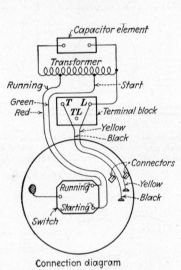

Connection diagram

FIG. 6-11.—Wiring diagram of a two-value capacitor motor used for a domestic refrigerator. The capacitor-transformer unit has a terminal block. (*Courtesy of Westinghouse Electric Corporation.*)

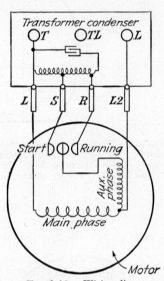

FIG. 6-12.—Wiring diagram of a transformer-condenser motor with terminal board in the capacitor. (*Courtesy of Delco Products.*)

the line leads. The corresponding arrangement for split-phase motors was shown in Fig. 4-24.

6-13. Motor with Terminal Block on Mounted Capacitor Unit.— The wiring diagram of a motor used in refrigeration service is shown in Fig. 6-11. A wiring diagram for a Delco motor of this same type is given in Fig. 6-12. The line is connected to L and TL, and the cold control to T and TL. To operate the motor without the use of an external line switch or cold control, connect the line to T and L. These motors are similar to the motor of Fig. 5-36 (discussed in Art. 5-27) except that they are two-value motors instead of capacitor-start motors. The stator connection diagram of a four-pole series-connected

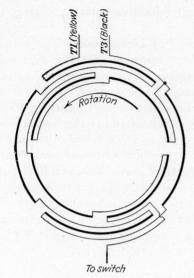

Fig. 6-13.—Stator connection diagram for the motor of Figs. 6-11, 6-12, and 6-14.

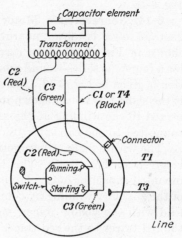

Fig. 6-14.—Wiring diagram of a two-lead, nonreversible two-value capacitor motor with mounted capacitor. (*Courtesy of Westinghouse Electric Corporation.*)

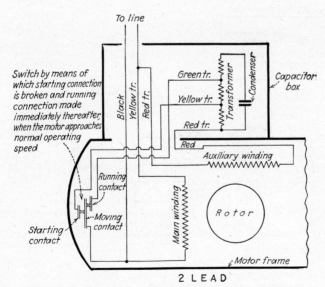

Fig. 6-15.—Wiring diagram of a two-lead, two-value capacitor motor. (*Courtesy of Wagner Electric Corporation.*)

motor of this type, arranged for counterclockwise rotation, is given in
Fig. 6-13.

6-14. Nonreversible Motor with Two Line Leads.—The wiring
diagram of a two-lead nonreversible two-value capacitor motor is
shown in Fig. 6-14. The corresponding stator connection diagram
for a four-pole series-wound motor arranged for counterclockwise rotation is given in Fig. 6-13. An interesting feature of this arrangement
is the short black lead shown in Fig. 6-14; one end of this lead is connected to the winding at the same point as $T1$, and the other end is
connected to the capacitor lead by means of a solderless connector.

The wiring diagram of another make of motor with two line leads
is given in Fig. 6-15. The line connections are made inside the
mounted capacitor box. To reverse this motor, interchange the leads
of the auxiliary winding by connecting the red motor lead to the motor
lead with the yellow tracer, and by connecting the motor lead with
the red tracer to the red-tracer lead of the capacitor box.

DUAL-VOLTAGE MOTORS

6-15. Dual-voltage Motor with Capacitor-transformer Unit.—
Wiring and line connection diagrams of a dual-voltage two-value
capacitor motor are given in Fig. 6-16. The corresponding **stator**

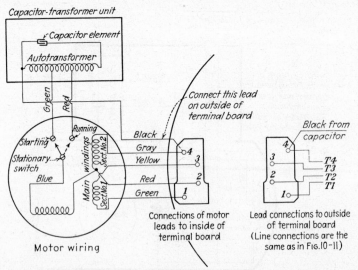

Fig. 6-16.—Wiring diagram of a dual-voltage, two-value capacitor motor with
built-in terminal board and attached capacitor. (*Courtesy of Westinghouse Electric
Corporation.*)

connection diagram for a four-pole series-connected motor is shown in Fig. 6-17. In principle of operation, the dual-voltage feature of this motor is similar to that of the motor discussed in Art. 5-15, except that a transfer switch is used to change taps on an autotransformer,

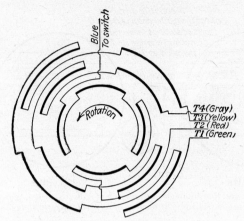

Fig. 6-17.—Stator connection diagram for the motor of Fig. 6-16.

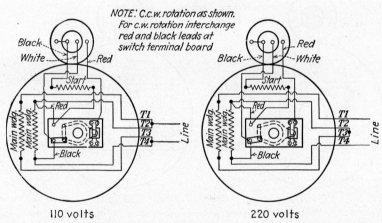

110 volts   220 volts

Fig. 6-18.—Wiring and line connection diagrams of a dual-voltage, two-value motor with double capacitor unit mounted on motor. (*Courtesy of General Electric Company.*)

instead of opening the capacitor circuit completely. On 220-volt circuits, the main winding of this motor serves the additional function of an autotransformer to step down the capacitor-phase voltage on either the starting or the running connection. This motor can be wound in the manner described in Art. 5-16.

6-16. Dual-voltage Motor Using Two Capacitors.—Figure 6-18 gives the wiring and line connection diagrams of a two-value motor using two capacitors.   The two capacitors are made into a double unit; the running capacitor is in a cylindrical can, and the electrolytic

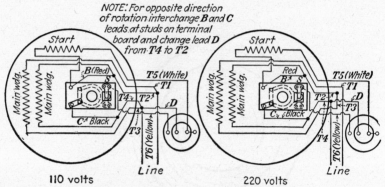

Fig. 6-19.—Wiring and line connection diagrams of a dual-voltage, two-value motor with separate capacitor.   (*Courtesy of General Electric Company.*)

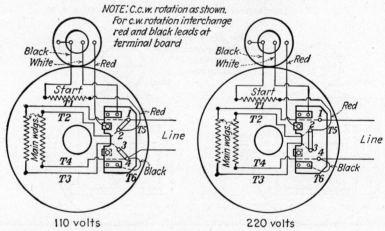

Fig. 6-20.—Wiring and line connection diagrams of a dual-voltage, two-value motor with built-in conduit box and mounted capacitor. (*Courtesy of General Electric Company.*)

starting capacitor is made in the form of a hollow cylinder into which the running capacitor fits.   Both capacitors are hermetically sealed as individual cans.   The motor of Fig. 6-18 has four line leads, and the capacitor is mounted on the motor.   The connections shown are for counterclockwise rotation; for clockwise rotation, it is necessary to remove the front (switch) end shield and interchange the red and black leads at the switch terminal board. A photograph of this motor is shown in Fig. 6-21.

Figure 6-19 gives the wiring and line connections of a motor that is the same as that shown in Fig. 6-18 except that the capacitor unit is separate from the motor. The method of reversing the direction of rotation is the same as for Fig. 6-18.

Fig. 6-21.—Two-value capacitor motor using two capacitors, an electrolytic for starting (outer one) and a Pyranol for running. (*Courtesy of General Electric Company.*)

Figure 6-20 gives the wiring and line connection diagram of a motor similar to that shown in Fig. 6-18 except that the motor has a built-in conduit box. Another important difference is that it is not necessary to remove an end shield to reverse the direction of rotation; it is necessary only to interchange the red and black leads on the terminal board in the conduit box.

MISCELLANEOUS SERVICE PROBLEMS

6-17. Rewinding or Reconnecting Motor for a Different Voltage but for Same Performance. *a. Changing from* 115 *to* 230 *Volts.*— About the only safe way for a serviceman to rewind a motor for 230 volts is to rewind for the dual-voltage connection, or for the swing connection; in this case, the same capacitor-transformer unit— or the same double-unit capacitor—and the same auxiliary winding are employed, but wire three sizes smaller should be used in each of the sections of the main winding, and each section must have the same number of turns as the 115-volt main winding. If, however, the main winding is already wound with two strands per conductor in parallel, it may be possible to separate the two strands making the two sections. (This is the second method described in Art. 5-16.) It would be advisable to test the insulation strength between the two strands at 500 volts before reconnecting as a dual-voltage motor.

The above procedure appears to be the only practical method for making this voltage change, for it is not feasible to attempt to alter the capacitor for 230 volts.

b. Other Voltage Changes.—Other voltage changes are not recommended because of the complications of the capacitor-transformer unit. It may be possible, however, to use the parts to wind a capacitor-start, split-phase, or polyphase induction motor.

6-18. Rewinding for Different Torques, Speed, or Frequency.— Because of the complications involved in the capacitor unit and also for the reasons outlined in Arts. 5-33 and 5-34, these types of changes are not to be recommended.

6-19. Changing a Two-value Motor to a Capacitor-start Motor.— It is often possible to substitute a simple electrolytic capacitor in place of the capacitor-transformer unit, thus converting the two-value motor into a capacitor-start motor. To make such a substitution, it is necessary to determine the proper number of microfarads to use. If a duplicate capacitor-transformer unit can be borrowed for test purposes, the effective microfarads can be checked in the manner described in Art. 6-8. An electrolytic capacitor having an actual capacity of 80 to 90 per cent of this value of *effective microfarads* is about the proper value to use. If a unit cannot be tested, it may be possible to determine the turns ratio of the autotransformer on the starting connection by (1) taking voltage measurements or (2) stripping the transformer coil and actually counting turns. Then, if the actual microfarads of the capacitor element can be determined by test or by inspection of its markings, the *effective microfarads* of the capacitor-transformer unit is approximately

$$0.95 \times (\text{turns ratio})^2$$
$$\times (\text{actual microfarads of capacitor element}) \quad (6\text{-}4)$$

An electrolytic capacitor of 80 to 90 per cent of this value can be used.

Substitution of an electrolytic capacitor for a capacitor-transformer unit is fraught with certain hazards, some of which will be discussed:

(1) In the first place, the breakdown torque of the motor may be reduced from 5 to 30 per cent. This point may or may not be important, but it should be considered. (2) The full-load losses, watts input, and resultant heating will increase, though perhaps not to an injurious extent. (3) Too severe voltages may be imposed upon the electrolytic capacitor in operation, shortening its life.

Any motor in which such a substitution is made will bear careful observation and testing; without doubt there will be times when the risks of such a substitution are wholly justified.

If the running capacitor of a motor of the type illustrated in Figs. 6-2, 6-18, 6-19, or 6-20 develops a short circuit, the motor will not operate properly; but if the defective capacitor is removed from the circuit, the motor should then operate satisfactorily as a capacitor-start motor (provided that there is no other defect), though with slightly impaired performance.

Bibliography

1. TRICKEY, P. H.: Design of Capacitor Motors for Balanced Operation, *A.I.E.E. Trans.*, September, 1932, p. 780.
2. MORRILL, WAYNE J.: The Revolving Field Theory of the Capacitor Motor, *A.I.E.E. Trans.*, April, 1929, p. 614.
3. SPECHT, H. C.: Fundamental Theory of the Capacitor Motor, *A.I.E.E. Trans.*, April, 1929, p. 607.
4. BAILEY, BENJAMIN F.: The Condenser Motor, *A.I.E.E. Trans.*, April, 1929, p. 596.
5. TRICKEY, P. H.: Equal Volt-ampere Method of Designing Capacitor Motors, *A.I.E.E. Trans.*, vol. 60, 1941, pp. 990–992.
6. MORRILL, WAYNE J.: The Apparent-impedance Method of Calculating Single-phase Motor Performance, *A.I.E.E. Trans.*, vol. 60, 1941, pp. 1037–1041.
7. TRICKEY, P. H.: Performance Calculations on Capacitor Motors, *A.I.E.E. Trans.*, vol. 60, 1941, pp. 662–663.
8. PUCHSTEIN, A. F., and LLOYD, T. C.: Capacitor Motors with Windings Not in Quadrature, *A.I.E.E. Trans.*, vol. 54, 1935, pp. 1235–1239.
9. LYON, W. V., and KINGSLEY, CHAS. JR.: Analysis of Unsymmetrical Machines, *A.I.E.E. Trans.*, vol. 55, 1936, pp. 471–476.
10. PUCHSTEIN, A. F., and LLOYD, T. C.: Cross-field Theory of the Capacitor Motor, *A.I.E.E. Trans.*, vol. 60, 1941, pp. 58–61.
11. McFARLAND, T. C.: Current Loci for the Capacitor Motor, *A.I.E.E. Trans.*, vol. 61, 1942, pp. 152–156.
12. ———: Turn Ratio of the Capacitor Motor, *A.I.E.E. Trans.*, vol. 62, 1943, pp. 892–898.
13. TARBOUX, J. G.: A Generalized Circle Diagram for a Four-terminal Network and Its Application to the Capacitor Single-phase Motor, *A.I.E.E. Trans.*, 1945.
14. SUHR, F. W.: Symmetrical Components as Applied to the Single-phase Induction Motor, *A.I.E.E. Trans.*, vol. 64, 1945, pp. 651–656.

CHAPTER VII

PERMANENT-SPLIT CAPACITOR MOTORS

(SINGLE-VALUE CAPACITOR MOTORS)

Permanent-split capacitor motors (also called "single-value capacitor motors") are generally used for special-purpose applications. Continuous-duty motors of this type have low inherent locked-rotor torque; they are used principally for unit heaters and for other shaft-mounted fans or blowers. They are especially suited for fans because of the relative ease with which their speed can be controlled when driving fans. These different applications are treated in this, and the following two, chapters. Intermittent-duty motors of this type can be designed for high locked-rotor torque; a popular use for such motors is for plug-reversing control motors for operating induction regulators, rheostats, dampers, etc.

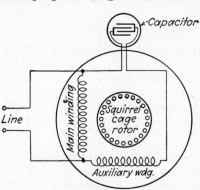

FIG. 7-1.—The permanent-split capacitor motor.

7-1. Permanent-split Capacitor Motor Defined.—This motor is defined in Art. 5-1 as "a capacitor motor having the same value of capacitance for both starting and running conditions." Other names applied to this type of motor are **permanent split-phase motor,** and **single-value capacitor motor.**

7-2. Essential Parts of a Permanent-split Capacitor Motor. The permanent-split capacitor motor is represented diagrammatically in Fig. 7-1. It is to be noted that the arrangement of windings and connections is exactly the same as in Fig. 5-1 except that the starting switch is omitted. Further it should be noted that the arrangement is exactly the same as in Fig. 6-21 except that the starting switch and starting capacitor both are omitted. The permanent-split capacitor motor is substantially a two-value motor operated on the running connection, with essentially the same torque characteristics as the

184

latter. These speed-torque characteristics are approximately as shown in Fig. 6-4. When designed and built as such, permanent-split motors may, however, have more full-load slip and more locked-rotor torque than a two-value motor on the running connection. They are used principally for fans, blowers, and oil burners, where quietness is essential and low locked-rotor torque is desirable or, at least, satisfactory.

7-3. Single-voltage Motors.—As pointed out in the preceding article, a permanent-split motor has the same arrangement of windings and capacitor as a capacitor-start motor, except that the starting switch is omitted. (This statement should not be construed to mean that a capacitor-start motor can be converted to a permanent-split motor merely by short-circuiting the switch! See Art. 5-5.) Generally speaking, all wiring and line connection diagrams for capacitor-start motors apply equally well to permanent-split motors, except that there is no starting switch.

Stator connection diagrams are the same as those for the corresponding capacitor-start motors, except that the switch leads are, in effect, connected to one another.

Rewinding a motor of this type with any winding other than the one originally used is hardly to be recommended unless the winding specification is obtained from the manufacturer. One exception is that the motor could be rewound for dual voltage or for the swing connection (see Art. 5-32).

Much of the general information given on split-phase motors is applicable to permanent-split motors. Specifically, the following articles may be of assistance:

Art. 4-8.   How to tell the windings apart and how to identify the leads.
Art. 4-15. Connecting motor windings for a definite direction of rotation.
Art. 4-16. Predetermining direction of rotation.

7-4. Dual-voltage Motors.—Currently, the most popular method of making dual-voltage motors is the same as that used for dual-voltage capacitor-start motors, *i.e.*, as shown in Fig. 5-10. If the starting switch is omitted, this wiring and line connection diagram applies equally well to the most popular form of dual-voltage permanent-split capacitor motor. The generalities of Arts. 5-14 to 5-17 all apply, as well as the diagrams discussed in those articles. For shaft-mounted fan applications, this type of motor can be used with a simple line switch as a single-speed dual-voltage motor; with nothing but a change in control, the motor can be used either as a two-speed or as an adjustable varying-speed motor.   (See Chap. VIII for a further description of the *all-purpose* motor.)

Earlier dual-voltage arrangements, as discussed in Arts. 7-5 to 7-7, have long been superseded by new applications.   However, the description of them is being retained for the benefit of the serviceman because there are still a large number of them in service.

7-5. Dual-voltage Motor with Capacitor-transformer Unit.—One type of dual-voltage permanent-split capacitor motor is illustrated schematically in Fig. 7-2.   There is a

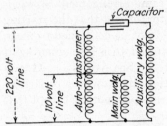

FIG. 7-2.—A dual-voltage, permanent-split capacitor motor using an autotransformer.

single main winding designed for operation on 110 volts; on a 110-volt circuit this winding is connected directly across the line, and on a 220-volt circuit the line voltage is stepped down to 110 volts by means of the autotransformer. The capacitor phase, including auxiliary winding plus capacitor, always operates on 220 volts, the voltage being stepped up from 110 if the motor is operated on 110 volts.   This arrangement is somewhat more economical than would be the use of merely an autotransformer in connection with the conventional permanent-split motor of Fig. 7-1 because

1. The autotransformer never has to handle more than one phase.
2. Operation of the auxiliary phase on 220 volts results in a more efficient use of the capacitor element and a more efficient use of winding space in the motor.

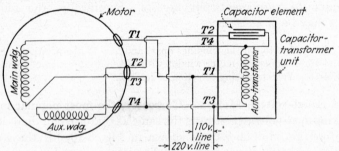

FIG. 7-3.—Wiring and line connection diagrams of a dual-voltage, permanent-split, capacitor motor using a capacitor-transformer unit.

A practical use of this arrangement is illustrated in Fig. 7-3, which is a wiring and line connection diagram showing one system of lead markings.   The capacitor-transformer unit is shown here as separately mounted, but it could equally well be attached to the motor.

In general, the **stator connection diagrams** for split-phase motors (Figs. 4-8 to 4-17) are applicable, except that no switch should be used.

Because of the complications involved in the capacitor-transformer unit, it is recommended that service shops do not attempt to rewind these motors, except to duplicate the original winding in case the latter burns out or becomes otherwise damaged. Modifications of this arrangement are used in dual-voltage adjustable-speed capacitor motors for fan duty.

7-6. Defective Capacitor-transformer Units.—If a capacitor-transformer unit, such as used in Fig. 7-3, is suspected of being defective, the first step should be to determine whether the defect is in the autotransformer or in the capacitor element. Disconnect the capacitor element from the autotransformer, and test the former for short circuits, open circuits, capacity in microfarads, and grounds. The method described in Art. 5-10 for checking electrolytic capacitors may be used here—except that the power factor is entirely too low to be read with commercial meters, unless the element is defective. If the capacitor element is found to be defective, it must be replaced.

The autotransformer should be checked by connecting $T1$ and $T3$ across a 110-volt line in series with a 5-amp fuse. If the transformer is badly short-circuited, the fuse will blow; if it is not short-circuited, connect meters in the circuit as shown in the diagram of Fig. 19-3, and read watts and amperes input. The watts input should be less than 10 watts, and the current input less than 1 amp. With 110 volts impressed across $T1$ and $T3$, a voltmeter should indicate 220 volts across $T3$ and $T4$; if no voltage is present, there is an open circuit in the transformer.

If the capacitor element is sound, though the autotransformer is defective and a new one is not obtainable, there is still a way of restoring the motor to service on a circuit of either voltage, as follows:

For a 110-volt Circuit.—Connect the motor and capacitor element only to the line, as shown in Fig. 7-1. The motor should operate this way, but with reduced breakdown torque, efficiency, locked-rotor torque, and full-load speed; but in many cases, the operation will be satisfactory. Insertion of 25 to 50 per cent more microfarads in parallel with the original capacitor element should help make the motor perform more nearly the same as originally, but this additional capacitance may not be necessary.

For a 220-volt Circuit.—Strip and rewind the motor so that the main winding has twice as many turns as originally, using wire that is three sizes smaller. Rewind the auxiliary winding, using wire of the same size and the same number of turns as in the original motor. Use the same capacitor element (if not defective), and connect as in Fig. 7-1. The motor should then operate as before with the same performance in all respects.

7-7. Dual-voltage Motor with Series-parallel Windings and Capacitor.—The wiring and line connections of a dual-voltage motor

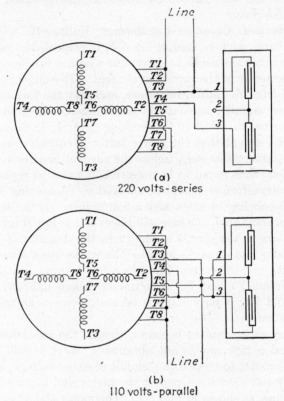

(a)
220 volts-series

(b)
110 volts-parallel

Fig. 7-4.—Wiring and line connection diagrams of a permanent-split, dual-voltage motor with series-parallel windings and series-parallel capacitor.

with series-parallel windings are given in Fig. 7-4. It will be noted that each winding is split into two sections which are connected in series in Fig. 7-4a and in parallel in Fig. 7-4b. The capacitor is split into two sections which are connected likewise either in series or in parallel.

In place of two capacitor elements, a single element and autotransformer may be used, as illustrated in Fig. 7-5. This arrangement is slightly simpler to connect for a 110-volt circuit because leads 1 and 3 are not connected together (they must not be!) as in Fig. 7-4.

7-8. Reversible, High-torque Motors.
In Art. 7-2, it was pointed out that a permanent-split capacitor motor was equivalent to a two-value motor operating on the *running connection*. As a consequence, the motor has low locked-rotor torque but will operate continuously. It will be remembered that, on the starting connection, the two-value motor has high torque, but it cannot operate continuously. High-torque permanent-split capacitor motors are built for intermittent duty with torques comparable to those of a two-value motor operating on the *starting connection;* the torques are comparable to those shown in Fig. 6-4.

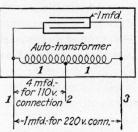

Fig. 7-5.—Capacitor-transformer unit which may be used with the motor of Fig. 7-4 in lieu of a series-parallel arrangement of capacitors as shown in Fig. 7-4.

Motors of this sort are widely used for operating valves, induction regulators, rheostats, arc-welding control, etc. To achieve simplicity of reversing control, a novel arrangement of windings and capacitor is employed. This arrangement is shown in Fig. 7-6. When the

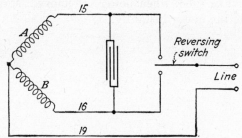

Fig. 7-6.—Electrically reversible, high-torque, permanent-split, intermittently rated capacitor motor.

reversing switch is in the "up" position, winding A becomes the main winding, and B becomes the auxiliary winding; when the switch is in the "down" position, A becomes the auxiliary winding, and B the main winding. Since—as was pointed out and explained in Art. 4-16—the direction of rotation is always from the auxiliary winding toward the main winding, it follows that interchanging main and auxiliary windings reverses the direction of rotation. The single-pole double-throw switch is both an "on-and-off" and a reversing switch. A simpler control could scarcely be devised.

Inasmuch as either winding acts as the main winding, depending upon the desired direction of rotation, it follows that both windings must be identical, both as to wire size and number of effective turns, if the motor is to develop the same torque in either direction of rotation. This type of motor is, therefore, frequently wound with a conventional two-phase diamond-coil lap winding, but single-phase concentric windings are often used. However, if a four-pole concentric winding is used in a stator that has 36 slots, there are 9 slots per pole, and the distribution of the phases cannot be made alike if the windings are to be displaced 90 electrical degrees. In such a case, the number of actual turns per phase will not be the same because of a difference between the distribution factors for the respective windings. This motor is virtually the only type of capacitor motor in which both windings are necessarily identical.

The **stator connection diagram** may be similar to the diagram for the corresponding polyphase motor or similar to the split-phase diagrams, switch omitted, depending on the type of winding used.

This motor, when used to operate an induction regulator, is usually provided with an electrically operated brake, the coil of which is connected across 15 and 16. When power is applied to the motor, for either direction of rotation, voltage is applied to the brake coil, releasing the brake shoe; when power is removed, springs apply the brake, stopping the motor instantly.

CHAPTER VIII

CAPACITOR MOTORS FOR UNIT HEATERS, SHAFT-MOUNTED FANS AND BLOWERS

Remarkable adaptability characterizes the new types of capacitor motors used for unit-heater service. They can be mounted in a number of ways and can be used with or without speed controllers.

8-1. General.—Speed control is desirable in a large number of fan and blower applications used for heating and ventilating service. A typical use is for unit-heater service, where it is desirable to operate the unit at a high speed to obtain quick initial warming up; once the room is warm, the speed can be reduced and a quieter and more uniform flow of heat is produced. Moveover, it is often desirable to increase the operating speed when the outside temperature decreases. Three different speed classifications have long been recognized for this service: single-speed, two-speed, and three-speed. Three different types of motors were formerly used to meet these requirements, and the choice of type for each specific installation depended a lot upon the ultimate user's own evaluation of whether or not the expense of obtaining more than one motor speed was justifiable. Since 1938, a quiet revolution has taken place in the design and application of these motors. A single motor type has been developed that can be used to replace the three former types. For want of a better name, this type will be called **all-purpose,** in order to distinguish it from earlier types of capacitor motors used for such applications. It is built in all common horsepower ratings from $\frac{1}{20}$ to $\frac{3}{4}$, for four-, six-, and eight-pole speeds.

ALL-PURPOSE CAPACITOR MOTORS FOR UNIT-HEATER SERVICE

8-2. Mechanical and Electrical Features.—One example of an all-purpose capacitor motor especially designed for unit-heater service is illustrated in Fig. 8-1. This example incorporates many novel mechanical and electrical design features:

a. Mechanical Features.—An outstanding characteristic is the fact that this motor can be mounted in any one of four ways: floor, wall, ceiling, or by means of a band around the motor (see Fig. 8-2). Resilient mounting isolates the double-frequency torque pulsations of the

191

motor* from the unit heater, thereby providing quiet operation. Cradle construction makes it very simple to change the base for floor, ceiling, or even side-wall mounting, or to remove it for round-frame mounting; it is necessary only to loosen or remove the two screws that tighten the clamps holding the motor in its cradle base. The capacitor is attached to the nose of the front end shield *inside the rubber mounting ring* in order to permit the cradle base to be turned around without

Fig. 8-1.—An all-purpose capacitor motor used for unit-heater service. Can be mounted on a floor, wall, or ceiling, or clamped in a mounting band. It is dual-voltage and can be used for single-speed, two-speed, or adjustable-speed service. (*Courtesy of Westinghouse Electric Corporation.*)

obstruction. A further advantage of mounting the capacitor on the front end shield is to keep it out of the air stream; if it were on top of the frame, as it is on capacitor-start motors, it might interfere with the air stream and cause unnecessary noise due to the fan blades passing too close to the capacitor. Sleeve bearings are used for applications where the shaft operates in a horizontal position, and the fan thrust is absorbed by a no-bump construction or thrust bearing (see Fig. 18-3). Ball bearings are usually used for vertical-shaft applications where the bearings have to carry the weight of the fan and rotor. Enclosed motors are used for applications where the motor is in the main air

* See Art. 18-12.

(a)   (b)

(c)   (d)

Fig. 8-2.—Unit heaters, showing different mounting arrangements for the motors. (a) Floor-mounted motor with foot. (*Courtesy of the Trane Co.*)   (b) Ceiling-mounted motor with foot. (*Courtesy of Fedders Manufacturing Company.*)   (c) Round-frame mounting without foot. (*Courtesy of the Carrier Corporation.*)   (d) Round-frame mounting without foot. (*Courtesy of the B. F. Sturtevant Company.*)

stream, but open motors are sometimes used if the motor is not in the main air stream.

b. Electrical Features.—This motor is designed so that it can be used

1. With line switch, as a single-speed motor on 115- or 230-volt circuits.

2. With two-speed switch (Fig. 8-3) as a two-speed motor on 115- or 230-volt circuits.

3. With speed controller (Fig. 8-4) as an adjustable varying-speed motor on 115- or 230-volt circuits.

So that the motor can be used as a single-speed motor without a controller, the capacitor is attached to the motor. (Formerly, it was often built into the controller, as shown in Figs. 8-15 and 8-17, for example.) Another important advantage gained by taking the capacitor out of the controller is that the number of controllers required to handle a given line of motors is considerably reduced. Two adjustable-speed controllers handle a line of 60- and 50-cycle motors from $\frac{1}{20}$ to $\frac{3}{4}$ hp. One two-speed switch handles the entire line of 60-, 50-, and 25-cycle motors.

Speed reduction of these motors is effected by increasing the slip, not by use of pole-changing windings. Two-speed operation is obtained by changing the winding connections and, in some cases, use of an external autotransformer (discussed further in Art. 8-7). Adjustable-speed operation is accomplished by use of a tapped, or adjustable, autotransformer that can be adjusted to impress different voltages on the motor windings. Usually the voltages impressed on the capacitor phase are not the same as those impressed on the main phase. A number of different systems of voltage control have been devised.

Fig. 8-3.—Two-speed switch used for controlling an all-purpose, capacitor-type, unit-heater motor. (*Courtesy of Westinghouse Electric Corporation.*)

8-3. Systems of Voltage Control.—Four systems of controlling the voltages on the windings of a **permanent-split capacitor motor** are illustrated in Fig. 8-5. Figure 8-5a shows a simple autotransformer used in conjunction with a permanent-split motor; with this system, the voltage on both phases (main and auxiliary) is the same at all times. Generally speaking, this system gives unsatisfactory starting characteristics on the low-speed connection. Figure 8-5b shows a system whereby only the voltage of the main phase is varied, the capacitor-phase voltage being fixed. Figure 8-5c shows a system in

(a)

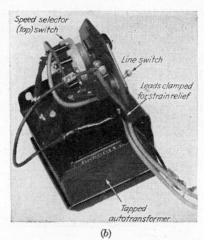

Speed selector
(tap) switch

Line switch

Leads clamped
for strain relief

Tapped
autotransformer

(b)

(c)

Autotransformer,
Gramme-ring-type

Line
switch

Adjustable
brush

Adjustable
stops

(d)

FIG. 8-4.—Speed controllers for all-purpose, capacitor-type, unit-heater motors. Both are suitable for either flush mounting or wall mounting. Both are designed so that the entire unit can be readily removed from the case to facilitate installation. (a) Eight-speed controller complete. (*Courtesy of Westinghouse Electric Corporation.*) (b) Transformer-and-switch assembly for 8-speed controller. (*Courtesy of Westinghouse Electric Corporation.*) (c) Adjustable-speed controller complete. (*Courtesy of the General Electric Company.*) (d) Adjustable-speed controller with cover removed. (*Courtesy of the General Electric Company.*)

which the voltage on the main phase is varied proportionately more than is the voltage on the auxiliary phase, though both are varied. In Fig. 8-5*d*, a decrease in the main-phase voltage is accompanied by an increase in the auxiliary-phase voltage. Systems *b, c,* and *d* have all been used successfully for speed control of unit-heater motors. In the three articles that follow, an explanation is given of the fundamental principles involved in the control of the speed of fan motors by varying the slip. Also, the inherent limitations of this method of speed control are discussed.

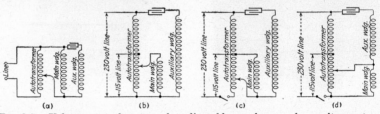

Fig. 8-5.—Voltage-control systems for adjustable varying-speed capacitor motors.

8-4. Fundamental Relationship between Slip, Voltage, and Torque.—In Art. 2-2, the principle of the induction motor was illustrated by means of a rotating magnet which caused a copper disc to rotate with it. It was there pointed out that if the magnet were revolved at a uniform speed, the disc would revolve at a lower speed than the magnet, and the difference between the speed of the magnet and the speed of the disc was called the **slip.** A strong magnet will cause the disc to rotate at a high speed, *i.e.,* with less slip than will a weak magnet revolved at the same speed as the strong magnet. The underlying reason is simply that the strong magnet will induce more eddy currents in the disc for any given slip. A little careful reasoning will lead to a fundamental relationship between slip, strength of the field, and torque.

At any given slip, the rate of cutting of lines of force is proportional to the number of lines of force in the field, *i.e.,* to the strength of the field. Therefore, the voltages tending to set up eddy currents in the disc—or secondary—are also proportional to the strength of the field. Since the eddy currents are proportional to the voltages generating them, they are likewise proportional to the strength of the field. The torque developed by the disc is proportional to the product of field strength and eddy currents. Since eddy currents are proportional to field strength, it follows that the torque developed is proportional to the *square* of the field strength. In a practical induction motor, the field strength is varied by changing the voltage.

This principle, then, is as follows: *The torque developed in any induction motor, at any given slip, is proportional to the square of the applied voltage.* For any given load torque, the stronger the field, the less will be the slip.

8-5. Speed Control by Means of Voltage Control.—The speed-torque curve of a typical adjustable varying-speed permanent-split capacitor motor with normal voltage on the windings is represented by the *high* curve of Fig. 8-6 and the speed-torque curve of a *normal fan* is likewise shown. The operating speed of the motor driving this fan is at point *a*, given by the intersection of the respective torque curves of the motor and fan. If the voltage on the windings is reduced

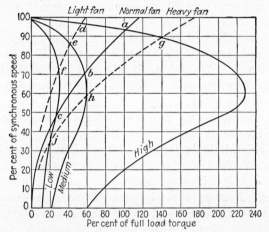

Fig. 8-6.—How speed control of a fan is obtained with an adjustable varying-speed capacitor motor. The *high*, *medium*, and *low* curves are the three speed-torque curves on the respective speed connections.

to a *medium* value, a corresponding speed-torque curve is obtained. (At any slip, the torque is less than on the *high* connection because the voltage is less.) The operating speed of the motor driving the same fan is at point *b*, the intersection of the two torque curves. It is to be noted that the operating speed of the fan was reduced approximately 25 per cent. If the voltage on the windings is reduced still further to a *low* value, a third speed-torque curve is obtained, the intersection of which with the fan speed-torque curve at *c* gives the operating speed of the motor driving the fan under this condition. The speed has now been reduced to about 50 per cent of normal full-load speed. Thus, speed control of this motor has been effected by means of controlling the voltage on the windings. This speed control can be obtained by one of the schemes of Fig. 8-5 or by a similar one.

8-6. Limitations of This System of Speed Control.—Motors with this type of speed control have been very successful when used with shaft-mounted fans and blowers, but this method of speed control does have limitations.

a. Speed Depends upon the Load.—At no load, the motor will operate at practically the same speed on the *high, medium,* and *low* connections. If a *light fan* requiring one-half the power of the *normal fan* is used, the motor will operate at speeds as shown by points *d, e,* and *f* on Fig. 8-6. It is to be noted that even on the *low* connection, a speed reduction of less than 25 per cent is obtained instead of the 50 per cent obtained when the *normal fan* was used. If a *heavy fan* is used, *i.e.,* one requiring 50 per cent more power than the rating of the motor, the three operating speeds are *g, h,* and *j.*

b. Locked-rotor Torque Necessarily Low.—The locked-rotor torque on the low-speed connection has to be lower than the fan torque at the desired low speed. At half speed, the fan torque is about 25 per cent of full-load torque, and the locked-rotor torque of the motor has to be less than this value.

c. Not Suited to Belted Drives.—Because of the inherently low locked-rotor torque and also because there is apt to be a considerable variation in belt friction, particularly if a V-belt is used, and because the low speeds would, therefore, be uncertain, this type of speed control is not suited to belt-driven applications.

d. Unstable Low-speed Connection.—Because, on the low-speed connection, the fan torque and motor torque curves cross at a very small angle, speed characteristics tend to be unstable, and the speed is sensitive to changes in voltage and also to restrictions in the inlet and outlet ducts of the unit heater or fan it is driving. Restrictions in the path or ducts of a propeller fan generally increase the load requirements and slow the motor down; restrictions in either the inlet or exhaust ducts of a centrifugal fan or blower unload the fan, causing the motor to operate at a higher speed. In general, this characteristic of instability is more pronounced in a motor having a low slip at full load than it is in a motor having a higher slip.

8-7. Connection Diagrams.—Connection diagrams vary somewhat among manufacturers and, generally speaking, motors and controllers of different manufacturers are not mutually interchangeable.

a. Westinghouse.—Wiring and line connection diagrams are given in Fig. 8-7. It is to be noted that the motor itself is essentially similar to the dual-voltage capacitor-start motor of Fig. 5-10 except that there is no starting switch; single-speed line connections are, therefore,

similar.   For the 115-volt two-speed connection, low speed is obtained
by connecting the two sections of the main winding in series, with the
capacitor phase across the 115-volt line.   On 230 volts a novel method
is used for obtaining low speed: The auxiliary winding is connected
in series with the two sections of the main winding and, to obtain
locked-rotor torque, the capacitor is shunted across the auxiliary
winding.   The speed reduction obtained is somewhat less than that

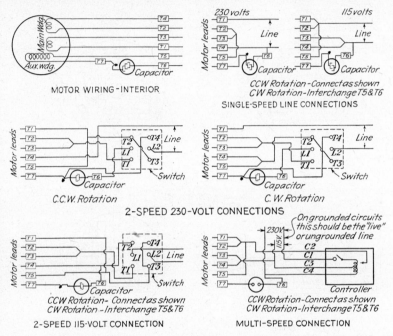

MOTOR WIRING - INTERIOR

CCW Rotation - Connect as shown
CW Rotation - Interchange T5 & T6

SINGLE-SPEED LINE CONNECTIONS

C.C.W. Rotation   C. W. Rotation

2-SPEED 230-VOLT CONNECTIONS

CCW Rotation - Connect as shown
CW Rotation - Interchange T5 & T6

2-SPEED 115-VOLT CONNECTION

CCW Rotation - Connect as shown
CW Rotation - Interchange T5 & T6

MULTI-SPEED CONNECTION

FIG. 8-7.—Wiring and line connection diagrams for Westinghouse Type FL unit-heater
motors.

obtained with the 115-volt connection but is sufficient to serve the
intended purpose.   The same switch—illlustrated in Fig. 8-3—is used
for two-speed operation on either 115- or 230-volt circuits; it is a
double-pole double-throw switch which connects

    $L1$ to $T1$ and $L2$ to $T3$ on the *high* speed connection.
    $L1$ to $T2$ and $L2$ to $T4$ on the *low* speed connection.

This switch should not be confused with the H. and H. switch in Fig.
8-9.   The adjustable-speed controller—illustrated in Figs. 8-4a and
8-4b—uses an autotransformer and eight-position tap switch, thereby
obtaining eight speeds.   The schematic arrangement is similar to

Fig. 8-5c.   A toggle switch is provided for use as a line switch; the motor can be started with the speed-selector tap switch in any position. Prior to 1946, a different type of speed controller was used.   This is practically the same identical controller as the one illustrated in Figs. 8-4c and 8-4d, *except for external markings and internal connections.*

b. *General Electric.*—Wiring and line connection diagrams are given in Fig. 8-8 for motors with terminal board; motors without

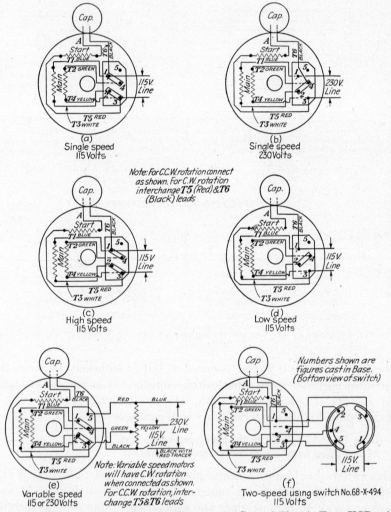

Fig. 8-8.—Wiring and line connection diagrams for General Electric Type KCP unit-heater motors.

terminal board have the external leads tagged as indicated in the figure. For single-speed operation, connections are the same in principle as in Fig. 8-7. Low speed on 115 volts is obtained by connecting the capacitor phase, also the two main-winding sections in series, across the line. Internal connections of switch 68-X-494 are given in Art. 8-7c. For two-speed operation on 230 volts, a special controller (connections not shown in the figure) incorporating an autotransformer is used. Connections for adjustable-speed operation are shown in the figure, which also gives the schematic diagram of the controller. The controller—illustrated in Figs. 8-4c and 8-4d— employs a continuously variable autotransformer of the Gramme-ring type, and a line switch mechanically interlocked so as to open in the extreme *high*-speed position. To close the line switch, the controller knob is turned clockwise until the switch is heard to snap; this position of the controller knob gives maximum speed. Turning the knob clockwise reduces the speed. To stop the motor, the knob must be turned counterclockwise to its extreme position.

c. Century Electric Co.—Wiring and line connection diagrams are given in Fig. 8-9. This motor makes use of the principles already discussed in connection with the two preceding motors. Connection diagrams are given for four different two-speed switches. Arrow-Hart and Hegeman switch No. 80788 is a special switch which makes the following connections:

Toggle up—High speed

L2 to T2 and T3 (Motor leads 1,4,6 connected to one line)
L1 to T1 (Motor leads 5,3,cap., to the other line)

Toggle down—Low speed

L2 to T3 (Motor leads 1,4 to one line)
L1 to T2 (Motor leads 5,6 connected together)
  (Motor leads 3, cap. to the other line)

This switch has been superseded by H. and H. switch No. 39947, which is a conventional three-pole double-throw switch, so connected to the motor as to give the same connections indicated above. (When the toggle is up, the three center terminals are connected, respectively, to the three bottom terminals, and vice versa.)

H. and H. switch No. 70232, also G.E. switch No. 68-X-494, make the following connections:

High: 1 to 2 and 3; 4 to 5
Low: 1 to 2; 3 to 4

Figure 8-9 shows use of an autotransformer to obtain two-speed operation on 230 volts. Variable-speed operation is obtained by using the same controller as in Fig. 8-8.

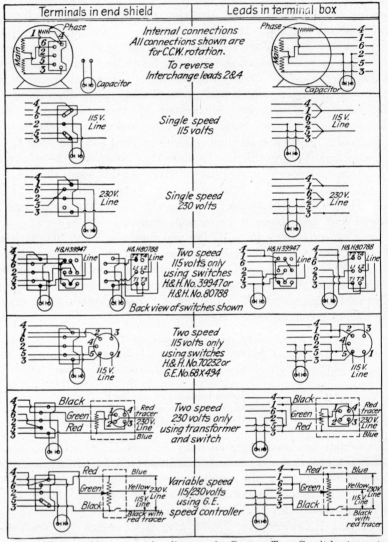

Fig. 8-9.—Wiring and line connection diagrams for Century Type C unit-heater motors.

8-8. Testing or Checking Adjustable-speed Controllers.—If an adjustable-speed controller is suspected of being defective, there are a number of simple checks that can be made:

1. Light-out for open circuits, referring to the proper schematic diagram, Fig. 8-7 or 8-8. (Controllers for Westinghouse motors, even those of Gramme-ring type, are wired as in Fig. 8-7, not as in Fig. 8-8.)

2. Apply 115 volts 60 cycles to the proper leads, using a fuse in series with the input line as a precaution against a short circuit. When the toggle switch is on, the transformer should be energized and drawing a small amount of current and power. The amount of current and watts input should be independent of the position of the speed-selector knob.

3. The voltage across the "230-volt" lines should be approximately 230 volts, and this voltage should be independent of the position of the speed-selector knob.

4. On Westinghouse controllers: the voltage between the $C2$ and $C3$ leads should be highest when the speed-selector switch is in the No. 1 position and lowest when it is in the No. 8 position, and should change by progressive steps from one position to the other; this voltage will range from a little less than line voltage down to the low twenties.

5. On General Electric controllers: the voltage between the *green* and *black* leads is nearly line voltage in the *high* speed position, *i.e.*, with the knob turned as far counterclockwise as it can without opening the toggle switch; the voltage from *green* to *black* decreases continuously as the speed-selector knob is turned clockwise. The extreme positions are determined by adjustable backstops in the controller. These stops can be adjusted after the U-shaped locking device is removed. The CCW stop must be adjusted so that the brush cannot drop off the winding and jam. The CW stop adjusts the lowest speed; it should not be set so low that the motor will fail to start on the lowest setting.

Usually it will be much less expensive to replace the entire controller than it will be to attempt to rewind the transformer.

THREE-SPEED DUAL-VOLTAGE MOTORS

Formerly, adjustable-speed capacitor motors for unit-heater service had the capacitor in the controller, and the motors could not be used independently of the latter. For new applications, these motors have been superseded entirely by the motors described above. However, because there are still a large number of these motors in service, a description of them is given below for the benefit of those who have to service and maintain them.

8-9. Motor Connections.—In general, in motors of this type, there are two windings, a main winding and an auxiliary winding displaced 90 electrical degrees, and a squirrel-cage rotor. Usually there is no centrifugal switch. As a rule, the main winding is put into the slots first, and the auxiliary winding, of finer wire and more turns, is placed on top of the main winding.

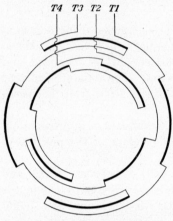

The **stator connection diagram** for a four-pole four-lead reversible series-connected motor is shown in Fig. 8-10. The stator connection diagrams for six-, eight-, and ten-pole four-lead reversible motors with both main and auxiliary windings parallel and cross-connected, are given in Figs. 8-11, 8-12, and 8-13, respectively.

FIG. 8-10.—Stator connection diagram for four-pole, series-connected, four-lead, externally reversible, permanent-split, capacitor motor.

Sometimes a reversible motor is not desired, and it is then necessary to bring out only three leads. The stator connection diagram for a six-pole parallel-wound motor is shown in Fig. 8-14; the rotation of this motor viewed from the connection end is counterclockwise. This

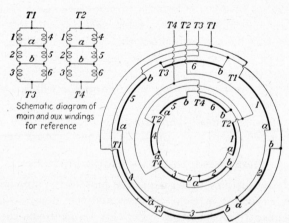

FIG. 8-11.—Stator connection diagram for six-pole, four-lead, externally reversible, permanent-split, capacitor motor. Both windings are parallel, cross-connected.

diagram is similar to that in Fig. 8-11, except that $T3$ and $T4$ are connected together internally and only the $T3$ lead is brought out.

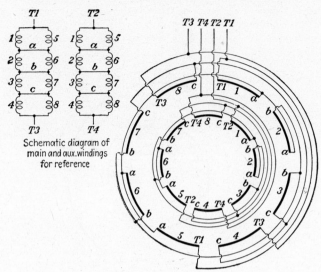

FIG. 8-12.—Stator connection diagram for eight-pole, four-lead, externally reversible, permanent-split capacitor motor. Both windings are parallel, cross-connected.

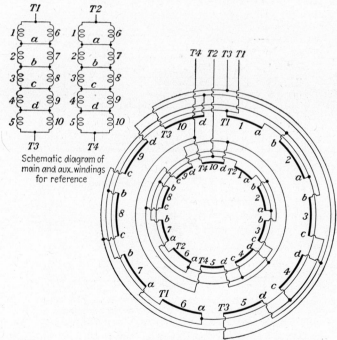

FIG. 8-13.—Stator connection diagram for ten-pole, four-lead, externally reversible, permanent-split, capacitor motor. Both windings are parallel, cross-connected.

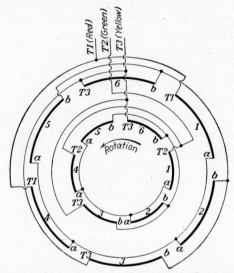

FIG. 8-14.—Stator connection diagram for six-pole, three-lead, nonreversible, permanent-split, capacitor motor.   Both windings are parallel, cross-connected.

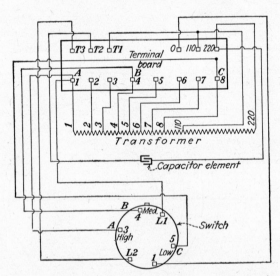

"High", "Med", and "Low" speeds can be varied by changing
leads A, B, C on terminals 1 to 8 on terminal board.
Terminal 1 is highest speed and terminal 8 is lowest speed

FIG. 8-15.—Internal wiring diagram of a three-speed controller. *Note:* This wiring is represented in schematic form in Fig. 8-5 (c). (*Courtesy of Westinghouse Electric Corporation.*)

8-10. Controller Connections.—The internal wiring diagram of a controller using the voltage-control system of Fig. 8-5c is illustrated in Fig. 8-15. This diagram shows the internal connections between the capacitor element, autotransformer, and snap switch, all of which are mounted in a single case. The switch shown is an Arrow Hart and Hegeman two-circuit three-speed snap switch. There are four positions making the following connections:

Switch position	First circuit	Second circuit
Off.........................	open	open
1......................./........	L1–1	L2–3 (high)
2..........................	L1–1	L2–4 (medium)
3..........................	L1–1	L2–5 (low)

The circuit L1 to 1, which is closed in three positions and open in the off position, is utilized to deenergize the transformer when the motor is idle. The function of this circuit is represented schematically in Fig. 8-5c by the single-pole single-throw switch shown there in the open position; the second circuit connects the common lead of the windings to different points on the autotransformer, as represented schematically by the movable tap on the transformer in Fig. 8-5c.

8-11. Line Connections to Motor and Controller.—In Fig. 8-16 are shown the motor and line connections to the controller; Fig. 8-16a is for a four-lead reversible motor using any one of the stator connection diagrams, Figs. 8-10 to 8-13; and Fig. 8-16b is for a three-lead nonreversible motor using a stator connection diagram such as is in Fig. 8-14. The internal wiring diagram of the controller is given in Fig. 8-15.

Now, to understand the principle of operation, compare the detailed diagrams of Figs. 8-15 and 8-16 with the schematic diagram of Fig. 8-5c: One end of the auxiliary winding T2 is connected through the capacitor element to the 220 tap of the transformer, and one end of the main winding T1 is connected to the midpoint or the 110 tap of the transformer. The other ends of the two windings are joined together, either on terminal post T3 (Fig. 8-16a) or inside the motor (Fig. 8-16b). Thus, in either case, T3 on the controller terminal board is the common point of the windings. From the common point T3 is a lead to post L2 on the switch; the latter connects L2 to leads A, B, and C in positions 1, 2, and 3, respectively. Lead A, B, or C can be connected to any one of the eight numbered taps from the autotransformer. Thus, the switch serves the same function as the adjustable arrow in Fig. 8-5c.

Terminals 1–2–3–4–5–6–7–8 are used for varying the speed; 1 gives the highest speed and 8 the lowest.   The high speed is adjusted by moving lead A to the desired tap; the medium and low speeds are adjusted with taps B and C, respectively.   The motor must be driving its fan with shutters and duct restrictions set as desired, and the switch must be set to position 1 when adjusting the A or *high* lead; similarly the switch must be in position 2 to adjust the B lead, and in position 3 to adjust the C lead.

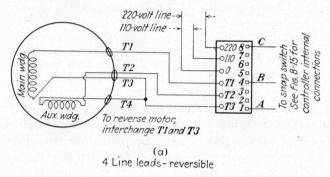

(a)
4 Line leads – reversible

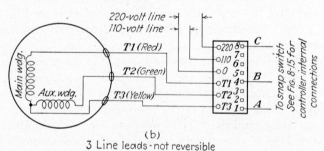

(b)
3 Line leads - not reversible

Fig. 8-16.—Line connection and motor wiring diagrams for a three-speed capacitor fan-duty motor.   (*Courtesy of Westinghouse Electric Corporation.*)

8-12. Controller with Nonadjustable High Speed.—Figure 8-17 shows the internal connections of a controller which also uses the voltage-control system of Fig. 8-5c.   In principle, it is similar to Fig. 8-15 except that only the *medium* and *low* speeds are adjustable.   The motor connections are made to terminals $T1$, $T2$, and $T3$ as in Fig 8-16.   The switch markings correspond to those of either a Bryant or a General Electric switch.

8-13. Testing Three-speed Controllers.   *a. Checking the Complete Controller.*—Before dismantling a controller that is supposed to be defective, a few simple checks can be made on the controller itself without connecting the motor to it.

1. Light-out for open circuits, referring to Fig. 8-15 or 8-17.

2. Apply 110 volts to 0 and 110 terminals, using a fuse in series to check for a possible short circuit in the transformer, and turn the switch to each of the four positions. On positions 1, 2, and 3, the transformer should be energized, drawing a small current, hardly large enough to detect on a 1-amp ammeter.

3. Connect a 110-volt voltmeter across T1 and T3, to which terminals the main winding is normally connected. Read the voltage in all three positions of the snap

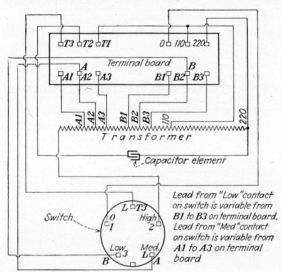

Fig. 8-17.—Internal wiring diagram of a three-speed controller. This diagram is similar to Fig. 8-15 except that the high-speed position is not adjustable. (*Courtesy of Westinghouse Electric Corporation.*)

switch. The voltage should be *high*, *medium*, and *low* in value, respectively, in these three positions.

4. A further test may be made by turning the switch to position 1, 2, or 3 and checking voltages 110 to 1, 110 to 2, 110 to 3, etc. Voltage 110 to 1 should be 110 volts, and voltage 110 to 8 may be as low as 20 volts or as high as 50 volts, with the other voltages spaced in progressive steps between these values.

b. Checking the Capacitor Element.—The foregoing tests generally will establish whether or not the autotransformer is defective. If it is all right, the next step is to check the capacitor element. The two leads from it are posts 220 and T2 on the terminal board. Using these two terminals and applying no voltage elsewhere, the capacitor can be tested for short circuits and for grounds; or its value of microfarads may be checked as described in Art. 6-8. This capacitor element is usually some type of oil-filled capacitor and, in general, is the same type of capacitor as that used in the motor shown in Fig. 6-1 or the running capacitor of the motor shown in Fig. 6-2.

c. Repairing.—A defective switch or capacitor element can usually be replaced, but it is not desirable to attempt to rewind the autotransformer. It may be well to caution the repairman here that, in small transformers like these, the tap is frequently made by bringing out a loop of wire, so that loops are connected to the terminal board at 2, 3, 4, etc.; consequently, if one of these strands breaks, it causes an open circuit in the transformer coil.

8-14. Rewinding.—Rewinding the motor, except to duplicate the original winding, is not to be recommended unless information for the new winding is obtained from the manufacturer.

TWO-SPEED VOLTAGE-CONTROLLED MOTORS

These motors are a simplified adaptation of the motors and controllers discussed in Arts. 8-9 to 8-14. They are likewise obsolete for

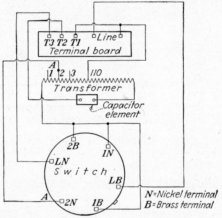

FIG. 8-18.—Internal wiring diagram of a controller for a voltage-controlled, two-speed, fan-duty motor rated at 110 volts. The arrangement of the switch terminals shown is for a Bryant switch, Cat. #2613. (*Courtesy of Westinghouse Electric Corporation.*)

new applications and the following description is primarily for the benefit of those who have to service and maintain them.

8-15. Single-voltage Motors.—Internal wiring diagrams of controllers used for two-speed voltage-controlled motors are given in Figs. 8-18 and 8-19. Both of these controllers use the voltage-control system of Fig. 8-5c, and speed control is obtained by the methods described in Arts. 8-4 to 8-6. These two controllers are actually simplifications of the controller of Fig. 8-15. The motor connections are made to terminals $T1$, $T2$, and $T3$, as in Fig. 8-16. The identical motor can be used with either controller, the choice of controller depending upon the circuit voltage. In fact, the 110-volt controller and motor could be used on 220 volts by connecting one side of the line to the 220 tap on the transformer and the other side of the line to the line terminal that goes to LB; all other connections are left alone. The 220-volt controller can be used on a 110-volt circuit by connecting

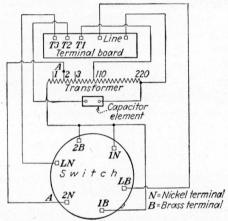

FIG. 8-19.—Controller wiring diagram similar to Fig. 8-18 except for a 220-volt motor. (*Courtesy of Westinghouse Electric Corporation.*)

one side of the line to $T1$ post and the other side to that line terminal which goes to LB.

Neither controller permits any adjustment of the *high* speed, but the *low* speed can be adjusted by connecting lead A to numbered lead 1, 2, or 3. The two leads that are not used must be individually taped to prevent a short circuit or a ground.

The switch shown is a double-pole double-throw snap switch making the following connections:

Position	Circuit 1	Circuit 2
1	LN–$1N$	LB–$1B$
2	LN–$2N$	LB–$2B$

N stands for nickel terminal.
B stands for brass terminal.

If one of these controllers is defective, it can be checked by following the principles outlined in Art. 8-13.

8-16. Special Mechanical Features.—Motors used on unit-heater service almost invariably have direct-connected propeller fans which draw air over the motor and through the heater. Since a large volume of air is drawn over the motor, it has been the practice of the industry to use totally enclosed motors to keep out dust and dirt.

Controllers are preferably mounted apart from the motor to avoid interference with the air stream; even a small obstruction such as a conduit box may be specially mounted on the front end shield to eliminate such interference.

Since the propeller fan is mounted on the shaft, special provision has to be made to accommodate the thrust of the fan. One such arrangement is shown in Fig. 18-3. Some designs of "no-bump" or spring thrust washers are built with sufficient thrust capacity to withstand this thrust. To keep the rotor from bumping or knocking against the bearings in earlier types of motors not equipped with no-bump bearings, the rotor core was sometimes offset, *i.e.*, displaced from the normal position, which is with stator and rotor laminations lining up with each other, as much as $\frac{1}{8}$ in. toward the shaft end; magnetic pull would then hold the rotor definitely against the front bearing until the fan got up to speeed, when the thrust of the fan would be sufficient to hold the rotor against the front bearing. Service shops may occasionally find this idea useful to eliminate bumping bearings. Too much offset is injurious to the performance of the motor; bearing friction is increased, as well as both watts and amperes input to the motor.

CHAPTER IX

TWO-SPEED TAPPED-WINDING CAPACITOR MOTORS

Tapped-winding capacitor motors were formerly used extensively for two-speed service on shaft-mounted fan and blower applications. This type is a **permanent-split capacitor motor,** and speed reduction is effected by changing the slip.

9-1. Principle of the Tapped-winding Motor.—The two-speed, tapped-winding capacitor motor is similar in principle of operation to the three-speed motors discussed in Chap. VIII. The three-speed motor, as pointed out in Arts. 8-3 to 8-6, varies the slip by varying the field strength; and the field strength is controlled by varying the voltage impressed upon the main winding. The two-speed, tapped-winding motor likewise varies the slip by varying the field strength; but the latter is varied by changing the number of effective conductors in the main winding, and not by changing the impressed voltage. The field strength of any given induction motor, at a given frequency, is proportional to the *volts per conductor;* in the three-speed motor, the volts per conductor is lessened by reducing the voltage, but in the tapped-winding motor, the volts per conductor is lessened by increasing the number of conductors. It will be shown subsequently how the number of series conductors in the main phase is varied.

9-2. Winding Arrangement of a Tapped-winding Motor.—A tapped-winding capacitor motor has three windings, which we shall call the **main winding, intermediate winding,** and **auxiliary winding.** The main winding and the intermediate winding are wound in space phase with each other; *i.e.,* the latter is wound on top of the former, in the same slots, with the same distribution but not necessarily with the same number of turns or with wire of the same size. In principle, the windings are similar in arrangement to the windings used in dual-voltage capacitor-start motors discussed in Arts. 5-14 to 5-16, except that, in the latter case, it is necessary to have both sections of the winding identical so that they can be paralleled. In the tapped-winding motor, the two sections never are connected in parallel so that they do not need to be identical. The third winding is the auxiliary winding, which is displaced 90 electrical degrees from the main and intermediate windings. The rotor is of squirrel-cage con-

213

struction, and no centrifugal switch is used.   Different methods exist for connecting these windings; two common ones are known as the **L-** and **T-connection,** respectively.

9-3. The L-connection.—How the three windings are connected for a 110-volt motor is shown schematically in Fig. 9-1a.   A vector diagram for the high-speed connection showing approximately the voltages existing and their phase relationships with one another is shown in Fig. 9-1b; a similar vector diagram for the low-speed connection is shown in Fig. 9-1c.

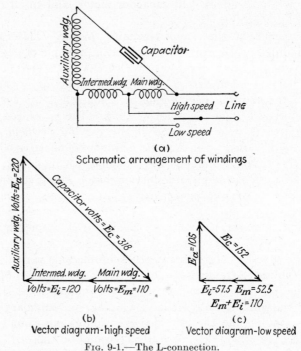

(a)
Schematic arrangement of windings

(b)
Vector diagram - high speed

(c)
Vector diagram - low speed

Fig. 9-1.—The L-connection.

Consider first the high-speed connection; 110 volts is impressed upon the main winding.   By transformer action, 120 volts is induced in the intermediate winding.   (In this illustrative example, the effective conductors in the intermediate winding were 9 per cent more than the effective conductors in the main winding; hence the voltage induced in the intermediate winding is 9 per cent more than the voltage induced in the main winding.)   Now, if the rotor is allowed to run near synchronous speed, a cross field will be set up by the rotor, as explained in Art. 2-10.   This cross field will induce a voltage in the auxiliary winding which is displaced 90 deg from the main winding, as shown in Fig. 9-1*b*. (Some find it easier to consider that it is a rotating field that is set up in the motor; how a rotating field is set up is described in Art. 2-11.) In the chosen example, there are twice as many conductors in the auxiliary winding as in the main winding; therefore, the voltage induced in the auxiliary winding is approximately twice the voltage induced in the main winding. The capacitor voltage is the hypotenuse of the right triangle and is found to be 318 volts. It can be seen that the intermediate winding acts as the secondary of an autotransformer and steps up the voltage on the auxiliary phase so that, while only 110 volts is impressed on the main phase, 230 volts (110 + 120 = 230) is impressed on the auxiliary phase.

On the low-speed connection, the voltages all bear approximately the same relative proportions with one another; but all are reduced in magnitude, as shown in Fig. 9-1*c*, because the line voltage is across two windings in series and the volts per conductor is thereby reduced. Observe, too, that the voltage across the main winding has been reduced from 110 to 52.5; in other words, the *volts per conductor* has been reduced in the ratio of 110: 52.5.

Voltage values given here should not be taken too literally; for the actual figures vary with different designs and, for any given design, vary with load, both in phase position and in magnitude. But these voltage values are sufficiently close to illustrate the principle involved.

9-4. The T-connection.*—A slightly different arrangement of windings is shown in Fig. 9-2. The capacitor phase is connected so that it has impressed on it the same voltage as on the main winding. The principal use for this connection is for 220-volt motors, and the reason for its use should be clearly apparent after studying the vector diagrams in Fig. 9-2. It will be seen that, by this connection, the capacitor element is operated at nearly the same voltage as the 110-volt L-connected motor of Fig. 9-1. However, if these windings were L-connected as in Fig. 9-1, the voltage across the auxiliary phase would be approximately 240 + 220 = 460 volts; and the voltage across the capacitor itself would be approximately 510 volts

$$(\sqrt{460^2 + 220^2} = 510).$$

In such a case, a 550-volt capacitor would have to be used; whereas if the T-connection is used, a 330-volt capacitor can be used.

* The T-connection discussed in this article should not be confused with the Scott T-connection used for connecting transformers to change two-phase to three-phase, or vice versa.

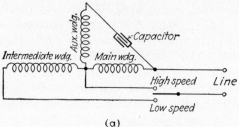

(a)
Schematic arrangement of windings

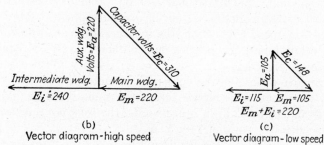

(b)
Vector diagram-high speed

(c)
Vector diagram-low speed

FIG. 9-2.—The T-connection.

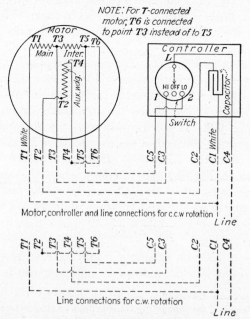

FIG. 9-3.—Motor, controller, and line connections for a two-speed, tapped-winding, permanent-split, capacitor motor with a separate controller. (*Courtesy of Westinghouse Electric Corporation.*)

9-5. Motors with Separate Controller.—Figure 9-3 shows the motor and controller wiring diagrams, also the line connection diagram, of a two-speed tapped-winding motor with separate controller. This diagram shows the connections for either an L-connected or a T-connected motor. That the external connections are the same for either arrangement is accomplished by bringing out the extra lead *T6*; if *T6* is connected internally to *T5*, the motor is L-connected; but if *T6* is connected to *T3*, the motor is T-connected. (If Figs. 9-1 and 9-2 are studied, it can be observed that the difference between the two connections is only a matter of where one end of the auxiliary

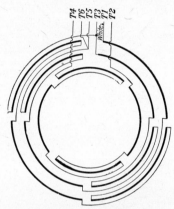

Fig. 9-4.—Stator connection diagram for a two-speed tapped-winding motor, four poles, series, L-connected.

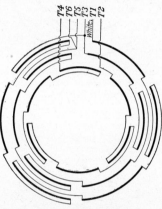

Fig. 9-5.—Stator connection diagram for a two-speed, tapped-winding motor, six poles, series, L-connected.

winding is connected, whether to the junction of main and intermediate windings or to the other end of the intermediate winding.)

The **stator connection diagrams** for four-, six-, eight-, and ten-pole motors with all three windings series-connected are given in Figs. 9-4, 9-5, 9-6, and 9-7, respectively. Similar stator connection diagrams for six- and eight-pole motors are shown in Figs. 9-8 and 9-9, except that in these two cases, both main and auxiliary windings are parallel, cross-connected, but the intermediate winding is series-connected. Stator connection diagrams for T-connected motors are exactly the same as in Figs. 9-4 to 9-9, except that *T6* is internally connected to *T3* instead of to *T5* as shown.

The motor, controller, and line connections of a two-speed tapped-winding capacitor motor with a built-in conduit box are given in Fig. 9-10. The controller is separately mounted. This motor is L-connected, and the arrangement of leads follows the schematic arrange-

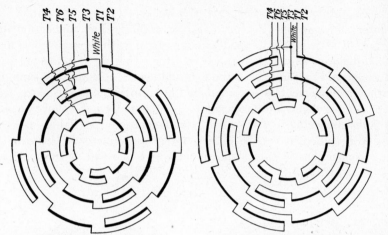

Fig. 9-6.—Stator connection diagram for a two-speed, tapped-winding motor, eight poles, series, L-connected.

Fig. 9-7.—Stator connection diagram for a two-speed, tapped-winding motor, ten poles, series, L-connected.

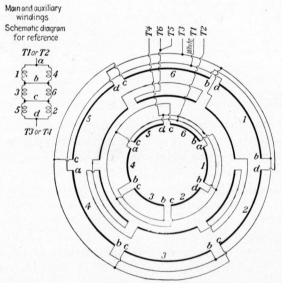

Fig. 9-8.—Stator connection diagram for a two-speed, tapped-winding motor, six poles, main and auxiliary windings parallel, cross-connected, intermediate winding, series; L-connection.

ment of Fig. 9-11*a*. The latter is similar to Fig. 9-1*a* except that the relative positions of the capacitor and auxiliary winding are interchanged.

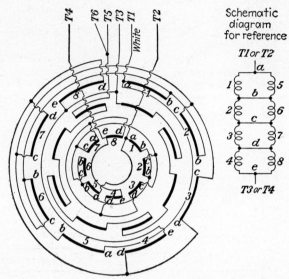

Schematic diagram for reference

FIG. 9-9.—Stator connection diagram for a two-speed, tapped-winding motor, eight poles, main and auxiliary windings parallel, cross-connected, intermediate winding, series; L-connection.

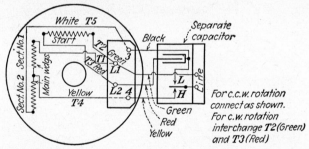

FIG. 9-10.—Motor, controller, and line connections for a two-speed, tapped-winding, permanent-split, capacitor motor with terminal board and separate controller. (*Courtesy of General Electric Company.*)

As a matter of interest, the capacitor and auxiliary winding in Fig. 9-2 were also interchanged; the result can be seen in Fig. 9-11*b*, which shows another form of the T-connection.

9-6. Motors with Capacitor Attached.—The motor wiring and line connection diagram of a two-speed tapped-winding capacitor motor with the capacitor mounted on the motor is given in Fig. 9-12. Like the motor shown in Fig. 9-10, this one also follows the schematic arrangement of Fig. 9-11a.

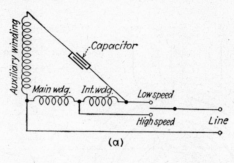

(a)

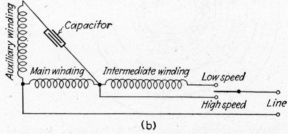

(b)

FIG. 9-11.—Other arrangements of two-speed tapped-winding motors.

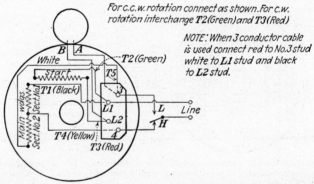

FIG. 9-12.—Motor and line connections for a two-speed, tapped-winding, permanent-split, capacitor motor with capacitor mounted on the motor. (*Courtesy of General Electric Company.*)

9-7. How to Tell the Windings Apart and How to Identify the Leads.—There are, of course, other ways to build tapped-winding motors than those just described, and the system of lead tagging may be different. Even if this system is used, the lead tags may be lost, making it necessary to identify the windings. A few simple principles may be helpful:

1. The main and intermediate windings are in space phase with one another. If the motor is running, the voltages of the two windings are in phase and add directly, as can be seen by referring to Fig. 9-1 or 9-2. If the end shield is removed, it is simple to find a pair of windings wound one on top of another; then these two must be the main and intermediate windings.

2. The intermediate winding is almost invariably of finer wire and higher in resistance than the main winding.

3. The auxiliary winding is displaced 90 electrical degrees from the main winding, and the voltage across it, when the motor is operating normally, is approximately 90 deg out of phase with the main-winding voltage.

9-8. Rewinding or Reconnecting.—In general, rewinding, except to duplicate the original windings, is to be discouraged unless the specification for the new winding is obtained from the manufacturer. There are some changes that can be made with a fair degree of safety, although the performance of the motor may or may not be slightly impaired. These changes will be discussed in turn.

a. Changing from 110 to 220 Volts.—The following applies only if the motor is L-connected. The turns in both the main and intermediate windings must be doubled, and wire three sizes smaller must be used for each. The original auxiliary winding should be duplicated both as to number of turns and wire size. The rewound motor should then be T-connected. If the main winding is parallel-connected, it may be possible to reconnect it in series without rewinding; however, the intermediate winding is probably series-connected so that it will have to be rewound.

b. Changing from 220 to 110 Volts.—The following applies only if the motor is T-connected. The turns in both the main and intermediate windings must be halved and wire three sizes larger must be used for each. The original auxiliary winding should be duplicated both as to number of turns and as to wire size. The rewound motor should then be L-connected. If the main and intermediate windings are series-connected—as is fairly probable—they can both be reconnected in parallel instead of being rewound; the original auxiliary winding will be used without reconnecting, and the three windings should be L-connected. The **stator connection diagram** for a six-pole motor reconnected in this manner is shown in Fig. 9-13.

c. Changing the Low Speed.—The operating speed on the low-speed connection can be decreased or increased by increasing or decreasing the number of turns in the intermediate winding. If such a change is made, it will be safer to use wire of the same size and not to change the turns more than 15 per cent.

Another and simpler way is to change the microfarads: to increase the speed, increase the microfarads, and vice versa.   If the motor is L-connected, the speed can be reduced by using the T-connection. (Do not reconnect a T-connected motor by the L-connection!)   Either of these changes will affect the high speed slightly.

d. Failure to Start on Low Speed.—If the motor fails to start on the low-speed connection, check to see that the motor is properly

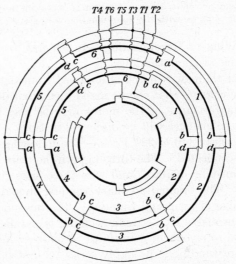

Fig. 9-13.—Stator connection diagram for a two-speed, tapped-winding motor, six poles, main and intermediate windings parallel, cross-connected, auxiliary winding, series; L-connection.

lubricated.   Spin the fan to see that the shaft turns freely.   Turn the controller to the low-speed position, and give the fan an initial start; if the motor fails to come up to speed, it is probable that an open circuit exists either in the controller or in one of the connecting leads. If these methods are fruitless, it may be necessary to disassemble the motor, set the rotor up on a lathe, and reduce the section of the resistance rings, thereby increasing the rotor resistance.

e. General Precautions.—If the motor is rewound or reconnected as described above, three precautions should be taken:

1. The capacitor volts should be checked on the high-speed connection with motor driving its fan.   (If motor is not driving a fan but is operating at no load, the capacitor volts will be 5 to 10 per cent higher.)   The voltage should not be too

great for the capacitor; 363 volts on a 330-volt capacitor or 10 per cent over rated voltage is permissible.

2. If the speed is reduced, care should be taken that the motor will start the fan on normal voltage or on any reduced voltage likely to be encountered.

3. The input watts, driving the fan on both the high- and low-speed connections, should be checked and compared with original values similarly taken before the motor was rewound. If the watts are substantially higher, it will be a wise precaution to take a temperature run to see that the motor will not burn out.

Bibliography

1. TRICKEY, P. H.: Performance Calculations on Tapped-winding Capacitor Motors, *A.I.E.E. Trans.*, vol. 62, 1943, pp. 1–3.

CHAPTER X

REPULSION-START INDUCTION MOTORS

The repulsion-start induction motor is, perhaps, the first type of single-phase induction motor that gained widespread commercial acceptance. Invented by Dr. Engelbert Arnold, it was used commercially in this country as early as 1896. Although widely popular until the middle thirties, it has now been generally supplanted for new applications by capacitor-start and two-value capacitor motors.

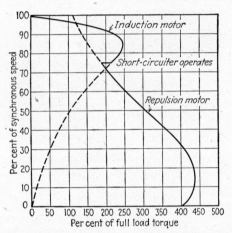

Fig. 10-1.—The speed-torque curve of a repulsion-start induction motor.

However, there are many thousands of this type still operating satisfactorily.

10-1. Repulsion-start Induction Motor Defined.—The repulsion-start induction motor is sometimes erroneously called a **repulsion induction motor** or simply a **repulsion motor.** The latter-mentioned types are defined in Arts. 11-1 and 11-2. The A.S.A. defines the repulsion-start induction motor as follows:

A repulsion-start induction motor is a single-phase motor having the same windings as a repulsion motor but at a predetermined speed the rotor winding is short-circuited or otherwise connected to give the equivalent of a squirrel-cage winding. This type of motor starts as a repulsion motor but operates

224

s an induction motor with constant-speed characteristics.—ASA C42—1941.
10.10.420.

10-2. Application and Torque Characteristics.—Repulsion-start
motors are used on such applications as pumps, compressors, and
miscellaneous general-purpose applications wherever high locked-rotor
torque and low locked-rotor current are desired. A representative
speed-torque curve is given in Fig. 10-1. For most applications, the
repulsion-start motor is now being replaced largely by the capacitor-
start motor, which has substantially the same torques (see Fig. 5-4).

The torque requirements for repulsion-start induction motors
established by Nema are given in Table VIII. This table of torques
was rescinded in June, 1946, by Nema, and replaced with the torques
given in Table II (see Art. 1-5).

TABLE VIII.—MINIMUM TORQUES OF REPULSION-START INDUCTION MOTORS*

Rating hp	Locked-rotor torque	Pull-up torque	Breakdown torque
60 cycles—1725 rpm			
1/8	350	200	200
1/6	350	200	200
1/4	350	200	200
1/3	350	200	200
1/2	350	200	200
3/4	350	200	200
60 cycles—1140 rpm			
1/8	300	150	185
1/6	300	150	185
1/4	300	150	185
1/3	300	150	185
1/2	300	150	185

These torques are expressed in percentage of full-load torque. Maximum permissible values of
locked-rotor currents are given in Table XXVI.
* These torques were Nema requirements until June, 1946.

10-3. Essential Parts of the Repulsion-start Induction Motor.—
Figure 10-2 is a cutaway view of a repulsion-start induction motor
showing clearly the essential and necessary parts:

a. The *stator winding* usually is a single, concentric winding of the
type discussed in Chap. III and may be hand-wound, or mold-wound
with progressive or concentric coils. Because of the fact that there
is only one winding, all the stator slots may not be wound. Some

manufacturers use the empty slots for ventilating ducts to keep the motor cool. Two empty slots are visible in this photograph. The stator core is laminated because it is excited with alternating current.

b. The *armature*, or rotor, is slotted and wound just as if it were a d-c armature. The core is, of course, laminated.

c, d. A *commutator* and *brushes* are necessary with a d-c type of winding.

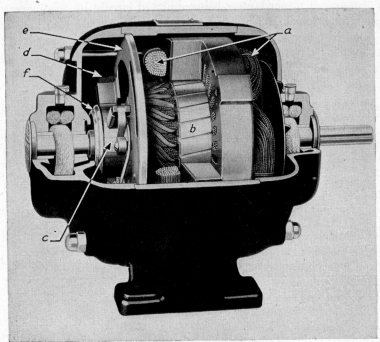

Fɪɢ. 10-2.—A cutaway view of a repulsion-start induction motor.　(*Courtesy of Maste Electric Company.*)

a. Stator winding.	*d.* Brushes.
b. Armature.	*e.* Rocker ring.
c. Commutator.	*f.* Short-circuiter.

e. The brushes are mounted on a *rocker ring*, or *brush yoke*, whicl can be shifted circumferentially to reverse the direction of rotation.

f. A centrifugally operated *short-circuiter* short-circuits all th commutator bars, making the armature, in effect, a squirrel-cag rotor. This particular short-circuiter is illustrated in Fig. 10-16 an discussed in more detail in Art. 10-32.

The motor just described is a **brush-riding motor;** *i.e.*, the brushe ride on the commutator continuously. In a **brush-lifting motor,** th brushes are lifted away from the commutator except during the starting period; such a motor is illustrated in Fig. 10-19.

PRINCIPLES OF OPERATION

10-4. Repulsion Motor Similar to a Series Motor.—The torque characteristics of a repulsion motor are quite similar to those of a series motor, and some idea of its principle of operation can be gained by comparing it with a series motor. A simple series motor is represented in Fig. 10-3; it consists of a field and an armature connected in series. The current flowing through the field winding sets up a magnetic field in the horizontal axis. The brushes and armature winding are arranged so

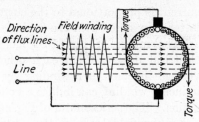

FIG. 10-3.—A simple series motor.

that current passing from one brush to the other flows through half of the armature conductors in one direction and through the other half in the other direction; these directions of current flow are indicated by the dots and plus signs in the figure. On one side of the armature an upward force is produced and on the other side a downward force,* the net result being torque or turning effort. (How torque is developed is elaborated in slightly more detail in Art. 17-3.)

A repulsion motor is represented in Fig. 10-4. Like the series motor of Fig. 10-3, it has an armature, brushes, and a **field winding,** but the brushes are short-circuited upon themselves, and there is a second, or **inducing winding,** displaced 90 electrical degrees from the field winding. This inducing winding induces current to flow in the armature in the same predetermined paths as in the series motor, and thus torque is produced just as in the series motor. The inducing winding acts as the primary of a two-winding transformer, the secondary of which is the short-

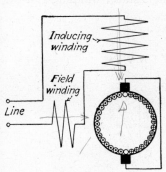

FIG. 10-4.—A simple repulsion motor with two stator windings.

* There is a left-hand rule for *motor* action similar to the Fleming right-hand rule for generator action explained in the footnote to Art. 2-10. *Extend the thumb and first and second fingers of the left hand mutually perpendicular. The thumb points in the direction of motion if the first finger is pointed in the direction of the lines of force and if the second finger points in the direction of current flow.*

circuited armature winding. Therefore, since the field winding and the inducing winding are both in series, it follows that the torque characteristics of the repulsion motor of Fig. 10-4 must be similar to the torque characteristics of the series motor of Fig. 10-3. To emphasize the similarity further—in the series motor, the armature current is equal to the field current at all times because the armature and field are in series; in the repulsion motor, the armature current is proportional to the current in the inducing winding, and the latter is in series with the field.

The motor of Fig. 10-4 has two stator windings displaced 90 electrical degrees from each other. Neither winding can induce a voltage in the other winding by transformer action, and only the inducing winding can induce a voltage in the armature by transformer action. The series motor of Fig. 10-3 can be reversed by interchanging either the field leads or the armature leads; the repulsion motor of Fig. 10-4 can likewise be reversed by interchanging either the field-winding leads or the inducing-winding leads.

10-5. The Simple Repulsion Motor.—The simple repulsion motor is illustrated in Fig. 10-5. It has but a single stator winding, and the

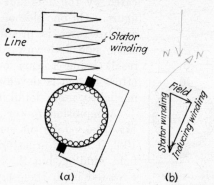

Fig. 10-5.—A simple repulsion motor with one stator winding and shifted brushes.

brush axis is shifted from the axis of this winding. Following the well-known process of dividing a vector into two components, the field set up by the stator winding can be resolved into two perpendicular component fields, one along the brush axis, the other perpendicular to it; the process of resolving the field into these two components is shown in vector form in Fig. 10-5b. Thus, a single winding with a shifted brush axis as shown in Fig. 10-5 is equivalent to two windings displaced 90 electrical degrees. (This point is developed more fully and from a different viewpoint in Art. 12-6.) Therefore, the simple repulsion motor of Fig. 10-5 is similar in characteristics to the repulsion motor of Fig. 10-4, which in turn is similar to the series motor of Fig. 10-3.

This type of repulsion motor cannot be reversed by changing connections but must be reversed by shifting the brushes.

10-6. Hard Neutral and Soft Neutral.—To determine experimentally how the locked-rotor torque and stator current of a repulsion motor vary with brush position, some tests were taken on a $\frac{1}{6}$-hp 110/220-volt 60-cycle repulsion-start induction motor. Instead of measuring locked-rotor torque—which varies considerably with rotor position—the torque and current were measured at 50 rpm, *i.e.*, with

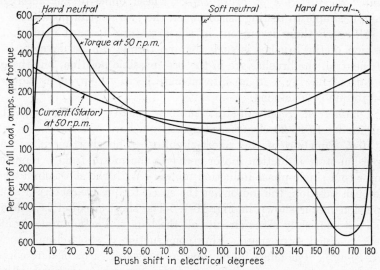

FIG. 10-6.—The effect of brush position on the torque and stator current of a repulsion-start motor at 50 rpm.

the rotor barely turning over; readings of current and torque were taken at a number of different brush positions. The results of these tests are plotted in Fig. 10-6.

In Fig. 10-6, a brush position of zero degrees indicates that the brushes were set for the position of maximum induced voltage and current in the armature circuit—this position would correspond to Fig. 10-4 if the field winding were left out of the circuit. In this position the torque is zero. This point is called **hard neutral**. Ninety electrical degrees from hard neutral is another point of zero torque, known as **soft neutral**. At this point, the relative positions of the brushes and stator winding are the same as in Fig. 10-3, and there is no voltage induced between brushes; hence, no current flows in the armature circuit.

Hard neutral and soft neutral are comparatively easy to distinguish in a practical motor. Hard neutral is very sharply defined—a slight shift in either direction will cause the armature to rotate. Another distinguishing characteristic of hard neutral is that, if the brushes are shifted in either direction when the stator is energized, the armature will start to revolve *in the same direction that the brushes are shifted.* Soft neutral is less sharply defined, and an appreciable shift is frequently necessary to cause the armature to rotate at all. When the shift is sufficient to cause rotation, the armature will revolve *against the direction of brush shift.* These opposite characteristics make it simple to distinguish between the two neutral positions.

Although there is current in the armature at hard neutral, the position of the brushes is such that no torque can be developed; at soft neutral, the brushes are in the best possible position, but there is no current flowing. At an intermediate position, current is induced, and torque is developed. .

Commercial repulsion-start motors usually operate with the brushes set 15 to 20 electrical degrees from hard neutral.

10-7. Function of the Short-circuiter.—The short-circuiter of a repulsion-start induction motor converts the motor from a repulsion motor to a single-phase induction motor. With the short-circuiter in the open position, the motor has the speed-torque characteristics of a repulsion motor shown in Fig. 10-1. The short-circuiter is a device that automatically short-circuits all the bars of the commutator at a predetermined rotor speed. (For construction of short-circuiters, see Art. 10-32.) The effect is the same as if several turns of bare copper wire were suddenly wrapped around the commutator. Since all the armature coils are mutually short-circuited upon each other, the armature then becomes, in effect, a squirrel-cage rotor, and the motor operates like any other single-phase induction motor. When the commutator bars are short-circuited, the brushes become inoperative, and sometimes a mechanism is provided to lift the brushes away from the commutator (see Art. 10-33).

STATOR WINDINGS

10-8. Dual-voltage Four-lead Motors.—Stator connection diagrams for dual-voltage two-, four-, six-, and eight-pole windings are shown in Figs. 10-7, 10-8, 10-9, and 10-10, respectively. The motor wiring and line connection diagram for any of these stator connection

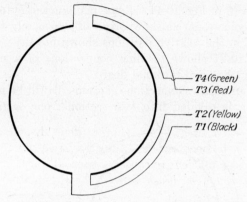

FIG. 10-7.—Stator connection diagram for a dual-voltage motor of the repulsion type, two poles.

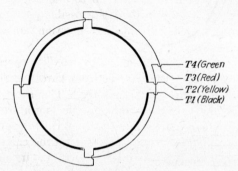

FIG. 10-8.—Stator connection diagram for a dual-voltage motor of the repulsion type, four poles.

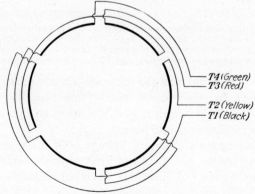

FIG. 10-9.—Stator connection diagram for a dual-voltage motor of the repulsion type, six poles.

diagrams is given in Fig. 10-11. Some manufacturers tag the leads as shown, some color them as shown, and others merely bring out four leads clamped in the relative positions shown but otherwise unidentified. Figure 10-21 shows the line connections of a motor using a built-in conduit box and terminal board.

In these four stator connection diagrams, it will be noted that the stator winding is divided into two sections: one section comprises

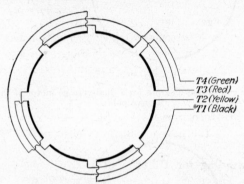

FIG. 10-10.—Stator connection diagram for a dual-voltage motor of the repulsion type, eight poles.

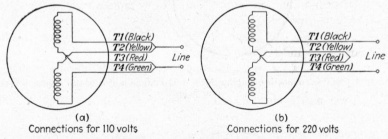

(a)   (b)
Connections for 110 volts   Connections for 220 volts

FIG. 10-11.—Wiring and line connection diagrams for a dual-voltage motor of the repulsion type. (NOTE: A.S.A. Standard C6.1—1944 shows terminal markings similar to the above except: (a) no color coding is given; (b) tags $T2$ and $T3$ are interchanged; i.e., $T1$ and $T2$ are connected to one section, and $T3$ and $T4$ are connected to the other.)

every alternate pole group, and the other section comprises the remaining pole groups. In other words, one section contains all the pole groups of one magnetic polarity, and the other section all the pole groups of the opposite magnetic polarity.

10-9. Rewinding for a Different Voltage.—Of the various types of single-phase motors so far discussed, the repulsion-start induction motor offers the fewest complications when it becomes a question of rewinding for a different operating voltage. A 110/220-volt motor can be rewound for 220/440 volts by using twice as many turns of wire three sizes smaller than was used in the original stator winding. To rewind a 220/440-volt motor for 275/550 volts, use 26 per cent more turns and wire one size smaller. To rewind a 110/220-volt motor for 275/550 volts, use two and one-half times as many turns and wire four sizes smaller. It is unnecessary to make any change in the armature winding when the stator is rewound for a different circuit voltage as described.

The General Rule.—To rewind to obtain the same performance on a circuit of a voltage higher or lower than rated voltage, rewind the stator with more or less turns in direct proportion to the increase or decrease in voltage. In general, use the largest size of wire that will permit the correct number of turns to be put into the slots: if the total circular mils of copper per slot is larger in the new winding, the performance will be slightly better than with the original winding; and, conversely, the performance will be slightly poorer if the circular mils per slot are less in the new winding. The armature winding should not be changed.

10-10. Rewinding for Different Torques.—The remarks in Art. 4-38 regarding changing the main winding of a split-phase motor to change the torques all apply directly to changing the stator winding of a repulsion-start induction motor, and like precautions should be taken to see that the rewound motor will not overheat. If the stator-winding turns are changed not more than 10 or 15 per cent, it will not be necessary to rewind the armature.

10-11. Rewinding for a Different Frequency or Number of Poles.— A 50-cycle repulsion-start motor can be safely operated on 60 cycles without rewinding, but the torques will probably be inadequate. The breakdown torque, in terms of full-load torque, may be as much as 15 per cent low; but the pull-up torque will be even more reduced, for it is reduced both by the decrease in breakdown torque and by the relatively slower operating speed of the short-circuiter. If the short-circuiter operated at 75 per cent speed on 50 cycles, it would operate at 62 per cent speed on 60 cycles because the change in frequency affects the full-load speed; if the operating speed of the short-circuiter of the motor of Fig. 10-1 is reduced from 75 to 62 per cent speed, the pull-up torque is reduced from 185 to 150 per cent, or a 20 per cent reduction in pull-up torque due to the use of a slow-speed short-circuiter. Therefore, when a 50-cycle motor is changed for operation on a 60-cycle circuit, a 60-cycle short-circuiter should be obtained; it may then be further necessary to rewind the stator, using 5 to 10 per cent less turns; whether or not rewinding the stator is necessary will depend largely upon the severity of the torque requirements of the load. It should not be necessary to rewind the armature.

A 60-cycle motor can seldom be operated successfully on a 50-cycle circuit, for the operating speed of the short-circuiter will be too high. If the short-circuiter operates at all, the contact pressures of the short-circuiting members on the commutator bars are likely to be too light. The proper 50-cycle short-circuiter must be used, and it may or may not be necessary to rewind the stator. Rewinding the stator with 5 to 10 per cent more turns of wire of the same size as the 60-cycle winding will improve the 50-cycle performance somewhat.

In changing a 25-cycle motor to operate on 30 cycles, the same considerations apply as in changing from 50 to 60 cycles. Likewise, in changing from 30 to 25 cycles, the same considerations apply as in changing from 60 to 50 cycles. For any other changes in frequency, the manufacturer should be consulted.

Rewinding for a different number of poles is not to be recommended for a number of reasons:

1. The armature would have to be rewound, and it would be difficult to formulate any general rules for such a change. Moreover, the number of slots and commutator bars might not be suitable, particularly when rewinding for a greater number of poles.
2. The spacing of the brushes would have to be altered, which means a new **rocker ring** or **brush yoke**.
3. If cartridge-type brush holders are used, changing the spacing is not feasible.
4. A new short-circuiter would have to be obtained.

ARMATURE WINDINGS

10-12. General.—The topic of armature windings is so extensively covered in the literature on the subject that no attempt will be made to treat it comprehensively here—only the high spots will be touched. Braymer and Roe,[1] for example, devote at least 10 chapters to the practical aspects of this subject. Langsdorf[2] gives excellent information on the subject for those who wish to pursue it further. **Simplex windings** are generally used in preference to **duplex windings**. **Wave** and **lap windings** are both used. When lap windings are used, it is a fairly common practice to cross-connect all commutator bars.

10-13. The Lap (or Parallel) Winding.—A simplex lap winding is shown in Fig. 10-12. In this example, the armature is wound for four poles; there are 28 slots and 56 bars, or 2 bars per slot; and the coil throw is 1 and 7, or slightly less than full pitch. Starting at bar 6,

[1] For numbered references, see Bibliography at end of chapter.

the winding progresses completely around the armature in an orderly fashion.

10-14. Lap Windings—Coil Connections to the Commutator.— Since there are two bars per slot, there are two coils per slot (four coil sides) as shown in Fig. 10-12. The connections to the commutator of the two coils lying in slots 1 and 7 are shown in full lines, whereas the other coil connections are shown dotted. These same coil connections are shown again in Fig. 10-13a, where only the connections of the coils lying in a single pair of slots are shown. Figure 10-13b gives an **armature connection diagram** for *any* simplex progressive lap-

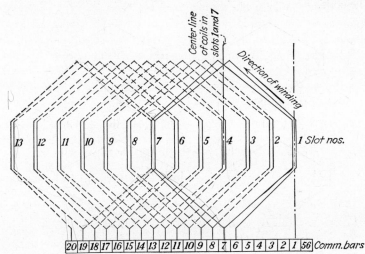

FIG. 10-12.—A simplex lap winding. Four poles, 28 slots, 1 and 7 throw, 56 bars, progressive.

wound armature having two bars per slot. Figure 10-13c and d show similar armature connection diagrams for simplex progressive lap-wound armatures having three bars per slot; note that if the coil throw is even, the mica to the right of bar 1 should be lined up with the center of slot 1, whereas if the coil throw is odd, the center of bar 1 lines up with the center of slot 1. After these first coil connections are made— as indicated by full lines—it is a simple matter to fill in the additional connections which are indicated by the dotted lines in Fig. 10-12.

10-15. Lap Windings—Position of the Brushes at Neutral.— With armature coil connections as shown in Fig. 10-12 and also in Fig. 10-13, the brushes will be in the soft-neutral position when they are opposite the centers of the stator coils comprising one pole group, *i.e.*, if a concentric winding is used, opposite the centers of the coils.

The brushes will be in the hard-neutral position when they are midway between the centers of the coils, *i.e.*, 90 electrical degrees from the soft-neutral position.

10-16. How to Lay Out Coil Connections of a Lap Winding for a Predetermined Brush Position.—Figure 10-12 illustrates how to lay out the coil connections so that hard neutral falls halfway between the centers of the stator pole groups.   The procedure is as follows (the use of squared paper is recommended):

1. There are two coils per slot, and the coil throw is 1 and 7; therefore, draw two straight lines in slot 1 and two more in slot 7 to represent the coils.

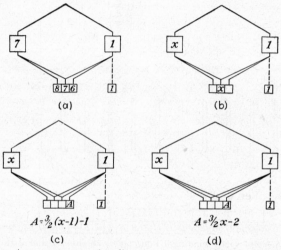

(a)   (b)

$A = \frac{3}{2}(x-1)-1$ $A = \frac{3}{2}x - 2$

(c)   (d)

Fig. 10-13.—Armature connection diagrams for lap windings.   (*a*) For the winding of Fig. 10-12.   (*b*) For any simplex winding with two bars per slot having a coil throw of 1 and *x*.   (*c*) For any simplex winding with three bars per slot, having an even coil throw (*x* is an odd number).   (*d*) For any simplex winding with three bars per slot, having an odd coil throw (*x* is an even number).

2. Draw a center line halfway between slots 1 and 7 as shown; this center line will fall either in another slot or on a tooth, depending upon whether the coil spans an even or an odd number of slots.   In Fig. 10-12, the throw is even, and the center line falls in a slot.

3. On a separate piece of scratch paper, draw the end connections of these two coils (as shown by full lines), making a picture similar to Fig. 10-13*b* except that the bars will not be numbered; note that from these two coils there will be three connections to the commutator (these are the connections to bars 6, 7, and 8, but we have not yet determined the numbering of these bars).

4. The center of these three commutator connections must coincide with the center line just drawn, *i.e.*, must fall halfway between slots 1 and 7. Therefore, we draw in a commutator bar with its own center line halfway between slots 1 and 7 and then draw in the rest of the bars.

5. We then number the bars as indicated. Further illustrative examples are given in Fig. 10-13, and simple rules are given therein for making up other **armature connection diagrams** in accordance with the principles just outlined.

The principle just outlined is valid for any combination; Fig. 10-13 is a short cut for arriving at the same result and is applicable to the majority of cases likely to be encountered.

If it is desired to have hard neutral fall in some position other than halfway between poles, the procedure is as follows: Lay out the armature connections as just described. Now, if hard neutral is to come one bar farther to the right, move all the commutator connections one bar to the right—*i.e.*, in Fig. 10-12, the commutator connections from the two coil sides in slot 1 will fall on bars 5 and 6 instead of on bars 6 and 7, as now shown. If hard neutral is to fall with brushes in the centers of the stator coils, the commutator connections in Fig. 10-12 will all have to be moved ½ pole pitch, or $56/(2 \times 4) = 7$ commutator bars, either to the right or to the left; *i.e.*, the connections now on bars 6 and 7 will then be on bars 55 and 56 or on bars 13 and 14.

10-17. Number of Brush Arms Required with a Lap Winding.— In any repulsion-type induction motor with a simplex lap-wound armature, not cross-connected, there must be as many brushes as there are poles, and these brushes must be spaced 1 pole pitch or 180 electrical degrees apart. The spacing, in mechanical degrees, is

> Two-pole motor—180 deg
> Four-pole motor—90 deg
> Six-pole motor—60 deg
> Eight-pole motor—45 deg

If the winding is cross-connected at every bar, two brushes may be sufficient regardless of the number of poles.

10-18. Cross-connected Lap Windings. *a. Cross Connections.*— Lap or parallel windings are frequently cross-connected at every bar. That is, all the commutator bars which are supposedly at the same potential are connected together. The bars at the same potential are

$$\text{Bar 1 and bar} \left(\frac{\text{number of commutator bars}}{\text{number of pairs of poles}} + 1 \right) \quad (10\text{-}1)$$

If the commutator has 56 bars and is wound for four poles, the bars to be connected together are

1 and 29
2 and 30
3 and 31
etc.

The most convenient way to make these cross connections is to use short lengths of double or triple cotton-covered wire *that has not been enameled,* for it is then unnecessary to scrape off the enamel. The cross-connection wires should be of the same gauge as the armature winding so that they will fit snugly into the sawed slots in the commutator necks. It is advisable to cross-connect the commutator before the armature is wound.

b. Sticking Brushes and Number of Brush Arms Required.—When all bars are cross-connected, it is necessary to use only two adjacent brushes, as pointed out in Art. 10-17, regardless of the number of poles.

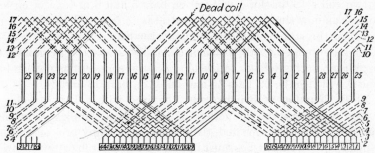

Fig. 10-14.—A simplex wave winding, four poles, 28 slots, 1 and 7 throw, 55 bars, one dead coil, commutator throw 1 and 29.

Four brushes may, however, be used in a four-pole motor with a cross-connected armature; in such a case, any two adjacent brushes can stick in their holders without any noticeable damage to torque or to performance. But, if the armature is not cross-connected and if a single brush sticks, the motor is likely to *fail to start.* In other words, the number of brushes actually required for a lap-wound cross-connected armature is the same as for a wave winding (see Art. 10-24).

10-19. The Simplex Wave Winding.—A simplex wave winding is shown in Fig. 10-14. It is comparable to the lap winding of Fig. 10-12 inasmuch as it is wound for four poles and has 56 wound coils; however, one coil is a dead coil, and there are only 55 commutator bars instead of 56. (A **dead coil** is a coil that is not connected in the circuit; its ends are taped. It is used to preserve the balance of the armature.) Note that the wave winding progresses around the armature in quite a different fashion from the lap winding. The lap winding progresses from one coil to the next and closes on itself after going once around the armature; in going once around the armature, the entire winding is traversed. The wave winding progresses from slot 1 to slot 7, thence to slots 15 to 21 under the next two poles, and thence back to the second coil side of slot 1; in other words, the simplex wave winding progresses around the armature, including one coil side under every pole, and comes back to a commutator bar adjacent to the one from which it started; it progresses as many times around the armature as necessary to include all the coil sides and then recloses upon itself.

In progressing around the armature, the winding touches all the commutator bars, before reclosing, in the following order: 1–29–2–30– 3–31–4–32–5–33–6–34–7–35–8–36–9–37–10–38–11–39–12–40–13–41– 14–42–15–43–16–44–17–45–18–46–19–47–20–48–21–49–22–50–23–51– 24–52–25–53–26–54–27–55–28–1. The winding closes on itself when it comes back to bar 1.

10-20. Progressive and Retrogressive Wave Windings.—The winding of Fig. 10-14 passes around the armature to the *left* and comes back to bar 2, the adjacent bar to the *left* of the starting point. This is a **progressive winding.** If the winding, after passing once around the armature, had returned to bar 55, the winding would have been known as a **retrogressive winding.** It may be well to mention here that, in repulsion motors where the armature currents are *induced*, either a retrogressive or a progressive winding will give the same direction of rotation; but in a d-c motor, or in any other type of motor wherein current is *conducted* directly into the armature, the two types of windings will give opposite directions of rotation. In a four-pole repulsion motor, a retrogressive winding generally is to be preferred to a progressive winding, for it gives fewer crossovers of the commutator connections.

The progress of a simplex retrogressive winding around the commutator bars would be: 1–28–55–27–54–26–53, etc. (Note that this progress chart is the same as the progress chart in Art. 10-19 in inverse order.)

10-21. Wave Windings—Number of Dead Coils and Commutator Throw.—Lap windings do not need to use dead coils, and the ends of a single coil are always connected to adjacent commutator bars (in simplex windings). Dead coils are common in wave windings, and the ends of all active coils are connected to bars approximately 360 electrical degrees apart. A simple rule for progressive wave windings is as follows:

$$\frac{\text{Number of coils} + 1}{\text{Number of pairs of poles}} = \text{quotient and remainder} \qquad (10\text{-}2)$$

Quotient = commutator throw (also called commutator pitch)   (10-3)

Remainder = number of dead coils   (10-4)

Number of commutator bars = (total number of coils) −

(number of dead coils)   (10-5)

For example, assume that a four-pole winding is to be placed in a 28-slot armature with two coils per slot or 56 coils total.

From Eqs. (10-2), to (10-5),

$$\frac{56 + 1}{2} = 28 \text{ with a remainder of } 1$$

Commutator throw = 28 bars or 1 and 29

Number of dead coils = 1

Number of commutator bars = 56 − 1 = 55

Now, compare this example with Fig. 10-14.

A similar rule for retrogressive windings is as follows:

$$\frac{\text{Number of coils} - 1}{\text{Number of pairs of poles}} = \text{quotient and remainder} \qquad (10\text{-}6)$$

Then Eqs. (10-3) to (10-5) apply.

Sometimes a retrogressive winding will lead to the use of fewer dead coils than a progressive winding, and vice versa. For example, attempt to put a six-pole winding into 29 slots with two bars per slot, or 58 coils. If the winding is progressive,

$$\frac{58 + 1}{3} = \frac{59}{3} = 19 \text{ with a remainder of } 2$$

and there are two dead coils. If the winding is retrogressive,

$$\frac{58 - 1}{3} = \frac{57}{3} = 19$$

and there are no dead coils.

10-22. Wave Windings—Coil Connections to the Commutator.— Refer now to Fig. 10-14. The **commutator throw** is 28 bars, or 1 and 29, as previously figured, which means that the ends of one of the coils lying in slots 1 and 7 are connected to bars 1 and 29 and the ends of the other coil to bars 2 and 30, as shown in solid lines in the figure. It is a simple matter, then, to connect the remainder of the coils, except that it must be remembered that one coil is dead and that its ends must be taped up. Which coil is taped up as dead is not of paramount importance, although its location has a minor effect on the neutral position; some tape up the dead coil first and then proceed to connect the remainder, and others tape up the last coil. In Fig. 10-14, one-fourth of the coils are connected, and then the next coil is made the dead one.

10-23. How to Lay Out Coil Connections of a Wave Winding for a Predetermined Brush Position.—Figure 10-14 is connected so that hard neutral is obtained when the brushes are midway between the centers of the stator coils, as in Fig. 10-12. To determine similar coil connections for any other winding, the procedure is illustrated by showing how Fig. 10-14 was derived: By using Eqs. (10-2) and (10-3), the commutator throw was found to be 28. The first coil lying in slots 1 and 7 was connected to bars 1 and 29 and the second coil to bars 2 and 30. The next step is to locate bar 1 with respect to slot 1. There have been made so far connections to four commutators bars, *viz.*, 1, 2, 29, 30. The center of these four bars must coincide with the center of the coils, *i.e.*, must fall halfway between slots 1 and 7. To meet this condition, bar 1 should be exactly as far to the right of slot 1 as bar 30 is to the left of slot 7. This consideration fixes the position of the bars with respect to the slots, and it is readily found that the mica between bars 9 and 10 falls opposite the center of slot 1.

Illustrative **armature connection diagrams** for wave windings are given in Fig. 10-15. These diagrams were derived by following the procedure described in the preceding paragraph and are to be considered merely as short cuts to facilitate making up the more common connection diagrams. To illustrate the use of these "short-cut" diagrams, let us check the winding of Fig. 10-14, where

$$x = 7$$
$$y = 28 \text{ (an even number, therefore use Fig. 10-15a)}$$
$$A = {}^{28}\!/_{2} + 2 - 7 = 9$$

It will be noted that bar 9 in Fig. 10-14 corresponds to bar A in Fig. 10-15a.

The diagrams just given will make hard neutral occur when the brushes are midway between the centers of the stator coils.

To obtain hard neutral in any position other than with the brushes midway between stator coils, lay out the connections as outlined in the preceding paragraphs, and then move all the connections on the commutator as many bars to the right or to the left as desired in order to move the brush position for neutral to the right or to the left, respectively. Often armatures are deliberately connected one or two bars off neutral.

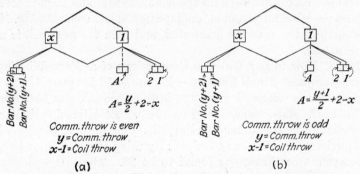

FIG. 10-15.—Armature connection diagrams for simplex wave windings with two coils (four coil sides) per slot. The winding may be full pitch or chorded.

10-24. Number of Brush Arms Required by a Wave Winding.—A wave winding requires only two brush arms, regardless of the number of poles. The spacing in mechanical degrees is

> Two-pole motor—180 deg
> Four-pole motor—90 deg
> Six-pole motor—60 or 180 deg
> Eight-pole motor—45 or 135 deg

Sometimes more brushes are used to keep down the current density in the brushes. When there are as many brushes as there are poles, the former are uniformly spaced 1 pole pitch apart. Four brushes are sometimes used for six-pole machines and also for eight-pole machines.

10-25. Number of Circuits in a Wave Winding.—A simplex wave winding has only two circuits, regardless of the number of poles. Therefore, since there are four circuits in Fig. 10-12 and two circuits in Fig. 10-14, the lap winding must have twice as many turns per coil as the wave winding for the same voltage from brush to brush or from bar to bar.

10-26. Dead Bars Used with a Wave Winding.—Sometimes a 55-bar commutator is required, and only a 56-bar commutator is available. In such a case, two adjacent bars can be connected together and used as a single bar. This procedure may reduce the locked-rotor torque,

particularly in one position of the rotor, but it is a justifiable emergency procedure.

10-27. Duplex Windings.—A **duplex winding** is a winding having twice as many circuits as a simplex winding. A duplex wave winding always has four circuits, regardless of the number of poles. How such a winding is arranged may be seen by referring to Art. 10-19, in which a simplex wave winding of 55 bars and 28 slots was described; if an armature had 110 bars and 56 slots, the simplex winding of Art. 10-19 could be put into alternate slots. After this winding was in place, a second winding identical with the first could be placed in the 28 empty slots, using the 55 unused bars. There would, therefore, be two electrically distinct windings on the armature. Such a winding would be a **duplex doubly reentrant** winding. If one starts at any conductor, the winding closes on itself after *only half the winding is traversed;* it is necessary to "enter" the winding a second time to traverse the remainder of the winding, hence the name doubly reentrant. A doubly reentrant winding closes upon itself twice.

A **singly reentrant duplex winding** is a duplex winding that closes upon itself once and only once.

The serviceman should note with caution that it is perfectly possible purely through accident to connect up a wave-wound armature to give a duplex winding. For example, suppose the winding of Fig. 10-14 had been connected to 55 bars with a commutator throw of 1 and 28 instead of 1 and 29. The result would have been a simplex two-circuit retrogressive winding. Suppose, however, that 56 bars were used, that the dead coil were not taped up, and that the commutator throw were again made 1 and 28; in this case, the result would be a duplex four-circuit retrogressive singly reentrant winding.

What is a simple test enabling one to identify a duplex winding? If there are 55 bars and the commutator throw is 27 bars or 1 and 28, the winding progresses

$$1\text{--}28\text{--}55$$

That is, after going once around the armature, the winding returns to bar 55, *which is adjacent to bar 1,* the starting point; this is the test for a simplex wave winding. Suppose now that there are 56 bars and that the commutator throw is again 1 and 28. Again the winding progresses

$$1\text{--}28\text{--}55$$

But this time bar 55 is not adjacent to the starting point, for bar 56 is between 1 and 55; this is the test for a duplex wave winding.

For further information on multiplex windings, the reader is referred to a more detailed treatise on the subject.[2]

10-28. Points to Note before Stripping an Armature.—It is probable that most service shops have their own system for marking and recording the connections of an armature winding. Braymer and Roe suggest a system in elaborate detail in Chap. II of their book.[1] Some of the important things to record are

1. Make an armature connection diagram (similar to those of Fig. 10-13 or 10-15).
2. Number of turns per coil.
3. Size of wire and kind of insulation used. If there are two strands per conductor, record the size of both strands.
4. Number of commutator bars.
5. Is commutator cross-connected (lap-wound armatures only)?
6. Number of wires per bar.
7. Distance commutator is pressed on shaft.
8. Thickness and kind of slot insulation.
9. Any other details noted that might be of importance.

10-29. Checking the Rewound Armature. *a. Commutator.*— Before rewinding an armature, test the commutator itself for grounds or for short circuits between bars. To test for grounds, wrap a few turns of a fine-gauge bare copper wire around the commutator, taking care to see that the wire touches all bars; then test from the wire to ground or from any bar to ground. Remove the wire and light-out between every bar with a 115-volt lighting-out light.

b. Check Winding before Soldering Connections.—It is suggested that the winding be thoroughly checked after the connections are made but before the connections are soldered in the commutator necks.

c. Short Circuits.—Short-circuited coils usually can be detected by means of a growler. The armature is placed in the growler and rotated slowly, while an iron knife, or other light piece of iron or steel, is held over the top of the slowly revolving armature. If a coil is short-circuited, the two slots in which the two sides of the short-circuited coil lie will attract the keeper. If the armature is assembled in the stator, there is another method of checking for a short-circuited armature coil; this method is described in Table XXVIII, Sec. *A*, 19.

d. Open-circuited Coils.—While the armature is being slowly rotated by hand in the growler, every pair of adjacent bars in the commutator can be successively short-circuited by means of the knife or by the keeper used in the test for short circuits. If the knife is kept in approximately the same position while the armature is rotated, the same amount of sparking should be observed between every pair of bars. If a coil is open, no spark can be obtained.

e. Reversed Coils with Direct Current and a Compass.—Apply low-voltage direct current from a battery, or other source, to two adjacent bars. Place a compass over a slot that gives the most definite action of the compass, and note the direction the needle points. Rotate the armature one bar, apply the same direct current to the next two adjacent bars, and note the direction the compass needle points. Continue until all bars have been checked. The compass should show up any reversed coils.

f. Reversed Coils by Use of a Growler and Wattmeter.—Another way to check for reversed coils is by using a wattmeter in conjunction with the growler. The armature is placed in a growler as in the preceding tests. The potential coil of a wattmeter is connected across the growler coil. The current coil is successively connected across each pair of adjacent bars by means of special pointed electrodes arranged for this purpose. The connections should be made by moving the armature but holding the test leads in approximately the same position. The deflections obtained with each coil should all be *in the same direction* and approximately the same in magnitude. If two ends of a coil are reversed, the fact will be indicated by a negative wattmeter reading. For such a test, a wattmeter with the zero in the center of the scale is preferable.

If a wattmeter sufficiently sensitive to obtain a readable deflection cannot be obtained, a slightly different hookup may give better results. Connect the current coil in series with a suitable current-limiting resistor which will limit the current to the rated ampere value of the current coil of the wattmeter; connect the current coil and its current-limiting resistor across the line in parallel with the growler, and connect the two potential leads across the bars. If too much deflection is obtained, the current in the current coil can be reduced by increasing the resistance of the series resistor.

It goes without saying that the connections should be carefully checked against the armature connection diagram to see that (1) the throw of the coils is correct, (2) the commutator is located correctly, and (3) the commutator throw is correct.

CONSTRUCTIONAL FEATURES AND CARE

10-30. Mark Position of End Shield.—Before any repulsion-start motor is dismantled for any purpose whatsoever, the position of the front (commutator) end shield with respect to the stator or to the frame must be marked carefully and positively. An excellent way to mark the position is by means of a cold chisel, a mark being made simultaneously on the frame and on the end shield as shown at *B* in Fig. 10-20. Often the manufacturer makes this mark himself. When the motor is reassembled, care should be taken to line up these marks exactly, for a serious loss in repulsion torque may be encountered unless the brushes are set correctly.

10-31. Commutators. *a. Radial and Axial Types.*—There are two principal types of commutator construction, **radial** and **axial.** The **radial type** is illustrated in Fig. 10-19; it presents its wearing surface in a plane perpendicular to the shaft, and the working surfaces of the commutator bars are wedge-shaped. This type of commutator is used principally in brush-lifting motors. The commutator in Fig. 10-2 is an **axial** commutator; it is cylindrically shaped, and the brushes ride on the outside of the cylindrical surface. This type of commutator is used more commonly on brush-riding motors.

b. Undercutting.—It is common practice to cut the mica away about $\frac{1}{32}$ in. below the working surface of the commutator by means of a small high-speed saw. The principal purpose of this undercutting is to eliminate high mica. **High mica** is a result of the wearing away of the commutator faster than the mica between bars. If the brushes carry no current, the mica and copper wear equally, but when current passes from commutator to brush, or vice versa, the copper frequently wears away faster than the mica. Undercutting generally is to be recommended to improve the life of the brushes and commutator; it may possibly minimize the radio interference during the starting period although it tends to make the brushes noisier. If the commutator was originally undercut by the manufacturer, the wisest policy for the serviceman is to keep it undercut.

10-32. Short-Circuiters.—A **short-circuiter** is a mechanism that short-circuits the armature coils or otherwise connects them to give the equivalent of a squirrel-cage winding. Types and designs vary somewhat; three specific types are described in the following paragraphs.

a. Master.—A Master short-circuiter is illustrated in Fig. 10-16. The device itself is shown in Fig. 10-16*a*; there are a large number of copper segments which are restrained from moving radially by means of a garter spring. In Fig. 10-16*b*, the position of these short-circuiting segments is shown when the motor is at rest. In Fig. 10-16*c*, the position of these segments when the motor is running is shown; centrifugal force has caused the segments to move in a radial direction against the commutator, short-circuiting the latter. Centrifugal force holds the short-circuiting segments against the commutator which is grooved to accomplish this result; the groove also limits the outer travel of the segments.

(a)   (b)   (c)

Fig. 10-16.—A Master short-circuiter. (*Courtesy of Master Electric Company.*) (a) The device itself. (b) Position when the motor is at rest. (c) Position when the motor is running.

b. Westinghouse.—Westinghouse slug-type short-circuiters are illustrated in Fig. 10-17. The action of the device can be understood by referring to Fig. 10-18, a sectional drawing of the short-circuiter. When the rotor begins to turn, the slugs tend to fly outward, bearing against the guide ring at the point C. At a predetermined speed, the centrifugal force acting on end portions B of the slugs overcomes the

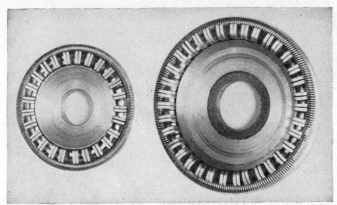

Fig. 10-17.—Westinghouse slug-type short-circuiters. (*Courtesy of Westinghouse Electric Corporation.*)

resistance of the garter spring, and the point C moves forward into contact with the end of the commutator, which is machined to a smooth surface. The slugs pivot about A. After B has moved out a short distance, the garter spring moves in, and the balance of the travel is snappy in action because the lever arm of the garter spring which restrains the movement is less after the spring has moved in toward the commutator.

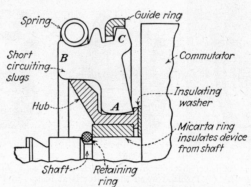

Fig. 10-18.—Sectional drawing of the slug-type short-circuiter. (*Courtesy of Westinghouse Electric Corporation.*)

Fig. 10-19.—Sectional view of the armature of a brush-lifting, repulsion-start, induction motor.   (*Courtesy of Wagner Electric Corporation.*)

a. Short-circuiting ring.	i. Brushes (connected pair).
b. Short-circuiting necklace.	j. Index pointer.
c. Spring barrel.	k. Spring-barrel extension.
d. Governor-weight rod.	l. Governor spring.
e. Governor-weight bumper.	m. Brush spring.
f. Governor weight.	n. Commutator.
g. Thrust washers.	o. Spring-barrel extension washer.
h. Rocker-arm brush-holder assembly.	

c. Wagner.—A somewhat different type of short-circuiter is shown in Fig. 10-19. The commutator is of the radial type. Between the commutator and armature laminations is a *short-circuiting ring* as shown. Inside the short-circuiting ring is carried a *necklace* of copper segments on a *spring barrel.* During the starting period, the short-circuiting necklace is not in contact with the commutator bars, the *governor spring* holding the spring barrel in the position shown. When the motor reaches a predetermined speed, the *governor weights* actuate the *governor-weight rods,* forcing the spring barrel forward until the short-circuiting necklace connects the commutator bars and the short-circuiting ring, thus short-circuiting all the commutator bars and making the motor operate as an induction motor.

10-33. Brush-lifting Mechanism.—The brush-lifting mechanism, if used, is usually made in conjunction with the short-circuiting device, as illustrated in Fig. 10-19. As pointed out in the preceding paragraph, the governor weights actuate the push rods to the left, forcing the spring barrel forward, which moves the brush holder forward, "lifting" the brushes away from the commutator.

10-34. Brush-holder Mechanisms.—The majority of repulsion-start motors are designed to be reversed by shifting the position of the brushes, and the brush holders are designed with that end in view. Also, provision has to be made to short-circuit the brushes upon each other. There are two popular types of construction, *viz.,* rocker-ring and cartridge type.

a. Rocker Ring.—In the rocker-ring type of construction, which resembles in principle the rocker rings used in large d-c machines, brush holders are mounted on an adjustable ring or circular plate. This rocker ring is referred to under various names, including **brush-holder plate, brush plate, brush ring,** and **brush-carrier ring;** Nema uses the term **brush yoke.**

b. Cartridge Type.—In Fig. 10-23 is illustrated a motor using a cartridge-type brush holder. In this motor, there are two brushes spaced 90 deg apart, and the brushes are carried in two holders.

c. Number of Brushes and Spacing Required.—For lap-wound armatures, not cross-connected, refer to Art. 10-17.

For lap-wound cross-connected armatures, refer to Art. 10-18.

For wave-wound armatures, refer to Art. 10-24.

10-35. How to Reverse a Motor Using a Rocker Ring.—Motors provided with a rocker ring usually are arranged so that the latter can be moved circumferentially to any position; means are provided for locking this rocker ring in any desired position. Two or three positions

of the rocker ring are marked in some manner or other.   If there are
three positions marked, the central position indicates the location of
the brushes for hard neutral; *the brushes must never be left in the neutral
position!*   If the rocker ring is turned in a clockwise direction to one

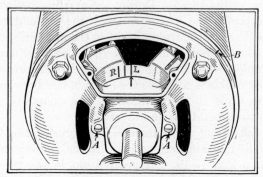

FIG. 10-20.—How to reverse a Marathon type SR motor.   (*Courtesy of Marathon
Electric Manufacturing Company.*)

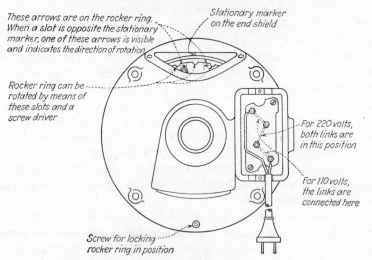

FIG. 10-21.—How to reverse a General Electric type RSA motor.   (*Courtesy of General
Electric Company.*)

of the other three positions, the motor will start and run in a clockwise
direction.   If the rocker ring is turned counterclockwise to the other
position, the motor will start and run counterclockwise.   If only two
positions of the rocker ring are marked, they are for opposite directions
of rotation.   In the following paragraphs, a few specific examples are
given.

a. Marathon Type SR *Motor.*—Refer to Fig. 10-20. Remove the small cover plate from the end shield by removing the round-head screws (cover and screws not shown). Loosen the setscrew clamping the brush-holder ring. On motors of ½ hp and larger, there are two screws, marked *A* in the figure, which must be loosened to unlock the rocker ring. If mark *L* is at the index mark, the motor will rotate counterclockwise facing the shaft-extension end, or clockwise when facing the end opposite the shaft extension; the mark *R* gives the opposite direction of rotation. After the rocker ring is set to the desired position, *lock it firmly in place,* and replace the cover.

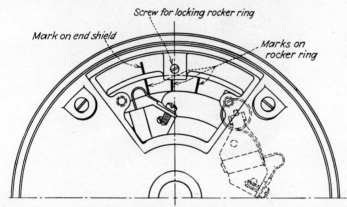

Fig. 10-22.—How to reverse a Westinghouse type AR motor. (*Courtesy of Westinghouse Electric Corporation.*)

b. General Electric Type RSA *Motor, Form* C.—Refer to Fig. 10-21. In this figure, the rocker ring is shown in the *central* position *i.e.,* on hard neutral; when shifted to either of the other two positions, an arrow on the rocker ring indicates the direction of rotation.

c. Westinghouse Types AR *and* FR *Motors.*—Refer to Fig. 10-22. *The screw for locking rocker ring, the mark on the end shield,* and *three marks on the rocker ring* are all visible. This motor is reversed as described in the first paragraph of this article. A similar arrangement is used for the type FR motors.

The examples just given should be sufficient to show the principles involved.

10-36. How to Reverse a Motor with Cartridge-type Brush Holders.—In Fig. 10-23, a motor using cartridge-type brush holders is illustrated. The direction of rotation is indicated by an arrow on top of each brush holder. This motor is a four-pole motor, and both arrows must point in the same direction. The brush holders are held

in position by two screws, as shown. At each brush position, there
are two holes through the end shield; the brush-holder cartridge passes

FIG. 10-23.—Repulsion-start induction motor with cartridge-type brush holders.
(*Courtesy of Westinghouse Electric Corporation.*)

through one of these two holes. To reverse the direction of rotation:
remove the four screws; withdraw the brush holders complete, turn
them around 180 deg, and insert them in the other two respective
holes in the end shield; and replace the four screws.
The motor then should run in the opposite direction.

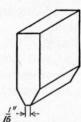

FIG. 10-24.—
Wedge-shaped
brush used for
setting neutral.

10-37. Checking or Setting Neutral. *a. Use
Wedge-shaped Brushes.*—The neutral position normally
is located and set by the manufacturer. If, however,
a motor is rewound, or even if it is dismantled and
reassembled, it is advisable to check the neutral
setting. The greater the number of poles, the more
important it is that the neutral be set correctly. The
brushes used for this purpose should be shaped in the
form of a wedge so that only a line contact can be
formed between the brush and commutator; this line of contact should
come at the center of the brush. A properly shaped brush is shown
in Fig. 10-24.

b. Checking Neutral—Motor with a Rocker Ring.—In Figs. 10-20 to 10-22, the setting of the rocker ring is plainly marked where neutral is supposed to occur. Using wedge-shaped brushes in all holders, set the brushes in the central position, and excite the stator; the armature should not rotate, but only a very slight movement of the brushes in either direction will cause the armature to rotate in the same direction.

c. Setting Neutral—Motor with a Rocker Ring.—If it is found that the neutral does not occur with the rocker ring in the center position, two different courses of procedure are open:

1. Lock the rocker ring in the central position, loosen the end-shield bolts, and turn the end shield slightly away from the direction of rotation of the armature. Continue turning the end-shield until the position is found where the armature will not rotate in either direction, and tighten up the end-shield bolts, locking the end shield in position. The rocker ring should then be shifted to one of the other two positions, depending upon the desired direction of rotation.

2. Turn the rocker ring in the end shield until the neutral position is found. Opposite the center of the three marks on the rocker ring, make a new mark to indicate the neutral setting, and obliterate the old mark. Then set either one of the other two markers on the rocker ring opposite this new stationary mark. It is necessary to use this procedure instead of (1) if the original stationary mark was on the frame instead of on the end shield or if it is not possible to turn the end shield far enough to find the neutral position. *Great care must be taken in setting neutral; this point is vitally important!*

d. Motors with Cartridge-type Brush Holders.—If cartridge-type brush holders are used, as in Fig. 10-23, the foregoing procedure is not applicable. The neutral position can be checked, preferably using wedge-shaped brushes, by measuring the torque and stator current in both directions of rotation at approximately 50 rpm. The torque and stator current at 50 rpm are measured first in one direction; next the brush holders are removed and turned around, and the torque and stator current are then measured in the opposite direction of rotation. The torques and stator currents should both be the same for each direction of rotation; if they are not the same, it is necessary to loosen the end-shield bolts and turn the end shield until this position is found. (It will be noted by referring to Fig. 10-6 that the torque may be the same for two different values of brush shift, but the corresponding stator currents would not be equal.)

10-38. Replacement of Brushes. *a. Grades.*—In general, whenever it is necessary to replace brushes, service shops should make an intensive and honest effort to use a new brush that is an exact duplicate of the original brush supplied by the manufacturer, in size, grade, and brand.   The proper brush to use has been determined by the manufacturer after a series of more exhaustive tests than the usual service shop can hope to make.   Successful substitutions of one brush for another undoubtedly are being made every day in many service shops, but care and judgment in these substitutions must be exercised. The safest rule, however, is to avoid these substitutions wherever and whenever possible.

b. Seating Brushes.—New brushes should be seated on the commutator.   Hold a piece of fine sandpaper so that it fits partly around the commutator, and insert the brush in the holder in which it is to be used.   Pushing radially against the brush with one hand, with the other hand rotate the commutator and sandpaper together in the direction the motor is to run.   Release the brush pressure, and turn the armature and sandpaper backward; then push against the brush and again rotate the commutator and sandpaper in the direction the motor is to run.   Repeat this process until the brush fits the commutator perfectly.   If the brush is properly seated, it should be shiny all over the contact surface after the motor has been in use for a short time.   If the motor has been disassembled for any reason, it will often be found easier to seat the brushes before the motor is reassembled, using only the armature and front end shield.   The use of a brush-seating compound which is an abrasive powder applied to the commutator surface is not recommended.

Another method of seating brushes is by scraping them—somewhat like scraping a bearing.   Run the motor long enough to develop shiny spots on the brushes; stop the motor, remove the brushes, and with a sharp-edged instrument carefully scrape off all polished spots. Again run the motor, and repeat the process just described until the brush is seated—*i.e.*, until it takes a polish over its entire surface. In some cases, particularly for very small motors, this method is easier than sandpapering.

10-39. Care and Maintenance—General.—In addition to the same care and attention as to lubrication, etc., required by all types of fractional horsepower motors, repulsion-start motors require attention to other features.

a. Commutator and Brushes.—If the commutator is dirty and blackened, it can be wiped off with a rag or cleaned with fine sandpaper (when running) but *never with emery*, because emery particles are conducting.   If the commutator is badly pitted and grooved, it is advisable to remove the armature and "true-up" the commutator on a lathe. If the commutator was originally undercut, it will be necessary to undercut it again. In any case, if high mica has developed—a condition that can be determined by running the fingers over the commutator—the latter should be trued-up and undercut. No more material should be taken off than is absolutely necessary. The brushes should be inspected to see that they all move freely and easily and that all make contact with the commutator at normal pressure. Worn-out brushes should be replaced. If there are two brushes on a single pigtail, the latter should be examined to see that it is not broken or unduly frayed. The surfaces of the commutator against which the short-circuiter operates should be kept reasonably clean and bright.

b. Short-circuiter and Brush Lifter.—The short-circuiter is a vital part of the motor and should be kept clean and in good condition; it should operate to short-circuit the commutator at about 75 per cent of full-load speed. The commutator surfaces against which it acts should all be clean and not pitted. The brush-lifting mechanism should work freely and should not be allowed to become fouled with dirt or jammed in any way. If the governor weights have cushion stops to minimize noise, these cushions should be inspected and replaced if necessary.

Bibliography

1. BRAYMER, DANIEL H., and ROE, A. C.: "Rewinding Small Motors," 2d ed., McGraw-Hill Book Company, Inc., New York, 1932.
2. LANGSDORF, ALEXANDER S.: "Principles of Direct Current Machines," McGraw-Hill Book Company, Inc., New York, 1931.
3. HAMILTON, JAMES L.: The Repulsion-start Induction Motor, *A.I.E.E. Trans.*, Oct., 1915, pp. 2443–2474. Disc. 2475–2482.
4. TRICKEY, P. H.: Performance Calculations on Repulsion Motors, *A.I.E.E. Trans.*, vol. 60, 1941, pp. 67–73.

CHAPTER XI

REPULSION AND REPULSION INDUCTION MOTORS

Repulsion and repulsion induction motors are two modifications of the repulsion-type motor. These various types are often confused with one another. The repulsion-start induction motor was defined in Art. 10-1. The other two major types are defined in the following paragraphs.

11-1. Repulsion Motor Defined.—The A.S.A. defines a **repulsion motor** as follows:

A repulsion motor is a single-phase motor which has a stator winding arranged for connection to the source of power and a rotor winding connected to a commutator. Brushes on the commutator are short-circuited and are so placed that the magnetic axis of the rotor winding is inclined to the magnetic axis of the stator winding. This type of motor has a varying-speed characteristic.—ASA C42—1941. 10.10.410.

11-2. Repulsion Induction Motor Defined.—According to the A.S.A.:

A repulsion induction motor is a form of repulsion motor which has a squirrel-cage winding in the rotor in addition to the repulsion motor winding. A motor of this type may have either a constant-speed or varying-speed characteristic.—ASA—C42—1941. 10.10.430.

DUAL-VOLTAGE MOTORS

11-3. Dual-voltage Repulsion Motor.—The repulsion motor is a single-phase motor that starts and runs as a repulsion motor. The principles of operation of this type of motor are discussed in Arts. 10-4 to 10-6. A representative speed-torque curve is given in Fig. 11-1. These torque characteristics resemble those of the repulsion-start motor of Fig. 10-1 when the latter is operated on the starting connection. The straight repulsion motor is similar in construction to the repulsion-start motor which is described in Art. 10-3 except for the omission of the short-circuiter and the fact that there is, of course, no brush-lifting mechanism. The brushes of a straight repulsion motor are usually shifted 20 to 30 electrical degrees from **hard neutral**, as compared with the usual shift of 15 to 20 deg for the repulsion-start motor.

The straight repulsion motor is classified as a **varying-speed motor** because the operating speed depends upon the load and may vary widely with changes in load.

The **stator connection diagrams** for four-lead dual-voltage motors for two-, four-, six-, and eight-pole windings are shown in Figs. 10-7, 10-8, 10-9, and 10-10, respectively. The motor wiring and line connection diagrams for any of these stator connection diagrams are given in Fig. 10-11. It will be noted that these are the same diagrams discussed in Art. 10-8 and used for repulsion-start motors.

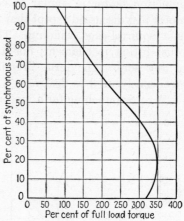

Fig. 11-1.—Speed-torque curve of a repulsion motor.

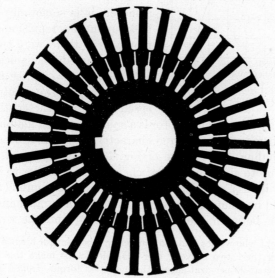

Fig. 11-2.—Rotor punching for a repulsion induction motor.

As to rewinding a straight repulsion motor, the considerations discussed in Arts. 10-9 to 10-11 apply. The discussion on armature windings (Arts. 10-12 to 10-29,) also applies to this type of motor.

11-4. Dual-voltage Repulsion Induction Motor.—The repulsion-induction motor is similar in construction to the straight repulsion motor just discussed except that, buried beneath the armature winding, is a squirrel-cage winding. This motor has no short-circuiter or brush-lifting mechanism; nor are there any centrifugal mechanisms of any sort. The term "repulsion induction" motor is sometimes erroneously used to designate a repulsion-start motor (see Art. 10-1).

A rotor punching for a motor of this type is illustrated in Fig. 11-2,

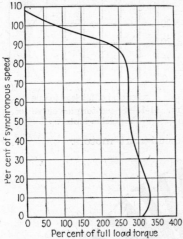

FIG. 11-3.—Speed-torque curve of a repulsion induction motor.

wherein can be seen the slots for putting in the repulsion winding and also the slots for the squirrel-cage winding. This squirrel cage may be wholly or partly made of copper, brass, or even iron, depending upon the torque characteristics desired. A typical speed-torque curve is shown in Fig. 11-3.

In order to gain a better understanding of the characteristics of such a motor, it is sometimes helpful to look upon the repulsion induction motor as if there were two distinct motors coupled mechanically to the same shaft; one of these motors is a straight repulsion motor having speed-torque characteristics similar to Fig. 11-1, and the second motor is a squirrel-cage single-phase induction motor having speed-torque characteristics similar to the "main (running) winding only" curve of Fig. 4-4. At any speed, these two torques add up to give a combined characteristic similar to Fig. 11-3.*

This analogy is wrong academically on at least two counts: (1) The two motors should be connected in series instead of in parallel and (2) there is interaction between the repulsion winding and the squirrel-cage

---

* Any student who wishes to do so can verify this point for himself by actually adding together these two curves. For example, let us make this addition on Fig. 11-1. Now at 20 per cent speed, the induction torque (from Fig. 4-4) is 25 per cent; then add 25 per cent (or half a large square) to the repulsion torque on Fig. 11-1, obtaining a new point. At a number of other speeds, such as 30, 40, and 50 per cent, read the induction torques from Fig. 4-4, and add them to the repulsion torques of Fig. 11-1, obtaining a series of points through which a new curve resembling Fig. 11-3 in shape can be drawn.

winding.   However, the comparison serves in a rough way to illustrate the principle of the repulsion induction motor.

The effect of the embedded squirrel cage is to give the motor more nearly the constant-speed characteristics and the high locked-rotor torque of the repulsion-start motor without the use of a short-circuiter. At no load, the repulsion induction motor usually will operate above synchronous speed and may actually run hotter than at full load. It can be classified as a constant-speed motor although the change in speed from no load to full load is slightly greater than in the case of the repulsion-start motor.   It generally has lower locked-rotor torque but better pull-up characteristics than the repulsion-start motor, and it has the advantage of requiring no short-circuiter or other automatic-switching means.   Moreover, this motor, with a suitable winding arrangement, can be used for **plugging service.**

This motor may use the same type of stator and armature, and the same connection diagrams for both stator and rotor as the repulsion-start motors described in Arts. 10-8 and 10-12 to 10-29.   As for rewinding this motor, the same general considerations discussed in Arts. 10-9 to 10-11 apply except that there is no short-circuiter to introduce complications.

ELECTRICALLY REVERSIBLE MOTORS FOR PLUGGING SERVICE*

11-5. Reversing Repulsion-type Motors Electrically.—Any of the three types of repulsion motors just discussed, *viz.*, repulsion-start, repulsion, and repulsion induction, can be reversed by shifting the brushes, and this is the usual method.   All three of these types may likewise be reversed by making changes in the stator connections—as intimated in Art. 10-4—*without changing* the brush position.   If the stator connections are suddenly changed to reverse the direction of rotation while the motor is running, the straight repulsion and also the repulsion induction motors will stop and then start up in the opposite direction, but the repulsion-start induction motor will continue running in the same direction unless the motor is allowed to slow down until the short-circuiter operates.

Instead of making changes in the connections of the stator windings, a different arrangement is sometimes used to obtain an electrically reversible motor of the repulsion type.   There is only one stator winding, the same as that shown in Fig. 10-11, and two sets of brushes. These two sets of brushes may both be on the same commutator or

* For a definition of these terms, see Glossary.

on two different commutators. For one direction of rotation, one set of brushes is short-circuited, and the other set is left open-circuited; and, for the opposite direction of rotation, the other set of brushes is short-circuited, and the first set is left open.

This type of reversal, *viz.*, from full speed in one direction to full speed in the opposite direction by a change of electrical connections, is known as **plugging.** Most of the types of single-phase motors discussed in this book so far will not plug, except for the motors of Arts. 5-30 and 7-8. In the case of general-purpose split-phase, capacitor-start, two-value capacitor, or repulsion-start motors, it is necessary to wait until the rotor has slowed down sufficiently to allow the centrifugal device to return the motor to the starting connection before the motor can be reversed electrically, unless a special control system such as described in Art. 5-30 is devised.

The repulsion induction motor is sometimes used for driving a lathe because it has essentially constant-speed characteristics and can be plugged. Likewise it, or the straight repulsion motor, may be used on such applications as valves, rheostats, or door openers, where the plugging characteristic is a necessity. The straight repulsion motor plugs much more energetically than does the repulsion induction motor.

Since the same stator winding arrangements can be used for either a repulsion or a repulsion induction motor, the winding arrangements that follow are applicable to either type of motor.

11-6. Electrically Reversible Motor with Single-phase Type of Winding.—In Fig. 10-4 is shown a repulsion-type motor with two

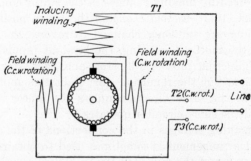

Fig. 11-4.—A three-lead, electrically reversible, repulsion or repulsion induction motor used for plugging service.

stator windings displaced 90 electrical degrees apart. This motor can be reversed by interchanging the two **field-winding** leads. A scheme that results in simpler connections is to use two field windings, as shown in Fig. 11-4, which may be considered and used as a **wiring and line connection diagram.** The **stator connection diagram** for a four-pole motor using this arrangement is Fig. 11-5. One field winding is inserted in the slots, there being one coil group for every pole; separators are inserted in the slots on top of the first winding, and a second field winding, identical with the first in distribution, wire size, and number of turns, is placed on top of the first winding. The **inducing winding** is then wound in the slots displaced 90 electrical degrees from the first two windings. An alternate method would be to wind the two field windings as a single winding with two strands in parallel. The insulation between strands would then have to be carefully tested.

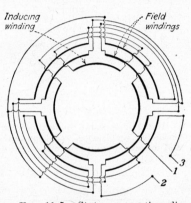

As for rewinding this type of motor, the same general considerations discussed in Arts. 10-9 to 10-11 apply, except that there is no short-circuiter to introduce complications.

11-7. Electrically Reversible Motor with Polyphase Type of Winding. *a. Balanced Polyphase Winding for 30-deg Shift.*—If the stator is wound as if for a three-phase star-connected winding with an equal number of coils per group and if the three leads are tagged *T*1, *T*2, and *T*3, the **wiring diagram** of Fig. 11-4 again is applicable. (It

FIG. 11-5.—Stator connection diagram for a four-pole, series-connected, electrically reversible, repulsion or repulsion induction motor.

may be found necessary to interchange tags *T*2 and *T*3 to make the direction of rotation agree with the figure.) In such cases, the two field windings and the inducing winding are all equal in number of turns, wire size, and distribution; and these three windings are spaced 120 electrical degrees apart. With this arrangement, a brush shift of 30 electrical degrees either side of neutral is invariably obtained.

b. Polyphase Winding with Unequal Coil Grouping.—If any brush shift other than 30 electrical degrees is desired with a polyphase type of winding, it is necessary to use unequal numbers of coils per group. For example, if a four-pole motor has 36 stator slots and 36 stator coils, there are 9 coils per pole or 9 coils for every three groups. The coils can then be grouped 2–5–2, 2–5–2, etc., and the *T*1 lead must be connected to a group containing 5 coils. This point is illustrated by means of the **stator connection diagram,** Fig. 11-6. With this arrangement, a brush shift of 20 electrical degrees either side of **hard neutral** is obtained.

c. Why a Coil Grouping of 2–5–2 Gives a Brush Shift of 20 *Electrical Degrees.*—It was simply stated in the preceding paragraph that a coil

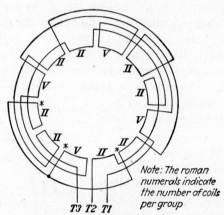

Note: The roman numerals indicate the number of coils per group

Fig. 11-6.—Stator connection diagram for a four-pole, series-connected, electrically reversible, repulsion or repulsion induction motor using a polyphase type of winding and unequal grouping of coils.

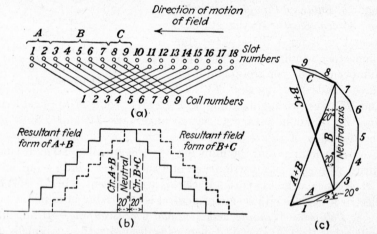

Fig. 11-7.—An electrically reversible repulsion or repulsion induction motor using a polyphase type of winding. (*a*) How the coil ends are connected and how the coils are grouped. (*b*) Resultant field forms shown by stepped waves. (*c*) Voltages induced in the coils of (*a*).

grouping of 2–5–2 gave a brush shift of 20 deg. The truth of this statement will be demonstrated. In Fig. 11-7*a* are represented the coils of a three-phase four-pole full-pitch winding with 36 stator slots.

Coils 1 and 2 are connected together for group A; coils 3 to 7, inclusive, are connected together for group B; and coils 8 and 9 for group C. Now, for one direction of rotation, groups A and B are connected in series to form the stator winding, and C is left idle; the field form for this condition is shown by the solid line in Fig. 11-7b. When B and C are connected in series and A is left idle, the field form is as represented by the dotted line in Fig. 11-7b. It is to be observed that the centers of the field forms are two slots (40 electrical degrees) apart and that either field is, therefore, displaced 20 electrical degrees from neutral.

Still another way to explain the 20-deg shift is as follows: Assume that there is a revolving field cutting the stator winding and that this field moves from right to left in Fig. 11-7a. Let 1, in Fig. 11-7c, represent the voltage induced in coil 1; 2 represents the voltage in coil 2, leading the voltage of coil 1 by 20 electrical degrees (1 stator slot = 20 deg) but equal to it in magnitude; similarly 3, 4, 5, etc., represent the voltages induced in coils 3, 4, 5, etc. The total voltage induced in A is 1 + 2 as shown; in like fashion, vectors representing B, $A + B$, and $B + C$ are drawn. The axis of B is the neutral axis. The axis of $A + B$ is displaced 20 deg from the neutral axis, and the axis of $B + C$ is likewise displaced 20 deg in the opposite direction from the neutral axis; therefore a brush shift of 20 electrical degrees either side of neutral is obtained.

d. How to Figure Equivalent Brush Shift with Unequal Coil Grouping. In general, if

B = total number of coils in group connected to $T1$ in Fig. 11-4

$A = C$ = total number of coils in groups connected to $T2$ and $T3$, respectively, in Fig. 11-4

P = number of poles

S = total number of stator coils

$$\text{Brush shift, in electrical degrees, } = \frac{AP}{S} \times 90 \qquad (11\text{-}1)$$

It is to be noted, however, that if Eq. (11-1) is to be valid,

$$A + B + C \text{ must equal } \frac{S}{P}$$

To illustrate the use of Eq. (11-1) by the example that has been discussed,

$$A = C = 2$$
$$B = 5$$
$$P = 4$$
$$S = 36$$

$$\text{Brush shift} = \frac{2 \times 4}{36} \times 90 = 20 \text{ deg}$$

11-8. Checking or Setting Neutral.—Install wedge-shaped brushes (see Fig. 10-24) in all the brush holders. Connect the power to leads $T1$ and $T2$, and find and mark the rocker-ring position for hard neutral (see Arts. 10-6, 10-37). When the brushes are in this position, the armature will not rotate; but a slight shift of the brushes in either direction will cause the armature to rotate in the same direction as the shift of the brushes. Now, connect the power to $T1$ and $T3$, and again find and mark the hard-neutral position. The brushes should be set and left halfway between these two positions.

A simpler but less reliable way is to connect $T2$ and $T3$ to the same line and $T1$ to the other line; now, find the hard-neutral position, which will be the correct position for the brushes, no further setting being necessary. This method has the one disadvantage that the hard neutral often is not so sharply defined. It is recommended that the method of the preceding paragraph be used in preference to this one.

OTHER TYPES OF REPULSION MOTORS

11-9. Synchronous Motor of the Repulsion Type.—A straight repulsion motor can be modified to operate as a synchronous motor. One way to accomplish this is to provide two collector rings, to which are connected taps from the armature winding or commutator. In a two-pole machine, there are two taps taken from points on the armature winding 180 deg apart. In a four-pole machine, the armature is tapped at four places 90 mechanical degrees apart, but there are only two collector rings as before; two diametrically opposite taps are connected to either ring. If the two collector rings are left open-circuited, the motor is a straight repulsion motor. If, however, the collector rings are short-circuited, the motor has definite synchronous tendencies; *i.e.*, over a certain range of loads, it will operate at synchronous speed. Much better characteristics will be obtained if the brushes are excited by direct current. With d-c excitation, the motor will operate at synchronous speed over a wider range of loads and will synchronize more readily. Moveover, the d-c excitation improves the power factor, reduces the line current, and gives more stable and satisfactory operation.

This motor was developed for driving a sound motion-picture projector and is described by Specht.[1] When a sound picture was shown, d-c excitation was used to hold the speed synchronous to maintain a true pitch; but the pictures could be speeded up by removing the d-c excitation and operating the motor as a repulsion motor. The variable speed was used when showing a silent picture. This type of motor was popular in the early days when sound and silent pictures were run on the same program.

11-10. Synchronous Motor of the Repulsion Induction Type.—A repulsion induction motor can be converted into a synchronous motor in much the same manner as any squirrel-cage induction motor (see Chap. XV) by cutting in the armature surface a number of equally (or approximately equally) spaced notches, there being as many notches as there are poles. A motor of this type is described by Haines,[2] who further increases the synchronizing torque by punching additional holes in the armature punchings *below* the repulsion winding slots; these additional holes are spaced halfway between the notches cut on the surface of the armature above the slots.

Bibliography

1. SPECHT, H. C.: The Synchronous-Repulsion Motor, *A.I.E.E. Trans.*, July, 1930, pp. 1027–1031.
2. HAINES, WILLIAM H.: Motors for Exact Speed Requirements, *Elec. Manufacturing*, February, 1934, pp. 24, 25.

CHAPTER XII

UNIVERSAL MOTORS

The universal motor has essentially the same performance and operating characteristics on alternating as on direct current. (The term "alternating current" here indicates frequencies of not over 60 cycles.) These motors are series-wound and have series characteristics on both alternating and direct current, except when governors are used to control the speed. With suitable governor control, the motors can be made to operate at constant speeds. Without governor control, the no-load speed is high; it may be as high as 10,000 or 20,000 rpm, but the armatures are designed so that they will not be damaged at these speeds. Continuous ratings up to as high as 1 hp are built; for intermittent service, ratings above 1 hp are built. The motors are usually designed for operating speeds of 3500 rpm or less, up to 10,000 or 15,000 rpm. At the higher speeds, better universal characteristics (*i.e.*, more nearly the same performance characteristics on both alternating and direct current) can be obtained, as well as more output per given weight of armature. A governor-controlled universal motor in use is illustrated in Fig. 12-1.

12-1. Universal Motor Defined.—The formal definition of a **universal motor** as given by the A. S. A., is as follows:

A universal motor is a series-wound or a compensated series-wound motor which may be operated either on direct current or single-phase alternating current at approximately the same speed and output. These conditions must be met when the direct-current and alternating-current voltages are approximately the same and the frequency of the alternating current is not greater than 60 cycles per second.—ASA C42—1941. 10.10.210.

12-2. Application and Torque Characteristics.—Very popular applications for universal motors are portable drills, saws, routers, vacuum cleaners, sewing machines, business machines of all kinds, home motion-picture projectors, food mixers, small washing machines, and many others. There are two major types of universal motors: **noncompensated** and **compensated**. The noncompensated motor usually is built with concentrated or salient poles. The speed-torque curve of a noncompensated concentrated-pole universal motor, for both a-c and d-c operation, is given in Fig. 12-2. Similar speed-torque curves for compensated motors are given in Fig. 12-3. It is to be noted that the compensated universal motor has better universal characteristics (*i.e.*, more nearly the same speed on both alternating and direct current) than the noncompensated motor. It is also to be

Fig. 12-1.—A governor-controlled universal motor driving an adding machine. (*Courtesy of Bodine Electric Company.*)

noted that the superiority of the compensated motor as regards universal characteristics is more marked at low speeds than at high speeds.

The noncompensated motor is less expensive and simpler in construction and is generally used for lower horsepower ratings and for higher speeds than the compensated motor, although there is an overlapping of ratings. Price is apt to be a deciding factor as to which type is used.

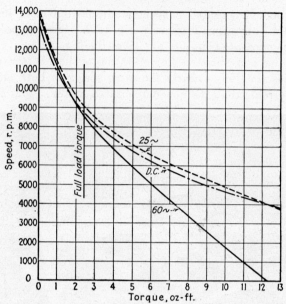

Fig. 12-2.—Speed-torque curves of a noncompensated concentrated-pole universal motor rated at ¼ hp, 8000 rpm.

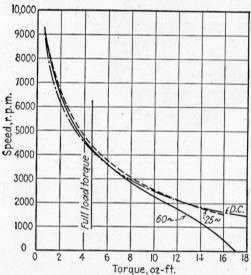

Fig. 12-3.—Speed-torque curves of a compensated universal motor rated at ¼ hp, 4000 rpm.

It is to be noted that with either type, the speed drops off rapidly with an increase in load and increases with a decrease in load. This characteristic is most desirable in vacuum-cleaner service; for, if the cleaner is used under conditions which decrease the volume of air handled, the load on the motor decreases. This decrease in motor load is accompanied by increased motor speed and increased vacuum, so that the cleaner will actually handle more air than it would if a constant-speed motor were used. Likewise, this characteristic of speeding

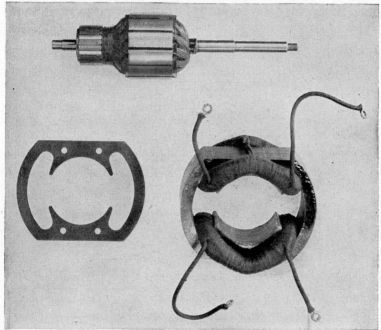

Fig. 12-4.—Parts for a concentrated-pole, noncompensated universal motor for a built-in application. (*Courtesy of Westinghouse Electric Corporation.*)

up on light loads is very desirable in the case of portable drills, for the motor will drive small drills at high speed and larger drills at a lower speed.

No industry-wide standards of horsepower and speed ratings have been established for universal motors, because these motors are often sold as sets of parts, because the choice of possible full-load operating speeds is virtually unlimited, and because most of the applications for them are highly specialized. However, the dimension standards in Table IX have been established by Nema.

TABLE IX.—STATOR CORE DIMENSIONS FOR UNIVERSAL MOTORS

Nominal outside diameter, in.*	Length of stacking, in.		
2.875	1	$1\frac{1}{4}$	$1\frac{5}{8}$
3.187	1	$1\frac{3}{8}$	$1\frac{3}{4}$
3.687	$1\frac{3}{8}$	$1\frac{3}{4}$	$2\frac{1}{8}$
4.125	$1\frac{1}{2}$	2	
4.375	$1\frac{3}{4}$	$2\frac{1}{8}$	$2\frac{1}{2}$
4.75	$2\frac{1}{4}$	$2\frac{3}{4}$	$3\frac{1}{4}$
5.5	$2\frac{1}{4}$	3	

* Tolerances for fits are negative; these are maximum dimensions.—From Nema Standards.

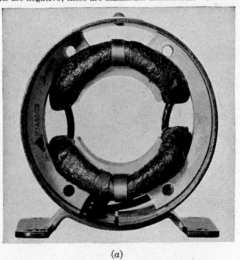

(a)

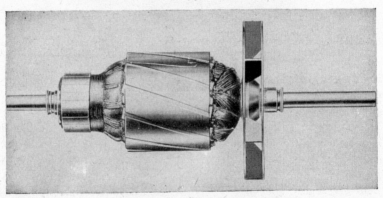

(b)

For descriptive legend see opposite page.

Standard shaft-extension diameters established by Nema are ¼, 5/16, ⅜, ½, ⅝ and ¾ in.; tolerances are the same as those given in Art. 20-9.

Standard direction of rotation is CCW facing end opposite shaft extension.

(c)

(d)

Fig. 12-5.—Exploded view of a universal motor. (*Courtesy of General Electric Company.*) (*a*) Stator structure, without brush holders. (*b*) Wound armature. (*c*) End shields. (*d*) Wound stator, with brush holders and leads.

12-3. Essential Parts of the Universal Motor. *a. The Concentrated-pole Noncompensated Motor.*—The parts for a concentrated-pole noncompensated universal motor for a built-in application are illustrated in Fig. 12-4. The shape of the stator punching and that of

FIG. 12-6.—Cutaway view of a noncompensated universal motor.   (*Courtesy of Westinghouse Electric Corporation.*)

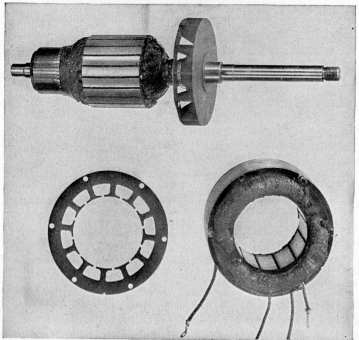

FIG. 12-7.—Parts for a distributed-field, compensated universal motor for a built-in application.   (*Courtesy of Westinghouse Electric Corporation.*)

the complete wound stator are shown. The armature has a commutator and is wound like the armature of a d-c motor or like the rotor of a repulsion-start induction motor. An exploded view of a complete motor of this type is shown in Fig. 12-5. A cutaway view of a complete universal motor of the concentrated-pole type is shown in Fig. 12-6.

b. *Distributed-field Compensated Universal Motors.*—In Fig. 12-7 are shown the parts for a distributed-field compensated series motor for a built-in application. The stator punching is seen to resemble the stator punching of an induction motor. This particular motor has only a single stator winding, as can be seen; some compensated series motors have a single winding which acts both as a **compensating winding** and as a **field winding,** whereas other compensated motors actually use two windings, located 90 deg apart. These winding arrangements and the reason for a compensating winding are discussed more fully in Art. 12-6. The armature is similar in appearance to the armature used in a concentrated-pole motor, or similar to the armature of a d-c machine.

PRINCIPLES OF OPERATION

12-4. Operation on Direct Current.—The theory of the operation of the d-c series motor is discussed in Arts. 17-3 and 17-6 and does not need to be repeated here.

12-5. Operation on Alternating Current.—If alternating current is applied to a series motor, it will start and run. The current in the armature circuit, of course, reverses 120 times per second (for 60 cycles), but the field excitation and stator flux likewise reverse 120 times per second; and these reversals take place *in time phase with the armature current.* On alternating current, the torque varies instantaneously 120 times per second, but the torque developed is always in one direction. (It is, perhaps, superfluous to say that the motor operates in the same direction of rotation on alternating current that it does on direct current.) However, there are some effects present on a-c operation that are not present on d-c operation.

a. *Laminated-field Construction.*—Because of the fact that the stator flux alternates, it is necessary to use a laminated-field structure in order to reduce hysteresis and eddy-current losses.

b. *Reactance Voltage.*—In a simple d-c circuit, the current is limited by the resistance. In a simple a-c circuit, the current is limited by the impedance and not solely by the ohmic resistance. The impedance is made up of two components, resistance and reactance. Reactance is present in an a-c circuit whenever a magnetic circuit is set up by the current flowing in the electric circuit. Reactance is, therefore, present to a marked degree in the case of a universal motor. This reactance voltage, which is present during operation on a-c but not under d-c operation, absorbs some of the line voltage, reducing the voltage applied to the armature, so that the speed of the motor, for any given current, tends to be lower on alternating than on direct current.* In other words, the effective voltage on the armature, for any given current, is less on a-c than on d-c operation.

c. Saturation Effect.—In the preceding paragraph, it was shown that the tendency of the reactance voltage is to make the speed lower on alternating than on direct current. There is another effect which gives the opposite tendency. This effect is simply that a given **root-mean-square value** of alternating current will produce less rms alternating flux than will a direct current of the same value because of saturation effects in the iron.† At low currents and high speeds, the reactance voltage is relatively unimportant; and this saturation effect usually causes the motor to operate at a higher no-load speed on alternating than on direct current. Likewise, under 25-cycle operation, the saturation effect is as pronounced as on 60 cycles, but the effect of the reactance voltage is appreciably less, in the ratio of 25:60. The net result is that the motor may sometimes operate at a higher speed on 25 cycles than it does on direct current.

d. Commutation and Brush Life.—The commutation on alternating current is substantially poorer than on direct current, and the brush life is likewise less. The principal reason for the poorer commutation on alternating current is because of the voltage induced in the short-circuited coils undergoing commutation by the transformer action of the alternating main field. No such transformer voltage exists when the motor is operated on direct current.

---

* The reactance voltage in the stator subtracts vectorially from the applied voltage, reducing the voltage applied to the armature. The IR drop and the reactance voltage of the armature are both subtracted vectorially from the voltage applied to the armature to obtain the **counter electromotive force.** The counter emf, hence speed, is reduced by the reactance voltage regardless of whether the latter appears in the field or in the armature.

† When the instantaneous value of the alternating current is exactly equal to the rms value, the magnetic flux will be substantially the same as it would be with the same amount of direct current flowing through the windings. Forty-five degrees later in time, the instantaneous value of the alternating current has risen to its **peak** value, which is 1.414 × its rms value. Owing to saturation of the iron parts of the magnetic circuit, the flux does not increase 41.4 per cent; and therefore, the effective, or rms value of the flux is less for a given effective value of alternating current than for the same value of direct current.

12-6. Compensated Universal Motors. *a. Purpose of Compensating Winding.*—It was mentioned in the preceding article that the principal reason why the speed is lower on alternating than on direct current under normal load conditions is the presence of the reactance voltage. The reactance voltage, or simply reactance, occurs both in the armature and in the field. The reactance voltage due to the field cannot be eliminated—unless the working field is eliminated—but the reactance voltage due to the armature can be practically eliminated by the use of a compensating winding. The compensating winding is a winding connected in series with the armature and so arranged that the ampere-turns of this winding oppose and neutralize the ampere-turns of the armature. To obtain this compensation, the compensating winding is displaced 90 electrical degrees from the field winding. When properly proportioned, the compensating winding virtually nullifies the effect of the reactance voltage due to the armature. There is another equally important effect, *viz.*, that the compensating winding eliminates the distortion of the main-field flux and improves the commutation; a slight overcompensation still further assists commutation.

One way to keep the field reactance down is to keep the product of field turns and flux as low as possible. The weaker the field is made, the stronger must the armature be (the more turns must it have) to develop the necessary torque and output. A strong armature will distort a weak field, and there are definite practical limits as to how low the ratio

$$\frac{\text{Field ampere-turns}}{\text{Armature ampere-turns}}$$

can be made. When a compensating winding is used, this ratio can be made lower than with a noncompensated motor.

To summarize: (1) The compensating winding neutralizes the reactance voltage that would be present in the armature; (2) it practically eliminates field distortion due to the armature, and for this reason, it permits the designer to take reactance out of the field and put it into the armature where it can be neutralized; and (3) it is a pronounced boon to commutation. As a matter of fact, it is really due to the assistance of commutation that the compensated motor can be operated at weak fields. The compensated universal motor is in reality a miniature edition of an a-c series motor used in railway service.

b. Two-field Compensated Motor.—As mentioned previously, the compensating winding is displaced 90 electrical degrees from the main

winding.   Such an arrangement is shown in the distribution chart of
Fig. 12-8*a*.   In Fig. 12-8*b*, the direction of current flow in each of the
stator slots and in each of the windings is shown.   Likewise, the neutral
position of the brushes is shown as opposite slots 18, 9, and 18.   (The
actual physical position of the brushes depends on how the connections
are made to the commutator, but these positions are shown as the
reference axes for the brushes.)

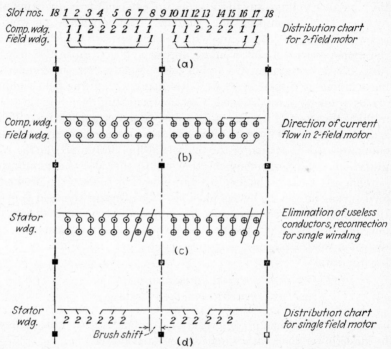

Fig. 12-8.—The equivalence of a single-field winding with shifted brushes to two
separate windings.

c. Single-field Compensated Motor.—A little study will reveal how
the two windings of Fig. 12-8*a* and *b* can be replaced by a single winding.   For example, it will be noted that, in slots 7, 8, 16 and 17, the
effect of one winding is to cancel the effect of the second winding.
Therefore, since these conductors mutually cancel one another, the
conductors themselves *could be omitted without affecting the operation
of the motor.*   These conductors are shown canceled in Fig. 12-8*c*.
Now then, we can reconnect the conductors in the various slots shown
in Fig. 12-8*c*, and we have here a single winding, the **distribution chart**
of which is shown in Fig. 12-8*d*.   Now the brushes were not moved,

but the flux conditions for the same current in the single winding shown in Fig. 12-8d are exactly the same as the flux conditions for that same current in the two windings given in Fig. 12-8a. It is to be noted, however, that the center of this new single stator winding is displaced one slot from the brushes. In other words, the one stator winding with shifted brushes is exactly equivalent* to the two windings.

Thus, the net result of all the foregoing is to show that a single winding, as Fig. 12-8d, can give the same magnetic fields as the two windings represented in Fig. 12-8a, provided that the brushes are shifted one slot from the neutral axis of the stator winding. The two-field motor, however, can be reversed by changing the connections of the main windings; but, in order to reverse the single-field motor, it is necessary to shift the brushes, just as in the case of a repulsion motor.

STATOR WINDINGS

12-7. Concentrated-pole Noncompensated Motors. *a. Nonreversible.*—The stator and brush-holder connections of a simple two-lead nonreversible concentrated-pole noncompensated universal motor are given in Fig. 12-9. It will be noted in this figure that the brushes are located halfway between the centers of the stator coils. When the brushes are so located, the connections from the armature coils to the commutator cannot be connected **on center,**† but they must be either **thrown left,**† or **thrown right;**† *i.e.*, the coil connections are brought straight out to commutator bars approximately opposite one of the two slots in which one of the two sides of the coils lies. In Fig. 12-9, arrows are drawn to assist in tracing the polarity of the stator coils. If the current is assumed to flow in through the upper leads and through the stator coils as indicated by the plus signs and dots and if, further, the armature connections are known, the direction of rotation can be predetermined as indicated in the tabulations of Figs. 12-9 and 12-10.

In Fig. 12-9, the armature is connected between two stator coils; and a variation from this procedure is shown in Fig. 12-10, where the armature is connected between one side of the line and two stator coils.

b. Caution—"Off-neutral" Connection.—In Figs. 12-9 and 12-10, it was shown that the armature could be caused to rotate in either direction simply by interchanging the leads on the brush holders. From this, it should not be inferred that a two-lead noncompensated

---

* For an explanation of this term, see Art. 3-1.

† See Fig. 12-22.

motor can be reversed satisfactorily simply by interchanging the brush-holder leads. It is a fairly common practice to connect the armature one or two bars "off neutral" in order to obtain better commutation, better torque characteristics, and better universal

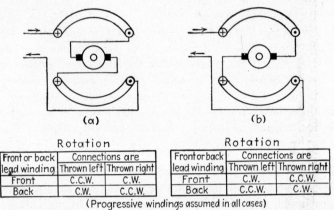

Front or back lead winding	Rotation Connections are	
	Thrown left	Thrown right
Front	C.C.W.	C.W.
Back	C.W.	C.C.W.

Front or back lead winding	Rotation Connections are	
	Thrown left	Thrown right
Front	C.W.	C.C.W.
Back	C.C.W.	C.W.

(Progressive windings assumed in all cases)

Fig. 12-9.—Motor wiring and brush-holder connection diagrams for a series motor. From these diagrams and the table, the direction of rotation can be predetermined.

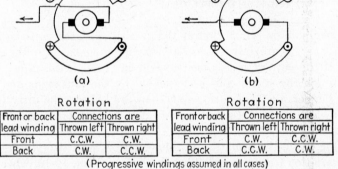

Front or back lead winding	Rotation Connections are	
	Thrown left	Thrown right
Front	C.C.W.	C.W.
Back	C.W.	C.C.W.

Front or back lead winding	Rotation Connections are	
	Thrown left	Thrown right
Front	C.W.	C.C.W.
Back	C.C.W.	C.W.

(Progressive windings assumed in all cases)

Fig. 12-10.—Motor wiring and brush-holder connection diagrams for a series motor. From these diagrams and the table, the direction of rotation can be predetermined.

characteristics. If an attempt is made to interchange the brush-holder connections on a motor having the armature connected off neutral, the motor will start and run in the opposite direction, as desired, but the commutation will be much poorer and the torque at any given normal operating speed may be reduced by as much as

50 per cent.   If a universal motor which is sent in for repairs seems to be commutating badly and has less torque than it apparently should have, the serviceman is advised to try interchanging the two brush-holder leads to find out if better torque characteristics and better commutation are obtained in the opposite direction of rotation.   If such is found to be the case, it is almost certain that the brush-holder leads were interchanged after the motor left the factory.   If such a motor is to be reversed, it will be necessary either to change the arma-

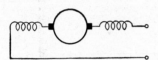

Fig. 12-11.—Connections for concentrated-pole, noncompensated, two-wire, nonreversible, universal motors.

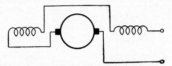

Fig. 12-12.—Connections for concentrated-pole, noncompensated, two-wire, nonreversible, universal motors.

ture connections (see Arts. 12-14 and 12-15) or to shift the brushes with respect to the stator, in addition to interchanging the brush-holder leads.

c. Reversible Motor.—The motors in Figs. 12-9 and 12-10 are represented schematically again in Figs. 12-11 and 12-12.   In Fig. 12-13 are shown the connections of a two-wire reversible motor.   The two brush-holder leads and also two leads from the stator coils are brought out and connected at a convenient point in the motor.   In the motor of Fig. 12-6, these connections are made under the nameplate, and

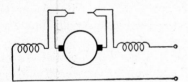

Fig. 12-13.—Connections for concentrated-pole, noncompensated, two-wire, reversible, universal motors.

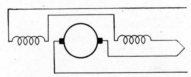

Fig. 12-14.—Connections for concentrated-pole, noncompensated, four-wire, reversible universal motors.

access may be had to them by removing it.   Another method of accomplishing the same result is to bring out four line leads, *viz.*, two from the armature and two from the stator, as shown in Fig. 12-14. It should be pointed out that for reversible motors, as shown in Figs. 12-13 and 12-14, the armature must be connected on neutral in order to obtain the same characteristics in both directions of rotation.

12-8. Split-series Electrically Reversible Motors.—The armature and field connections of a split-series three-wire reversible concen-

trated-pole universal motor are shown in Fig. 12-15. With this
arrangement, one stator coil is used to obtain one direction of rotation,
and the other stator coil to obtain the other direction of rotation, only
one stator coil being in the circuit at a time. Needless to say, the
armature connections must be on neutral in order to obtain satisfactory operation in both directions of rotation. It is interesting to
note that the external reversing control of such a motor is identical

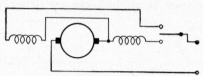

FIG. 12-15.—Connections for concentrated-pole, noncompensated, split-series, three-
wire, reversible, universal motors.

with the control of a reversible high-torque capacitor motor described
in Art. 7-8; the split-series motor is **electrically reversible** and may
be used for **plugging service.**

12-9. Tapped-field Winding.—Speed control of concentrated pole
noncompensated universal motors is sometimes effected by using
tapped-field windings. Such an arrangement is represented in Fig.
12-16. There may be three taps as shown there, or simply the two
taps 1 and 2. Taps 1, 2, and 3 give *low, medium,* and *high* speed,
respectively. Sections *A* and *B*
may comprise one field coil, and
section *C* the other; it is to be noted,
however, that the wire sizes in these
three sections may all differ from
one another.

It should be pointed out that
the tapped-field universal motor still
has **varying-speed** characteristics,

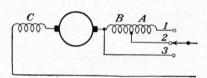

FIG. 12-16.—Connections for concentrated-pole, noncompensated, tapped-
field, two- or three-speed, nonreversible,
universal motors.

regardless of which tap is used; but for fans, blowers, and many other
applications satisfactory control of the speed can be obtained.

Sometimes a tapped field is employed merely to obtain the same
speed operating on direct current as on alternating current; for operation on alternating current, tap 2 is used, and for operation on direct
current, tap 1. With such a tap properly located, it is possible to
make the motor operate at the same speed on 60 cycles as it does on
direct current for any *one* given torque load; but the speeds on direct
and on alternating current will not be the same at any other load,
although they will be closer together than if no tap were used.

12-10. Two-field Compensated Windings.—The stator and brush-holder connections for two-lead nonreversible compensated windings are shown in Figs. 12-17 and 12-18. The two diagrams are similar

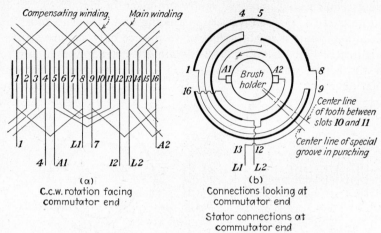

(a)
C.c.w. rotation facing
commutator end

(b)
Connections looking at
commutator end

Stator connections at
commutator end

Fig. 12-17.—Stator connection and brush-holder connections for a two-field, two-winding, compensated series motor. Counterclockwise rotation.

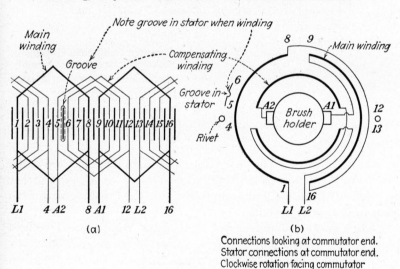

(a)

(b)
Connections looking at commutator end.
Stator connections at commutator end.
Clockwise rotation facing commutator

Fig. 12-18.—Stator and brush-holder connection diagram similar to Fig. 12-17, except for clockwise rotation.

except for slight differences in marking of the leads and the fact that one is for clockwise rotation and the other for counterclockwise rotation. It will be noted that in these two diagrams the brushes are located opposite the centers of the main-winding coils.   The armature connections, therefore, must be on center (see Fig. 12-22).

The stator and brush-holder connections for a reversible two-winding compensated universal motor are given in Fig. 12-19.   It is to be noted that the compensating winding and armature must be reversed as a unit; it is not sufficient to reverse only the armature.

Figures 12-17a, 12-18a, and 12-19a are directly applicable only to a certain definite number of stator slots, but the corresponding connection diagrams, Figs. 12-17b, 12-18b, and 12-19b are applicable to

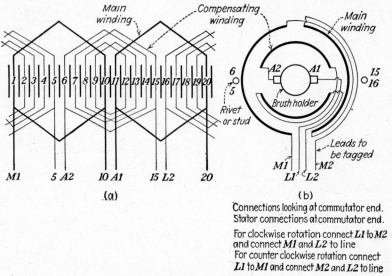

(a)

(b)

Connections looking at commutator end.
Stator connections at commutator end.

For clockwise rotation connect *L1* to *M2* and connect *M1* and *L2* to line
For counter clockwise rotation connect *L1* to *M1* and connect *M2* and *L2* to line

Fig. 12-19.—Stator and brush-holder connections for a reversible, two-winding, compensated universal motor.

any number of slots.   The (a) portions of these diagrams are given to illustrate the details of the connections better.   It is to be further noted that all these diagrams carefully locate the brush position with respect to the stator winding.

12-11. Two-field Compensated Split-series Windings.—Two-field compensated universal motors can be connected as split-series motors. The stator and brush-holder connections for such a motor are given in Fig. 12-20.   Here again it is to be noted that the compensating winding and armature are permanently connected in series as a single unit, regardless of the direction of rotation.

12-12. Single-field Compensated Motor.—In Art. 12-6, it was explained that a single distributed field winding could accomplish the same results as two windings displaced 90 deg apart, provided that the brush axis is shifted slightly from the axis of the stator winding. The stator and brush-holder connections of such a motor are given in Fig. 12-21. In this diagram, the brushes are shown shifted *with*

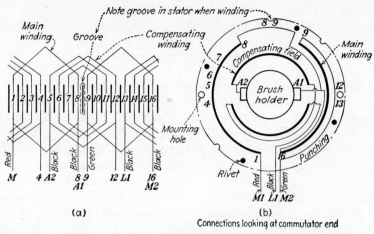

(a)

(b)

Connections looking at commutator end

M1 and L1 to line = clockwise rotation
M2 and L1 to line = counter clockwise rotation

FIG. 12-20.—Stator and brush-holder connections for a split-series, compensated universal motor.

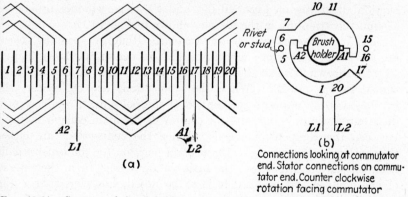

(a)

(b)

Connections looking at commutator end. Stator connections on commutator end. Counter clockwise rotation facing commutator

FIG. 12-21.—Stator and brush-holder connections for a single-field, compensated universal motor, counterclockwise rotation.

rotation. The armature connections for this motor are on center. The single stator winding corresponds to the compensating winding on a two-field motor, and the normal brush position would be between the coils; but, in this figure, they are shown displaced slightly in a counterclockwise direction because the armature is to rotate counterclockwise.   It should be pointed out, however, that the brushes might be located between the centers of the stator coils, and the brush shift obtained by making the armature connections 2, 3, or 4 bars off neutral.

The single-field compensated motor can be reversed not by changing the connections of the winding but only by shifting the brushes.

ARMATURE WINDINGS

12-13. General.—Universal motors almost invariably are wound for two poles.   Therefore, the windings are all lap windings, and cross-connected commutators cannot be used.   In principle, the windings are the same as the windings used in a d-c or in a repulsion-start motor.   These lap windings are, likewise, very similar in principle to the lap windings used on large d-c machines.   But in universal motors (and also in small d-c motors) another type of winding, known as the **back-lead winding,** is used.

12-14. Front-lead Windings.—In **front-lead windings,** the commutator connections from the armature coils are brought out in front of the armature, *i.e.,* on the commutator side of the laminations. Three methods of making these armature connections to the commutator are illustrated in Fig. 12-22.   (Figure 12-22a resembles the connection diagrams of Figs. 10-13a and b.)   The winding progresses around the armature in the manner shown in Fig. 10-12.

a. Three Main Types of Connections.—Roughly speaking, there are three main types of connections: *viz.*, **on center,** as shown in Fig. 12-22a; **thrown left,** as shown in Fig. 12-22b; and **thrown right,** as shown in Fig. 12-22c.   When the connections are on center, the brushes will fall opposite the centers of the poles or, in the case of a distributed winding, opposite the centers of the main coils or halfway between the compensating coils.   When the connections are either thrown left or thrown right, the neutral position for the brushes falls between the poles, between the main-winding coils, or in the centers of the compensating coils.   It is to be noted, however, that if the connections are thrown left, the direction of rotation will be opposite to what it would be if they were thrown right.   This point is shown in tabular form in Figs. 12-9 and 12-10.   The method of connecting the armature leads to the commutator determines the position of the brushes—for neutral position—with respect to the stator, as has just been explained.   The corresponding brush positions for the three methods of connection are shown in Fig. 12-22.

b. *"On-neutral"* and *"Off-neutral"* *Connections.*—When the armature connections are on neutral, the armature is suitable for rotation in either direction. However, a noncompensated series motor usually gives better commutation, longer brush life, and generally more satisfactory operation if the brushes are shifted against rotation. The effect of a shift of the brushes *against rotation* can be obtained by moving the armature connections to the commutator *with rotation.* Such a con-

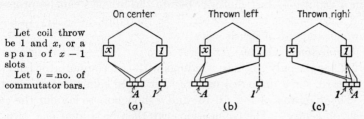

Let coil throw be 1 and x, or a span of $x - 1$ slots
Let $b = $ no. of commutator bars.

IF THE NUMBER OF SLOTS IS EVEN:

Brush position	Opposite centers of poles or opposite main coils	Between poles or opposite centers of compensating coils	Between poles or opposite centers of compensating coils	
If brushes are on neutral for CW or CCW rotation......	$A = x$	$A = x + \dfrac{b}{4}$	$A = x + \dfrac{3}{4}b$	Note: If, from formula, $A > b$, subtract b from result to find A.
1 bar off neutral for CCW rotation.................	$A = x + 1$	$A = x + \dfrac{b}{4} + 1$	$A = x + \dfrac{3}{4}b + 1$	
1 bar off neutral for CW rotation.....................	$A = x - 1$	$A = x + \dfrac{b}{4} - 1$	$A = x + \dfrac{3}{4}b - 1$	
2 bars off neutral for CCW rotation.................	$A = x + 2$	$A = x + \dfrac{b}{4} + 2$	$A = x + \dfrac{3}{4}b + 2$	
2 bars off neutral for CW rotation.....................	$A = x - 2$	$A = x + \dfrac{b}{4} - 2$	$A = x + \dfrac{3}{4}b - 2$	

IF THE NUMBER OF SLOTS IS ODD:

$b/4$ comes out a fraction—as $5\frac{1}{2}$. In such a case, drop the $\frac{1}{2}$ and locate bar No. 1 to the left of the center line of slot No. 1 so that mica to right of bar No. 1 is opposite center line of slot No. 1. Otherwise follow the formulas above.

FIG. 12-22.—Armature connections to the commutator. Front-lead windings, two bars per slot. This figure shows how to lay out an armature connection diagram for any lap-wound armature with two bars per slot and front-lead windings.

nection is an off-neutral connection and is frequently used in universal motors, as mentioned in Art. 12-7*b.* Diagrams for off-neutral connections are shown in Fig. 12-22. When an armature is connected off neutral, it is suitable only for a single direction of rotation—unless the brushes themselves can be shifted.

c. Single-field Compensated Motors.—In the case of single-field compensated motors, the neutral position of the brushes with respect to the stator can be determined by use of the diagrams in Fig. 12-22.

In this case, there is only a single winding, and this single stator winding must be considered—for purposes of location of neutral—as the compensating winding. For example, on center armature connections make the brushes fall midway between the coils; and on the other two connections make them fall in the centers of the coils. However, it must be remembered that the normal operating position of the brushes of single-field motors is displaced off neutral slightly, just the same as it is in a repulsion-start motor. Before the brushes can be properly located with respect to the stator, it is, therefore, necessary to know the correct amount of brush shift.

d. Connection Diagrams for Three Bars per Slot.—The diagrams of Fig. 12-22 apply only to those windings with two commutator bars per slot, whereas some universal motors have three commutator bars per slot. The diagrams of Fig. 10-13c and d show how to lay out the connections on center. The connections can then be shifted one, two, or three commutator bars to the left or the right for off-neutral operation, as explained in detail in Fig. 12-22. Likewise, these diagrams in Fig. 10-13 can be used as a starting point for the thrown-left or thrown-right connections by moving the commutator connections 90 deg around the commutator, to the left or to the right as desired. A concrete example illustrating the use of these principles is given in Art. 17-18.

12-15. Back-lead Windings. *a. General.*—In back-lead windings, the wire is started at the back (the end opposite the commutator) of the armature, and all the commutator connections are brought out at that end. The progress of a typical winding around the armature is illustrated in Fig. 12-23. When there are two bars per slot, a short and a long loop are brought out of each slot. Short and long loops are for connections between coils, and the two different lengths identify the first and second coils in each slot. When the winding is complete, the *start* and *finish* wires form another loop. After the armature is completely wound and before wedging, the loops are pulled through the slots and connected to the commutator.

b. Armature Connection Diagrams.—Figure 12-22 gives the **armature connection diagrams** for various front-lead windings. These diagrams apply equally well to back-lead windings, and the principles therein explained can be used to determine to which bars the various loops are connected. For example, in Fig. 12-23, loop 2 is connected to the bar A, as represented in Fig. 12-22. This point can be illustrated for

$$x = 7$$
$$b = 26$$

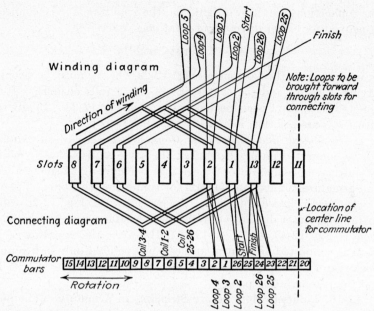

Fig. 12-23.—Winding and connection diagram of a back-lead winding. Thirteen slots, 26 bars, connections are *thrown right* and *on neutral*. Reversible.

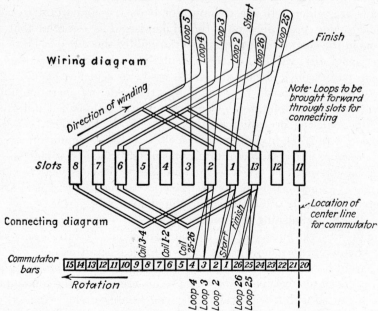

Fig. 12-24.—Winding and connection diagram of a back-lead winding similar to Fig. 12-23 except connected two bars *off neutral* for counterclockwise rotation.

The connections are thrown right, and the armature is to be connected on neutral for either direction of rotation. Therefore,

$$A = 7 + 19\frac{1}{2} = 26\frac{1}{2}$$

As explained at the bottom of Fig. 12-22, the $\frac{1}{2}$ must be dropped, leaving $A = 26$; and the center line of slot 1 falls on mica. It will be noted that loop 2 is connected to bar 26 in Fig. 12-23. In any case, with two bars per slot, loop 2 is connected to bar A.

c. *On-neutral and Off-neutral Connections.*—Back-lead windings can be connected on or off neutral, the same as front-lead windings, by shifting the commutator connections. Figure 12-24 shows a back-lead **armature connection diagram** for connecting two bars off neutral for counterclockwise rotation. The armature of Fig. 12-23 can be operated in either direction of rotation or used in any reversible motor such as Fig. 12-13, 12-14, or 12-15. However, the armature of Fig. 12-24 is connected off neutral and can be operated only in a counterclockwise direction. If operated clockwise, the torque will be low, and the commutation poor.

12-16. Points to Note before Stripping an Armature.—The points to be noted before stripping an armature are discussed in Art. 10-28.

12-17. Notes on Rewinding and Reconnecting.—When armature leads are soldered to the commutator bars, it is important to use a good solder, preferably pure tin. Likewise, it is essential that the slots in the commutator necks, also the ends of the wires, be clean and free from dirt, varnish, or other insulation. A neutral flux, such as rosin and alcohol, should always be used; an acid flux should never be used. Care should be taken during the soldering operation not to overheat the commutator. Commutators can be loosened and ruined if the soldering operation gets them too hot. Moreover, excessive heat can ruin the insulation that is close to the commutator.

Because universal motor armatures usually operate at high speeds, special care must be taken to wind and shape the coils so as to obtain a good balance. It is highly desirable to balance the complete armature dynamically after refinishing the commutator surface.

12-18. Refinishing the Commutator.—After the dipping and baking process, the outside of the commutator should be turned on a lathe to true it up, to remove excess solder, to clear short circuits between adjacent bars, and to prepare it for the final finish on the brush surface. Mica insulation between bars should be undercut up to the commutator necks, or to within approximately $\frac{1}{8}$ in. from the rear (winding) end of the commutator. This mica can be removed with a hand scraper, or preferably by means of a circular saw. The saw used for this purpose should be about 0.005 in. thicker than the mica; a standard thickness is 0.025. It should be from $\frac{3}{8}$ to $\frac{3}{4}$ in. in diameter, with 12 to 16 teeth per inch of circumference, and hollow-ground on both sides. A speed of 7500 rpm or greater is recommended. The cuts should be made to a depth of 0.032 in. from the final finished surface of the commutator.

Final finish to the commutator surface should be cut with either a diamond-point or carboloy-point cutting tool. This tool should have a tip rounded off to a radius of approximately 0.005 in., and ground for a rake of 5 deg and a clearance angle of 18 deg. Tool must be firmly clamped and rigidly held for the turning process, which should be done at a high speed—of the order of 6000 to 7500 rpm. Feed should be adjusted so that the tool does not advance more than 0.0005 in. per revolution, nor should the depth of the final cut be more than 0.0005 in. If the finish cut is taken in this manner, the burrs in the slots will be few and can easily be removed with a stiff brush.

For good commutation and brush life, it is important that the commutator surface be concentric with the shaft journals. After the finish cut, set the armature up on V-blocks and indicate the commutator surface with a dial indicator, preferably one reading 0.0001 in. per division. Rotate the armature slowly and note maximum and minimum readings over a revolution. For high-speed armatures, the total variation in reading should not exceed 0.0005 in. (eccentricity of 0.00025). Moreover, the maximum variation from one bar to an adjacent one should not exceed 0.0002 in.

12-19. Checking the Rewound Armature.—In general, the rewound armature of a universal motor can be tested by the same procedure used for checking the armature of a repulsion-start motor. This procedure is fully discussed in Art. 10-29.

GOVERNOR-CONTROLLED MOTORS

12-20. General.—The underlying idea of governor control is to make and break the stator circuit of a universal motor by centrifugal means of some sort. This idea is old, having been credited to Edison as early as 1882. It was not used to any great extent in universal motors until after 1927.

a. Principle of Governor Operation.—The governor is so arranged that, above any certain predetermined speed, the contacts will stay open, but below this speed the contacts will stay closed. Instead of opening the circuit completely, the usual arrangement is to have the governor insert a resistance in series with the motor. To improve the contact life, a capacitor is put across the governor contacts, in parallel with the resistor.

b. Speed-torque Characteristics.—The speed-torque characteristics of a universal motor with and without a governor and with two different values of resistance are shown in Fig. 12-25. These curves are sufficient to show that, if a low resistance is used across the governor

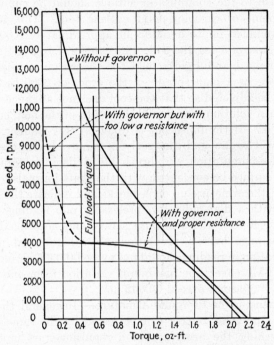

Fig. 12-25.—Speed-torque characteristics of a governor-controlled universal motor rated at $\frac{1}{40}$ hp, 4000 rpm.

contacts, the governor may not be able to hold the speed down under light load. It is the usual procedure, however, to make the resistance as low as it can be made and still not have the operating speed too high under light-load conditions.

12-21. Two-brush Governors.—*a. Principle of the Lee Governor.* One very popular and widely used governor was invented by Dr. Royal Lee; photographs of this governor are shown in Fig. 12-26. The contacts are mounted on a disc of a phenolic material, and current is passed into the governor through two brushes which ride on separate collector rings. The contact points of the governor are mounted on two flexible strips of steel. The inner contact is stationary, but the outer contact is movable and can be actuated by centrifugal force. When in operation, the governor contacts make and break rapidly, at approximately one hundred to two hundred times per second. The speed of make and break is governed by the natural resonant frequency of the moving contact. This contact vibration is said to be maintained by the explosive force of the arc, and the high-speed operation of the contact is held to be responsible for the accurate speed control than can be obtained with this type of governor. Centrifugal force, within a narrow range near the operating speed, does not actually hold the contacts open; nor does it allow them to remain closed, for they are vibrating continuously. But when the speed gets slightly above

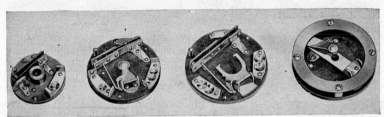

Fig. 12-26.—Some governors used to control the speed of universal motors. (*Courtesy of Lee Engineering & Manufacturing Company.*)

normal, the centrifugal force tends to hold the movable contact away from the stationary contact a relatively large percentage of the time; whereas, if the speed is low, the two contacts remain closed a relatively greater portion of the time.

b. *Adjustment of Governors to Change Operating Speed.*—The smallest governor shown in Fig. 12-26 can be adjusted only while the motors are stationary. The adjustment is made by means of a setscrew which moves the position of the stationary contact. The other governors shown in Fig. 12-26 have a link mechanism and a lever, as shown. The end of the lever comes in the center of the governor, so that its position may be adjusted by means of a screw moving in an axial direction. A mechanism effecting this type of speed adjustment is shown in Fig. 12-27.

c. *Special Governor for D-c Operation.*—When a governor of the type just described is used on direct current, there is a distinct tendency to pit one contact and build up the other, thus causing early failure of the governor. To get around this difficulty, another form of the Lee governor has been developed. In this form of governor, there are, likewise, two brushes, but only a single collector ring, split in

halves, is used.   (The collector ring might be called a two-bar commutator.)   The two brushes are connected in series with the motor
just the same as the two brushes used on the two collector rings in
the governor described above.   One governor contact is connected to
one segment of the collector ring, and the other contact to the other

Fig. 12-27.—A governor-controlled series motor.   The speed adjustment is by
means of the long lever shown at the left; movement of this lever changes the axial
position of the central stud which bears against the link in the governor shown in the
center.   This motor is rated 0.067 hp, 3600 rpm.   (*Courtesy of General Electric Company.*)

segment of the collector ring.   In operation, the direction of current
flow through the governor contact is thus reversed twice for each
revolution of the armature.

12-22. Single-brush Governors.—A photograph of a single-brush
governor having one stationary contact is shown in Fig. 12-28.   The
current is fed into the rotating member through a single brush and a

Fig. 12-28.—A governor-controlled universal motor.   (*Courtesy of General Electric
Company.*)

collector ring to the movable contact of the governor, which is located
at the end of a lever in the center of the governor.   The stationary
contact is located coincident with the axis of the shaft.   The lever
carrying the movable contact has an extension, bent back about 90
deg; centrifugal force acts on this extension to pull the movable con-

tact away from the stationary contact at a predetermined speed. When the motor is running, there is a very definite wiping action of the governor, which improves the contact life. The speed can be adjusted by moving the stationary contact in or out, toward or away from the armature, in an axial direction.

12-23. Other Governors.—There are a number of other governors made, some of which do not conduct any current into the rotating part at all but merely use the rotating member to actuate the contacts that are both on the stationary member.

12-24. Care and Adjustments of Governors.—The methods of adjusting the speeds of the various governors have been discussed separately under each type of governor. With all types of governors, the contacts must be kept clean and free from pitting, just like any other electrical contacts in any control circuit. If the contacts are worn or badly burned, it is advisable to check the capacitor for short circuits, open circuits, or grounds. Likewise, the resistors should also be checked for short circuits, open circuits, or grounds.

Proper Size of Resistors.—The resistor should have sufficient resistance so that the motor will not run too fast for the appliance when the highest d-c voltage likely to be encountered is applied to the motor. If the resistance is too high in value, the contact life will be reduced, and the motor will be more noisy (the noise being due to the sudden changes in motor torque caused by the governor's interruptions of the power supply).

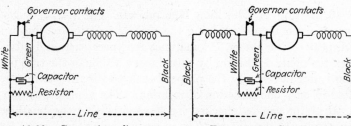

Fig. 12-29.—Connection diagrams for governor-controlled, three-wire, nonreversible, universal motors. (*Courtesy of Bodine Electric Company.*)

Fig. 12-30.—Connection diagrams for governor-controlled, four-wire, nonreversible, universal motors. (*Courtesy of Bodine Electric Company.*)

12-25. Wiring Diagrams of Governor-controlled Motors.—The wiring diagram of a three-wire nonreversible governor-controlled motor is given in Fig. 12-29. The wiring diagram of a four-wire nonreversible governor-controlled motor is given in Fig. 12-30. Since neither of these motors is reversible, off-neutral armature connections can be used; but, of course, the armature connections should be displaced in the correct direction.

The connections of a five-wire reversible governor-controlled motor are given in Fig. 12-31. The wiring diagram of a split-field five-wire reversible governor-controlled motor is given in Fig. 12-32. In both of these diagrams, the armature connections must be on neutral, for the armature may be operated in either direction of rotation.

It will be noted that these connections are similar to the conventional connections for a universal motor, except for the insertion of the governor, capacitor, and resistor in the circuit.

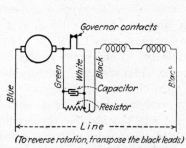

Fig. 12-31.—Connection diagrams for governor-controlled, five-wire, reversible, universal motors. (*Courtesy of Bodine Electric Company.*)

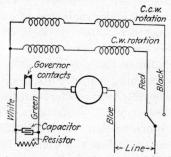

Fig. 12-32.—Connection diagrams for governor-controlled, split-series, five-wire, reversible, universal motors. (*Courtesy of Bodine Electric Company.*)

MISCELLANEOUS SERVICE PROBLEMS

12-26. Setting or Checking Neutral.—In Fig. 12-22, suggested rules were given for determining the neutral position of the brushes with respect to the stator. Sometimes it is necessary and advisable to check the neutral position by actual tests, although the true neutral position is not necessarily the proper brush position if the motors are operated in only one direction of rotation. The neutral position of a universal motor can be checked by short-circuiting the brushes and applying power to the stator. The procedure is the same as for finding the neutral of a repulsion motor described in Art. 10-37. For concentrated pole noncompensated motors, the brushes must be set on soft neutral. For two-field compensated motors, excite the compensating winding, and set the brushes on hard neutral. In single-field compensated universal motors, there is no way of checking the actual brush position unless the correct shift is known; if the amount of shift is known, the neutral position can be determined by exciting the windings and determining the hard neutral position and then displacing the brushes therefrom in the direction of rotation by the known amount of shift.

12-27. Predetermination of Direction of Rotation.—The direction of rotation can be determined in advance before assembling the motor by comparing the armature connections with Fig. 12-22 and the corresponding stator and brush-holder connections with Fig. 12-9 or 12-10. For two-winding compensated motors, the direction of rotation can be predetermined from Fig. 12-17 or 12-20.

12-28. Rewinding for Different Characteristics.—The rewinding of a universal motor for characteristics different from those for which it was designed almost invariably necessitates rewinding both stator and armature windings. In the case of a two-field compensated motor, the compensating winding must always be rewound if the armature is rewound.

Rewinding for a Different Voltage.—To rewind to obtain the same performance on a circuit of a voltage higher or lower than rated voltage, rewind the stator (including both windings if there are two) with more or less turns in direct proportion to the increase or decrease in voltage. Likewise, rewind the armature with more or less turns per coil in direct proportion to the increase or decrease in voltage. In general, use in all windings wire of the largest size that will permit the correct number of turns to be put into the slots. If the total circular mils of copper per slot in all slots are larger in the new windings than in the old windings, the performance will be slightly better than with the original windings; and, conversely, the performance will be slightly poorer if the circular mils of copper per slot are less in the new windings.

For Different Torques or Speed.—Before attempting to rewind a universal motor to obtain a different speed with any given device or for a different torque, a careful application test should be made with the original winding. The applied voltage should be adjusted until the desired torque or speed characteristics are obtained. A temperature run should then be taken to determine whether or not the motor can safely operate on the newly found circuit voltage. By this procedure, a new operating voltage will be found; say this new voltage is 150 volts, for purposes of illustration. Consider now the motor as if it had been originally rated for a 150-volt circuit; and, on this basis, rewind for a circuit of the voltage on which it must be operated, say 115, following the rules laid down in the preceding paragraph.

12-29. Use of an External Resistor for Speed Reduction.—The speed of a universal motor is often varied by means of an external resistor connected either in series with the motor or across the brushes.

Sometimes this resistor may be a variable resistor, as in the case of a sewing-machine motor; or it may be a fixed resistor inserted in the circuit to reduce the speed.   When an external series resistor is used, a much more drooping speed-torque characteristic is obtained, and the locked-rotor torque is consequently reduced considerably.   This effect is shown in Fig. 12-33.   With such a drooping torque characteristic, the motor may fail to start, and there will be wide variations in speed for relatively small variations in load.   This characteristic of a universal motor has often given rise to difficulty in service, and the universal motor has sometimes been severely and unjustly criticized because of these characteristics.   The best cure for such a difficulty is

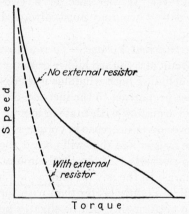

FIG. 12-33.—How the speed-torque curve of a universal motor is affected by an external resistor connected in series with the motor windings.

to rewind the motor to obtain the proper operating characteristics without the use of an external resistor or else to use an autotransformer to obtain the desired speed reduction.

Bibliography

1. PACKER, L. C.: Universal Type of Motors, *A.I.E.E. Trans.*, 1925, p. 587.
2. PUCHSTEIN, A. F.: Universal Electric Motors, *Ohio State Univ. Eng. Expt. Sta.*, *Bull.* 53, 1930.
3. GROOT, R. W.: Governor Controlled Fractional Horsepower Motors, *Product Eng.*, June, 1936, pp. 216–218.
4. Where Constant Speed Motors Are of First Importance, *Elec. Manufacturing*, January, 1936, pp. 25–27.
5. Motorizing the Business Machines, *Elec. Manufacturing*, July, 1935, pp. 25–27.
6. Where to Use High Speed Motors, *Elec. Manufacturing*, August, 1935, pp. 24–27.
7. FROMM, W. H.: Why Use Universal Motors?   *Elec. Manufacturing*, July, 1936, pp. 19–23.

CHAPTER XIII

SHADED-POLE INDUCTION MOTORS AND FANS

Shaded-pole motors are used for nearly all applications requiring an induction motor of $\frac{1}{20}$ hp or less. In the subfractional range—horsepower ratings below $\frac{1}{20}$—it is the standard general-purpose constant-speed a-c motor. It is simple in construction, low in cost, and extremely rugged and reliable—like a polyphase induction motor—because it employs no commutator, switch, collector rings, brushes, governor, sliding or make-and-break contacts of any sort. It is low in efficiency, but this factor is not usually important because power inputs are low; however, the characteristically low efficiency does keep it from being built and used in the larger horsepower ratings. It is used for such applications as advertising devices, barber poles, damper controllers, fans, humidifiers, radio controls, hair driers, and others.

CHARACTERISTICS OF SHADED-POLE MOTORS

13-1. Shaded-pole Motor Defined.—This motor type is partly described by the following definition of the A. S. A.:

A shaded-pole motor is a single-phase induction motor provided with an auxiliary short-circuited winding or windings displaced in magnetic position from the main winding.—ASA C42—1941. 10.10.355.

This definition does not recognize synchronous shaded-pole motors, discussed in Chap. XV; the latter are widely used in clocks and timing devices. Only the induction type is discussed in this chapter. In the usual form of construction, salient poles are used, and the "auxiliary short-circuited winding" consists of a single turn placed around a portion of the main pole. This coil is known as a "shading coil" because it causes the flux in that portion of the pole surrounded by it to lag behind the flux in the rest of the pole. Sometimes two, or even three, shading coils are used on each pole, each coil encompassing a different percentage of the main pole face (see Fig. 13-6).

13-2. Essential Parts of a Shaded-pole Motor.—Figure 13-1 gives a schematic representation of a simple shaded-pole motor. There is but a single winding, which is connected to the line, a second winding permanently short-circuited upon itself, and a squirrel-cage

rotor.   This short-circuited winding is displaced from the main winding by an angle which can never be 90 electrical degrees.   It has to be
shifted a definite amount in order to set up a component field along
an axis in space different from that of the main winding; furthermore,

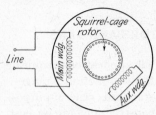

this shift has to be less than 90 deg so
that a voltage can be induced in the short-
circuited winding by transformer action of
the main winding.   Constructions may
vary considerably in detail, but the above
are the essential elements found in all
shaded-pole induction motors.   Some of
these constructions are described in more
detail below.

Fig.   13-1.—The   shaded-pole
induction motor.

13-3. Construction of Shaded-pole Motors.—At least three
typical constructions are recognizable: salient-pole, skeleton, and
distributed-winding.

   a. Salient-pole Constructions.—Figure 13-2 illustrates a popular
type of punching design for the larger ratings—from 0.005 to 0.1 hp.
There are as many main-winding coils as there are poles, in this case,

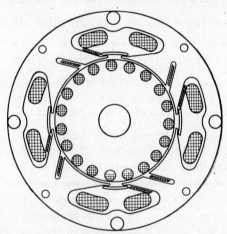

Fig. 13-2.—A shaded-pole motor with tapered poles and magnetic wedges.   (*Reprinted
from Electrical Engineering.*)

four.   The shading coils, one for each pole, are put on before the main-
winding coils; the latter may be wound as form coils and slipped on
over the poles and held in place by wedges.   It has been found that, if
these wedges are made of a magnetic material such as iron, the performance of the motor is improved.

Figure 13-3 shows another construction, which uses a solid and permanent magnetic bridge. In this case, the stator core is made in two parts and the pole sides are straight and parallel. There are four shading coils, as shown. The four stator coils can be wound directly on the poles quite easily, or they can be wound on molds and readily slipped onto the pole projections, after which the internal part of the core and its windings are pressed into the outer ring of punchings. Sometimes, when this construction is used, two diametrically opposite coils are omitted for economy in winding; in this case, however, there are twice as many turns on each of the two poles as there would be in a single coil if there were four coils.

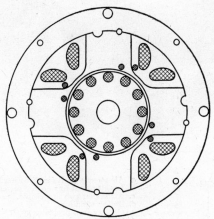

Fig. 13-3.—A shaded-pole motor with a two-piece stator.   (*Reprinted from Electrical Engineering.*)

A cutaway view of a complete shaded-pole motor is given in Fig. 13-4. The inset shows details of the bearing construction. Oil circulates through the porous bearing material to the shaft and out to the oil reservoir to the wick to the bearing, completing the cycle. A shaded-pole refrigerator-fan motor is illustrated in Fig. 13-5.

b. Skeleton-type Construction.—Figure 13-6 illustrates the skeleton construction used for motors rated from 0.00025 to 0.03 hp. Note that this particular motor employs triple shading, *i.e.*, three shading coils of different throw for each pole. The construction is very simple. Self-aligning oilite bearings are mounted in diaphragms and surrounded by wick-type oilers; the entire bearing assembly is in the bearing plate, which is extended to serve as a mounting foot.

c. Distributed-winding Motors.—Stator punchings are similar to those used for single-phase or polyphase induction motors. The main

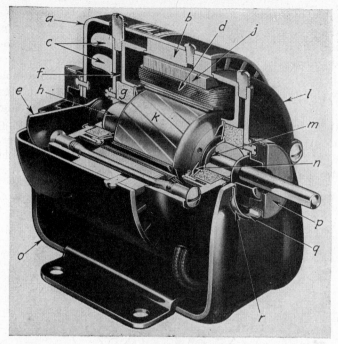

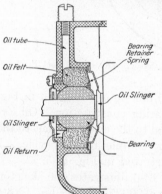

a. Air-stream shell for directing air past cooling fins.
b. Longitudinal fins on the die-cast frame.
c. Air inlets; two are visible.
d. Stator windings.
e. Cooling fan, propeller type.
f. Oiling tube.
g. Felt wicking surrounding the bearing.
h. Self-aligning porous bronze bearings (see inset).
j. Stator laminations.
k. Rotor laminations.
l. Frame of three-piece die-cast construction.
m. Steel thrust washer.
n. Oil retainer to prevent loss of lubricating oil.
o. Cradle base of drawn steel.
p. Rubber mounting ring.
q. Lock ring. Locks motor in cradle base without use of nuts or bolts.
r. Release slot. Motor can be removed from cradle base by inserting screw driver and applying half twist against lock ring.

FIG. 13-4.—Cutaway view of a totally enclosed, fan-cooled, shaded-pole, induction motor with self-aligning sleeve bearings. Inset shows details of the bearing construction. (*Courtesy of the A. G. Redmond Company.*)

winding is similar to that of any single-phase motor, and the short-circuited auxiliary winding is similar to a starting winding except that it is short-circuited upon itself, and it is displaced from the main winding by less than the usual 90 deg. Such a winding is illustrated in the distribution chart of Fig. 13-15.

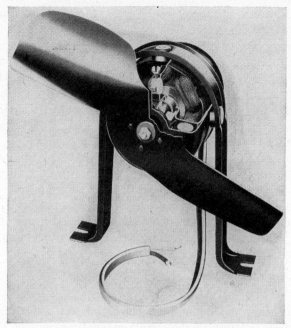

Fɪɢ. 13-5.—A shaded-pole refrigerator-fan motor. (*Courtesy of Delco Products.*)

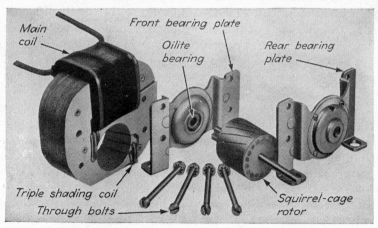

Fɪɢ. 13-6.—Exploded view of skeleton-type, small, shaded-pole motor. Note use of triple shading coil. (*Courtesy of the Barber-Colman Company.*)

13-4. Principle of the Shaded-pole Motor.—Like any other induction motor, the shaded-pole motor is caused to run by the action of a revolving magnetic field set up by the primary windings. The method of obtaining the revolving field is slightly different from that of other types of induction motors. It was seen in Chap. II that the revolving field in a two-phase motor is the resultant of two stationary fields displaced 90 deg apart in space and 90 deg apart in time. In a split-phase motor at standstill, the fields are 90 deg apart in space, but they are displaced considerably less than that in time, as shown in Fig. 4-2; however, there is enough of a rotating field to produce considerable torque. Actually, it is not necessary that the fields be displaced in space by a full 90 deg in order to set up a sort of rotating field; it is necessary only that there be two component fields, displaced both in time and space. This condition is fulfilled in all shaded-pole motors, as will be shown. Each pole may be considered as split into two sections:

1. *Main body* of the pole.
2. *Shaded portion,* i.e., the portion surrounded by the shading coil.

An elementary understanding of the action of the shading coil may be gained from a study of the simple magnetic circuit of Fig. 13-7a, which shows a single pole divided into two equal parts, one of which is shaded. Consider the instant of time when the current flowing in the primary coil is actually zero, but is just starting to increase positively. In the main portion, the flux ϕ_m is just starting to build up in phase with the current. Likewise the flux ϕ_s in the shaded area is starting to build up, but this change in flux induces a voltage in the shading coil which causes current to flow. Since an induced current always flows in such a direction as to oppose the change in flux which induces it,* the current in the shading coil delays the building up of the flux ϕ_s. Further, when the current in the primary coil starts to decrease, flux ϕ_m starts to decrease immediately. However, the current induced in the shading coil by a decreasing flux still tends to oppose the change in flux; i.e., in this case, the induced current tends to maintain the flux. Hence, flux ϕ_s continues to lag behind ϕ_m during the second part of the cycle. By similar considerations, it is evident that flux ϕ_s always lags behind flux ϕ_m in time. Hence, the net effect of this time and space displacement is to produce a shifting flux in the air gap which shifts always toward the shading coil. *Therefore, the*

* This is an application of Lenz's classical law, which is discussed in practically every elementary text on electricity.

direction of rotation of a shaded-pole motor is always from the unshaded to the shaded portion of the pole.

A somewhat more rigorous and precise explanation of the action of a shading coil is given in the following article.

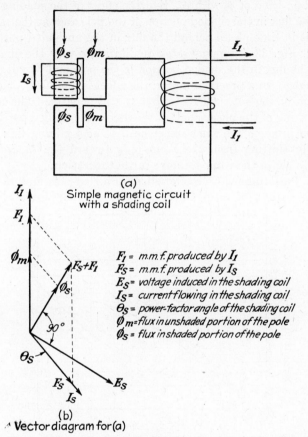

(a)
Simple magnetic circuit
with a shading coil

F_I = m.m.f. produced by I_I
F_S = m.m.f. produced by I_S
E_S = voltage induced in the shading coil
I_S = current flowing in the shading coil
θ_S = power-factor angle of the shading coil
ϕ_m = flux in unshaded portion of the pole
ϕ_S = flux in shaded portion of the pole

(b)
Vector diagram for (a)

FIG. 13-7.—How a shading coil reduces the flux threading it and delays it in time phase.

13-5. Vector Diagram of a Simple Shading Coil.—Figure 13-7*b* is the vector diagram for the simple shading coil illustrated. It was constructed so as to fulfill simultaneously the following conditions, all of which must be satisfied in accordance with elementary principles; these determine the diagram:

1. ϕ_m is proportional to, and in phase with, F_1.
2. ϕ_s is proportional to, and in phase with, $F_s + F_1$.
3. E_s is proportional to, and 90 deg in time behind, ϕ_s.

4. I_s is proportional to, and θ_s deg behind, E_s.

5. F_s is proportional to, and in phase with, I_s.

After the diagram is constructed to fulfill simultaneously the conditions outlined above, it becomes at once apparent, by comparing the magnitude and position of ϕ_s with ϕ_m, that the effect of the shading coil is to reduce the flux in the shaded portion of the pole and, at the same time, to shift it in time phase behind the flux in the unshaded portion.

Thus, Fig. 13-7 demonstrates qualitatively why the shading coil reduces the flux in the shaded portion of the pole and why it shifts the phase angle. In a practical motor, the effect is modified somewhat by the action of the rotor currents, but it still persists. The net result of the shifting of the phase angle of the flux in the shaded portion of the pole is to produce the same effect as that of a gliding flux which is constantly shifting from the *main body* toward the *shaded portion*, tending to cause the rotor to move in that direction.

13-6. Performance Characteristics.—Shaded-pole motors are built in a wide variety of ratings and performance characteristics.

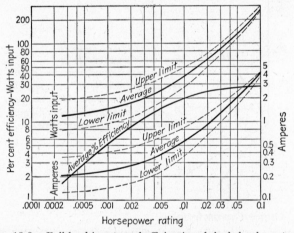

Fig. 13-8.—Full-load inputs and efficiencies of shaded-pole motors.

a. Horsepower Ratings.—Motors are frequently rated at nearly the maximum output, or near the breakdown torque, in order to obtain best efficiencies and highest outputs. Horsepower ratings cover a wide range—from about 0.00025 to 0.1. In the upper end of this range, most of the motors are of four-pole construction; whereas in the medium and lower ranges, two-pole construction is more common.

b. Full-load Inputs.—Full-load watts input and full-load amperes for shaded-pole motors are given in Fig. 13-8, which shows that, even for a given horsepower rating, the input may vary over quite a wide range. It also shows that the efficiency is low, though the total input is so low that efficiency is usually unimportant. This curve was plotted from the performance data on about 70 different shaded-pole motor designs published by four different manufacturers, and should be fairly representative.

c. Speed-torque Characteristics.—Performance characteristics of a typical 0.008-hp motor, taken from data published by Trickey,[1] are given in Fig. 13-9. The speed-torque curve is generally similar in shape to that of a polyphase motor, except that both breakdown and locked-rotor torques are considerably lower in terms of full-load

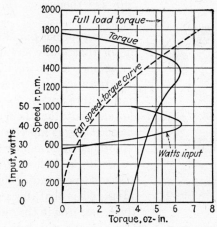

Fig. 13-9.—Performance curves of a shaded-pole motor.

torque. Although the shape of this curve is typical, shaded-pole motors are also made for very high slips, with the breakdown torque occurring at standstill; such motors have lower than normal efficiencies. It is of interest to note, in Fig. 13-9, that the watts input with rotor locked is only about 40 per cent greater than at full load. For this reason, many of the smaller ratings can be stalled indefinitely without harm.

d. Locked-rotor and Breakdown Torques.—Locked-rotor torques range from 40 to 90 per cent of full load, with a tendency toward the higher torques in the lower horsepower ranges. Breakdown torques are low—of the order of 115 to 130 per cent of full load.

e. Speeds.—Most motors in the medium and low horsepower ranges are two-pole motors. For 60-cycle motors, no-load speeds are

[1] For numbered references, see Bibliography at end of this chapter.

from 2700 to 3500 rpm, and full-low speeds are from 1600 to 3000 rpm. In the larger horsepower ratings, four-pole motors are the most common. Sixty-cycle motors have no-load speeds from 1750 to 1770 rpm, and full-load speeds from 1450 to 1620 rpm. Many of these motors are supplied with built-in reduction gearing, with ratios up to 450:1, permitting a wide choice in output shaft speeds.

13-7. Reluctance-start Motor.—In Fig. 13-10 is shown a **reluctance-start motor,** which is not to be confused with the **reluctance motor;** the latter is a synchronous motor, the former is not (see Chap. XV). This motor, although not a shaded-pole type, since it has no shading coil, has about the same general performance characteristics and is, therefore, included in this chapter.

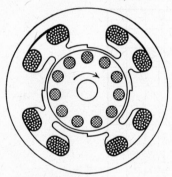

It is a curious paradox that often the motor that is the simplest structurally is the one that is the hardest to understand; for example, single-phase induction motors are simpler than polyphase motors, but the theory of the single-phase motor is more involved. Why a reluctance-start motor has any locked-rotor torque is less obvious than why a shaded-pole motor has. One theory advanced is that, because there is relatively less iron in the magnetic circuit—

Fig. 13-10.—A reluctance-start motor. (*Reprinted from Electrical Manufacturing.*)

compared with the amount of air—on the wide-gap side of the pole, there is less relative damping of the flux due to eddy currents in the iron; therefore, the flux in the wide-gap section leads the flux in the narrow-gap section, producing flux shifting from the wide to the narrow gap, so that the motor runs from the wide to the narrow gap.

John L. Baum[6] made an extensive mathematical analysis of this type of motor and he ascribes locked-rotor torque to two causes:

1. The difference in leakage inductance of the rotor bars on one side of the pole from that on the other causes a different current to flow on each side, producing a resultant torque, as in a repulsion motor.

2. The difference in mutual reactance on the two sides of the poles gives the rotor current under the two sides some difference in phase, which also produces a resultant torque.

13-8. Reversible Shaded-pole Motors.—None of the motors so far discussed in this chapter is reversible, but there are at least three different ways of building reversible shaded-pole motors:

a. With Two Main Windings.—One form of reversible motor employs two main windings and a single shaded-pole winding. For one direction of rotation, one main winding is used; and for the other direction of rotation, the other main winding is used. Such an arrangement is represented schematically in Fig. 13-11. This arrangement is adaptable only to distributed windings, but it can also be used with a motor of the reluctance-start type. If used with a motor of the

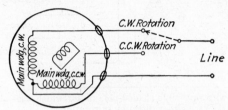

Fig. 13-11.—A reversible shaded-pole motor with two main windings.

reluctance-start type, the tips of the stator teeth halfway between the two main coils are cut off, providing a larger air gap at that portion.

b. With Two Shaded-pole Windings.—Another scheme employed is to use a single main winding and two shaded-pole windings. Such an arrangement is represented schematically in Fig. 13-12. In this case, the two shaded-pole windings are displaced 90 electrical degrees from each other and 45 electrical degrees from the main winding. If one shaded-pole winding is short-circuited, the motor operates in one direction; if the other shaded-pole winding is short-circuited, the motor operates in the other direction of rotation. This reversing arrangement is adaptable to motors either of the distributed-winding type or of the

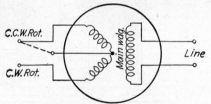

Fig. 13-12.—A reversible shaded-pole motor with two auxiliary windings.

salient-pole type. If used with the salient-pole type, there are a slot in the center of the pole and a shading coil around each half of the pole instead of around only one-half of the pole (see Fig. 13-14).

c. With Continuous Main Winding.—There is another type of reversible shaded-pole motor—used only with distributed windings—in which the full stator winding is used. The arrangement is represented schematically in Fig. 13-13. The main winding is a continuous winding, closing upon itself like the winding of the armature of a d-c motor. There is also a shaded-pole winding short-circuited upon itself. The main winding is tapped at points 90 electrical degrees apart. Care is taken to see that the winding is tapped at points displaced 45 electrical degrees from the center of the shading coils. If, now, two of the taps that are displaced 180 electrical degrees apart are connected to opposite sides of the line, the motor will rotate in

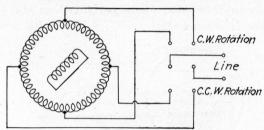

FIG. 13-13.—A four-wire reversible shaded-pole motor which uses all the winding for either direction of rotation.

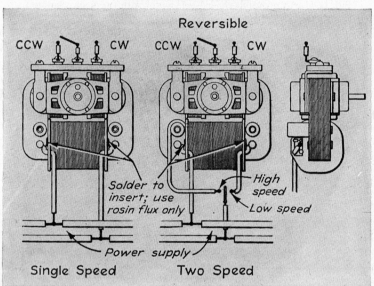

FIG. 13-14.—Reversible shaded-pole motors using two shaded-pole windings. Note that the arrangement is suitable for both single-speed and two-speed motors. (*Courtesy of Barber-Colman Company.*)

one direction; if the other two diametrically opposite taps are used, the rotation will be in the opposite direction. In either case, the entire stator winding will be used. With this arrangement, slightly better efficiency is obtained because the full winding space is utilized. This arrangement can also be used in either a reluctance-start or a shaded-pole motor.

13-9. Variable-speed Motors.—One method of controlling the speed of shaded-pole motors when they are used to drive fans is by means of an external reactor (also known as a "choke coil") connected in series with the motor. This reactor can have one or more taps to provide as many operating speeds as desired; or, variable resistance can be inserted in series with the motor. Speed control can also be effected by using an autotransformer to vary the applied voltage. Tapped windings are also used; an example of a tapped-winding two-speed reversible shaded-pole motor is given in Fig. 13-14. For low speed, the full number of turns is used and, for high speed, a lesser number of turns.

These methods of speed control have the same general limitations discussed in Art. 8-6; *viz.*, speed depends upon the load; locked-rotor torque is necessarily low; these methods are not suited to belted drives; and the low-speed connection is liable to be somewhat unstable.

REWINDING SHADED-POLE MOTORS

13-10. Rewinding for the Original Characteristics.—Form-wound coils can be used for rewinding most shaded-pole motors. For salient-pole motors, the coils are similar in shape and appearance to those

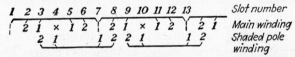

Fig. 13-15.—Stator distribution chart of a shaded-pole motor with distributed windings. Six poles, 36 slots.

used in salient-pole universal motors, and the same general technique and precautions apply. When there is one coil per pole, the coils are connected so that adjacent poles are of opposite magnetic polarity, and the coils may have parallel circuits, as in any other motor. If there are only two coils in a four-pole motor, they go on diametrically opposite poles and are connected for the *same* magnetic polarity. If the stator is of the two-pole skeleton type illustrated in Fig. 13-6, the motor is somewhat harder to rewind, for it is necessary to disassemble the stator laminations—a rather difficult task if the whole motor has been impregnated in varnish. The coil for such a motor is ordinarily wound on a universal winding machine.

If the motor has a distributed winding, the punchings, coils, and winding are similar to that of a split-phase motor. Usually the shading winding is wound on top of the main winding and, when a motor is stripped, it is necessary to remove the shading winding first. Especial care must be taken to record the distribution chart of the motor before stripping, since the shading winding is never displaced by 90 deg from the main winding. A typical stator distribution chart is given in Fig. 13-15, and a stator connection diagram in Fig. 13-16.

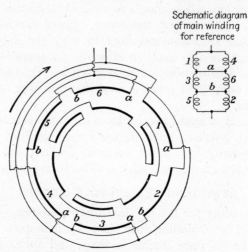

Schematic diagram of main winding for reference

Fig. 13-16.—Stator connection diagram for a shaded-pole motor with distributed windings, six poles, parallel, cross-connected.

13-11. Rewinding for Different Characteristics.—The procedure for determining the correct number of turns and correct wire size for rewinding the shaded-pole motor for any desired voltage or torque characteristics is much the same as the procedure to be followed for determining the windings of a universal motor, except that there is no armature to rewind. In general, the shading coil does not need to be changed, although it may have to be removed in order to remove the main winding. Of course, if there are two main windings, as shown in Fig. 13-11, it will be necessary to strip and rewind both of these windings. In all the types discussed, however, the following procedures are applicable:

a. For Different Voltage.—To rewind to obtain the same performance on a circuit of a voltage higher or lower than rated voltage, rewind the coils with more or less turns in direct proportion to the increase or decrease in voltage. After the number of turns has been determined, use in all windings wire of the largest size that can be used and still allow the required number of turns in the slots. If the total cross section of copper in the new winding is the same as, or greater than, in the old winding, the performance should be equal to, or slightly better than, the performance of the old motor; but if the total amount of copper used in each slot is less, the performance will be slightly poorer.

b. For Different Torques or Speed.—Before an attempt is made to rewind a shaded-pole motor to obtain a different speed or a different torque when operating a given device, a careful application test should first be made with the original winding. The applied voltage should be adjusted until the desired torque or speed characteristics are obtained. A temperature run should then be taken to determine whether or not the motor can safely operate at the desired circuit voltage. (If the watts input at the newly found voltage is not greatly different from the watts input at the original voltage, a temperature test is unnecessary.) By this procedure, a new operating voltage will be found; say, for purposes of illustration, that this new voltage is 150 volts. Now consider the motor as if it had been originally rated for a 150-volt circuit, and, on this basis, rewind for a circuit of the voltage on which it may be operated, say 115, following the rules laid down in the preceding paragraph.

FAN-MOTOR WINDINGS

13-12. General.—A brief history of the development of fan-motor windings is given in the two following articles. For a more complete story, see an article by E. W. Denman[4] or the book by Braymer and Roe.[5]

13-13. Series Motor.—Some of the earliest fans used a series type of motor. Speed control was effected by using a tapped resistor built into the base of the fan. Also, in some of the designs, speed control was obtained by shifting the brushes. In some of these earlier motors, it is interesting to note that only one field coil was used.

13-14. Induction-type Motors. *a. Shaded-pole.*—Some of the earliest type of induction-motor windings used for small fans were of the salient-pole type, using a shading coil.

b. Split-phase.—A later development of fan-motor windings was to use a split-phase motor. In some of these split-phase motors, a centrifugal starting switch was used to open the starting winding. In other designs, the starting switch was omitted, and the starting winding was left in the circuit all the time. The omission of the starting switch increased the watts input, but the performance was comparable to the performance of a shaded-pole motor and, therefore, acceptable. In this type of winding—where the starting switch was not used—the starting winding was displaced about 30, and not 90, deg, from the main winding.

c. *Tapped-field, Split-phase.*—Fans were also built using a tapped-field arrangement similar to the arrangement used in the two-speed tapped-winding motors discussed in Chap. IX and shown in Fig. 9-1a, except that the capacitor shown in this figure should be replaced with a starting switch. In this type of winding, as described in Chap. IX, there are two main windings; or it may be considered that there are a main winding and an intermediate winding, both wound in the same slots. For three-speed motors, a tap was brought out from the center of the intermediate winding and used for the medium-speed connection.

d. *Special Split-phase Winding for High Locked-rotor Torque.*—Another type of winding was developed for fan motors and was found to give high locked-rotor torque, high efficiency, high running speeds, and large speed reduction and that required no starting switch. This winding is represented schematically in Fig. 13-17. It can be seen

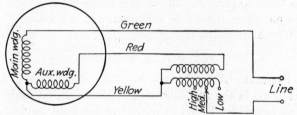

Fig. 13-17.—A special split-phase motor used for desk fans. This motor employs no starting switch.

that there is a tapped transformer used with this arrangement, and the main winding is connected in series with the primary of this transformer; the starting or auxiliary winding is connected permanently across the secondary of this transformer. With this arrangement, it has been found that, under starting conditions, nearly 90-deg phase displacement can be obtained between the currents in the two stator windings and high locked-rotor torque thereby obtained. Moreover, the losses under the running conditions are lower than when the auxiliary winding is connected directly across the line. Speed control is effected by changing the taps on the primary of the autotransformer.

13-15. Capacitor Windings.—Capacitor windings, which have recently been used in fans, have been found to reduce the weight of the motor body considerably, and, in many cases, it was found that the watts input could be reduced as much as 25 per cent by using capacitor-type windings. There are two principal types of connections, one of which is used for 115-volt fans and the other for 230-volt fans.

a. 230-volt Fans.—For 230-volt fans, the windings are the same as those of a conventional permanent-split motor of the same type and arrangement shown in Fig. 7-1 and discussed in Art. 7-3. For the connections of such a motor, refer to Fig. 13-18. For speed control, a variable reactor is used in series with the motor winding, as shown in the figure.

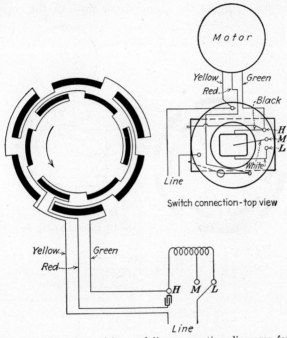

Fig. 13-18.—Stator connection, wiring and line connection diagrams for a capacitor motor used for desk-fan service, 230 volt motors. (See Art. 13-15.)

b. 115-volt Fans.—For 115-volt motors, a slightly different arrangement of windings is used in order to increase the voltage on the capacitor. This arrangement is shown in Fig. 13-19. To understand just how these connections operate, connect the line to the high-speed (*H*) contact instead of to the low-speed (*L*), as shown in the figure. Now, if we examine the circuit arrangement, we shall see that the motor is a conventional permanent-split motor of the same type shown in Fig. 13-18, except for the capacitor; the capacitor unit, in this case, consists of an autotransformer used to step up the voltage on the capacitor element itself in much the same manner that an autotransformer is used in the two-value motor shown in Fig. 6-1. It may be considered that this autotransformer steps up the voltage on the capacitor, or it may be considered that the autotransformer has the effect of increasing the effective capacitance, as discussed in Chap. VI. Now, then, for medium or low speed, the switch is moved to either the *M* or *L* position, thereby inserting reactance in series with both motor windings. This insertion of reactance reduces the voltage on both of the windings because of the drop in the reactance and also reduces the effective capacitance by changing the transformer ratio of the capacitor unit.

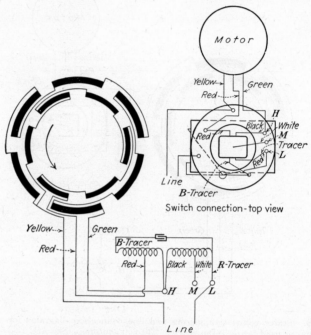

Fig. 13-19.—Stator connection, wiring and line connection diagrams for a capacitor motor used for desk-fan service, 115-volt motors.

Bibliography

1. Trickey, P. H.: An Analysis of the Shaded Pole Motor, *Elec. Eng.*, September, 1936, pp. 1007–1014.
2. Rall, Carl A.: This Motor Meets Many Product Needs, *Elec. Manufacturing* June, 1937, pp. 31–35.
3. Veinott, C. G.: Discussion on Trickey's Paper, *Elec. Eng.*, May, 1937, pp. 612–613.
4. Denman, E. W.: Development of Fan Motor Windings, *Elec. J.*, June, 1919.
5. Braymer, Daniel H., and Roe, A. C.: "Rewinding Small Motors," Chap. XX, McGraw-Hill Book Company, Inc., New York, 1932.
6. Baum, John L.: The Asymmetrical Stator as a Means of Starting Single-phase Induction Motors, *A.I.E.E. Trans.*, vol. 63, 1944, pp. 245–250.

CHAPTER XIV

POLYPHASE INDUCTION MOTORS

In the field of integral horsepower motors, the polyphase induction motor dominates the industry, and very few single-phase motors are used. In the field of fractional horsepower motors, exactly the opposite is true; for nearly all the motors used are for operation on single-phase circuits, and relatively few polyphase motors are found. The principal reason for the use of single-phase motors is simply that, in most installations where fractional horsepower motors are used, polyphase alternating current is not available. If polyphase power does happen to be available, single-phase motors can always be used, but polyphase motors cannot be operated on a single-phase source. In general, in fractional horsepower sizes, single-phase induction motors sell at lower prices than polyphase induction motors, principally because of their larger activity; and price is another reason why single-phase motors are often used even in some cases where polyphase motors could be used.

The polyphase induction motor has been widely discussed in literature, and excellent books for the repairman have been written.[1,2,3] Because so much has already been published about polyphase induction motors, the treatment of the subject in this chapter is purposely made brief. In general, the information published about the larger induction motors is more or less applicable to fractional horsepower polyphase motors, but there are fewer modifications in the smaller size motors. In this chapter, the polyphase induction motor is treated from the standpoint of fractional horsepower sizes.

14-1. Essential Parts of a Polyphase Induction Motor.—A polyphase induction motor is illustrated in Fig. 14-1. The essential parts are

1. A **primary winding,** usually placed on the stator, but sometimes on the rotor. The primary winding is the winding connected directly to the source of power, regardless of whether it is on the stator or on the rotor. In the case of a two-phase motor, there are two electrically distinct windings displaced by 90 electrical degrees. In the three-

[1,2,3] For numbered references, see Bibliography at the end of this chapter.

phase induction motor, there are three windings, or phases, displaced 60 electrical degrees from each other.   The connections of the center phase are reversed so that the voltages induced in the three windings

FIG. 14-1.—A polyphase induction motor.   (*Courtesy of Emerson Electric Manufacturing Company.*)

are 120 deg apart.   These three phases may be connected in the circuit by any one of the common connections discussed in Art. 1-11 and illustrated in Fig. 1-7.

2. A **secondary winding,** usually placed on the rotor, which may

a. Be of squirrel-cage construction, or
b. Have phase windings like the primary.   If a phase-wound rotor is used, it is the customary practice to use a three-phase winding,

regardless of whether the primary is wound for two or for three phases.

3. There are no switches, short-circuiters, or other mechanisms required, except that collector rings and brushes are required for wound-rotor induction motors, also for motors that have a revolving primary.

14-2. Principle of the Polyphase Induction Motor.—The principle of operation of a two-phase induction motor is discussed in Chap. II, wherein it was shown that polyphase windings, excited by polyphase currents, set up a rotating magnetic field which causes the rotor to follow it and thereby act as a motor. The speed of this rotating field is known as the **synchronous speed.** The motor always runs slower than synchronous speed, and the difference between the actual operating speed and synchronous speed is known as the **slip.** The slip is usually expressed as a percentage of the synchronous speed.

Following are the minimum torque requirements that have been established by Nema for fractional horsepower, 60-cycle, squirrel-cage, polyphase induction motors:

	4-pole motors	6-pole motors
Locked-rotor, per cent of full load...............	150	135
Breakdown, per cent of full load.................	200	200

Torques of commercially available motors may exceed the above values by quite a margin.

WINDINGS AND CONNECTIONS

14-3. Lap Winding for Polyphase Motors.—Most fractional horsepower motors use diamond-shaped mush-wound coils; *i.e.*, the coils are wound from round wire and are inserted into partly closed slots, a few wires at a time. Usually there are as many stator coils as there are slots, or, in other words, two coil sides per slot, making what is known as a two-layer winding. All the coils are identical in number of turns and size of wire, and the phase coils are usually better insulated than the other coils. (A **phase coil** is a coil adjacent to a coil of a different phase.) The typical way in which such a winding progresses is shown in Fig. 3-1. The coils are connected in groups; *e.g.*, in Fig. 3-1 there are four coils per group. A **group** is simply a given number of individual coils connected in series, with only two leads brought out, and the stator winding is then connected from these groups. So far as the winding itself is concerned, the lap winding used in a polyphase motor is very similar to the lap winding used in a d-c armature. However, in the d-c winding all the coils are connected in series, and

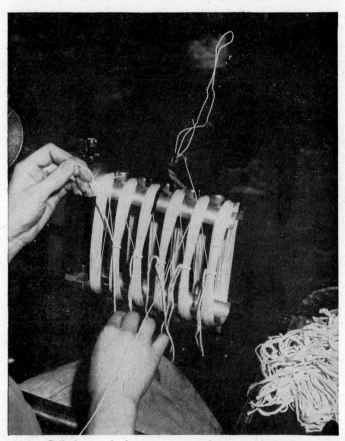

Fig. 14-2.—Coils for a polyphase motor wound on a mold of a light weight which permits fast winding. Six coils, enough for two groups in this case, are wound from a continuous strand of wire. Start and finish leads of each group are marked by dark- and light-colored sleeves threaded onto the wire before winding. Figure 14-3 shows removal of these coils. (*Courtesy of Westinghouse Electric Corporation.*)

a closed winding is formed; whereas in polyphase motors the coils are connected in a number of groups.

In the mush-wound coils used in fractional horsepower motors, it is a fairly common practice to wind all the coils of a single group from a continuous strand of wire (see Figs. 14-2 and 14-3). If there are the same number of coils in all groups, this is a very desirable practice because it eliminates a number of connections and simplifies the final connections of a wound stator. If, however, the number of coils is not the same in all groups (see Art. 14-9), it may be less confusing to bring out the connections from each individual coil and to connect them in groups after the stator is wound.

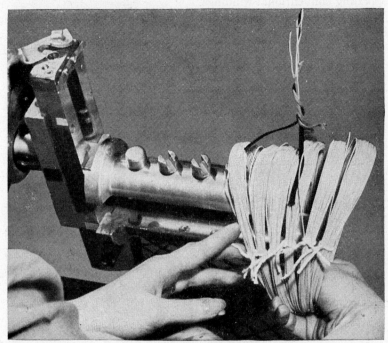

Fig. 14-3.—Easy collapsibility of this mold, shown in Fig. 14-2 before collapsing, permits ready removal of both coil groups together. The two groups can be left connected or can be cut apart by cutting the single loop of wire. Coil perimeter can be varied over a wide range by adjusting the separation of the two halves of the mold. (*Courtesy of Westinghouse Electric Corporation.*)

14-4. Number of Groups and Number of Coils per Group.—In the ordinary winding (as distinguished from a consequent-pole winding), there is one group per phase per pole. Therefore,

$$\text{Number of groups} = \text{number of poles} \times \text{number of phases} \qquad (14\text{-}1)$$

$$\text{Number of coils per group} = \frac{\text{total number of coils}}{\text{number of groups}} \qquad (14\text{-}2)$$

If the number of coils per group works out to be a whole number, each group has this number of coils—but if a fractional number is obtained, an unequal grouping of the coils must be used, as explained in Art. 14-9, and shown in Tables X and XI. Windings that have an integral number of coils per group are often referred to as **integral-slot windings.** Similarly, windings with a fractional number of coils per group are often called **fractional-slot windings.**

Consequent-pole windings have half as many groups as the corresponding conventional windings.

14-5. "Throw-up" and "Throw-down" Windings.—In the usual two-layer lap winding, each and every coil has one side in the bottom of a slot and the other side in the top of some other slot. This means

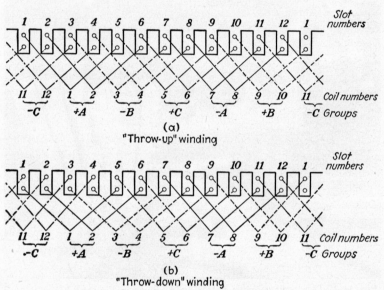

Fig. 14-4.—Two types of polyphase windings.

that when the first coils are inserted, only the bottom coil side can be placed in the slot, and the top coil side must be left inside the stator bore, but not in a slot, until the winding is nearly completed. In the case of two-pole induction motors, where the throw is large, there would normally be a large number of these coil sides in the bore. As the bore of a two-pole motor is relatively small, the large number of coil sides interferes with the winding process so that it is a fairly common practice to wind the coils **throw down.** In the throw-down winding, both coil sides of all the first coils are inserted in the slots, which means that the first coils wound have both sides in the bottoms of the slots. This point is illustrated in Fig. 14-4b. As a result, the last coils wound have both coil sides in the tops of the slots. This throw-down winding is compared with the conventional, or throw-up, winding, which is shown in Fig. 14-4a.

The throw-down winding does cause a slight electrical unbalance but usually not enough to have serious consequences.

14-6. "Short-throw" and "Long-throw" Connections.—In integral horsepower motors, there are two types of connections between the groups which are recognized:

1. Top-to-top, using short jumpers.
2. Top-to-bottom, using long jumpers.

In this chapter, the terms **short throw** and **long throw** are used because they are less confusing than the other terms, particularly in the case of a throw-down winding.

In the short-throw connection (top-to-top), each group is connected to another group displaced 180 electrical degrees. In the long-throw connection (top-to-bottom), a group is connected to another group displaced 360 electrical degrees away. In single-phase windings, there are similarly two such connections, as discussed in Art. 4-12.

When parallel connections are used, it is desirable to use the long throw if possible, in order to balance the magnetic pull on the rotor. However, in the case of unequal grouping of coils (Arts. 14-9 to 14-12), it is usually necessary to use the short throw. If the stator is series-connected, it makes no difference whether the long or short throw is used; whichever is the more convenient connection may be employed. For example, if a motor is parallel-connected using the long throw, it can be reconnected in series more easily by also using the long throw on the series connection.

14-7. Stator (or Rotor) Connection Diagrams, Single Voltage, Two- and Three-Phase.—Diagrams for the more common connections used in fractional horsepower polyphase motors are given in Figs. 14-5 to 14-28. These diagrams are reproduced, by permission, from Dudley's book "Connecting Induction Motors."[1] Many other connection diagrams for polyphase induction motors are given by Dudley, also by Braymer and Roe.[2,3]

14-8. How to Check a Diagram or Winding.—There are so many possible methods of connecting polyphase induction motors that it is impossible to give them all in a book of this scope. It is, therefore, desirable that the serviceman know how to check the correctness of a diagram, for he may often be called upon to make up his own connection diagrams or to try to check the correctness of another diagram or

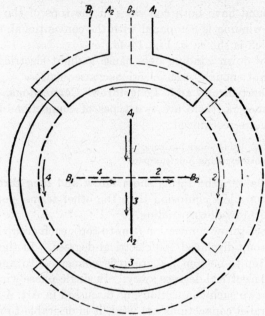

FIG. 14-5.—Stator connection diagram, two poles, two phase, series, short throw. (*After Dudley.*)

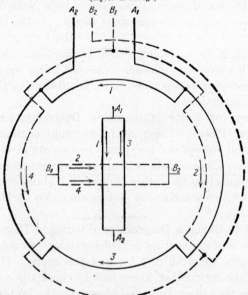

FIG. 14-6.—Stator connection diagram, two poles, two phase, parallel, short throw. (*After Dudley.*)

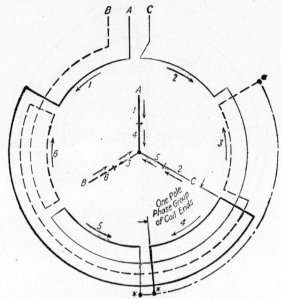

Fig. 14-7.—Stator connection diagram, two poles, three phase, series Y, short throw. (*After Dudley.*)

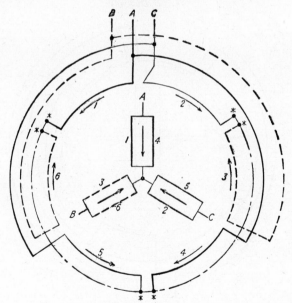

Fig. 14-8.—Stator connection diagram, two poles, three phase, parallel Y, short throw. (*After Dudley.*)

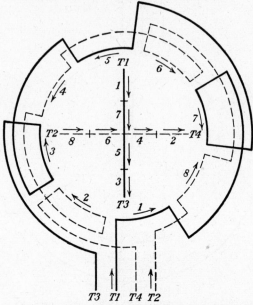

Fig. 14-9.—Stator connection diagram, four poles, two phase, series, short throw. (*After Dudley.*)

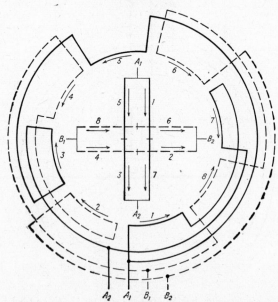

Fig. 14-10.—Stator connection diagram, four poles, two phase, parallel, short throw. (*After Dudley.*)

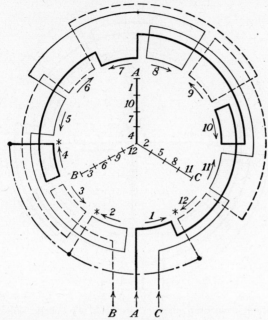

Fig. 14-11.—Stator connection diagram, four poles, three phase, series Y, short throw. (*After Dudley.*)

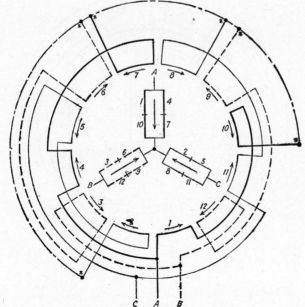

Fig. 14-12.—Stator connection diagram, four poles, three phase, parallel Y, short throw. (*After Dudley.*)

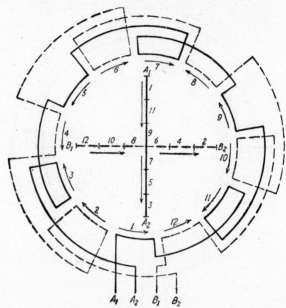

Fig. 14-13.—Stator connection diagram, six poles, two phase, series, short throw. (*After Dudley.*)

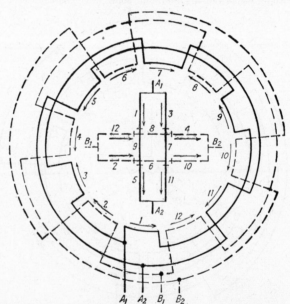

Fig. 14-14.—Stator connection diagram, six poles, two phase, parallel, long throw. (*After Dudley.*)

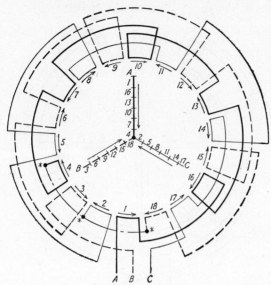

Fig. 14-15.—Stator connection diagram, six poles, three phase, series **Y**, short throw. (*After Dudley.*)

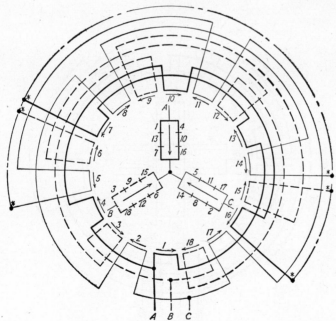

Fig. 14-16.—Stator connection diagram, six poles, three phase, parallel **Y**, long throw. (*After Dudley.*)

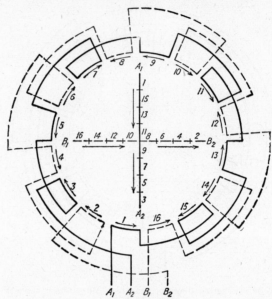

Fig. 14-17.—Stator connection diagram, eight poles, two phase, series, short throw. (*After Dudley.*)

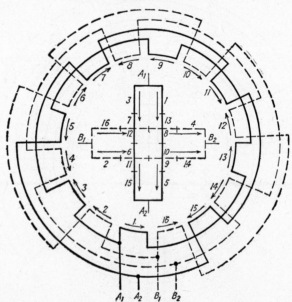

Fig. 14-18.—Stator connection diagram, eight poles, two phase, parallel, long throw. (*After Dudley.*)

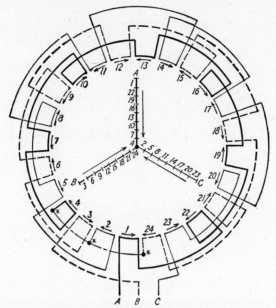

Fig. 14-19.—Stator connection diagram, eight poles, three phase, series Y, short throw. (*After Dudley.*)

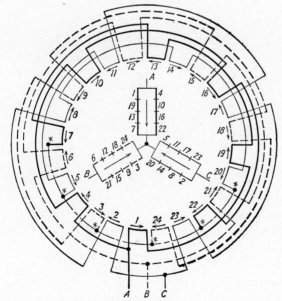

Fig. 14-20.—Stator connection diagram, eight poles, three phase, parallel Y, long throw. (*After Dudley.*)

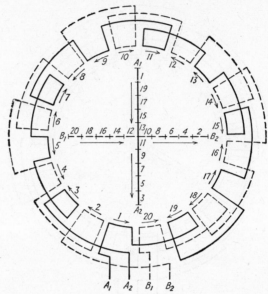

FIG. 14-21.—Stator connection diagram, 10 poles, two phase, series, short throw. (*After Dudley.*)

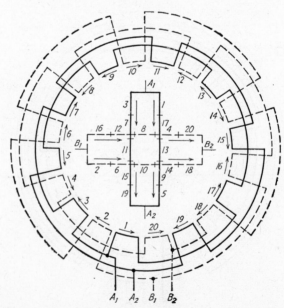

FIG. 14-22.—Stator connection diagram, 10 poles, two phase, parallel, long throw. (*After Dudley.*)

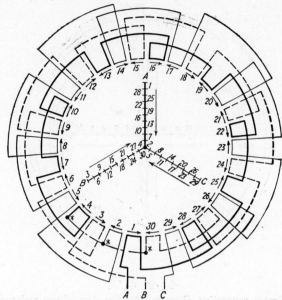

Fig. 14-23.—Stator connection diagram, 10 poles, three phase, series Y, short throw. (*After Dudley.*)

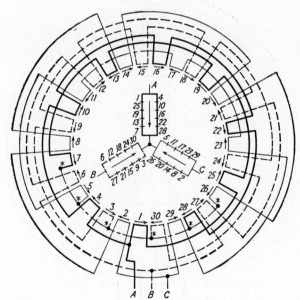

Fig. 14-24.—Stator connection diagram, 10 poles, three phase, parallel Y, long throw. (*After Dudley.*)

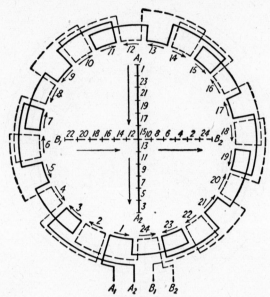

Fig. 14-25.—Stator connection diagram, 12 poles, two phase, series, short throw. (*After Dudley.*)

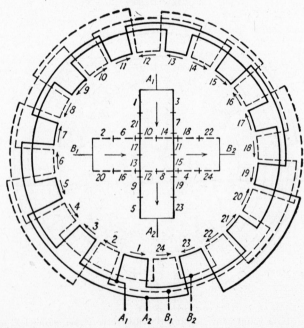

Fig. 14-26.—Stator connection diagram, 12 poles, two phase, parallel, long throw. (*After Dudley.*)

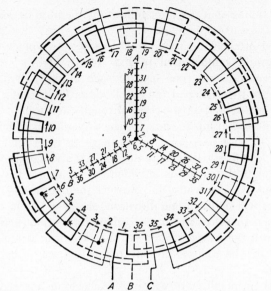

FIG. 14-27.—Stator connection diagram, 12 poles, three phase, series Y, short throw. (*After Dudley.*)

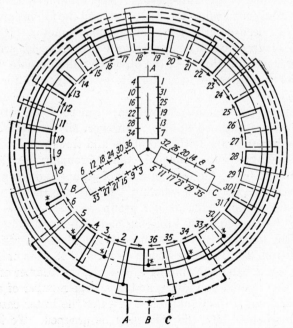

FIG. 14-28.—Stator connection diagram, 12 poles, three phase, parallel Y, long throw. (*After Dudley.*)

of another winding that does not follow any diagram he may have but that may, nevertheless, be correct.

A method of checking the correctness of a two-phase stator connection diagram is illustrated in Fig. 14-9. Arrows are drawn to assume current flow *into* one lead of each of the two phases. The connections are then traced from one lead, as $T1$, through each of the groups and out at $T3$; as we trace through each group, an arrow is marked beside the group to indicate the direction in which the pencil traced through that particular group in going from $T1$ to $T3$. The process is repeated, starting in at the $T2$ lead and again marking each group to indicate the direction in which the group was traversed, until we finally come out at lead $T4$. Now, if the diagram is correct, two of the arrows will point in one direction, the next two in the opposite direction, then the next two in the original direction, and so on; *i.e.*, the arrows will point first clockwise, then counterclockwise, in alternate pairs. If the arrows do not point this way, the diagram is incorrect.

The same principles are applied in checking a three-phase connection diagram, as illustrated in Fig. 14-11. Current is assumed to flow *into* each one of the three leads. The winding is traced three times, once from each lead to the star point, and the groups are marked as has already been described for the two-phase motor. Now if the three-phase diagram is to be correct, no two adjacent arrows will point in the same direction; *i.e.*, the direction will alternate with each coil. Unless this direction does alternate with every coil, the diagram is not correct.

Diagrams for consequent-pole windings can be checked by following the procedure outlined above. However, all arrows must point in the same direction, for both two-phase and three-phase windings.

14-9. Windings with Unequal Coil Grouping.—Article 14-4 explained how to figure the total number of groups and the number of coils per group in a polyphase winding. It was also therein explained that the total number of coils per group was not always a whole number, so that unequal coil grouping had to be used. In Table X are shown the possibilities for balanced three-phase lap windings for windings of from 2 to 12 poles, inclusive, for 6 to 48 slots or coils. In each case where a balanced winding is possible, the number of coils per group has been figured and given, and in a large number of cases this number comes out a fractional number. For the latter cases, Table XI is given to show how the coils may be grouped. To illustrate: assume that it is desired to put a four-pole winding into 15 stator slots. The number of coils per group is $1\frac{1}{4}$, from Table X. In Table XI we find that with $1\frac{1}{4}$ coils per group, the grouping is 2–1–1–1–2–1–1–1–2–1–1–1. This means that the first group in phase *A* has 2 coils per group; then, progressing around the stator, the next three groups have 1 coil each; the next group, 2 coils; the next three groups, 1 coil each; and so on, progressing completely around the stator. If there are $1\frac{1}{4}$ coils per group, this grouping is the same whether the winding is 4 poles in 15 slots, 8 poles in 30 slots, or 12 poles in 45 slots.

In Table X under Circuits is given the maximum number of parallel circuits into which it is possible to divide a balanced winding for the combination shown. If a parallel winding is used, it is not necessary to connect into so many parallel paths as the maximum number indicates, but the number of parallel paths used may be any factor of the maximum number of possible parallels. For example, if 6 parallels are possible, 6, 3, or 2 parallel paths may be used. If 10 parallels are possible, 10, 5, or 2 parallels may be used.

TABLE X.—BALANCED THREE-PHASE LAP WINDINGS
(Maximum number of parallel circuits, number of coils per group, for equal and unequal groupings)

Num- ber of slots or coils	2 poles		4 poles		6 poles		8 poles		10 poles		12 poles	
	Circuits	Coils per group	Circuits	Coils per group	Circuits	Coils per group	Circuits	Coils per group	Circuits	Coils per group	Circuits	Coils per group
6	2	1										
9	1	$1\frac{1}{2}$										
12	2	2	4	1								
15	1	$2\frac{1}{2}$	1	$1\frac{1}{4}$								
18	2	3	2	$1\frac{1}{2}$	6	1						
21	1	$3\frac{1}{2}$	1	$1\frac{3}{4}$	0							
24	2	4	4	2	0	...	8	1				
27	1	$4\frac{1}{2}$	1	$2\frac{1}{4}$	3	$1\frac{1}{2}$	1	$1\frac{1}{8}$				
30	2	5	2	$2\frac{1}{2}$	0	...	2	$1\frac{1}{4}$	10	1		
33	1	$5\frac{1}{2}$	1	$2\frac{3}{4}$	0	...	1	$1\frac{3}{8}$	1	$1\frac{1}{10}$		
36	2	6	4	3	6	2	4	$1\frac{1}{2}$	2	$1\frac{1}{5}$	12	1
39	1	$6\frac{1}{2}$	1	$3\frac{1}{4}$	0	...	1	$1\frac{5}{8}$	1	$1\frac{3}{10}$	0	
42	2	7	2	$3\frac{1}{2}$	0	...	2	$1\frac{3}{4}$	2	$1\frac{2}{5}$	0	
45	1	$7\frac{1}{2}$	1	$3\frac{3}{4}$	3	$2\frac{1}{2}$	1	$1\frac{7}{8}$	5	$1\frac{1}{2}$	3	$1\frac{1}{4}$
48	2	8	4	4	0	...	8	2	2	$1\frac{3}{5}$	0	

0 indicates no balanced winding is possible.
If the coils per group is a whole number, all groups have the indicated number of coils.
If the coils per group is not a whole number, refer to Table XI for the grouping.

In general, when the coil grouping is unequal, the short-throw connection must be used for parallel-connected windings. In the single-voltage diagrams (Figs. 14-5 to 14-28), the parallel diagrams, except for two- and four-pole motors, are long throw and should not be used with unequal coil grouping. The dual-voltage diagrams (Figs. 14-29 to 14-34) are all short throw and may be used in such cases for reference. However, only the three leads necessary need actually be brought out of the winding. (That is, referring to Fig. 14-31, for example, $T1$ and $T7$ are connected together internally, and one lead $T1$ is brought out; also one lead only, $T2$, is brought out from the two leads $T2$ and $T8$; one lead $T3$ is brought out from the two leads $T3$ and $T9$; and the leads $T4$, $T5$, and $T6$, are all connected to the star point inside the winding.) Thus, for windings with unequal

TABLE XI.—BALANCED THREE-PHASE LAP WINDINGS WITH UNEQUAL COIL GROUPING

Average number of coils per group	Group number																													
	1	2	3	4	5	6	7	8	9	10	11	12	13	14	15	16	17	18	19	20	21	22	23	24	25	26	27	28	29	30
1 1/10	2	1	1	1	1	1	1	1	1	1	2	1	1	1	1	1	1	1	1	2	1	1	1	1	1	1	1	1	1	1
1 1/8	2	1	1	1	1	1	1	1	2	1	1	1	1	1	1	1	2	1	1	1	1	1	1	1						
1 1/6	2	1	1	1	1	1	2	1	1	1	1	1	2	1	1	1	1	1												
1 1/4	2	1	1	1	2	1	1	1	2	1	1	1																		
1 3/10	2	1	1	2	1	1	2	1	1	1	2	1	1	2	1	1	2	1	1	2	1	1	1	2	1	1	2	1	1	1
1 3/8	2	1	2	1	1	2	1	1	2	1	2	1	1	2	1	1	2	1	1	2	1	1	2	1						
1 2/5	2	1	2	1	1	2	1	2	1	1	2	1	2	1	1	2	1	2	1	1										
1 1/2	2	1	2	1	2	1																								
1 3/5	2	2	1	2	1	2	2	1	2	1	2	2	1	2	1	2	2	1	2	1										
1 5/8	2	2	1	2	2	1	2	1	2	2	1	2	2	1	2	1														
1 3/4	2	2	2	1	2	2	2	1	2	2	2	1																		
1 7/8	2	2	2	2	2	2	1	2	2	2	2	2	2	1	2	2														
2 1/4	3	2	2	2	3	2	2	2	3	2	2	2																		
2 1/2	3	2	3	2	3	2																								
2 3/4	3	3	3	2	3	3	3	2	3	3	3	2																		
3 1/4	4	3	3	3	4	3	3	3	4	3	3	3																		
3 1/2	4	3	4	3	4	3																								
3 3/4	4	4	4	3	4	4	4	3	4	4	4	3																		
4 1/2	5	4	5	4	5	4																								
5 1/2	6	5	6	5	6	5																								
6 1/2	7	6	7	6	7	6																								
7 1/2	8	7	8	7	8	7																								

If a parallel connection is used, the short-throw or top-to-top connection must be used with the grouping given in the table.

coil grouping, the dual-voltage connection diagrams can be used for single-voltage motors as well as for dual-voltage motors.

An explanation of how the coil groupings given in Table XI were determined is explained in Art. 14-10 for the benefit of those who may have occasion to work out combinations that are not listed.

14-10. How to Determine Coil Groupings for Three-phase Fractional-slot Windings.

—Coil groupings for fractional-slot windings are not so difficult to determine as popularly supposed. The first step is to compute the number of coils per group, as explained in Art. 14-4; for any fractional-slot winding this comes out a number and a fraction. Next step is to reduce this number and fraction to an improper fraction, *i.e.*, a fraction in which the numerator is larger than the denominator, thereby eliminating the whole number. Now, call the numerator of this improper fraction R and the denominator N; *i.e.*, there are R/N coils per group, or R/N slots per pole per phase. Numerical values of both R and N are very significant:

$N = 3\ N.G.$

1. For three-phase windings, if $N = 3$ or any multiple of 3, a balanced winding is impossible.

2. N equals the minimum number of poles in any circuit of the winding; the maximum number of parallel paths is equal to the number of poles divided by N. However, the actual number of parallel paths can be any factor of the maximum number.

$\#\ \text{paths} = \frac{poles}{N}$

3. Distribution factor of the fractional-slot winding is the same as the distribution factor for an integral-slot winding with R slots per pole per phase.

NOTE: It can be shown from (1) that a balanced three-phase winding can be put into any number of slots divisible by 3 unless the number of poles is divisible by 6. If the winding has 6, 12, or 24 poles, the number of slots must be divisible by 9; if the winding has 18 or 36 poles, the number of slots must be divisible by 27.

Now, lay out on a piece of plain paper a group of dots consisting of N horizontal rows with R dots in each row; similarly, lay out two more identical groups as shown in the illustrative example below, so that there are actually N rows with $3R$ dots per row, with the dots divided into three major groups by two vertical lines. The procedure can best be explained by the use of a practical example.

Example: Lay out a 10-pole 3-phase winding in 48 slots.
Solution:

$$\text{Coils per group} = \frac{48}{3 \times 10} = 1\tfrac{3}{5} = \tfrac{8}{5}$$

Hence,

$$R = 8 \quad \text{and} \quad N = 5$$

Since N is not a multiple of 3, a balanced winding is possible. There must be a minimum of 5 poles per circuit, so that the maximum number of parallel paths is equal to $1\tfrac{0}{5} = 2$. Now, to determine the coil grouping, we lay out a first block of dots consisting of 5 rows of 8 dots in each row, and repeat this group twice more as shown below:

	Phase A	Phase B	Phase C
Pole 1	✓ ✓	✓ ✓	✓
Pole 2	✓ ✓	✓	✓ ✓
Pole 3	✓ ✓	✓	✓ ✓
Pole 4	✓	✓ ✓	✓ ✓
Pole 5	✓	✓ ✓	✓

Starting with the first dot in the first row, a check mark is placed just above it; N dots are counted and a second check mark placed over the dot, and so on. In this case, $N = 5$, so a check mark is placed over the 1st, 6th, 11th, 16th dots, etc. Now, the number of check marks shows the number of coils in the group for each phase for each of the first 5 poles. Hence, the number of coils in each successive group, starting at the top and reading across and down in normal fashion, is 2-2-1-2-1-2-2-1-2-1-2-2-1-2-1. (Compare this with the grouping given in Table XI.) For the next 5 poles, this same grouping repeats itself.

The reader is cautioned that it is seemingly possible to lay out a balanced winding for any case where the number of slots is divisible by 3, even if N is equal to 3 or any multiple of 3. Such windings are not balanced, however, but three special cases of this kind are discussed in Art. 14-12.

14-11. Two-phase Fractional-slot Windings.—Fractional-slot windings for two-phase machines can be laid out following the same general process that was described for three-phase windings in Art. 14-10. First, the number of slots per pole per phase is determined and reduced to an improper fraction, R/N. If N is not equal to 2 or to any multiple of 2, the coil grouping can be determined by the process described in Art. 14-10 for three-phase machines except that there are only two groups of dots consisting of N rows of R dots in each row. *However, if $N = 2$, the process gives erroneous and false results.* For example, consider a 4-pole 36-slot winding. Here, $R = 9$ and $N = 2$, or the number of coils per group is $4\frac{1}{2}$. Following the procedure of Art. 14-10 gives a coil grouping of 5-4-5-4-5-4-5-4. All the groups in one phase would have 5 coils per group, and all groups in the other phase would have 4 coils per group; *obviously, the phases would not be balanced!* But balance can be achieved by grouping the coils 5-5-4-4-5-5-4-4, provided a short-throw connection diagram is used. In general, as stated in Art. 14-9, short-throw diagrams must be used when the coil grouping is unequal.

14-12. Irregular Windings.—In Table X it was shown by a 0 that balanced windings are not possible with certain numbers of slots, notably for 6- and 12-pole motors. In many cases, however, there is

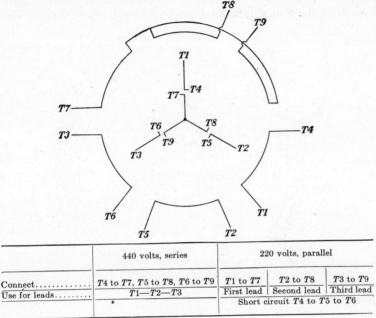

	440 volts, series	220 volts, parallel		
Connect.............	T4 to T7, T5 to T8, T6 to T9	T1 to T7	T2 to T8	T3 to T9
Use for leads........	T1—T2—T3	First lead	Second lead	Third lead
		Short circuit *T4* to *T5* to *T6*		

Fig. 14-29.—Stator connection diagram, dual-voltage, two poles, three phase, short throw, series and parallel star.

a possible winding arrangement which is nearly enough balanced to use. Three such arrangements are given below:

Slots or coils	Poles	Grouping
24	6	2–1–1–1–1–2–1–2–1 and repeat
48	6	2–3–3–3–3–2–3–2–3 and repeat
48	12	2–1–1–1–1–2–1–2–1 and repeat

These winding arrangements are satisfactory for ordinary squirrel-cage motors. However, if an irregular winding arrangement such as one of these is used for either the primary or secondary winding of a wound-rotor induction motor, a serious loss in torque may be encountered, due to this irregular winding.   This reduction may be as much as 25 per cent, as reported by Hellmund and Veinott.[5]

14-13. Wound-rotor Motors.—In the case of wound-rotor motors, the secondary or rotor windings are usually of the same type as the stator, *i.e.*, using mush-wound diamond-shaped coils, with two coil sides per slot.   The rotor is usually wound for three phases, regardless of whether the stator is wound for two or for three phases.   In the

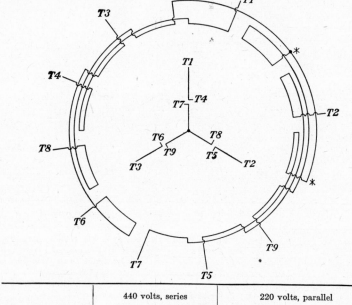

	440 volts, series		220 volts, parallel		
Connect............	T4 to T7, T5 to T8, T6 to T9		T1 to T7	T2 to T8	T3 to T9
Use for leads........	T1—T2—T3		First lead	Second lead	Third lead
			Short circuit T4 to T5 to T6		

Fig. 14-30.—Stator connection diagram, dual-voltage, four poles, three phase, short throw, series and parallel star.

case of a wound-rotor induction motor, the speed, at any given load, can be reduced by the use of external resistors connected in series with the secondary circuit.   It is this possibility of speed reduction that constitutes the principal reason for using motors of this type.   However, motors of this type are often used as synchronous-drive motors (see Chap. XVI).

14-14. Dual-voltage Motors.—Stator connection diagrams for dual-voltage motors are given in Figs. 14-29 to 14-34.   A schematic diagram is given with each one of these figures, all of which are for series and parallel star. The terminal markings of all of these diagrams are in conformance with the latest American standards.[6]

It is to be noted here that there are certain combinations of slots and poles into which it is not possible to put a dual-voltage winding;

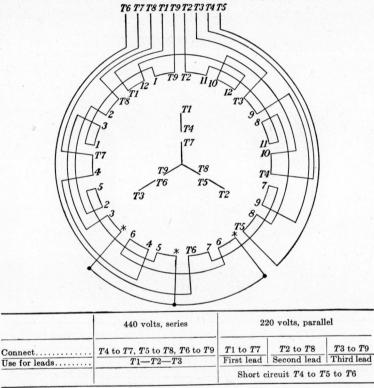

	440 volts, series	220 volts, parallel		
Connect.............	T4 to T7, T5 to T8, T6 to T9	T1 to T7	T2 to T8	T3 to T9
Use for leads........	T1—T2—T3	First lead	Second lead	Third lead
		Short circuit T4 to T5 to T6		

Fig. 14-31.—Stator connection diagram, dual-voltage, six poles, three phase, short throw, series and parallel star.

these arrangements are those in which only one circuit per phase is possible and these combinations are shown in Table X. For example, a two-pole winding in 9, 15, 21, 27, etc., slots, or any other combination in which the maximum number of circuits is one, cannot be connected for dual voltage.

REWINDING OR RECONNECTING

14-15. General.—Probably the most popular change to be made in polyphase induction motors is to rewind or reconnect the motor for one of the following:

1. Different voltage
2. Different number of phases
3. Different frequency
4. Different number of poles
5. Different horsepower

Fundamentally, the soundest way for determining such possibilities is to figure the magnetic inductions for the new winding desired,

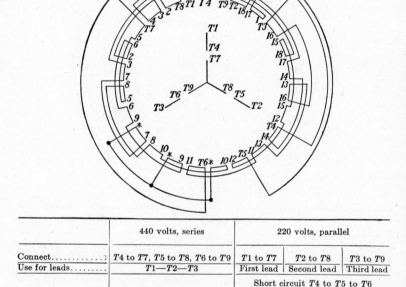

	440 volts, series		220 volts, parallel		
Connect..............	T4 to T7, T5 to T8, T6 to T9		T1 to T7	T2 to T8	T3 to T9
Use for leads........	T1—T2—T3		First lead	Second lead	Third lead
			Short circuit T4 to T5 to T6		

Fig. 14-32.—Stator connection diagram, dual-voltage, eight poles, three phase, short throw, series and parallel star.

designing the winding to operate the magnetic parts at a maximum permissible safe value. This method is essentially the same as the one followed by a design engineer in making up new designs and is probably the safest method that can be used. Before attempting to discuss this method in detail (as will be done in Art. 14-21), we shall first discuss a number of short cuts which will eliminate much unnecessary labor and give the serviceman a rough idea of what is to be expected of any given change.

As mentioned in the preceding paragraph, there are five basic changes that can be made in polyphase induction motor windings. It is best to take up these changes one at a time. In the following articles, changing each one of these major factors is discussed; and, in each case, it is assumed that all four of the other factors remain unchanged. If it is necessary to alter more than one of these factors,

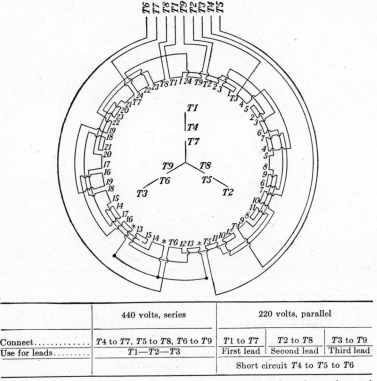

	440 volts, series	220 volts, parallel		
Connect............	T4 to T7, T5 to T8, T6 to T9	T1 to T7	T2 to T8	T3 to T9
Use for leads........	T1—T2—T3	First lead	Second lead	Third lead
		Short circuit T4 to T5 to T6		

Fig. 14-33.—Stator connection diagram, dual-voltage, 10 poles, three phase, short throw, series and parallel star.

it is suggested that, starting from the old winding, a new winding be proportioned changing only one of the factors; then a second new winding can be proportioned from the first new winding by changing the second factor, and so on until a final winding is reached. These trial windings need exist only on paper, and only the final winding is put into the motor. It is believed that such a procedure is really simpler to learn than to attempt to learn rules for changing several factors at once; *e.g.*, if it is desired to change a two-pole 25-cycle motor to a four-pole 60-cycle motor, the method herein suggested is to change the two-pole 25-cycle motor, first to a two-pole 60-cycle motor, and then from a two-pole 60-cycle winding to a four-pole 60-cycle winding. When more than one factor is changed, it is recommended that the new winding be checked by the method of Art. 14-21.

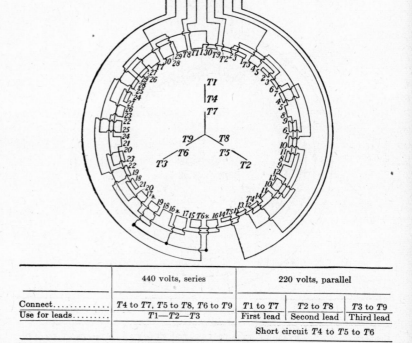

	440 volts, series		220 volts, parallel		
Connect.............	T4 to T7, T5 to T8, T6 to T9		T1 to T7	T2 to T8	T3 to T9
Use for leads........	T1—T2—T3		First lead	Second lead	Third lead
			Short circuit T4 to T5 to T6		

Fig. 14-34.—Stator connection diagram, dual-voltage, 12 poles, three phase, short throw, series and parallel star.

Before explaining the simplified rules for changing these windings, it will first be necessary to explain the terms **chord factor, distribution factor,** and **effective conductors.**

14-16. Chord Factor, Distribution Factor, and Effective Conductors.   *a. Chord Factor.*—If the two sides of a coil are a full pitch apart (180 deg), the voltages induced in these coil sides—we are now considering the motor as a generator—are also 180 deg apart and add directly, so that the total coil voltage is the arithmetical sum of the two voltages induced in the two coil sides.   If, however, the coil sides are not a full pitch apart, the induced voltages are not 180 deg apart, and the resultant voltage is, therefore, less than the simple sum of the voltages; *i.e.*, the voltage is reduced, owing to the fact that the winding is not a full-pitch winding. Allowance is made for this reduction in voltage by the use of a **chord factor**, which is defined as

$$\text{Chord factor} = \frac{\text{actual voltage generated in the coil}}{\text{voltage of a full-pitch coil}}$$

$$= \sin \tfrac{1}{2} \text{ (coil span in electrical degrees)} \quad (14\text{-}3)$$

$$= \sin \left(\frac{\text{slots throw} \times 90}{\text{slots per pole}} \right) \quad (14\text{-}4)$$

A table of chord factors for cases most commonly encountered is given in Table XII. Factors for a throw of more than full pitch are given because, in reconnecting motors for a different number of poles or in pole-changing windings, it is often necessary to use a throw greater than full pitch. This table does not apply to windings with unequal coil groupings, the chord factors for which must be figured by formula. For example, it is desired to know the chord factor for a 4-pole 27-slot winding with a throw of 1-7. From Eq. (14-4), and

TABLE XII.—CHORD FACTORS FOR POLYPHASE WINDINGS

Throw	Slots per pole												
	24	18	16	15	14	13	12	11	10	9	8	7	6
1–25	1.000	0.866											
1–24	0.998	0.906											
1–23	0.991	0.940	0.831										
1–22	0.981	0.966	0.882										
1–21	0.966	0.985	0.924	0.866									
1–20	0.947	0.996	0.956	0.914	0.847								
1–19	0.924	1.000	0.981	0.951	0.901	0.833							
1–18	0.897	0.996	0.995	0.978	0.944	0.884	0.793						
1–17	0.866	0.985	1.000	0.995	0.975	0.935	0.866	0.756					
1–16	0.832	0.966	0.995	1.000	0.994	0.971	0.924	0.841	0.707				
1–15	0.793	0.940	0.981	0.995	1.000	0.993	0.966	0.910	0.809				
1–14	0.752	0.906	0.956	0.978	0.994	1.000	0.991	0.960	0.891	0.766			
1–13	0.707	0.866	0.924	0.951	0.975	0.993	1.000	0.990	0.951	0.866	0.707		
1–12	0.659	0.819	0.882	0.914	0.944	0.971	0.991	1.000	0.988	0.940	0.831		
1–11	0.609	0.766	0.831	0.866	0.901	0.935	0.966	0.990	1.000	0.985	0.924	0.782	
1–10	.....	0.707	0.773	0.809	0.847	0.884	0.924	0.960	0.988	1.000	0.981	0.901	
1– 9	.....	0.643	0.707	0.743	0.782	0.833	0.866	0.910	0.951	0.985	1.000	0.975	0.866
1– 8	.....	.....	0.698	0.669	0.707	0.749	0.793	0.841	0.891	0.940	0.981	1.000	0.966
1– 7	.....	.....	0.570	0.616	0.624	0.663	0.707	0.756	0.809	0.866	0.831	0.901	1.000
1– 6	.....	.....	.....	0.530	0.532	0.566	0.609	0.655	0.707	0.766	0.831	0.901	0.966
1– 5	.....	.....	.....	.....	.....	.....	.....	.....	0.588	0.643	0.707	0.782	0.866
1– 4	.....	.....	.....	.....	.....	.....	.....	.....	.....	.....	0.570	0.624	0.707

since there are $6\frac{3}{4}$ slots per pole with a throw of 6 slots, the chord factor becomes

$$\text{Chord factor} = \sin\frac{6 \times 90}{6.75} = \sin 80 = 0.9848 \text{ (Table XXXIII)}$$

b. Distribution Factor.—The second factor, known as the distribution factor, is necessary to take care of the fact that the voltages generated in all coils of a group are not in phase; for example, in Fig. 14-4*a*, the voltages in the adjacent coils are 30 deg out of phase, and consequently the total voltage induced in the group is less than it would be if all the individual coil voltages were in phase. To take care of this reduction in voltage, it is necessary to use a **distribution factor,** which may be defined as

Distribution factor

$$= \frac{\text{vector sum of voltages of the coils in a group}}{\text{arithmetic sum of voltages of the coils in a group}} \quad (14\text{-}5)$$

A table of distribution factors is given in Table XIII.

TABLE XIII.—DISTRIBUTION FACTORS FOR POLYPHASE WINDINGS

Slots per pole per phase, or number of coils per group	Two-phase	Three-phase
1	1.000	1.000
2	0.924	0.966
3	0.911	0.960
4	0.906	0.958
5	0.904	0.957
6	0.903	0.956
Infinity	0.900	0.955
$1\frac{1}{2}$	0.911	0.960
All other fractional-slot windings	0.900	0.955

c. Effective Conductors.

Effective conductors per phase = actual series conductors
$\times$ chord factor $\times$ distribution factor   (14-6)

Thus, the number of effective conductors is always less than the actual number of conductors. Physically, the number of effective conductors is the actual number of conductors that would be required in a full-pitch polyphase winding having one slot per phase per pole (or one coil per group) to give the same magnetic field (neglecting harmonics) and the same torque as obtained with the actual chorded winding of more than one slot per pole per phase.

The actual number of series conductors is given by the expression

Series conductors

$$= \frac{\text{total number of coils} \times 2 \times \text{turns per coil}}{\text{number of phases} \times \text{number of parallel circuits}} \quad (14\text{-}7)$$

14-17. Changes in Voltage. *a. General Rule.*—The number of effective conductors should be increased or decreased in direct ratio as the increase or decrease in applied circuit voltage. For small changes of 10, or sometimes even 15, per cent, rewinding is usually unnecessary for the same winding may generally be used with satisfactory results.

b. Voltage Changes through Reconnecting without Rewinding.—A two-parallel winding may be reconnected in series for double line voltage without rewinding. A three-phase Y-winding can be connected for 57 per cent voltage by connecting in delta. Other possibilities of reconnecting to obtain a different circuit voltage are given in Table XIV. This table is a partial reproduction of a larger table given by Dudley.[1]

TABLE XIV.—RECONNECTING A POLYPHASE MOTOR

(If a motor connected originally as shown in any horizontal column had a normal voltage of 100, its voltage when reconnected as indicated in any vertical column, is shown at the intersection of these two columns.)

Form of connection	3-phase series Star	3-phase 2-parallel Y	3-phase 3-parallel Y	3-phase 4-parallel Y	3-phase 5-parallel Y	3-phase 6-parallel Y	2-phase series	2-phase 2-parallel	2-phase 3-parallel	2-phase 4-parallel	2-phase 5-parallel	2-phase 6-parallel
Three-phase series Y.......	100	50	33	25	20	17	81	41	27	20	16	14
Three-phase 2-parallel Y....	200	100	67	50	40	33	162	81	54	40	32	27
Three-phase 3-parallel Y....	300	150	100	75	60	50	243	122	81	60	48	41
Three-phase 4-parallel Y....	400	200	133	100	80	67	324	163	108	80	64	54
Three-phase 5-parallel Y....	500	250	167	125	100	83	405	203	135	100	80	68
Three-phase 6-parallel Y....	600	300	200	150	120	100	486	243	162	120	96	81
Two-phase series..........	125	63	42	31	25	21	100	50	33	25	20	17
Two-phase 2-parallel.......	250	125	84	63	50	42	200	100	67	50	40	33
Two-phase 3-parallel.......	375	188	125	94	75	63	300	150	100	75	60	50
Two-phase 4-parallel.......	500	250	167	125	100	84	400	200	133	100	80	67
Two-phase 5-parallel.......	625	313	208	156	125	105	500	250	167	125	100	84
Two-phase 6-parallel.......	750	375	250	188	150	125	600	300	200	150	120	100

14-18. Changes in Number of Phases.—To change from three-phase series star to a two-phase series connection, increase the number of turns per coil from 15 to 20 per cent for the same line-to-line voltage.

To change from a two-phase series winding to a series star winding, decrease the turns per coil to 80 or 85 per cent of the two-phase turns per coil.

In passing, it may be mentioned that a 550-volt three-phase star-connected motor can be reconnected for a 440-volt two-phase series connection. To make this change, it is necessary to regroup the coils. A change of this nature is hardly to be recommended as good practice, for the phase coils of the reconnected winding will not be properly insulated.

14-19. Changes in Frequency.—Changes in frequency may well be made with caution. However, a number of short-cut rules will be given here which may be followed with more or less safety.

60 to 50 Cycles.—Most 60-cycle fractional horsepower polyphase motors will operate successfully on 50 cycles; in fact, the usual practice is to rate polyphase motors for 50/60 cycles. Strictly speaking, however, for the same horsepower, the effective conductors or turns per coil should be increased 10 per cent when changing from 60 to 50 cycles.

50 to 60 Cycles.—The 50-cycle motor will usually operate satisfactorily on 60 cycles, but to obtain the same torque the turns or effective conductors should be decreased approximately 10 per cent. The turns can be decreased 20 per cent, in which case approximately 20 per cent more horsepower can be developed on 60 than on 50 cycles.

30 to 25 Cycles.—For such a change, the same considerations apply as for changing from 60 to 50 cycles.

25 to 30 Cycles.—In such a case, the same considerations apply as in changing from 50 to 60 cycles.

60 to 25 Cycles.—In changing from 60 to 25 cycles, the horsepower rating should be cut in half. The effective conductors or turns per coil should be increased to approximately 220 per cent of the value for 60 cycles.

50 to 25 Cycles, or 60 to 30 Cycles.—For such changes, the horsepower rating should be cut in half, and the number of effective conductors should be doubled, which means doubling the number of turns per coil if the number of poles and coil throw is not changed.

25 to 50 Cycles, or 30 to 60 Cycles.—For such a change, the horsepower rating can be doubled. The number of effective conductors should be cut in half.

25 to 60 Cycles.—The horsepower rating can be doubled. The effective conductors should be reduced to 45 per cent of the 25-cycle effective conductors.

60 *to* 40 *Cycles.*—The horsepower rating should be reduced one-third. The effective conductors should be increased approximately 35 or 40 per cent.

40 *to* 60 *Cycles.*—The horsepower rating can be increased 50 per cent. The effective conductors should be decreased 35 to 40 per cent.

14-20. Changes in Number of Poles.—This is one of the more difficult types of change and one most apt to be fraught with difficulty.

TABLE XV.—REWINDING INFORMATION FOR CHANGING THE NUMBER OF POLES

Poles		Effective conductors *		Horsepower rating		Core density		Tooth density	
Old	New	Old	New	Old	New	Old	New	Old	New
2	4	1.00	1.82	1.00	0.43	1.00	0.55	1.00	1.10
2	6	1.00	2.68	1.00	0.24	1.00	0.37	1.00	1.12
2	8	1.00	3.48	1.00	0.165	1.00	0.29	1.00	1.15
2	10	1.00	4.24	1.00	0.125	1.00	0.23	1.00	1.18
2	12	1.00	4.92	1.00	0.10	1.00	0.20	1.00	1.22
4	6	1.00	1.39	1.00	0.64	1.00	0.72	1.00	1.08
4	8	1.00	1.82	1.00	0.43	1.00	0.55	1.00	1.10
4	10	1.00	2.25	1.00	0.31	1.00	0.44	1.00	1.11
4	12	1.00	2.68	1.00	0.24	1.00	0.37	1.00	1.12
6	8	1.00	1.25	1.00	0.73	1.00	0.80	1.00	1.06
6	10	1.00	1.53	1.00	0 55	1.00	0.65	1.00	1.09
6	12	1.00	1.82	1.00	0.43	1.00	0.55	1.00	1.10
8	10	1.00	1.21	1.00	0.76	1.00	0.82	1.00	1.03
8	12	1.00	1.39	1.00	0.64	1.00	0.72	1.00	1.08
10	12	1.00	1.18	1.00	0.79	1.00	0.85	1.00	1.02
4	2	1.00	0.91	1.00	0.86	1.00	1.10	1.00	0.55
6	2	1.00	0.89	1.00	0.72	1.00	1.12	1.00	0.37
6	4	1.00	0.925	1.00	0.95	1.00	1.08	1.00	0.72
8	2	1.00	0.87	1.00	0.66	1.00	1.15	1.00	0.288
8	4	1.00	0.91	1.00	0.86	1.00	1.10	1.00	0.55
8	6	1.00	0.94	1.00	0.97	1.00	1.06	1.00	0.795
10	2	1.00	0.85	1.00	0.62	1.00	1.18	1.00	0.235
10	4	1.00	0.90	1.00	0.78	1.00	1.11	1.00	0.445
10	6	1.00	0 92	1.00	0.92	1.00	1.09	1.00	0.65
10	8	1.00	0.97	1.00	0.95	1.00	1.03	1.00	0.825
12	2	1.00	0.82	1.00	0.61	1.00	1.22	1.00	0.204
12	4	1.00	0.89	1.00	0.72	1.00	1.12	1.00	0.37
12	6	1.00	0.91	1.00	0.86	1.00	1.10	1.00	0 55
12	8	1.00	0.925	1.00	0.95	1.00	1.08	1.00	0.721
12	10	1.00	0.98	1.00	0.95	1.00	1.02	1.00	0.85

* Total, not per pole; see Eqs. (14-6) and (14-7).

Rewinding is practically always involved, and the throw should be changed. For two-pole motors, a throw of two-thirds full pitch is recommended, and for other numbers of poles, approximately five-sixths of full pitch is recommended.

Whenever a motor is rewound for a different number of poles, it is usually necessary to derate it. Practical assistance in rewinding a motor for a different number of poles is afforded in Table XV, which is to be used in the following manner:

1. Under Poles, select the desired winding change.
2. To obtain the total number of effective conductors per phase required for the new winding, multiply the total number of effective conductors per phase in the old winding by the factor in the column headed New.
3. To obtain the horsepower rating of the new winding, multiply the horsepower rating of the old winding by the factor in the column headed New.
4. How this change affects the core density and the tooth density is shown merely for reference purposes in the columns headed accordingly.

This table was figured out on the assumptions (1) that the "old" winding represented nearly the maximum rating possible and (2) that the punching was properly designed for the "old" number of poles. If the old winding was not the maximum rating, the rating of the new winding can usually be increased. Moreover, the old winding may be a six-pole winding on a four-pole punching and the "new" winding may be for four poles; in this case, the new, or four-pole, winding may be rated much higher than would be indicated in the table. The most satisfactory way to obtain a winding that utilizes the parts of the motor to best advantage is to figure the magnetic densities.

14-21. Figuring Magnetic Densities to Check a Proposed Winding.—As pointed out in Art. 14-15, the rules given in Arts. 14-17 to 14-20 are merely short cuts to be used with caution. The fundamental way is to figure the magnetic densities in the iron parts in order to determine the maximum safe output that can be obtained for any given set of conditions desired. Briefly, the method to be outlined is to assume a winding of the proper number of poles, to figure the magnetic inductions in the stator at the proper circuit voltage and frequency, and to compare these densities with the table of allowable values. The densities in the iron parts will then be adjusted to an allowable value by increasing or decreasing the number of turns, and the motor wound accordingly. The final actual horsepower can then be determined by testing the complete motor. This first trial winding may be simply a guess, or it could be arrived at by following the rules given in Arts. 14-17 to 14-20. If this trial winding is determined from the old winding by following these rules, the approximate horsepower rating of the new winding will be known. If, after figuring the magnetic densities, it is found that they can be increased, the horsepower rating can likewise be increased *as the square of the increase in density;* for example, if the density is increased from 100 to 110 per cent, the horsepower rating will increase from 100 per cent to (110 per cent)^2 = 121 per cent. The principal thing to be determined is the number of effective conductors and, from this, the number of turns per coil and the coil throw.

a. Figuring the Amount of Magnetic Flux per Pole.

$$\text{Flux per pole} = \frac{\text{volts per phase} \times 45 \times 1,000,000}{\text{effective conductors per phase} \times \text{cycles}} \qquad (14\text{-}8)$$

The above formula gives the total amount of magnetic flux per pole under no-load conditions. It is to be noted that

In star-connected motors,

$$\text{Volts per phase} = \frac{\text{line voltage}}{\sqrt{3}} = 0.577 \times \text{line-to-line voltage} \qquad (14\text{-}9)$$

In delta-connected motors,

$$\text{Volts per phase} = \text{line voltage} \qquad (14\text{-}10)$$

In two-phase motors,

$$\text{Volts per phase} = \text{line voltage} \qquad (14\text{-}11)$$

The number of effective conductors per phase can be figured by use of Eq. (14-6), Art. 14-16.

To figure the magnetic densities, it is necessary to figure the areas of the magnetic circuit, of which there are two important areas to figure, *viz.*, the stator core area and stator teeth area.

b. The Area of the Stator Core.

$$\text{Stator core area} = 2 \times \text{DBS} \times \text{width of iron} \times 0.93 \quad (14\text{-}12)$$

The factor **2** is used because the flux divides in half at the pole centers, and half goes in either direction away from the pole (see Fig. 2-4).

The **DBS** (depth below slots) can usually be measured with calipers or an ordinary steel scale (see Fig. 14-35). If a slot has a round bottom, measure the minimum DBS. Neglect bolt holes and rivets when measuring DBS.

The **width of iron** is also called the length of stack. It should be measured at a rivet to eliminate errors due to flaring of the punchings, or else a suitable allowance should be made for the flare. This width of iron should be the actual width that the iron would be if it were clamped tightly.

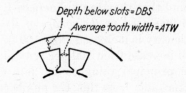

Depth below slots=DBS

Average tooth width =ATW

○

FIG. 14-35.—Dimensions used for figuring the areas of the magnetic circuit of a simple stator punching.

The figure **0.93** is a stacking factor used because the core is laminated and it is necessary to make an allowance for the thickness of the varnish, air space, etc., between the punchings.

c. Area of the Stator Teeth.

Stator tooth area =

$$\frac{\text{ATW} \times \text{number of slots}}{\text{number of poles}} \times \text{width of iron} \times 0.93 \qquad (14\text{-}13)$$

The **ATW** (average tooth width) can often be measured best by bending one tooth of one lamination away from the core and actually measuring it with an accurate pair of calipers or with micrometers.

TABLE XVI.—ALLOWABLE DENSITIES

	Stator core			Stator teeth		
	60 cycles	50 cycles	25 cycles	60 cycles	50 cycles	25 cycles
Quiet motors, open or enclosed:						
2 poles.............	70,000	77,000	87,000	85,000	93,000	106,000
4 poles.............	70,000	77,000	87,000	87,000	95,000	108,000
6 poles.............	70,000	77,000	87,000	89,000	98,000	110,000
8 or more poles......	70,000	77,000	87,000	90,000	100,000	
High-torque, open motors:						
2 poles.............	90,000	99,000	110,000	105,000	115,000	120,000
4 poles.............	95,000	104,000	112,000	110,000	118,000	125,000
6 poles.............	98,000	107,000	115,000	113,000	120,000	130,000
8 or more poles......	100,000	110,000	....	115,000	122,000	

This dimension is illustrated in Fig. 14-35.

d. Magnetic Densities.

$$\text{Stator core density} = \frac{\text{flux per pole}}{\text{area of stator core}} \qquad (14\text{-}14)$$

$$\text{Stator tooth density} = \frac{\text{flux per pole}}{\text{area of stator teeth} \times 0.637} \quad (14\text{-}15)$$

The factor 0.637 has to be used in figuring the stator tooth density because the flux density over the pole face is not uniform; it varies rom zero, halfway between poles, to a maximum in the center of the poles following approximately a sinusoidal distribution. The factor 0.637 is to allow for this sinusoidal distribution.

14-22. Allowable Densities.—The allowable magnetic density in a motor varies with a large number of factors; it depends upon whether

TABEL XVII.—INDEX OF STATOR CONNECTION DIAGRAMS FOR POLYPHASE INDUCTION MOTORS

Phases	Poles	Series or parallel	Throw	Voltage	Fig. No.	Page No.
2	2	Ser.	Short	Single	14- 5	322
2	2	2 par.	Short	Single	14- 6	322
2	4	Ser.	Short	Single	14- 9	324
2	4	2 par.	Short	Single	14-10	324
2	6	Ser.	Short	Single	14-13	326
2	6	2 par.	Long	Single	14-14	326
2	8	Ser.	Short	Single	14-17	328
2	8	2 par.	Long	Single	14-18	328
2	10	Ser.	Short	Single	14-21	330
2	10	2 par.	Long	Single	14-22	330
2	12	Ser.	Short	Single	14-25	332
2	12	2 par.	Long	Single	14-26	332
3	2	Ser. Y	Short	Single	14- 7	323
3	2	2 par. Y	Short	Single	14- 8	323
3	4	Ser. Y	Short	Single	14-11	325
3	4	2 par. Y	Short	Single	14-12	325
3	6	Ser. Y	Short	Single	14-15	327
3	6	2 par. Y	Long	Single	14-16	327
3	8	Ser. Y	Short	Single	14-19	329
3	8	2 par. Y	Long	Single	14-20	329
3	10	Ser. Y	Short	Single	14-23	331
3	10	2 par. Y	Long	Single	14-24	331
3	12	Ser. Y	Short	Single	14-27	333
3	12	2 par. Y	Long	Single	14-28	333
3	2	Ser.-par.	Short	Dual	14-29	339
3	4	Ser.-par.	Short	Dual	14-30	340
3	6	Ser.-par.	Short	Dual	14-31	341
3	8	Ser.-par.	Short	Dual	14-32	342
3	10	Ser.-par.	Short	Dual	14-33	343
3	12	Ser.-par.	Short	Dual	14-34	344

the motor is open or enclosed and, if open, upon what kind of ventilation it has; it also depends upon whether noise is an important factor or not and upon many other factors, including grade of iron. For most practical purposes, however, the grade of iron can be neglected, so far as the serviceman is concerned, when a new winding is being figured.

It is not without hesitation and some reluctance that a table of allowable densities is given. However, if windings are redesigned to give maximum densities as indicated in this table, the repairman is fairly safe in assuming that he is getting as near the maximum output out of his rewound motor as can be obtained without running into danger of burnouts.

The rewound motor can be designed to have approximately the densities given in Table XVI; finally the motor should be checked by careful tests after the motor has been rewound. It is then advisable to take a temperature run of the motor under normal operating conditions to see that the motor does not overheat or burn out.

It may be pointed out, in connection with using Table XVI, that when the number of poles is changed, as in changing from two to four poles, it will be found, for example, that if the stator tooth density is worked up to the maximum value given in the table, the stator core density may be considerably below, maybe half as much as indicated. In such a case, it is usually perfectly safe to increase the stator tooth density above the value shown in the table. The values shown are based on the assumption that *both* stator core and stator teeth are worked at the densities given. If either one is considerably below the maximum allowable value, the other density can be increased above the value given. In Table XV, allowances of this sort have been made.

Bibliography

1. DUDLEY A. M.: "Connecting Induction Motors," McGraw-Hill Book Company, Inc., New York, 1936.
2. BRAYMER, DANIEL H., and ROE, A. C.: "Repair Shop Diagrams and Connecting Tables for Induction Motors," McGraw-Hill Book Company, Inc., New York, 1927.
3. ——— and ———: "Rewinding and Connecting Alternating-Current Motors," McGraw-Hill Book Company, Inc., New York, 1932.
4. RIKER, C. R., and DUDLEY, A. M.: Lap Windings with Unequal Coil Groups, *Elec. J.*, January, 1925, pp. 25–29.
5. HELLMUND, R. E., and VEINOTT, C. G.: Irregular Windings in Wound Rotor Induction Motors, *Elec. Eng.*, February, 1934, pp. 342–346.
6. Rotation, Connections, and Terminal Markings for Electrical Apparatus, ASA C6.1—1944, published by National Electrical Manufacturers' Association.

CHAPTER XV

SYNCHRONOUS MOTORS

Exactness of speed is the outstanding characteristic that has made synchronous motors so popular in fractional horsepower sizes. Speed of a synchronous motor is exactly proportional to the line frequency, which is regulated on all large 60-cycle systems so closely that clocks can be driven by synchronous motors; the frequency is rarely in error by more than a small fraction of 1 per cent, and these small errors are averaged out over a period of time.

15-1. General.—Synchronous motors cover probably the widest range of horsepower and speed ratings of any type of motor. Horsepower ratings range from 5,000 or more down to one-millionth of a horsepower; output speeds, for 60-cycle motors, range from 3600 to 0.00003 rpm, or 1 revolution per month. In integral horsepower ratings, their popularity is due in large measure to their ability to correct system power factor but, in fractional horsepower sizes, d-c excitation is almost never used, and the power factor is poorer than for induction motors of comparable ratings. In sizes from ⅛ hp down to about 0.001 hp, synchronous motors are used for such applications as teleprinters, facsimile picture transmission, recording (graphic) instruments, sound-recording or -reproducing apparatus. In miniature ratings (below 0.001 hp) they are widely used for clocks and all kinds of timing devices, control apparatus, and time-delay mechanisms. Most of them are self-starting, but some clock motors require manual starting. Use of synchronous motors for such applications is rapidly growing with the ever-increasing number of automatic devices being developed for our present-day civilization.

15-2. Types of Synchronous Motors.—Synchronous motors are built in a wide variety of types and constructions. However, most of them have one feature in common with induction motors; a stator structure with windings which, when properly energized with alternating current, set up a revolving magnetic field as explained in Chap. II. The speed of this magnetic field—known as the **synchronous speed**—is exactly proportional to the frequency. Synchronous motors are so built that they lock into step with the rotating magnetic field and rotate at exactly the same speed as the latter. Induction motors,

355

on the other hand, always rotate at a speed a little slower than synchronous. It is the construction of the rotor that determines whether the latter locks into step with the rotating field, or whether it rotates at a slightly slower speed. Hence, synchronous motors are usually classified (1) by the type of rotor construction and (2) by the stator winding arrangement. Large synchronous motors use a salient-pole rotor with a d-c-excited field coil on each pole, and a squirrel-cage damper winding for starting and to prevent hunting when in synchronism. However, d-c excitation is rarely used in fractional horsepower synchronous motors, though permanent magnets are used to provide excitation for synchronous inductor motors, which are built in ratings from 0.0002 to 0.010 hp. These are quite special in construction. Two popular and basic types of nonexcited synchronous motors, which are essentially induction motors except for rotor construction, are **reluctance motors** and **hysteresis motors.** Either of these basic types may use a number of different stator winding arrangements, giving rise to many types.

RELUCTANCE MOTORS

15-3. Reluctance Motor Definitions.—According to the A. S. A.:

A reluctance motor is a synchronous motor similar in construction to an induction motor, in which the member carrying the secondary circuit has salient poles, without direct-current excitation. It starts as an induction motor, but operates normally at synchronous speed.—ASA C42—1941. 10.10.305.

A variation of the reluctance motor is the **subsynchronous reluctance motor**, which is defined as follows:

A subsynchronous reluctance motor is a form of reluctance motor, which has the number of salient poles greater than the number of electrical poles of the primary winding, thus causing the motor to operate at a constant average speed, which is a submultiple of its apparent synchronous speed.—ASA C42—1941.   10.10.310.

15-4. Construction.—As implied in the above definition, the reluctance motor is really a special case of a d-c-excited synchronous motor with an open field circuit. However, the small reluctance motor usually is built from induction motor parts, except that some teeth are cut out of the squirrel-cage rotor.

Even the large synchronous d-c-excited motors start as induction motors using the damper winding as a squirrel cage; the damper winding is likewise necessary in the case of the reluctance motor, which also starts as an induction motor. A typical rotor punching is shown in Fig. 15-1, which happens to have been made up for a six-pole motor, as can be seen. In each of six places, teeth have been removed. If—as in the example—the sizes or locations of these cutout portions are slightly unsymmetrical, better locked-rotor torque is obtained than if the cutouts were uniform in size and spacing. (Obviously, uniform size and spacing are impossible with a 47-slot punching.) Although teeth have been removed, the end rings (resistance rings) are left intact, and all the squirrel-cage conductors are used, even those which are in the cutout portions, in order to obtain better starting characteristics.

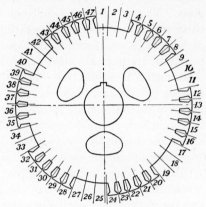

Fig. 15-1.—Rotor punching used in a reluctance motor.

Reluctance motors may use any one of a number of types of stator windings: polyphase, split-phase, and capacitor.

15-5. Polyphase Reluctance Motors.

Construction and characteristics of reluctance motors were discussed in an *Electric Journal* article by P. H. Trickey,[1] who has more recently published a method for calculating the performance of polyphase reluctance motors.[2] In the polyphase reluctance motor, the rotor is the same shape as that shown in Fig. 15-1, and the stator windings are regular polyphase windings of the type discussed in Chap. XIV. The motor starts as an induction motor but runs synchronously once up to speed.

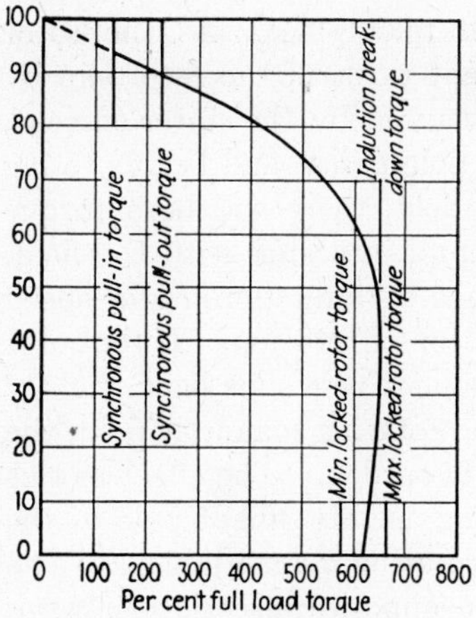

The relation between the performance of the synchronous motor and the performance of the same machine as a polyphase induction motor without the salient poles is fairly constant. A typical speed-

Fig. 15-2.—Speed-torque curves of a polyphase, reluctance motor.

[Figure axis labels: 100, 90, 80, 70, 60, 50, 40, 30, 20, 10, 0 (vertical); 0 100 200 300 400 500 600 700 800 Per cent full load torque (horizontal); curve labels: Synchronous pull-in torque, Synchronous pull-out torque, Min. locked-rotor torque, Max. locked-rotor torque, Induction breakdown torque]

[1] For numbered references, see Bibliography at end of this chapter.

torque curve, taken from Trickey's article,[1] is shown in Fig. 15-2.
The induction-motor breakdown torque and the average locked-rotor
torque will not change materially with the cutout rotor, although the
minimum locked-rotor torque is appreciably reduced because of cogging.   The synchronous pull-out torque will be approximately one-
third the induction-motor breakdown, and consequently, in most small
motors, it is necessary to derate the induction motor to one-half or
one-third its normal rating when a synchronous rotor is used.   This
relationship is so generally true that the dimensions of synchronous
motors usually are determined by the dimensions of an induction
motor of three times the rating.   It is, nevertheless, sometimes possible
to obtain half as much rating in a synchronous motor as in a straight
induction motor by working the iron parts somewhat harder or by
accepting proportionately lower torques.

If the required locked-rotor torque is about the same as the full-load
torque, the rotor resistance of the polyphase motor can be made low,
and the pull-in torque will then be very nearly the same as the pull-out
torque.   If the required locked-rotor torque is high, the rotor resistance probably will be increased until the pull-in torque is as low as the
requirements will allow.   The effect of rotor resistance on pull-in
torque is best explained by saying that, for a given amount of inertia
of the rotor and connected load, there is a minimum speed that must
be attained before synchronization will take place.   As the rotor
approaches synchronous speed, the salient poles of the rotor slip by
the poles of the rotating magnetic field caused by the stator current,
at a constantly slower rate.   As a rotor pole passes and begins to lag
behind a pole of the rotating magnetic field, there will be a torque
exerted tending to make the rotor pole pull into step with the field.
This torque will accelerate the rotor above its induction-motor speed
because it is pulling the rotor in the direction of rotation.   If the rotor
has not pulled into step by the time its salient pole slips back slightly
more than halfway to the next pole of the rotating magnetic field, the
latter will try to pull the rotor pole *back* toward it.   The effect of this
tendency is to decelerate the rotor as long as this salient pole of the
rotor is ahead of the nearest pole of the rotating magnetic field.   The
average effect of these successive pulls in opposite directions is zero;
and therefore, unless the rotor can accelerate from the induction speed
to synchronous speed while the rotor pole passes a pole of the stator
field, the motor will not synchronize at all.

The synchronizing or pull-in torque does not depend directly upon
rotor resistance.   However, for good pull-in torque characteristics, the

rotor resistance should be low. The reason for this is simply that, as has just been explained, there is a definite speed up to which the rotor must be brought by induction-motor action before the motor will lock in as a synchronous motor; the lower the rotor resistance, the higher will be the torque at this pull-in speed, hence the higher will be the pull-in torque.

The apparent synchronous pull-in torque is *greatly affected by the inertia of the connected load*, since, when synchronizing, it is necessary that the rotor change its speed suddenly, *i.e.*, in less time than it takes for the rotor to slip ½ pole pitch.

Although, as mentioned above, the average locked-rotor torque will be very nearly that of the induction motor, the motor will be subject to "cogging," *i.e.*, variation of locked-rotor torque with rotor position. This effect will usually be negligible on high locked-rotor torque motors but may be of some account on low locked-rotor torque motors. This cogging effect is minimized to some extent by skewing the rotor core or by using a number of rotor slots not divisible by the number of poles.

Power factor and efficiency are slightly lower than for the same motor as an induction motor operated at one-third full load, and quite a bit less than the full-load efficiency and power factor of an induction motor of the same horsepower and speed rating.

15-6. Split-phase Reluctance Motors.—In a split-phase reluctance motor, the rotor construction is similar to that for a polyphase motor, but the stator windings are the windings of a split-phase motor. A starting switch, such as is found in a split-phase motor, is used. The switch operates at the same speed as in a conventional split-phase motor so that the starting winding is out of the circuit before the motor "pulls into" synchronism.

As a reluctance motor, a single-phase induction motor will have a horsepower rating of approximately one-third its rating as an induction motor. If rewound for fewer turns, it may be possible to obtain one-half normal rating, however. The cogging will be relatively worse than in the case of the polyphase motor because of the inherently lower locked-rotor torque.

15-7. Capacitor-type Reluctance Motors.—In the capacitor-type reluctance motor, the rotor construction is the same as for the poly-phase motor or for the split-phase motor, but the stator windings are the windings of a capacitor motor which may be any one of three types: (1) a capacitor-start motor, as discussed in Chap. V; (2) a two-value capacitor motor, as discussed in Chap. VI; or (3) a permanent-split capacitor motor, as discussed in Chap. VII. If the stator windings are arranged for operation either as a capacitor-start or as a two-value capacitor motor, the usual switch is, of course, required. A small reluctance motor of the permanent-split capacitor type, with built-in gear reduction, is illustrated in Fig. 15-3. This motor is a three-lead electrically reversible motor with windings illustrated schematically in Fig. 7-6.

As a capacitor motor, the synchronous-motor performance and induction-motor performance bear much the same relation as in the polyphase motor. That is, the capacitor motor has approximately

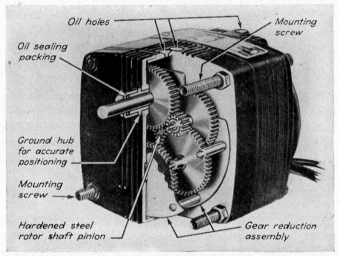

Fig. 15-3.—Small capacitor-type reluctance motor with built-in reduction gear. Standard output speeds for 60-cycle motors are from 300 to 1 rpm; output torques are from 1.3 oz-in. to 120 oz-in., respectively. Motor has three leads and is electrically reversible. (*Courtesy of Bodine Electric Company.*)

one-third, or possibly one-half, the rating as a synchronous motor that it would have as a normal capacitor motor.

All reluctance motors exhibit marked cogging tendencies; but in the case of the two-value motor or of the capacitor-start motor, usually so much locked-rotor torque is provided that little difficulty is experienced with this effect. In the case of a permanent-split motor, cogging may present real difficulties.

15-8. Making a Synchronous Motor in the Repair Shop.—A reluctance motor can usually be made in any repair shop from either a polyphase or a split-phase motor or from any one of the capacitor types of motors. To do this, it is recommended that the easiest way will probably be to mill flats on the rotor surface, equally spaced,

there being as many flats as there are poles.   The total area of these
flats should be approximately 40 per cent of the total cylindrical area
of the rotor before the flats are milled.   In such a case, the rotor
resistance rings and the conductors in the flat part will be partially,
but not entirely, removed.   Usually this partial removal of conductors
and resistance rings will do little appreciable harm.   The motor
should be able to carry roughly about one-third its nameplate rating.

An alternative, and probably a better although a more tedious,
way is to chisel out 35 to 40 per cent of the rotor teeth, without dis-
turbing the conductors or resistance rings.   The teeth should be cut
out at approximately equal intervals, there being as many cutouts as
there are poles, as shown in Fig. 15-1.

A motor of this type is particularly useful for checking tachometers,
as well as for numerous other applications.

A synchronous motor can be made out of any wound-rotor polyphase induction motor by connecting two of the three-phase secondary
leads to one side of a d-c source, and the third secondary lead to the
other side of the d-c source.   The motor is first brought up to speed as
an induction motor with secondary leads shorted; then the d-c excitation is applied.   Such a motor is known as a **synchronous induction
motor.**

HYSTERESIS MOTORS

15-9. Hysteresis Motor Defined.

A hysteresis motor is a synchronous motor without salient poles and
without direct-current excitation, which starts by virtue of the hysteresis
losses induced in its hardened steel secondary member by the revolving field
of the primary and operates normally at
synchronous speed due to the retentivity of
the secondary core.—ASA C42—1941.
10.10.315.

15-10. Construction.—Rotor con-
struction for a typical hysteresis motor
is illustrated in Fig. 15-4.   Hysteresis
rings of a special magnetic material,
such as chrome or cobalt steel, are
carried on a supporting arbor made of

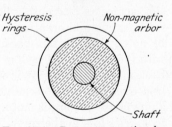

Fig. 15-4.—Rotor construction for
a hysteresis motor.

a nonmagnetic material such as brass; the assembly is carried on the
shaft.   Hysteresis rings are usually from thin stock and several of
them are assembled to give a built-up laminated rotor.   In the
smallest sizes, the rotor may consist of a single solid ring.

Variations in construction are legion.   For example, in the hysteresis motor of Fig. 15-6, the hysteresis rings are made in the form of wheels; the rims of the wheel act as hysteresis rings, and the spokes support the latter.   In Fig. 15-7, the hysteresis element consists of a thin strip of hardened steel carried inside a lightweight aluminum cup. The latter motor is of the umbrella type of construction; *i.e.*, the stator, which sets up the revolving field, is actually surrounded by the umbrella-shaped rotor.

Almost any form of stator construction that sets up a rotating magnetic field can be used; polyphase stators set up more uniform rotating fields than single-phase induction motors, but the latter are quite successful and widely used.   Mechanical arrangements of the stator vary widely.   Principles of operation of both polyphase and single-phase motors are discussed in the following paragraphs.

15-11. Polyphase Hysteresis Motors.—Assume that the rotor of Fig. 15-4 is placed inside a conventional polyphase stator which, when energized, sets up a rotating field such as shown in Fig. 2-4.   In the stator iron, the field is an alternating or pulsating field.   This point can be more easily understood by referring to Fig. 2-4 and noting what happens to the strength and direction of the flux in the iron back of slot 7 at each of the four times illustrated.

Time 1—Strength—4; direction—clockwise
Time 2—Strength—1; direction—clockwise
Time 3—Strength—2; direction—counterclockwise
Time 4—Strength—4; direction—counterclockwise

Similarly, it can be shown that the iron back of each and every stator slot carries an alternating flux.   Likewise, the hysteresis rings on the rotor carry an alternating flux when the rotor is stationary.   (It is to be noted that the flux back of each slot is slightly out of time phase with the flux back of each of the other slots, but it is an *alternating flux* back of every slot.)   It is well known that an alternating flux in an iron circuit causes losses due to eddy currents and to hysteresis.   In a polyphase hysteresis motor, the torque is directly proportional to the hysteresis loss in the rotor.   In fact, the hysteresis torque, expressed in synchronous watts, is equal to the hysteresis loss in the rotor at standstill.   This is another way of saying that a hysteresis loss of, say, 5 watts, under locked-rotor conditions, produces a locked-rotor torque numerically equal to the running torque required at synchronous speed to develop an output of 5 watts.   An interesting comparison is afforded by the polyphase induction motor, in which the locked-rotor torque, expressed in synchronous watts, is numerically equal to the locked-rotor copper loss.

In other words, if the rotor of Fig. 15-4 is placed inside the stator of a polyphase motor that is excited to produce a rotating magnetic field, two kinds of iron losses will be produced in the hysteresis rings: Eddy-current losses produce induction-motor torque; hysteresis losses produce hysteresis-motor torque. There is an important distinction between these two kinds of torque. Induction-motor torque decreases to zero at synchronous speed, whereas, in an "ideal" hysteresis motor, the hysteresis torque is constant at all speeds from standstill to synchronism; *i.e.*, *locked-rotor*, *pull-in*, and *pull-out torques* are all mutually equal to one another. Such a speed-torque curve is shown in Fig. 15-5. In a practical motor, the shape of the speed-torque is modified somewhat from the theoretical curve shown by harmonics in the rotating field and by other irregularities.

For a more extended and mathematical treatment of the theory of hysteresis motor torque, the reader is referred to a paper on the subject by B. R. Teare, Jr.[3]

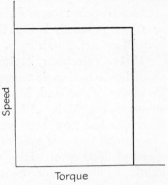

Fig. 15-5.—Speed-torque curve of an "ideal" polyphase hysteresis motor.

15-12. Capacitor-type Hysteresis Motors.—Capacitor-type hysteresis motors are essentially the same as polyphase motors except that the rotating field is set up by a capacitor-motor stator. Rotating fields set up by a capacitor motor are generally elliptical in shape (see Art. 2-12) rather than circular, as in a polyphase motor. Also, the shape of the ellipse varies with the load because the capacitor cannot maintain balanced conditions at more than one load. Consequently, the actual speed-torque of a capacitor hysteresis motor departs more from the "ideal" curve of Fig. 15-5 than does that of a polyphase hysteresis motor.

Capacitor hysteresis motors can be built in fractional horsepower ratings down to 0.001 hp but, in these sizes, reluctance motors appear to have found wider usage.

15-13. Shaded-pole Hysteresis Motors.—Of all the varieties of hysteresis motors, the shaded-pole type has probably enjoyed by far the most widespread use. It is used for clocks and all kinds of timer applications, of which the hold-fire control of a stoker is but a single example.   These motors are usually supplied with a reduction gear of very high ratio to give output speeds from 60 rpm down to one revolution per month.   Efficiencies are very low, but unimportant, because the total inputs are of the order of 1.6 to 12 watts.   Horsepower outputs are extremely low—of the order of a few millionths of a horsepower —but, because of the low output speeds, very little horsepower is required to operate clocks or timing mechanisms.   Shaded-pole hysteresis motors, because of their availability, are often used for applications such as advertising displays which require a slow-speed motor with low power consumption.

Shaded-pole motors differ from polyphase motors in principles of operation primarily in that the rotating field is set up by a shaded-pole stator (see Art. 13-4).

15-14. Telechron   Motors.—Telechron is the trade name for shaded-pole hysteresis motors manufactured by the Warren Telechron Company of Ashland, Mass.   A cutaway view of a typical motor is shown in Fig. 15-6.   Although originally designed for electric clocks, their use has now been extended to many industrial applications. They are of two-pole construction with a 60-cycle rotor-shaft operating speed of 3600 rpm.   They are made in three general basic sizes for light-, medium-, and heavy-duty applications.   Standard output speeds are from 60 rpm to one revolution per month, but specially constructed motors can be furnished with speeds up to 3600 rpm. Motors are rated in terms of torque instead of horsepower.   Torque ratings represent the torque load that can be started, brought up to speed, and carried continuously.   Torque ratings for 1-rpm motors range from 0.0625 to 2.0 lb-in.   Inputs are from 2 to 12 watts, depending upon the motor size.

Reversible motors are made by building two motors in tandem, with two stators, and two rotors on the same shaft; one coil or the other is energized, depending upon the desired direction of rotation. Explosion-proof motors are also built.   They are built for line voltages from 12 to 250; for higher circuit voltages, a reactor is connected in series.

15-15. Multipolar Shaded-pole Hysteresis Motor with a Single Stator Coil.—A shaded-pole hysteresis motor of novel construction used for demand meters, two-rate meters, recording instruments, and time switches is illustrated in Fig. 15-7.   Figure 15-8 is an exploded view of the motor.   There is but a single cylindrical stator coil 1, into which the center core 2 is assembled.   Stampings 4 and 5, when assembled onto the ends of this core, provide 12 main poles, all excited by the single coil. Hence the motor operates at the synchronous speed of a 12-pole motor, which is 600 rpm for a 60-cycle circuit. Stampings 3 and 6 are likewise assembled onto core 1 with the two

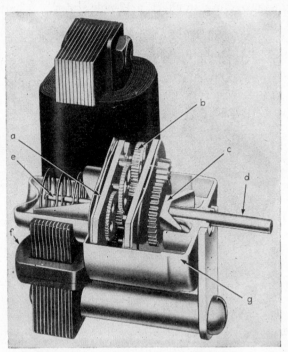

Fig. 15-6.—Telechron motor used in clocks and timing devices. It has two poles and is of the shaded-pole hysteresis type. (*Courtesy of the Warren Telechron Company.*)

  a. Capillary oiling system. Capillary action in the space between each bearing and capillary plate causes the bearing and the pivot surfaces to be covered with a thin film of oil drawn from the oil reservoir at the bottom of the gear case. Additional lubrication is accomplished by oil creepage along the shafts, pinions and gears.
  b. Gear and pinion assembly. Gears are mounted with steel pinions on stainless-steel shafts, and the entire gear train is supported between two bearing plates.
  c, d. Terminal shaft assembly. A brass baffle *c*, which is an integral part of the terminal gear, is mounted on a stainless-steel terminal shaft *d* controlling oil creepage to the terminal bearing. A secondary baffle surrounds the terminal-gear baffle. These two baffles together effectively control the amount of oil for lubricating the terminal-shaft bearing.
  e. Rotor shaft assembly, designed for high-speed operation, consists of lightweight rotors and steel pinions mounted on a steel rotor shaft.
  f. Shading coils. Copper shading coils are arranged on one-half of each pole face of the bipolar field structure.
  g. Sealed gear-case assembly. Gear-case assembly is first filled with the proper amount of oil at the factory, and then sealed to keep the oil in, and to exclude dust.

shading coils 7 and 8 separating them from the main-pole stampings. Thus, 12 more polar projections are provided, but these are shaded poles. For example, the six projections of 4 provide six poles all of the same magnetic polarity; stamping 3 provides six poles all having the same polarity as those of 4 but these six are all shaded by the single copper washer 7.   Thus, the assembly 4-7-3 provides six poles of one polarity, each having a *main body* and a *shaded portion*.   Similarly, assembly 5-8-6 provides six more poles of the opposite magnetic polarity, thus providing, in effect, a 12-pole stator.   A hardened steel ring 9, serving as the hysteresis element, is carried in the aluminum cup 10.   A single self-lubricating bearing 11 is contained within the central core 2; 12 is the oil-seal cap.

Fig. 15-7.—Multipolar shaded-pole hysteresis motor used for demand meters, timing switches, etc.   Motor runs at 600 rpm, drawing 1.6 watts, and delivering an output of 0.000005 hp. (*Courtesy of Westinghouse Electric Corporation.*)

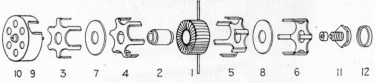

10 9   3   7   4   2   1   5   8   6   11   12

Fig. 15-8.—Exploded view of the motor of Fig. 15-7.   Note single stator coil.   (*Reprinted from the Instrument Maker.*)

INDUCTOR MOTORS

Inductor-type motors are essentially inductor-type synchronous generators operated as motors.   However, the small synchronous inductor motors described in the following paragraphs use permanent-magnet excitation, instead of d-c excitation as used in conventional inductor alternators.

15-16. Construction.—Parts and assemblies of three inductor motors are illustrated in Fig. 15-9.   Rotor punchings are mounted on an alnico disc-shaped hub.   Either one or two rotors may be mounted on the shaft, as shown.   Figure 15-10 shows the path of the permanent-magnet flux in a motor with double-rotor construction; all the teeth of one rotor are of the same magnetic polarity, and all the teeth of the second rotor are of the opposite magnetic polarity.   (With a single-disc rotor, the path of the return flux is through the end shields and shaft.)   There are eight polar projections to the stator punchings, and each of these has a toothed pole face with teeth having the same pitch as the rotor teeth. The stator winding consists of eight coils, each one wound around one tooth; these coils are connected as in a conventional two-phase winding.

Fig. 15-9.—Synchronous inductor motors, dissassembled. Top line: Type SMY-54-H, double-rotor, ball-bearing, 115-volt, 60-cycle, 75-rpm, 75- to 150-oz-in. torque. Middle line: Type SMY-50-H, double-rotor, 115-volt, 60-cycle, 75-rpm, 40-oz-in. torque. Bottom line: Type SMY-50-L, single-rotor, 115-volt, 60-cycle, 75-rpm, 20-oz-in. torque. (*Courtesy of General Electric Company.*)

15-17. Principles of Operation.—Principles of operation are best explained by the help of Fig. 15-11, which shows eight stator teeth—one per coil—and ten rotor teeth. Stator coils are connected as a four-pole two-phase winding, and excited, say, so as to produce a clockwise-rotating field. Assume, for purposes of discussion, that all the rotor teeth are magnetized as south poles due to the alnico disc. Now, consider the instant of time when coils 1 and 3 are energized so that 1 is a north pole and 3 a south pole. It is obvious that the rotor locks in the position shown because pole 1 attracts A and pole 3 repels teeth C and D equally. (At this same instant, coils 2 and 4 are not excited. Although teeth B and E are attracted to poles 2 and 4 because of the permanent-magnet excitation, these two forces balance each other and produce no net torque.) If the rotor is displaced slightly from the position shown in Fig. 15-11, the magnetic forces tend to return it to that position. One quarter of a cycle later, pole 2 becomes a north pole, and poles 1 and 3 are not excited. Since pole 2 is now a north pole, the rotor will turn clockwise until B and 2 are in alignment, with

C displaced only one quarter of a tooth pitch from 3; thus, the rotor has turned a quarter tooth pitch in a quarter cycle of the applied voltage. Poles 3, 4, and 1' successively become north poles at one-quarter cycle intervals, and at each interval the rotor moves a quarter of a tooth pitch. Thus, in one cycle of power frequency, the rotor moves *one rotor tooth pitch*, and not one stator pole pitch. Therefore,

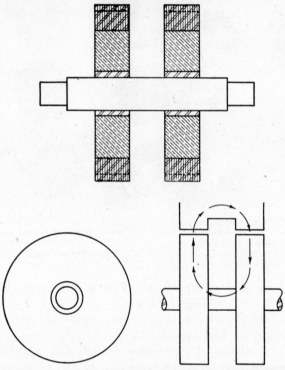

Fig. 15-10.—Schematic sectional view of double-rotor inductor motor showing path of permanent-magnet flux. (*Courtesy of General Electric Company.*)

when the speed of an inductor-type motor is figured, each rotor tooth must be counted as *two* poles. In Fig. 15-9 the rotor has 48 teeth; hence, from the equation in Art. 2-17 the synchronous speed, for 60-cycle excitation becomes

$$\frac{120 \times 60}{2 \times 48} = 75 \text{ rpm}$$

Motors of the double-disc construction are built with two rotor-stator units spaced apart as shown in Fig. 15-9 in order to prevent excessive magnetic leakage in the axial direction. However, common stator coils thread like poles of both units. Rotors, of course, are magnetized so that opposite polarities appear at the peripheries. Stator slots are in alignment, but the teeth in two rotors are displaced circumferentially by 180 electrical degrees.

Windings, instead of being two-phase, are usually of the permanent-split capacitor type.

A smaller inductor motor has been developed, using the same basic principles of operation but differing considerably in the arrangement of the active elements, which are shown in Fig. 15-12. The rotor consists of four cup-shaped stampings, each having 36 teeth. These

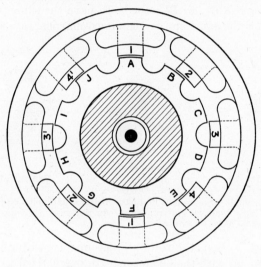

Fig. 15-11.—Schematic sectional view of inductor motor with one stator tooth for each stator coil. Actual motor has several teeth per coil (see stator punching in Fig. 15-9), but principles of operation are the same. (*Courtesy of General Electric Company*).

punchings are arranged in two pairs, back to back, and adjacent to the opposite ends of a cylindrical alnico magnet with a large clearance hole for the shaft. The entire assembly is held in a fixture and die-cast as a single unit; since the die-cast material is nonmagnetic, it does not affect axial magnetization of the magnet. The outside diameter is then ground. The stator likewise consists of four cup-shaped metal stampings, each having 36 teeth. These punchings are arranged in two pairs adjacent to each other axially, with the two middle punchings back to back. The entire assembly is encased in a single plastic-molded unit resembling a double spool. The inside bore is ground to expose four complete rings of uniformly spaced teeth in axial alignment.

Principles of operation are similar to those of the larger motor. In this motor, the stator teeth are axially aligned, while the two rotor punchings comprising one pair are displaced from each other circumferentially by one-half tooth pitch. The second pair of rotor punchings, identical with the first, is displaced circumferentially from the first pair by one-quarter tooth pitch. Consider the moment when the current in one winding is maximum and the current in the other zero; consider only the two stator punchings and the two rotor punchings associated with the excited coil. All 36 teeth of one of the stator punchings are magnetized as north poles; all 36 teeth of the other as 36 south poles. Now, all 72 rotor teeth have the same polarity since they are all on the same end of the alnico magnet; say, that they are

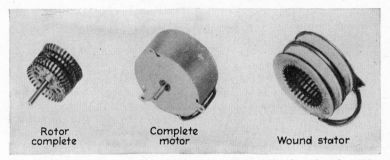

Rotor complete　　　Complete motor　　　Wound stator

Fig. 15-12.—Small synchronous inductor motor. 115-volt, 60-cycle, 100-rpm, 2-oz-in. torque. Also built with internal spur-reduction gearing giving 48 oz-in. torque at 1 rpm. (*Courtesy of the General Electric Company.*)

all south poles. Then, the rotor will assume a position such that 36 rotor teeth line up with the 36 stator teeth magnetized as north poles, like *A* and 1 in Fig. 15-11; the other 36 rotor teeth will fall halfway between the other 36 stator teeth magnetized as south poles, just as 3 falls between *C* and *D* in Fig. 15-11. One-half cycle later, the rotor will have moved one-half a tooth pitch—it might be in either direction without the second phase, which acts similarly but which imparts a definite predetermined direction of rotation to the motor.

15-18. Characteristics and Applications.—These motors are practically instantaneous in starting, since they have to reach full synchronous speed in something less than half a cycle, or they will not start at all. This feature is useful in many applications such as interval timers and follow-up mechanisms. This feature is a definite handicap if the connected load has appreciable inertia. Usually the slight amount of angular slack in the driving connection is sufficient to allow the motor to come up to synchronous speed but, in some cases, additional flexibility may have to be provided in the coupling to obtain satisfactory operation.

The smaller unit described above gives 2 oz-in. torque at 100 rpm and is available with built-in reduction gears to give 1, 2, or 4 rpm with torques of 48, 24, and 12 oz-in., respectively.

These motors have very definite pull-out torques; if a load exceeds the pull-out torque of the motor, the latter will pull out of step and come to a dead stop. When power is removed, they come to a stop almost instantly because of their low speed, low inertia, and the permanent-magnet excitation. They can be stalled indefinitely without injury.

Bibliography

1. TRICKEY, P. H.: The Non-excited Synchronous Motor, *Elec. J.*, April, 1933.
2. ———: Performance Calculations on Polyphase Reluctance Motors, *A.I.E.E. Trans.*, 1946, pp. 191–193.
3. TEARE, B. R., JR.: Theory of Hysteresis Motor Torque, *A.I.E.E. Trans.*, vol. 59, 1940, p. 907.
4. PEARCE, R. M.: Small Synchronous Timing Motors Can Assist Automatic Operation, *Elec. Manufacturing*, March, 1945, p. 109.
5. MACGAHAN, PAUL: A Slow-speed Synchronous Time Motor Operates on the Remanence or Hysteresis Principle, *The Instrument Maker*, July-August, 1942.

CHAPTER XVI

POSITION-INDICATING AND SYNCHRONOUS-DRIVE SYSTEMS

Machines used in position-indicating and synchronous-drive systems are not, strictly speaking, motors, but control devices. However, since they are small rotating machines usually built by manufacturers of fractional horsepower electric motors, a description of them is included in this book.

16-1. General.—Electrical systems for transmitting an angular motion of one shaft to a remotely located second shaft have long been known and used by industry. Reding[1] likens such a system to "an invisible shaft that can turn corners or go upstairs, that can at any speed, fast or slow, maintain an exact mechanical relation between two or more machines; that can drive a machine at precisely the same speed, or exactly at some speed greater or less than that of the one driving it . . . ." Numerous electrical systems are used to perform the above-described function of a long flexible shaft. A better understanding of how these systems work is often gained by comparing them with equivalent mechanical systems.

Extreme usefulness of such systems in many varieties of combat equipment caused them to be produced during the war in large quantities by a number of manufacturers. However, these systems had many prewar industrial applications: remote indication of positions of meters, valves, water-level gauges, drawbridges, radio antennas, etc.; remote control or positioning of valves, rheostats, bridges, etc. There is no inherent limit to the amount of torque or power that can be transmitted or controlled by these systems, which offer interesting possibilities for an even greater number of postwar uses.

16-2. These Systems Are Known by Many Names.—No small confusion has been caused by the fact there are no universally accepted names for the components of position-indicating and synchronous-drive systems, or for the systems themselves. Some of these names are as follows:

---

[1] For numbered references, see Bibliography at end of this chapter.

Autosyn
Diehlsyn
Position indicator
Self-synchronous
Selsyn
Synchronous-drive
Synchro-tie

Some of these are copyrighted trade names and may be used as nouns or as adjectives, to describe either the system as a whole or individual units of it. Still other names have been applied to the systems described in this chapter. In any of these systems, the sending unit may be known as either the **generator** or the **transmitter**. In some systems, the receiving unit is known as either the **motor** or the **receiver**. In other systems, a **control transformer** is used. Magnesyn[6] remote-indicating systems used on airplanes accomplish similar results, but the units are basically different in construction from the units discussed in this chapter and make use of different principles of operation. Likewise, **self-synchronous motors** should not be confused with **synchronous motors**. A synchronous motor keeps in step with the power supply, whereas a *self-synchronous motor* keeps in step with another *self-synchronous machine*.

For instrument and control applications that involve small torques, single-phase and d-c systems are widely used. For applications where appreciable mechanical power has to be transmitted, polyphase excitation is more often used.

MOTOR-AND-GENERATOR SYSTEM WITH SINGLE-PHASE EXCITATION

16-3. Components and Connections of the System.—Figure 16-1 is the schematic diagram of a system used for transmitting a single angular motion to a remote location. When the two units are connected as shown and energized, they operate much as if they were connected mechanically by means of a long, slender, and flexible shaft. If the generator shaft is turned, the motor shaft turns likewise, lagging behind by a very slight angle. If the motor is locked in position so that it is not free to turn, a torque will be exerted upon its shaft tending to turn it; for small angles of movement of the generator, of the order of 20 deg, the torque exerted upon both motor and generator shafts is nearly proportional to the angle through which the generator is turned. To displace the generator, a torque must be applied to it which is substantially equal to the torque load on the motor. These characteristics are the same as would be obtained with a flexible mechanical coupling. Generators and motors may be of either salient-pole or distributed-winding construction.

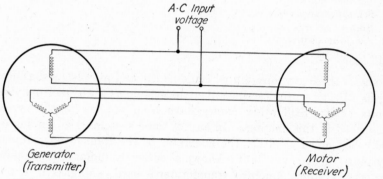

FIG. 16-1.—System for transmission of a single angular motion to a remote location.

16-4. Construction of Salient-pole Generators and Motors. *a. Generator.*—In the schematic diagram of Fig. 16-1, the generator has two windings. The single-phase winding is the **primary winding**, and the three-phase winding, the **secondary**. Some generators are built with the primary winding on the stator. In this case, the stator

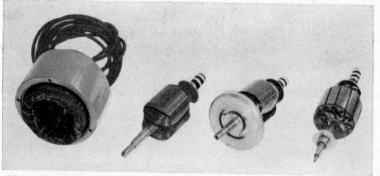

FIG. 16-2.—Selsyn stator and three rotors. View shows stator, generator rotor, motor rotor (showing damper), and differential rotor. (*Courtesy of General Electric Company.*)

punchings bear some resemblance to the punchings of a concentrated-pole universal motor, such as shown in Fig. 12-4; the rotor punchings then have uniformly spaced slots and a balanced three-phase winding. Three collector rings and brushes are required; these are especially designed for low contact drop by use of gold or silver alloys. Other designs of generators use a revolving-primary construction. One of these rotors is illustrated in Fig. 16-2; the punchings are shuttle-shaped and carry two coils. Two collector rings are required.

Self-synchronous generators are somewhat similar to large two-pole three-phase generators except for the size, and except that a laminated-field construction is essential because the field is excited with alternating current. Another difference is that the span of the pole face of a conventional synchronous generator is of the order of 120 deg, whereas the pole span of a self-synchronous generator is nearer 90 deg. Still another difference is the fact that the self-synchronous generator does not have a squirrel-cage damper winding. These comments apply to both revolving-primary and revolving-secondary generators.

b. Motor.—Self-synchronous motors are identical electrically and mechanically with self-synchronous generators except for added refinements, one of which, often incorporated, is a mechanical damper. This damper consists essentially of a flywheel which is loose on the shaft but which is coupled to it through a friction clutch. One such damper, illustrated in Fig. 16-2, serves to damp out mechanical oscillations of the rotor; it also prevents the motor from running as a single-phase induction motor. It is to be noted that, if the secondary leads of a self-synchronous motor are short-circuited, the machine becomes in fact a single-phase induction motor with a three-phase secondary winding; it will run once it is started. If the self-synchronous motor happens to be displaced from its position of correspondence when it is energized, the self-synchronizing torque gives the rotor a momentary impulse to bring it to the correspondence position; now, the secondary is short-circuited through the relatively low impedance of the generator secondary, so that the motor can, and often does, start and continue running if a damper is not used. Because the damper is mounted on the shaft, it does not restrict the slow movements incident to normal operation; but, because of its high inertia, the damper cannot follow rapid movements or accelerations of the shaft such as occur when the rotor attempts to start as a motor or when it attempts to oscillate angularly at its natural frequency. In either case, the friction clutch slips, effectively damping out any oscillations and preventing operation as a motor.

Specially selected ball bearings of high accuracy are used to keep the static friction low.

Very small units may use a Gramme-ring construction, as shown in Fig. 16-6 and described in Art. 16-11.

16-5. Construction of Distributed-winding Machines.—Conventional wound-rotor polyphase induction motors can be, and often are, used for the units of a single-phase self-synchronous system. An illustration of how these can be used is given in Fig. 16-3. Secondaries, which are usually three-phase whether the primary is two- or three-phase, are interconnected. The transmitter is shown as having a two-phase primary winding; one phase is connected to the a-c input voltage while the other one is short-circuited. Satisfactory operation can be obtained without short-circuiting the second phase, but the effect of the short circuit is to give a stiffer system, *i.e.*, more torque gradient when the machines are near correspondence, although it takes less torque to break the system apart completely. The receiver of Fig. 16-3 has a three-phase primary. It will be noted that two of the leads are connected to the same a-c input line; this arrangement gives the equivalent of the two-phase machine, *i.e.*, a short-circuited

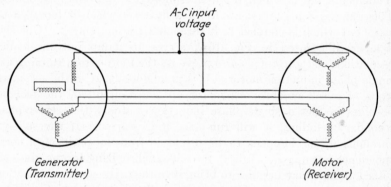

Fig. 16-3.—Single-phase system similar to Fig. 16-1, except that wound-rotor polyphase induction motors are used for both machines. Ordinarily, both machines would be identical. Different machines are used above to illustrate two different primary connections.

winding in quadrature with the single-phase exciting winding. The effect of no short-circuited winding can be obtained by connecting the single-phase input to two of the line leads, leaving the third one open-circuited.

Connections such as shown in Fig. 16-3 are not recommended for an actual system because of the difficulty in matching secondary voltages. For example, suppose both motors are designed so that, for the same line voltage, the same secondary voltages are obtained (polyphase excitation is assumed); now if these machines are connected as in Fig. 16-3, the output voltage of the motor will be approximately 15 per cent greater than that of the generator. *It is better to use identical machines.*

16-6. Principles of Operation.—As shown in Figs. 16-1 and 16-3, a simple motor-and-generator system consists of two machines connected together electrically. Considering, say, only the generator, there will be a voltage induced in each of the three secondary windings by transformer action. This voltage will be of the same frequency as, and in time phase with, the primary voltage; however, the magnitude of this voltage depends upon the rotor position. When the rotor position is such that the axis of a particular secondary phase coincides with the axis of the primary winding, the voltage induced in that phase has its maximum value; as the rotor is turned from this position, the voltage induced decreases as the cosine of the angle of displacement from this position. In Fig. 16-1, maximum voltage is being induced in the phase shown in the vertical position, and only half as much voltage in each of the other two phases. If the voltage induced in the vertical phase is, say, 100 volts, the voltage induced in each of the other two phases is 50 volts; therefore, in the position shown, the secondary voltage between the two top secondary lines is zero, but between either top line and the bottom line, the voltage is 150. In general, a different set of secondary voltages is produced for each different position of the rotor.

Now consider the system of Fig. 16-1 as a whole. The principle of operation is fairly simple, although it has been made the subject of extensive mathematical analysis.[2] When power is applied, the rotors assume "corresponding positions" as shown. If generator and motor are identical in design, this is the position in which the voltage induced in each secondary phase of the motor is exactly equal and opposite to the voltage induced in the corresponding secondary phase of the generator. Hence, in this position of "correspondence," the voltage between each pair of motor leads is exactly equal and opposite to the voltage between the pair of generator leads to which it is connected; therefore, no secondary currents will flow. If, now, the generator rotor is turned a little, the voltage induced in each generator secondary phase is changed a little, so that it is no longer equal to and opposite the voltage of the corresponding motor winding. Therefore, currents will flow between secondaries, and the effect of these circulating currents is to develop a torque in both machines. The torque developed by the generator is in a direction to restrain the movement of the generator, and the motor torque is in the direction that turns the motor rotor, if it is free to turn, to the position of correspondence where there are no secondary currents. If the machines are not designed for the same secondary voltage, the rotor will, nevertheless, assume corresponding positions of equilibrium, but current will flow even in this position, although no torque will be produced.

Table XVIII.—Characteristics of Self-synchronous Motor Systems

A. Alternating-current types

Model No.	Primary volt	Application*	Static error max.	Torque gradient at various frequencies, oz-in. per deg				Voltage gradient (volt/deg) (60 or 400)	Weight, lb
				25 cyc.	50 cyc.	60 cyc.	400 cyc.		
1	115	G	....	....	....	0.1	0.1	...	1.2
		M	1.5 deg	....	....	0.1	0.1		
		CT	0.6 deg	....	....	....	....	1.0	
		DG	†	....	....	....	0.06		
2	110	G	1.0 deg	....	0.13	0.16	....	....	4.0
		M	1.0 deg	....	0.13	0.16			
		DG	†	....	0.1	0.12			
		DM	2.0 deg	....	0.1	0.12			
3	115	G	....	....	....	0.45	0.35	...	5.5
		M	0.6 deg	....	. . ..	0.45	0.35		
		CT	0.3	....	....	....	....	1.0	
		DG	†	....	....	0.35	0.28		
		DM	1.2 deg	....	....	0.35			
4	110 or 220	G	1.0 deg	0.17	0.37	0.4	....	...	7
		M	1.0 deg	0.17	0.37	0.4			
		DG	†	0.13	0.27	0.3			
		DM	2.0 deg	0.13	0.27	0.3			
5	115	G	....	....	....	1.2	....	...	7
		DG	†	....	....	1.0			
6	110 or 220	G	1.0 deg	0.7	1.5	1.7	....	...	17
		M	1.0 deg	0.7	1.5	1.7			
		DG	†	0.5	1.1	1.4			
		DM	2.0 deg	0.5	1.1	1.4			
7	115	G	....	....	....	3.4	....	...	17
		DG	†	....	....	3.0			

B. Direct-current types

Model No.	Application	Voltage	Torque gradient, oz-in. per deg	Weight, lb
3	Motor	115	0.6	5
5	Motor	115	1.2	7
7	Motor	115	2.72	17
8	Motor	115	7.5	55

* G = Generator
M = Motor
CT = Control transformer
DG = Differential generator
DM = Differential motor
† The introduction of a differential generator decreases the available torque of a system. The over-all error is increased approximately 50 per cent.

Reprinted from Electrical Manufacturing.

16-7. Performance Characteristics.—Torque gradients and maximum static errors for representative self-synchronous systems are given in Table XVIII, which is taken from an article in *Electrical Manufacturing* by Chestnut and Johnson.[4]

Torque gradient is a measure of the stiffness of the system. Values of torque gradient given in Table XVIII represent the amount of torque necessary to displace the rotor 1 deg from its position of correspondence. For small angles of displacement—20 deg or less—the torque gradient can be taken as the ratio of torque to angle of displacement from correspondence. More generally, *torque gradient* refers to the increase or decrease in torque necessary to increase or decrease the displacement by one degree. In any system, the torque gradient is highest in the position of correspondence and decreases as the displacement angle is increased. Torque gradients given, then, are maximum values. In the table, identical machines are assumed, so that the torque gradients are the same for both motor and generator. If a motor is used with a larger generator, more torque gradient can be obtained. These torque values also assume neglible resistance in the leads interconnecting the secondaries; if the resistance of each interconnecting line is comparable to the line-to-line secondary resistance, the torque gradient may be reduced as much as 50 per cent, according to Chestnut and Johnson.

Static error refers to the maximum angular error by which the motor, when free of external load, fails to follow the movement of the generator. For example, if the generator is moved 60 deg and the motor turns either 59 or 61 deg, the static error in that position is 1 deg.

Several motors can be operated by a single generator. For example, a single generator installed on the operating drum of an elevator can operate a motor on each floor and so give simultaneous indication on all floors of the position of the elevator. For such an application, the generator has to be larger than the motors need be, but the secondary voltages of all machines must be the same in the position of correspondence.

In any of these systems, the mechanical power output of the motor or motors all has to be supplied by mechanical power input to the generator.

OTHER SELF-SYNCHRONOUS SYSTEMS

16-8. Use of a Control Transformer and Generator.—An electrical system for detecting the relative angular displacement between two shafts is illustrated schematically in Fig. 16-4, which introduces a new element, the **control transformer.** For the moment, in order to simplify this discussion, let it be assumed that the control transformer is another generator, identical with the one just discussed. When the generator primary is excited, an alternating magnetic field is set up in the generator along the axis of the primary winding. This field induces voltages in the three secondary phases; these voltages cause current to flow and set up an alternating magnetic field in the control transformer. The latter field is stationary in space, but its position in the control transformer moves forward or backward as the generator rotor does, *and by the same amount within very close limits.* Now,

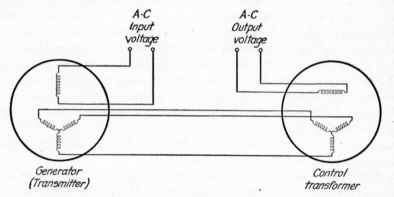

FIG. 16-4.—System for detecting angular displacement between two shafts. Amount and direction of this displacement are indicated by magnitude and phase position of the a-c output voltage.

since this field in the control transformer alternates at line frequency, there is a voltage induced in the single-phase winding of the transformer, the magnitude of which varies with the position of the winding with respect to the magnetic field set up by the three-phase winding. When the output winding of the control transformer (this corresponds to the primary winding of the generator) is displaced by 90 deg from the field, the voltage induced in it is zero. The windings in Fig. 16-4 are shown in this position of zero output voltage, which is, then, the position of "correspondence." The output voltage of the control transformer is proportional to the sine of the displacement from correspondence, which means that, for angles of 20 deg or less, the voltage is substantially proportional to the angle of displacement. It does not matter whether the generator shaft or the control-transformer shaft is turned; the effect on the transformer output voltage is the same. Voltage per degree of displacement is called **voltage gradient,** values of which are given in Table XVIII. It is to be noted that the phase angle of the output voltage of the control transformer changes by 180 deg when its rotor is moved through the correspondence position, *i.e.*, through the zero-voltage position. It is also to be noted that the output voltage in any position is also proportional to the voltage impressed upon the primary of the generator, but as the output voltage is generally used to actuate a control circuit to restore the control transformer to the position of zero voltage, variation in line voltage is not important.

There is an important difference between the functioning of a motor-and-generator system and a transformer-and-generator system. In the first system, the generator shaft is driven mechanically, and the motor shaft follows just as if a long flexible shaft coupled the two units mechanically. In the second case, the shafts of both generator and transformer are driven mechanically and independently of one another, but the relative movement of the two shafts with respect to each other is indicated by the amount and phase position of the output voltage from the control transformer. A mechanical analogy would be this: Suppose that the control transformer were equipped with a dial rigidly fastened to its shaft, and on this shaft an indicating pointer were mounted, free to turn about the shaft; now suppose that this pointer were mechanically coupled to the generator shaft by means of a long, flexible, and fairly rigid shaft. Further, suppose that generator and transformer shafts are turned independently of one another. So long as the motion of both shafts is identical, the position of the pointer on the dial does not change but, if the movement of the shafts is not the same, the difference will be shown up by a movement of the pointer on the dial, and this movement indicates the difference in angular motion between the transformer and generator shafts. However, in the transformer-and-generator system, the control transformer indicates the amount and direction of the difference in movement between the two shafts by the amount and direction of the output voltage, and not by a visual indication. In practice, this output voltage is generally used to control the motor driving the shaft to which the transformer is connected. The control, which may be electronic, is arranged to position the transformer shaft to the zero-output, or correspondence, position. Thus, the position of the second shaft is effectively controlled by the transformer-and-generator system; but torque and power are not directly transmitted through the self-synchronous system, as they are in the motor-and-generator system of

Fig. 16-1.   Since neither torque nor mechanical motion is transmitted, large amounts of power can be controlled by use of small instruments, and mechanical friction introduces no error in the system.

16-9. Construction of a Control Transformer.—It was stated in the preceding article that a control transformer is similar to a generator.   Essentially this is true, but two important differences should be pointed out: (1) The secondary winding of the control transformer is wound to obtain relatively high impedance, in order to reduce the current drain on the generator.   (2) The control transformer has a

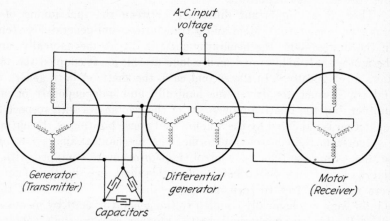

FIG. 16-5.—System for transmitting sum or difference of two angular motions to a remote location.

uniform air gap, primarily so that the impedances of all three phases will be equal to one another in all positions of the rotor.   It is desirable to keep the impedances equal so as not to unbalance the generator signal and thereby introduce errors into the system.   Moreover, with a salient-pole arrangement, a mechanical torque would be exerted on the transformer shaft.

16-10. Differential Generators and Motors.—Figure 16-5 shows the use of a differential generator in a motor-and-generator system. The differential generator has three-phase windings on both stator and rotor.   If the differential generator shaft is held motionless, the motor follows the motion of the generator just as it does in the system of Fig. 16-1.   If the generator shaft is stationary and the differential generator is turned, the motor follows the differential generator.   If both generator and differential generator are turned together, the motor turns by an amount equal to the sum or the difference of the movements of the two generators, depending upon how the system is connected.   In other words, the differential generator transmits the system of voltages from a self-synchronous generator, either with or without modifying them.   Turning the differential generator by, say, 30 deg modifies the voltages just the same as if the main transmitting generator were itself turned 30 deg.

The differential generator is wound to have a low primary imped-ance, and capacitors are used in parallel with it to furnish exciting current and lessen the drain on the generator.

It is, perhaps, obvious that the differential generator could be used between the generator and transformer in Fig. 16-4 to modify the signal sent to the control transformer.   Another possible modifica-tion of the system of Fig. 16-5 is to substitute another generator for the motor; in this case, the differential generator, if its shaft is free to turn, becomes a differential motor, and the shaft turns by an amount equal to the sum or difference of the motions of the two generator shafts.

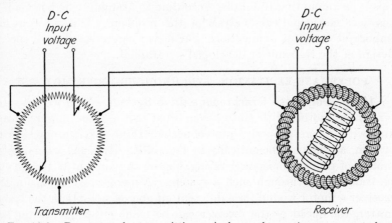

Fig. 16-6.—D-c system for transmitting a single angular motion to a remote loca-tion.   Use of same input voltage for both units is optional, but a relative change in polarity introduces an error of 180°.   If the receiver is made exclusively for a d-c system, a permanent-magnet rotor can be used, eliminating the coil and d-c excitation.

16-11. Position-indicating System for Direct Current.—Figure 16-6 shows in schematic form a position-indicating system which uses a d-c supply.   The transmitter consists of a special closed-circuit resistor wound uniformly around a ring of refractory insulating material, as indicated schematically in the figure.   This resistor is tapped at three points equally spaced around the circumference; further, a pair of diametrically spaced moving contacts is provided.

A conventional self-synchronous motor, similar to the ones already described, can be used as a receiver, but a receiver of different construction is shown in the figure. This receiver has a stator consisting of a laminated iron ring which is uniformly wound around the outside with insulated copper wire; this coil is tapped at three points equally spaced around the ring. Inside the ring a simple shuttle-type armature wound with a single coil of wire is shown. Such a receiver can be used equally well with a single-phase generator in the system of Fig 16-1. Ring-type stator construction is used for receivers as small as 1 in. in outside diameter. If the receiver is intended to be used only on direct current, a permanent magnet can be used as the movable element, thus eliminating coil, collector rings, and d-c excitation.

There is no torque reaction against the transmitter, and all the power to turn the receiver is supplied electrically from the source of power. Such a system does not have such high accuracy as a single-phase a-c system; in addition to the errors due to friction and manufacturing variations, there is a natural error inherent to a system of this type amounting to 1.1 deg, according to Manildi[7] who has made a rigorous mathematical analysis of the problem. This error is not important for most applications, but it can be corrected by a special design of the transmitter developed by Manildi.

POLYPHASE EXCITATION (SYNCHRONOUS–DRIVE MOTORS)

16-12. Polyphase Synchronous-drive System.—Two wound-rotor polyphase motors with stators connected to the same power source, and with rotors properly interconnected, form a synchronous-drive system, as shown schematically in Fig. 16-7. By using wound-rotor motors of proper horsepower rating, almost any amount of torque can be transmitted through such a system. Moreover, by using for the receiver a motor wound for a different number of poles than the transmitter, the speed of the receiver can be made either greater or less than that of the transmitter.

Torque and Speed Characteristics.—When the primaries are excited with polyphase, there is a rotating field produced, as in any polyphase induction motor. The torque and speed characteristics depend upon whether the transmitter is turned in the same direction as the rotation of this field or against the direction of rotation of this field. In Fig. 16-8 are shown the torque characteristics of a representative synchronous-drive system as given by C. W. Drake in the *Electrical World*.[3] It is noted that if the transmitter is turned with the field, the receiver develops more torque than the transmitter, but that if the rotation is against the field, the receiver develops less torque than the transmitter. If the operation is with the field, the receiver and transmitter torques decrease rapidly as the transmitter speed is increased.

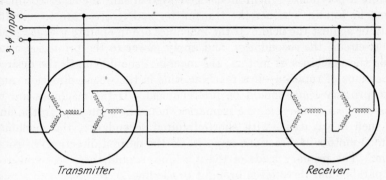

Fig. 16-7.—Polyphase system for transmission of a single angular motion to a remote location. Torques of motor magnitudes can be transmitted.

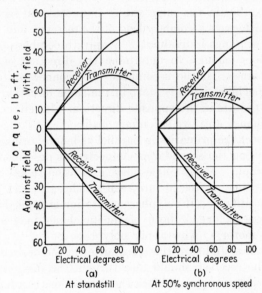

Fig. 16-8.—Torque angle characteristics of two synchronous-drive motors.

In general, if the operating speeds are less than 50 to 60 per cent of synchronous speed, better characteristics will be obtained if the transmitter is driven in the direction of rotation of the field. However, if the operating speeds are higher, more satisfactory performance will be obtained, as will also somewhat higher losses, if the operation is against the field.

16-13. Connecting Up a Polyphase Synchronous-drive System.— Before a polyphase synchronous-drive system can be connected up, it must be known whether the transmitter and receiver are to operate with or against the field. If the machines are to operate *with the field*, short-circuit the secondaries, and apply power to the primaries, running the machines as motors; the machines should run in the desired directions of rotation—if a machine runs in the wrong direction, any two primary leads should be interchanged. If the machines are to operate *against the field*, the primaries should be connected to the line in such a way that, with short-circuited secondaries, the machines run as motors in directions opposite to the desired directions of rotation. The primary leads of the machines should then be connected in parallel and three leads brought to the line.

The next step is to connect the secondaries together correctly. Tag, or otherwise mark, the primary leads so that they can again be connected together in the same way. Connect each secondary lead of the transmitter to a secondary lead of the receiver, and short-circuit the primary windings individually. Apply three-phase power to the secondaries long enough to determine the direction of rotation of the two machines. If the secondaries are connected together correctly, *both* machines will (1) start in the same direction they are to operate or (2) rotate in the opposite direction. If neither condition is found, interchange any two secondary leads.

Now connect the primaries in parallel as before, bringing out three leads and leaving the secondaries connected as described in the preceding paragraph. Apply single-phase excitation to any two primary lines. Both rotors, if free to turn, will synchronize, *i.e.*, take up corresponding positions. (If polyphase excitation is applied immediately to both primaries, one or both of the machines may start up and operate as a motor). Now apply polyphase power to the primaries of both machines, and turn the transmitter in the desired direction of rotation. The receiver should also turn in the desired direction of rotation; but if it does not, recheck the connections carefully. If there is more than one receiver, it is suggested that each individual one be connected to the transmitter one at a time, taking care to get all leads connected correctly. Once all the receivers are connected to the transmitter, it is no longer necessary to connect them individually to start them up, but it is always necessary to synchronize the machines at standstill by first applying single-phase power.

MISCELLANEOUS SERVICE PROBLEMS

Self-synchronous machines such as are described in Arts. 16-3 to 16-11 are instruments, and any repairs or adjustments on them should take this fact into consideration. It is suggested that, when possible, the manufacturer's recommendations be obtained before any extensive repairs are undertaken. However, the resourceful serviceman is often not content to wait for such recommendations. For his benefit a few comments are given.

16-14. Rewinding Self-synchronous Machines.—The only safe rule that can be laid down is to duplicate the original winding. If only one machine of a system is rewound, this provision is a necessity. In any case, if all the machines of a system are rewound, the ratio of effective conductors in the primary to the number of effective conductors in the secondary must be kept the same in all machines that are to operate in the same system, in order to avoid circulating current when the rotors are in corresponding positions.

All the units of a system can be rewound for a different primary voltage, if desired; but all the primaries should be wound alike, thus keeping the ratio between primary and secondary turns the same in all machines. If this is done, it should not be necessary to rewind the secondaries unless they have a defective winding.

16-15. Reversing a Self-synchronous Motor.—If it is found that, when the rotor of a generator is moved as desired, the motor moves in the wrong direction, the situation can be corrected by interchanging two of the secondary leads (three-phase member) of either the generator or the motor. If there are one generator and several motors and if some motors operate in the correct direction and some in the wrong direction, it will be better to correct the direction of rotation by correcting each motor individually, instead of by changing the connections to the generator.

16-16. Building Position Indicators in the Repair Shop.—For him who may have the temerity to build a self-synchronous system in his workshop, the following suggestions are reluctantly and hopefully given:

a. From a Wound-rotor Polyphase Induction Motor.—If two or more duplicate polyphase wound-rotor induction motors are available, they can be used for position indicators, as discussed in Art. 16-5, or as discussed in Arts. 16-12 and 16-13.

b. From the Parts of a Universal Motor.—Sometimes it is possible to build position indicators from the parts of a universal motor, particularly if the number of rotor slots is a multiple of three, permitting the rewinding of the rotor with a three-phase winding. It is necessary to strip the armature, remove the commutator, and provide three collector rings and brushes. The armature then should be wound with a straight three-phase winding. For want of a better rule, the number of turns per coil in the armature can be selected so as to give approximately 55 volts per phase (line-to-neutral) in the armature. In order to find the number of turns to give approximately 55 volts per phase, it will first be necessary to design the stator field winding. If the stator is of the concentrated-pole type, it is necessary to rewind the field coils to operate across the line. It is suggested that the number of turns be proportioned so as to make the maximum density in any portion of the magnetic circuit, neglecting bolts and rivets, about 80,000 lines per square inch. In order to find the correct number of turns for the field coils, any number of turns can be assumed, and then the total flux per pole can be figured from Eq. (14-8), Art. 14-21. When using this formula, it should be borne in mind that one turn of the field coil is the equivalent of two series conductors (moreover, with a concentrated coil such as this, the chord factor and distribution factor are both equal to 1). The minimum section through which the magnetic flux passes can then be figured and divided by the total flux to obtain the density. When computing the area of the core, care should be taken to multiply the core area by two, as in Eq. (14-12), Art. 14-21. With the maximum magnetic density known for any number of stator turns, the number of turns can then be adjusted to give the correct magnetic density. It will then be possible to calculate the number of effective series conductors per phase for the secondary and, from this information, the number of turns per coil.

If the stator is of the compensated type with a distributed winding, the field winding can be designed to operate across the line, as explained in the preceding paragraph. A compensating winding—the number of turns is immaterial—short-circuited upon itself should be used.

It should not be expected that a machine made in this crude way, particularly if sleeve bearings are used, can compete in accuracy with machines especially designed and built for this service; but if too great accuracy is not demanded, satisfactory results may be obtained.

16-17. Rewinding a Polyphase Synchronous-drive Motor.—The polyphase synchronous-drive motor is simply a wound-rotor polyphase induction motor. Synchronous-drive motors may be rewound the same as polyphase induction motors, following the rules and principles set down in Chap. XIV. It is important to remember, however, that the secondaries of all machines that operate on the same system must be wound to give the same voltage, as otherwise there would be excessive losses due to circulating currents between the various machines.

Bibliography

1. REDING, H. W.: Synchronized Drives without Mechanical Connection, *Elec. J.*, July, 1933, pp. 277–280.
2. LINVILLE, T. M., and WOODWARD, J. S.: Selsyn Instruments for Position Systems, *Elec. Eng.*, June, 1934, pp. 953–960.
3. DRAKE, C. W.: Synchro-ties to Handle Torques of Motor Magnitudes, *Elec. World*, August 25, 1934, pp. 240–243.
4. CHESTNUT, HAROLD, and JOHNSON, T. C.: Self-synchronize for Remote Control. *Elec. Manufacturing*, December, 1944, p. 96.
5. JOHNSON, T. C.: Selsyn Design and Application, *A.I.E.E. Trans.*, vol. 64, 1945, pp. 703–708.
6. CHILDS, ROBERT S.: Magnesyn Remote Indication, *A.I.E.E. Trans.*, vol. 63, 1944, pp. 679–682.
7. MANILDI, JOSEPH: Analysis and Design of a D-c Selsyn System, *A.I.E.E. Trans.*, vol. 64, 1945, pp. 512–516.

CHAPTER XVII

DIRECT-CURRENT MOTORS

In the field of fractional horsepower motors, d-c motors represent less than 10 per cent of the total activity. They are used as a rule only if alternating current is not available. They may sometimes be used, however, because of the variable-speed characteristics of the shunt motor.

It should be pointed out, however, that d-c motors cannot be depended upon to operate so closely to their rated full-load speed as do a-c motors. At full load, single-phase a-c motors will, in general, operate within 2 per cent of their rated speed, whereas d-c motors may vary as much as $7\frac{1}{2}$ per cent above or below their rated speed.

17-1. Types of D-c Motors.—Major types of d-c motors are represented schematically in Fig. 17-1.

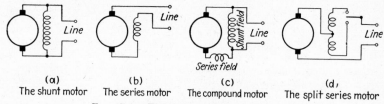

(a) The shunt motor (b) The series motor (c) The compound motor (d) The split series motor

Fig. 17-1.—The major types of d-c motors.

a. Shunt Motors.—**Shunt-wound motors** have the field connected in shunt with the armature, and have essentially constant-speed characteristics similar to the speed characteristics of induction motors. (The shape of the speed-torque curve of a shunt motor is somewhat similar to the shape of the combined-winding speed-torque curve shown in Fig. 5-4 for a capacitor-start motor.) **Stabilized shunt-wound motors** are shunt-wound motors with a light series winding added to stabilize the speed characteristics, *i.e.*, to prevent any rise in speed when load is added. Tendency to rise in speed is due to the field-weakening effect of armature reaction, as explained in Art. 17-4*f*. Stabilized shunt-wound motors are very rarely used in fractional horsepower sizes.

b. Series Motors.—**Series-wound motors** have the field connected in series with the armature and have the varying-speed characteristics of universal series motors, representative curves for which are shown in Figs. 12-2 and 12-3. A modified form of this type is the **split-series motor** shown in Fig. 17-1*d*. Its chief advantage is ease of reversibility, requiring only a single-pole double-throw switch for control; it is discussed further in Art. 17-13.

c. Compound Motors.—**Compound-wound motors** employ both a series and a shunt field, and have speed characteristics intermediate between those of shunt and series motors, depending upon the amount of the compounding. The series winding is connected in such a direction as to assist the shunt field, thereby increasing the flux. Compound-wound motors are normally known as varying-speed motors. ("Differentially compounded motors," wherein the series field is connected so as to oppose the shunt field, are seldom used because of their unstable speed characteristics.)

d. Permanent-magnet Motors.—**Permanent-magnet motors** have armature windings, but no field windings; a permanent-magnet material is used in the field structure to set up the required flux. Motors of this type are built in miniature sizes of the order of 0.001 hp for control devices, timing motors, model railroads, etc.

17-2. Essential Parts of a D-c Motor.—A fractional horsepower d-c motor is illustrated in Fig. 17-2; it has essentially the same parts as an integral horsepower direct-current motor.

a. A field structure is necessary to provide a magnetic circuit for the flux and to hold the field coils. This may consist of two or more poles and a solid or laminated yoke. The poles are usually laminated because, with this type of construction, the pole face and the pole body itself are from the same stamping and it is usually necessary to laminate the pole face to keep down the pole-face surface losses. The laminated poles are riveted together, and the whole pole bolted to the inside of the yoke after the field coils have been slipped on over the poles. Another form of construction is similar to the construction of a universal motor as shown in Fig. 12-4; with this form of construction the yoke, pole body, and pole shoe are integral.

b. The *field coils* may consist of

1. Shunt coils wound with many turns of small wire, connected in series with each other and across the line, or in parallel with the armature.
2. Series coils with fewer turns and larger wire, which are connected in series with the armature or in series with the line.
3. Both shunt and series coils for a compound motor.

c. The *armature* is the rotating element, consisting of slotted punchings pressed onto the shaft. These punchings perform the dual purpose of providing a path for the magnetic flux and of carrying the armature winding, which is usually a drum winding of a closed circuit type such as illustrated in Figs. 10-12 and 10-14.   Ordinarily, fractional horsepower d-c motors built for industrial applications have but two poles.   However, aircraft d-c motors often use four or more poles. Sometimes the armature is skewed to reduce noise.

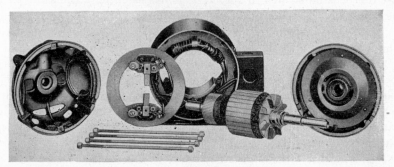

Fig. 17-2.—A fractional horsepower d-c motor. (*Courtesy of Emerson Electric Company.*)

d. A *commutator* and *brushes* are necessary to feed the current to the armature.   The construction of the brush holders may be similar to that of the brush holders of a repulsion-start motor, except that it is absolutely necessary that the brush holders of a d-c motor be insulated. Both cartridge-type and rocker-ring constructions are common.

e. *Commutating poles*, also called *interpoles*, are occasionally used in fractional horsepower d-c motors to improve commutation.   These are small auxiliary poles placed halfway between the main poles and connected in series with the armature. There may be as many inter-poles as main poles, or only half as many.

PRINCIPLES OF OPERATION

17-3. How Torque Is Developed.—Some idea of how torque is developed may be gained by referring to the schematic figure of a simple two-pole series motor as shown in Fig. 10-3. The armature windings, together with the commutator and brushes, are so arranged that the flow of current is in the same direction in all of the conductors on one side of the armature and in the opposite direction in all of the conductors on the other side of the armature. This condition is represented in Fig. 10-3 by the use of dots to indicate that the current is flowing perpendicularly toward the observer, and by plus signs to indicate that the current is flowing perpendicularly away from the observer. The field windings set up a magnetic field, the axis of which is perpendicular to the armature axis, as shown in the figure. It is a simple fundamental law of motor action that if current is passed through a conductor which is perpendicular to a magnetic field, a mechanical force will be exerted mutually perpendicular both to the field and to the current or conductor. The direction of this mechanical force depends upon the direction both of the field and of current flow. A rule for the direction of this force, expressed in terms of current and flux, is given in the left-hand rule appended as a footnote to Art. 10-4. Applying this rule to our own particular case, the force exerted on all of the conductors to the left of the brushes is in an upward direction, and in a downward direction on all of the conductors to the right of the brushes, so that a torque or turning effort is developed when the field is excited and when the armature is carrying current.

17-4. How the Shunt Motor Works.—Schematic arrangements showing how a shunt motor is connected to the line are given in Figs. 17-1a and 17-3. These connections are given in greater detail in the **wiring around frame diagrams,** Figs. 17-6, 17-7, and 17-12. Since the theory of operation of the d-c shunt motor is fully explained in almost every elementary text on d-c machines, the following discussion should be considered as only a review of the subject. For a more complete treatment of this subject, the reader is referred to any good elementary text. *Counter electromotive force* plays an important part in the operation of the d-c motor, and its effect must be understood if an understanding of how the motor works is to be gained.

a. Counter Emf.—At standstill, the armature current of a d-c motor is determined by the resistance and applied voltage, in accordance with Ohm's law. The armature current is, therefore, very high because the armature resistance is low. But when the motor is running, the armature generates a counter emf, which limits the current. Since the d-c motor and generator are essentially the same machine, it follows that, when the armature of a motor rotates, the armature conductors cut the field flux and, therefore, a voltage must be induced in these conductors by generator action. This induced voltage is known as the **counter emf**; it always opposes the line voltage when the machine is acting as a motor. The difference between the applied voltage and the counter emf is the net voltage that drives current through the armature. In any motor

$$\text{Counter emf} \propto \text{flux} \times \text{speed}$$

b. No-load Speed Is Fixed.—In a shunt motor, the flux is constant, so that

$$\text{Counter emf} \propto \text{speed}$$

Now at standstill, the motor current is very high and so is the torque, so that the motor accelerates rapidly. As the motor builds up speed, the counter emf builds up proportionately. As the counter emf builds, up, the net voltage—*i.e.*, the difference between the line voltage and the counter emf—decreases, decreasing the armature current. If the counter emf were exactly equal to the line voltage, no current would flow, hence no torque would be developed, and the motor could not accelerate to this point. However, the motor does actually accelerate up to the point where the counter emf is practically equal to the line voltage, drawing only enough current to supply friction and windage and armature core losses. Thus, a shunt motor has a very definite and fixed no-load speed which, for all practical purposes, may be said to be the speed at which the counter emf equals the line voltage.

c. How Field Control Affects the Speed.—In the foregoing paragraph it was stated that at no load the counter emf practically equals the line voltage. If the field is weakened by inserting resistance in the field circuit, the speed of the motor will increase. This point is easy to understand. Since the counter emf is proportional both to flux and to speed, it necessarily follows that if the flux is weakened, the motor will have to operate faster to generate a counter emf equal to the applied voltage. A motor of this type is known as an **adjustable-speed motor.** Under load conditions, changing the field strength affects the speed in a similar fashion; *i.e.*, weakening the field increases the speed, and strengthening the field decreases the speed. *The* *shunt-field circuit should never be opened while the armature is connected to the line.*

d. Change in Speed with Load.—If the motor is operating at no load and load is applied, the motor slows down because it was developing only sufficient torque to overcome its own losses. When the motor slows down, the counter emf—which is proportional to the speed—decreases, allowing more current to flow in the armature, thereby developing more torque. The speed drops to the point where this increased torque is just sufficient to carry the load. The amount of this speed change from no load to full load for shunt and compound motors is given in Table XIX.

e. Effect of Resistance in the Armature Circuit.—Suppose that a shunt motor is operating at full load. It is then operating at a speed such that the difference between the counter emf and the applied voltage is just enough to cause the right amount of current to flow to develop full-load torque. Now, if resistance is suddenly introduced into the armature circuit, the armature current will be reduced and the motor will no longer develop the torque necessary to maintain full speed. Therefore, the speed of the motor decreases, reducing the counter emf and thereby allowing more current to flow. This effect continues until a new equilibrium point is reached at a lower speed. Thus, the effect of introducing resistance into the armature circuit is to reduce the operating speed; this effect is greatest at heavy loads and almost negligible at light loads. With armature-resistance control, the constant-speed shunt motor becomes an **adjustable varying-speed motor.**

f. Armature Reaction—Interpoles.—Consider the schematic representation of a d-c motor in Fig. 10-3. In all the conductors to the left of the brushes, the current is flowing out of the paper; in all the conductors to the right of the brushes, the current is flowing into the paper. This is exactly the effect that would be produced by a coil of wire wrapped around the armature with its axis vertical. This coil would produce a magnetic field along the brush axis and perpendicular to the main field axis. In general, that is exactly what the armature current does: it sets up, or tends to set up, a magnetic field which is displaced 90 electrical degrees from the main-field flux. Such an effect is known as **armature reaction.** The magnetic field produced by armature reaction has at least two harmful effects: it distorts the main field, usually weakening it somewhat in the process; it causes a voltage to be induced in coils undergoing commutation, tending to produce sparking at the brushes. Commutation can be improved by shifting the brushes *against rotation*, if the construction of the motor permits; this procedure is practicable only if the motor is operated in only one direction of rotation. If the brush-holder positions are fixed, the effect of shifting the brushes can be obtained by shifting the coil connections to the commutator as illustrated in Fig. 12-22; this procedure is practicable only if the direction of rotation is known before the coil connections are soldered to the commutator.

Armature reaction can be overcome by the use of compensating windings such as used in universal motors. Interpoles provide another means for overcoming the harmful effects of armature reaction. These are small auxiliary poles placed between the main poles, and the interpole winding is always connected in series with the armature. By selecting the proper number of turns for the interpole winding, the armature-reaction mmf could be exactly canceled at all load currents, since the interpole carries armature current. In practice, the interpole winding is usually made a little stronger than this in order to improve commutation by setting up a little net flux at right angles to the main flux; a little interpolar flux aids commutation.

Interpole windings of *motors* must be connected so as to have the same magnetic polarity as that of the main pole just behind. This means that an armature conductor passes under an interpole that has the same polarity as the main pole just left behind. Interpole windings of *generators* are connected so that they have the same magnetic polarity as that of the main pole just ahead, *i.e.*, opposite to what they are in a motor.

17-5. How the Compound Motor Works.—How the compound motor is connected is shown schematically in Figs. 17-1c and 17-5, and more completely in the **wiring around frame diagrams** of Figs. 17-8 to 17-11. As pointed out in Art. 17-1, the series field is connected cumulatively, *i.e.*, so that the armature current through the series-field coils increases the field flux. As in the case of a shunt motor, the armature will come up to a definite no-load speed where the counter emf is equal to the applied voltage; the armature current will be very low, so that the effect of the series field is negligible. If the motor is loaded, the speed drops, just as in a shunt motor, allowing more current to flow through the armature, thus developing more torque to carry this load. Principally because of the increased flux due to the series field, the speed of a compound-wound motor will decrease more with an increase in load than will that of a shunt motor; *i.e.*, the speed regulation will be greater, as given in Table XIX.   Moreover, as the armature current increases, the resistance of the series field that is connected in the armature circuit tends to reduce the speed still further, for the reasons explained in Art. 17-4*e*.

Compound motors are usually classified as **varying-speed motors.**   With armature-resistance control, they become **adjustable varying-speed motors.**

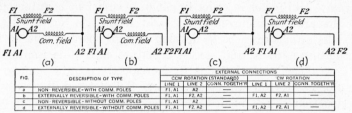

FIG.	DESCRIPTION OF TYPE	EXTERNAL CONNECTIONS					
		CCW ROTATION (STANDARD)			CW ROTATION		
		LINE 1	LINE 2	CONN. TOGETH'R	LINE 1	LINE 2	CONN. TOGETH'R
a	NON-REVERSIBLE-WITH COMM. POLES	F1, A1	A2	—			
b	EXTERNALLY REVERSIBLE-WITH COMM. POLES	F1, A1	F2, A2	—	F1, A1	F2, A1	—
c	NON-REVERSIBLE-WITHOUT COMM. POLES	F1, A1	A2	—			
d	EXTERNALLY REVERSIBLE-WITHOUT COMM. POLES	F1, A1	F2, A2	—	F1, A2	F2, A1	—

Fɪɢ. 17-3.—Standard terminal markings and connections for d-c shunt motors.   (*From A.S.A. Standards.*)

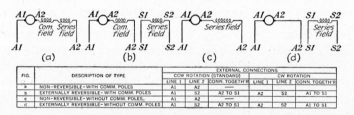

FIG.	DESCRIPTION OF TYPE	EXTERNAL CONNECTIONS					
		CCW ROTATION (STANDARD)			CW ROTATION		
		LINE 1	LINE 2	CONN. TOGETH'R	LINE 1	LINE 2	CONN. TOGETH'R
a	NON-REVERSIBLE-WITH COMM. POLES	A1	A2				
b	EXTERNALLY REVERSIBLE-WITH COMM. POLES	A1	S2	A2 → S1	A2	S2	A1 TO S1
c	NON-REVERSIBLE-WITHOUT COMM. POLES	A1	A2				
d	EXTERNALLY REVERSIBLE-WITHOUT COMM. POLES	A1	S2	A2 TO S1	A2	S2	A1 TO S1

Fɪɢ. 17-4.—Standard terminal markings and connections for d-c series motors.   (*From A.S.A. Standards.*)

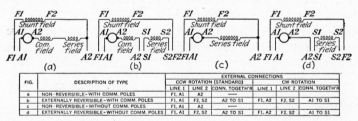

FIG.	DESCRIPTION OF TYPE	EXTERNAL CONNECTIONS					
		CCW ROTATION (STANDARD)			CW ROTATION		
		LINE 1	LINE 2	CONN. TOGETH'R	LINE 1	LINE 2	CONN. TOGETH'R
a	NON-REVERSIBLE-WITH COMM. POLES	F1, A1	A2				
b	EXTERNALLY REVERSIBLE-WITH COMM. POLES	F1, A1	F2, S2	A2 TO S1	F1, A1	F2, S2	A1 TO S1
c	NON-REVERSIBLE-WITHOUT COMM. POLES	F1, A1	A2	—			
d	EXTERNALLY REVERSIBLE-WITHOUT COMM. POLES	F1, A1	F2, S2	A2 TO S1	F1, A2	F2, S2	A1 TO S1

Fɪɢ. 17-5.—Standard terminal markings and connections for d-c compound motors. (*From A.S.A. Standards.*)

17-6. How the Series Motor Works.

—The series motor is known as a **varying-speed motor** and has a very high no-load speed, as can be seen in Figs. 12-2 and 12-3.   The speed regulation is very much higher than for a shunt or compound motor.   At standstill, the counter emf is zero, and the current is high—as is the field flux—so that the motor accelerates rapidly.   As the motor accelerates, the counter emf increases with the speed.   Now, in the case of a shunt motor, the counter emf increases directly in proportion to the speed because the flux remains constant.   However, in the case of a series motor, as the speed increases, the increased counter emf *decreases* the armature current, and this decreased armature current in turn decreases the field excitation.   Therefore, as the motor accelerates, the weakening field makes it necessary that the armature rotate still faster in order to generate sufficient counter emf to limit the armature current.   At light loads, the motor literally races—the armature races to develop enough counter emf to limit the armature current, and, as the armature current is limited, the field is weakened, which tends to decrease the counter emf, so that the motor has to run still faster.   Large d-c motors will usually race to destruction if not loaded, but fractional horsepower d-c series motors, as well as universal motors, usually are designed to withstand these high speeds.

APPLICATION CHARACTERISTICS

17-7. Ratings.   *a.   Voltage.*—Standard voltage ratings are 32, 115, and 230 volts.   However, standard motors will operate successfully at any voltage within 10 per cent of rated, though the operating characteristics will be affected somewhat.   Field windings of standard 32-volt d-c motors are generally so designed that they can be run continuously on 40 volts without injury.

b. Horsepower and Speed Ratings.—Fractional horsepower d-c motors are built in the same horsepower and speed ratings as 60-cycle single-phase induction motors, which are listed in Table XXVI. Smaller horsepower ratings are also built, but there are no universally accepted standards for these ratings.   Standard winding arrangements are

Below $\frac{1}{20}$ hp............................... Series, shunt
$\frac{1}{20}$, $\frac{1}{12}$ hp................................. Shunt
$\frac{1}{8}$, $\frac{1}{6}$, $\frac{1}{4}$ hp.............................. Compound
$\frac{1}{2}$, $\frac{3}{4}$ hp.................................. Shunt, compound

Actual full-load operating speeds of individual motors may vary as much as plus or minus $7\frac{1}{2}$ per cent because of manufacturing variations.

17-8. Operating Characteristics.   *a. Change in Speed Due to Load.*—Direct-current motors are not nearly so constant in speed as split-phase and capacitor-start motors.   Usually, however, the reduction in speed will not be greater than shown in Table XIX taken directly from Nema standards,[1] which lists the *speed regulation* of standard motors. **Speed regulation** is defined as the change in speed from no load to full load, expressed as a percentage of *full-load speed*.

TABLE XIX.—SPEED REGULATION OF D-C MOTORS (MAXIMUM VALUES)

Motor rating		Shunt-wound, per cent	Compound-wound, per cent
Horsepower	Speed, rpm		
$\frac{1}{20}$–$\frac{1}{8}$	1725	20	30
$\frac{1}{20}$–$\frac{1}{8}$	1140	25	35
$\frac{1}{6}$–$\frac{1}{3}$	1725	15	25
$\frac{1}{6}$–$\frac{1}{3}$	1140	20	30
$\frac{1}{2}$–$\frac{3}{4}$	1725	12	22
$\frac{1}{2}$	1140	15	25

b. Change in Speed Due to Heating.—As a shunt motor warms up, the no-load speed steadily increases because the resistance of the shunt field increases, decreasing the field current and flux. At full load, the speed may increase or decrease with an increase in temperature because the increase in armature resistance with heating tends to cause the full-load speed to *decrease*. This change in full-load speed as the motor warms up from ambient temperature to normal operating temperatures generally will not exceed 10 per cent of the latter speed, which is a Nema standard.

c. Effect of Variation in Line Voltage.—A 10 per cent change in line voltage will change the operating speed, but usually by less than 10 per cent, for reasons to be explained. Increasing the line voltage increases both the shunt-field flux and the voltage applied to the armature. Increasing the shunt-field flux tends to *decrease* the speed, whereas increasing the voltage applied to the armature tends to *increase* the speed. These two effects do not cancel each other entirely for the reason that a 10 per cent increase in shunt-field current does not cause a 10 per cent increase in field flux because of saturation effects. Therefore, the speed of a shunt or compound motor does not change so much percentagewise as the line voltage.

d. Reversibility.—Direct-current motors may be either non-reversible or externally reversible, depending upon the number of leads brought out. The possibility of using them as electrically reversible motors for plugging service is discussed in Art. 17-14.

[1] See Bibliography at end of this chapter.

DIAGRAMS FOR GENERAL-PURPOSE MOTORS

17-9. Standard Lead Markings.—Standard markings established by the A. S. A.[2] for motors with external leads are given as follows:

For shunt motors	Fig. 17-3
For series motors	Fig. 17-4
For compound motors	Fig. 17-5

These standards have been widely followed by industry.

Many d-c motors are supplied with a terminal board inside a conduit box cast integral with the front end shield, similar to the one shown in Fig. 5-18 for a-c motors.

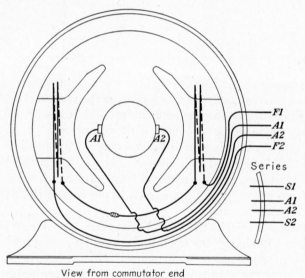

View from commutator end

Fig. 17-6.—Wiring around frame diagram of a d-c motor; four leads, externally reversible, brushes at centers of poles. Shunt or series.

Shunt:

For counterclockwise rotation connect $A1$ to one line wire and $A2$ to other line wire, and connect $F1$ to $A1$, and $F2$ to $A2$ (on a generator, $A1$ should be $+$). For clockwise rotation reverse $A1$ and $A2$ or $F1$ and $F2$ (on a generator, $A2$ should be $+$).

Series:

For counterclockwise rotation connect $A1$ to one line wire, connect $A2$ to $S1$, and connect $S2$ to other line wire. For clockwise rotation connect $A2$ to one line wire, connect $A1$ to $S1$, and connect $S2$ to other line wire.

17-10. Wiring around Frame Diagrams—Shunt and Series Motors. A **wiring around frame diagram** of a d-c motor gives more information than the schematic diagrams of Figs. 17-3 to 17-5. It shows the polarity of each of the field coils together with the tagging of the external leads; examples are Figs. 17-6 to 17-13, inclusive, which are classified and discussed in this and the following articles.

a. Four Leads—Brushes at Pole Centers.—Figure 17-6 is the wiring around frame diagram. In this diagram, the brushes are shown opposite the centers of the poles. When the brushes are so located, the armature connections must be **on center.*** Four line leads are brought out so that this motor can be externally connected for either direction of rotation. For this reason, the armature connections themselves must be **on neutral.*** Direction of rotation can be determined in advance from Fig. 17-6.

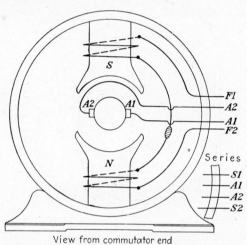

View from commutator end

FIG. 17-7.—Wiring around frame diagram of a d-c motor; four leads, externally reversible, brushes between poles. Shunt or series.

Shunt:
    For counterclockwise rotation connect *A*1 to one line wire and *A*2 to the other line wire, connect *F*1 to *A*1 and *F*2 to *A*2 (on a generator, *A*1 should be +). For clockwise rotation reverse *A*1 and *A*2 or *F*1 and *F*2 (on a generator, *A*2 should be +).
Series:
    For counterclockwise rotation connect *A*1 to one line wire, connect *A*2 to *S*1, and connect *S*2 to the other line wire. For clockwise rotation connect *A*2 to one line wire, connect *A*1 to *S*1, and connect *S*2 to the other line wire.
Armature connection:
    Front lead—thrown left; back lead—thrown right. (See Fig. 12-22.)

b. Four Leads—Brushes Midway between Poles.—Figure 17-7 is the wiring around frame diagram. When the brushes are between poles, it is necessary to offset the armature connections to the commutator 90 deg; the direction of rotation given in Fig. 17-7 is based on throwing these leads 90 deg to the left for a front-lead winding, or 90 deg to the right for a back-lead winding.

17-11. Wiring around Frame Diagrams—Compound Motors.—Wiring around frame diagrams for compound motors can be used for shunt motors by omitting the series winding; also, since all the dia-

* See Art. 12-14 for an explanation of these terms.

grams listed in this article are for cumulative compound motors, they can be used for series motors.

*a. Six Leads, Externally Reversible, Brushes at Pole Centers.—*Figure 17-8 is the wiring around frame diagram.   Because the brushes are at the pole centers, the armature connections must be *on center*.

*b. Three Leads, Nonreversible, Brushes at Pole Centers.—*Figure 17-9 is the wiring around frame diagram.   The *A*1 armature lead

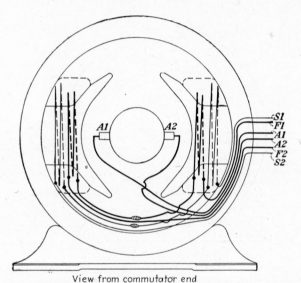

View from commutator end

FIG. 17-8.—Wiring around frame diagram of a d-c motor; six leads, externally reversible, brushes at centers of poles.   Compound wound.

Motor connections:
    For counterclockwise rotation connect *A*1 to line (+), connect *F*1 to line (+), connect *A*2 to *S*1, and connect *S*2 and *F*2 to line (−).   For clockwise rotation connect *A*2 to line (+), connect *F*1 to line (+), connect *A*1 to *S*1 and connect *S*2 and *F*2 to line (−).
Generator connections:
    For counterclockwise rotation connect *A*1 to line (+), connect *A*2 and *F*2 to *S*2, connect *S*1 to line (−), and connect *F*1 to field rheostat (when used), thence to *A*1.   For clockwise rotation connect *A*2 to line (+), connect *A*1 and *F*2 to *S*2, connect *S*1 to line (−), and connect *F*1 to field rheostat (when used), thence to *A*2.

is brought out separate from the field lead *F*1 in order to permit insertion of resistance in series with the armature circuit to reduce the motor speed, or in series with the field to increase the speed.   This motor is not externally reversible but can be reversed by interchanging the leads at the brush holders.   Armature connections must be on center and, if provision is made for reversing the brush-holder leads, the armature connections should also be on neutral.

*c. Three Leads, Nonreversible, Brushes between Poles.—*Figure 17-10 is the wiring around frame diagram.   Except for brush position, this

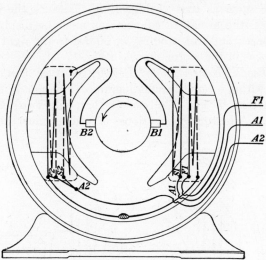

View from commutator end

Fig. 17-9.—Wiring around frame diagram of a d-c motor; three leads, not externally reversible, brushes at centers of poles.   Compound wound.

Counterclockwise rotation as shown.   For clockwise rotation interchange leads *B*1 and *B*2.
Connections:
Connect *A*2 to one line wire and *A*1 and *F*1 to the other line wire.

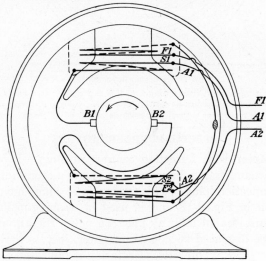

View from commutator end

Fig. 17-10.—Wiring around frame diagram of a d-c motor; three leads, not externally reversible, brushes between poles.   Compound wound.

Counterclockwise rotation as shown.   For clockwise rotation interchange leads *B*1 and *B*2.
Connections:
Connect *A*2 to one line wire and *A*1 and *F*1 to the other line wire.
Armature connections:
Front lead—thrown left; back lead—thrown right.   (See Fig. 12-22.)

motor is the same as that of Fig. 17-9. Because the brushes are between poles, the armature connections must be displaced 90 deg to the left for a front-lead winding, or 90 deg to the right for a back-lead winding, as in the motor shown in Fig. 17-7.

   d. Two Leads, Nonreversible, Brushes at Pole Centers.—Figure 17-11 is the wiring around frame diagram. This motor is essentially the same as that of Fig. 17-9 except that only two line leads are brought out. Armature connections, of course, must be on center.

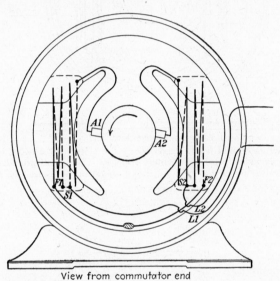

View from commutator end

FIG. 17-11.—Wiring around frame diagram of a d-c motor; two leads, not externally reversible, brushes at centers of poles. Compound wound.
Counterclockwise rotation as shown. For clockwise rotation interchange leads $A1$ and $A2$.

SPECIAL-PURPOSE MOTORS

   17-12. Motor with Direction-connection Plug.—Figure 17-12 is the wiring around frame diagram for a shunt motor equipped with a direction-connection plug. This motor is a companion to the a-c motor shown in Fig. 4-18 and is used in washing-machine service. As brushes are located midway between poles, the armature connections must be displaced 90 deg from center, just as they are for the motor of Fig. 17-7. Direction of rotation is indicated by the arrows on the escutcheon plate on the outside of the motor. For CCW rotation, the direction-connection plug connects 1 and 4 to one line and 2 and 3 to the other line. (The figures on the terminal plate are shown backward in Fig. 17-12 because they are inside the motor on the back side of the plate; the wiring diagram is drawn looking at the outside of the commutator end.)

17-13. Split-series Motors.—Figure 17-13 is the wiring around frame diagram for a three-lead split-series motor. In the drawing, the brushes are opposite the centers of the poles so that **on-center** and **on-neutral** armature connections are used, as in Fig. 17-6. This diagram shows only two field coils, one on each pole; hence only one

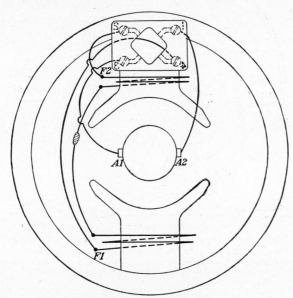

View from commutator end

FIG. 17-12.—Wiring around frame diagram of a d-c motor with a direction-connection plug; brushes between poles. Shunt wound.

   For counterclockwise rotation connect 1 and 2 to one line, 3 and 4 to the other line. For clockwise rotation connect 1 and 4 to one line, 2 and 3 to the other line.
Armature connections:
   Front lead—thrown left; back lead—thrown right. (See Fig. 12-22.)

pole is excited at a time, the other pole being consequent. Sometimes two coils are wound on each pole; in this case, half the winding on both poles is excited for either direction of rotation. This arrangement gives somewhat better balanced flux conditions but involves a few extra complications (see Fig. 12-32). Split-series motors are usually designed for plugging service.

17-14. Electrically Reversible (Plug-reversing) Motors.—Electrically reversible motors are used for hoists, machine tools, and electrode feeders for electric furnaces and arc welders. Figure 17-14 shows schematically the connections for a compound motor arranged for this service. (Commutating-pole windings, if used, would be in the armature-winding circuit as shown in Fig. 17-5b.) Note that the armature connections are reversed while the shunt field is left connected to the line. It is preferable to leave the shunt field excited

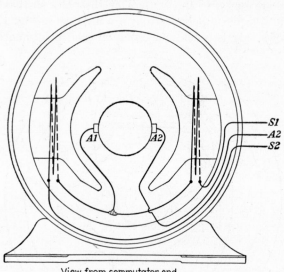

View from commutator end

Fig. 17-13.—Wiring around frame diagram of a split-series d-c motor; three leads, externally reversible, brushes at centers of poles.

For counterclockwise rotation connect *A2* to one line wire and connect *S1* to the other line wire. For clockwise rotation connect *A2* to one line wire and connect *S2* to the other line wire.

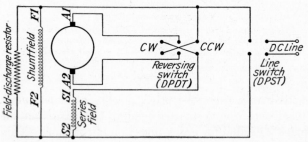

Fig. 17-14.—Schematic diagram of connections for an electrically reversible (plug-reversing), compound-wound d-c motor. If the line switch is not operated simultaneously with the reversing switch, the field-discharge resistor can be omitted.

during the changing of the reversing switch so as to avoid interrupting the shunt-field circuit (see next paragraph). The line switch is shown as a separate switch, not mechanically coupled to, and preferably not operated simultaneously with, the reversing switch.

Control is simplified if the line switch is made single-pole and combined with the reversing switch; in this case only a three-pole double-throw switch is required. This arrangement has the added advantage that the motor is always deenergized in the open position of the three-pole switch. These advantages have made the use of this arrangement attractive and frequently used. However, this arrangement has the serious disadvantage that the shunt field is opened at each reversal, causing a very high voltage surge across the field and causing a severe spark under the brushes, which may cause flashover between adjacent brushes. Voltage surges of several thousand volts have been measured on fractional horsepower motors, requiring extra-heavy insulation of the field windings. This difficulty can be minimized by connecting a field-discharge resistor across the field as shown; a 25-watt resistor often serves the purpose. In addition, special insulation of the field windings is required.

Many general-purpose fractional horsepower d-c motors can be used for this service, but it is safest to check the manufacturer to determine: (1) how many reversals the motor can stand per minute, if any; (2) his recommendations on the use of a field-discharge resistor; (3) whether or not special insulation of field windings is required. Upper ratings of 1725- and 3450-rpm motors are more apt to be unsuitable for this service than motors rated lower in speed or horsepower rating or both. Another factor to be considered is the heavy inrush of current drawn by the motor at the instant of closing the reversing switch; this may be from one and one-half to two times the locked-rotor current.

17-15. Adjustable Varying-speed Motor for Fans and Blowers. The usual practice for adjustable varying-speed d-c motors for fan and blower service is to insert resistance in series with the armature. Such a connection is shown

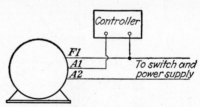

Fig. 17-15.—Wiring diagram for a d-c motor using armature control to obtain speed reduction.

in Fig. 17-15. This wiring diagram is applicable to a motor wired in accordance either with Fig. 17-9 or 17-10. It is generally pretty well known—but it may not be amiss to point it out again here—that, when armature control is used, the operating speed depends very much upon the load, just as it does in the case of the adjustable-speed capacitor motors which are used for fan and blower service (Chap. VIII).

17-16. Two-speed Motor.—An ingenious two-speed d-c motor is shown in the schematic wiring and line connection diagram of Fig. 17-16. The motor is designed to operate as a cumulative compound

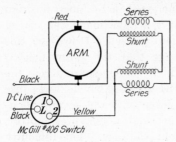

Fig. 17-16.—Wiring and line connection diagram for a 2-speed, d-c motor. (*Courtesy Marathon Electric Manufacturing Company.*)

motor on the low-speed connection. For high-speed operation, the motor is connected as a shunt motor, but the series field is connected in series with the shunt field in such a manner that the series field opposes the shunt field, thereby reducing the effective number of turns in the shunt field. As a result, the shunt field is weaker on the high- than on the low-speed connection; moreover, on the low-speed connection, the speed is reduced still more by the cumulative series field. A performance curve of a typical motor of this type is illustrated in Fig. 17-17, which shows a speed change of 2:1 at full load.

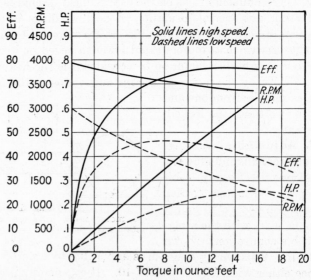

Fig. 17-17.—Performance curves of a 2-speed, d-c motor rated ⅓ hp, 115 volts, 3450/1725 rpm. (*Courtesy of Marathon Electric Manufacturing Company.*)

17-17. Motor for Material-handling Electric Trucks.—Figure 17-18 is a wiring and line connection diagram for an electrically reversible d-c motor designed and built especially for material-handling trucks operated by storage batteries. It is to be noted that the field coils are connected in two parallel paths. These motors are usually wound for 24 to 30 volts, though they may be wound for a higher voltage. They are equipped with a magnetic brake.

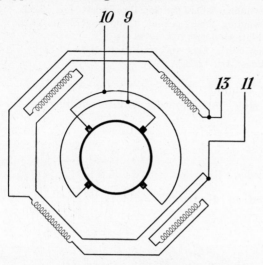

EXTERNAL LINE CONNECTIONS			
ROTATION	LINE 1	LINE 2	CONN. TOGETHER
CCW	9	13	10 TO 11
CW	10	13	9 TO 11

Fig. 17-18.—Wiring and line connection diagram for a 4-pole, electrically reversible, d-c, series motor used on material-handling trucks that are operated by storage batteries. Field winding is 2-parallel. (*Courtesy of Electric Specialty Company.*)

SERVICE PROBLEMS

17-18. Armature Windings—Lap.—Lap windings are discussed in Arts. 10-12 to 10-18 and 12-13 to 12-19. These two discussions were written for repulsion-type and universal motors, respectively, but they apply equally well to d-c motors. However, the reader is cautioned that armature windings for repulsion-type motors are usually laid out with respect to the **hard neutral** position, whereas for d-c motors there is only one neutral position of interest, which corresponds to the soft neutral position for repulsion motors (Art. 10-6). These two neutral positions are one-half a pole pitch apart. Bearing this point in mind, the reader may be helped by the following specific references:

How to lay out coil connections to commutator: Arts. 10-15, 10-16
Armature connection diagrams for front-lead windings:
    Any simplex winding, 2 bars per slot, on center: Fig. 10-13*b*
    Any simplex winding, 3 bars per slot, on center: Fig. 10-13*c,d*
    Any simplex winding, 2 bars per slot, on center: Fig. 12-22*a*
    Any simplex winding, 2 bars per slot, thrown left: Fig. 12-22*b*
    Any simplex winding, 2 bars per slot, thrown right: Fig. 12-22*c*
Cross-connected lap windings: Art. 10-18
Stripping and rewinding: Arts. 10-28, 10-29, 12-16 to 12-19
Back-lead windings: Art. 12-15

Back-lead windings discussed in Art. 12-15 are specifically for
two bars per slot. An armature connection diagram for a back-lead

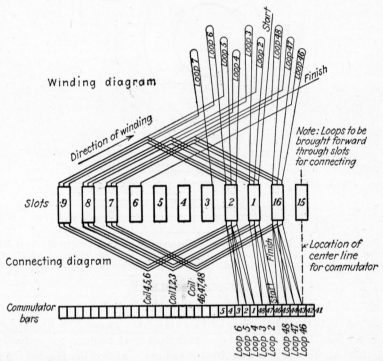

Fɪɢ. 17-19.—Armature connection diagram for a back-lead, d-c armature winding.
Sixteen slots, 48 bars, on neutral, brushes between poles, connections thrown right.

winding with three bars per slot is given in Fig. 17-19, which applies
to a popular make of d-c washing-machine motor. Because this
diagram is for three bars per slot, its development will be discussed
for the purpose of assisting the reader in making up any similar diagrams of this type that he may require. This particular motor has

16 armature slots, 48 commutator bars, with armature connections on neutral; the armature is back-lead wound, and the connections to the commutator are thrown right. The throw of the coil is 1 and 8, or 7 slots. Our problem is to make up an armature connection diagram for this armature:

Refer now to Art. 12-14*d*. Here the instruction is given to lay out the connections for a front-lead winding with connections on center, referring to Fig. 10-13*c* and *d*. Refer now to this figure. In our example, the throw is 1 and 8, or $x = 8$, an even number; so we use Fig. 10-13*d*. Now then,

$$A = \tfrac{3}{2}x - 2 = \tfrac{3}{2} \times 8 - 2 = 12 - 2 = 10$$

Therefore, bar A is bar 10, and the center line of bar 1 is opposite the center line of slot 1. Now then, referring back again to the last paragraph of Art. 12-14, we are told to move the commutator connections 90 deg around the commutator either to the left or to the right—in our case, it is to the right. Since there are 48 bars, 90 deg is equivalent to 12 bars. We should then move the connection on bar A 12 bars to the right, and then this connection will fall on bar 46. It is to this bar, 46, that we connect the *start* of the back-lead winding. The complete diagram can then be laid out, and it will appear as shown in Fig. 17-19. In this diagram, it will be noted that bar 43 is lined up as opposite slot 15; this makes bar 1 fall opposite the center of slot 1; the dotted line for location of the center line of commutators bars was drawn from slot 15 to bar 43 merely so that it would not be confused with the armature connections to the commutator.

17-19. Armature Windings—Wave.—These are used comparatively little in general-purpose fractional horsepower d-c motors, and so there is no necessity for elaborating upon the discussion contained in Arts. 10-19 to 10-26.

17-20. How to Change the Speed without Rewinding.—The speed of a d-c motor can be increased without rewinding

1. By inserting resistance in the field circuit (shunt or compound motors only).
2. By increasing the air gap. The air gap can be increased by grinding down the outside diameter of the armature, by grinding out the stator bore, or, if the poles are separate from the yoke, by grinding off a part of the poles, either from the face or from the body next to the yoke.
3. If the poles are separate from the yoke, by putting shims of *nonmagnetic* material between the poles and the yoke.

The speed of a d-c motor can be *decreased* without rewinding

1. If the poles are separate from the yoke, by putting shims of magnetic material between the poles and the yoke. Shims may be made from any convenient shim stock of iron or steel (do not use brass, copper, or lead). Cut out a shim that is approximately ⅛ in. larger than the body of the pole at the yoke, and put a hole in this shim for the pole bolt.

2. By inserting resistance in the armature circuit. This procedure increases the speed regulation and makes the speed vary more with changes in load. Insertion of armature resistance does not affect the no-load speed appreciably.

17-21. How to Reverse a D-c Motor.—Electrically reversible motors are discussed in Art. 17-14. If it is desired to change the direction of rotation by changing the connection when the motor is at rest and not energized, the following comments apply:

a. Shunt Motor.—To reverse a shunt motor, it is necessary to reverse the field with respect to the armature, or vice versa. Standard connections are given in Fig. 17-3.

b. Series Motor.—To reverse a series motor, it is necessary to reverse the field with respect to the armature, or vice versa. If there is a compensating winding, the compensating winding and armature together must be reversed as a unit, and not simply the armature winding (see Fig. 12-19). Standard connections are given in Fig. 17-4.

c. Compound Motor.—If, when a compound motor is being reversed, the armature leads are reversed, the series-field leads must not be reversed also, as this would cause the series field to buck the shunt field, making a differentially compounded motor which is very unstable in speed characteristics. If the shunt field is reversed, the series field must likewise be reversed. Standard connections are given in Fig. 17-5.

17-22. Rewinding for a Different Voltage.—Both the armature and the field must be rewound; if there are two fields, *e.g.*, a shunt field and a series field, both of them must be rewound. Likewise, if there is a commutating pole, the field coil on this pole must also be rewound. So far as determining the number of turns to use for a different voltage is concerned, the same rule applies to both armature and field, and this rule is the same rule as is used in rewinding any other type of electric motor; *i.e.*, the number of turns must be increased or decreased in direct ratio as the voltage rating is increased or decreased. For slight changes in voltage, say 10 to 20 per cent, it may not be necessary to rewind the fields. (If the shunt field does not get too hot at the higher voltage, it may be unnecessary to rewind it.) The wire size of the new winding should be selected to give as nearly the same weight of copper as possible in all the windings as was used in the original windings.

17-23. Rewinding for a Different Speed.—When rewinding for a different speed, at the same voltage, it is usually necessary to rewind only the armature. The speed, at any current, is inversely proportional to the number of armature conductors or turns per coil. Therefore, the first step is to determine the actual operating speed of the motor when it is developing the torque that the load requires when the latter is driven at the desired operating speed. Then

Armature turns per coil for desired speed
$$= \frac{\text{actual operating speed}}{\text{desired operating speed}} \times \text{actual armature TPC}$$

This simple formula will give correct results if the armature is rewound with the number of turns indicated and with wire of the size used in the original winding. However, if the number of turns is increased in order to reduce the speed, it becomes a practical necessity to use wire of a smaller size in order to get the required number of turns in the slots; the smaller size of the wire will reduce the speed slightly, so that it is not necessary to put quite so many turns in the rewound armature as would be indicated by the formula. Conversely, if turns are taken out to increase the speed and if wire of a larger size is used, slightly more turns than are indicated by the formula should be used. Generally, it is advantageous to use wire of a size to fill the slots.

17-24. Finding the Neutral Position.—A satisfactory way of finding the neutral position in a d-c motor is by means of the **kick neutral method.** Connect a 15-volt voltmeter across the brushes, and make and break the field circuit; if the brushes are off neutral, a deflection of the voltmeter needle will be observed. Shift the brushes until no deflection can be observed when the field circuit is made or broken. For more accurate results, it may be necessary to repeat this process, using a voltmeter having a full-scale reading of 1.5 volts. Wedge-shaped brushes such as are shown in Fig. 10-24, will contribute further to the accuracy of the setting.

If the motor is to operate in either direction of rotation or if it has a commutating pole, the brushes should be left in the neutral position. If the motor operates only in one direction and if it has no commutating pole, the brushes may be shifted approximately 10 deg *against* the direction of rotation of the armature.

17-25. Brushes.—The brushes usually selected for d-c motors are those found best suited for the particular designs after exhaustive tests have been made of motors operating under conditions duplicating as nearly as possible those expected in actual service. For replacement, the serviceman should obtain duplicates of the original brushes, securing the same make and grade, if possible.   If the original type of brush cannot be obtained, one having as nearly as possible the same characteristics should be selected.

Bibliography

1. "Nema Motor and Generator Standards," Publication No. 45-102, 1946, National Electrical Manufacturers' Association, 155 E. 44th St., New York.
2. "American Standard Terminal Markings for Electrical Apparatus," ASA Standard., C6.1—1944, American Standards Association.
3 GERLACH, F. H.: Better Commutators for Small Motors, *Elec. Manufacturing*, December, 1944, p. 124.

CHAPTER XVIII

CONSTRUCTIONAL FEATURES COMMON TO MORE THAN ONE TYPE

Many features of construction are common to more than one type of motor. Rather than repeat these discussions for each motor type involved, they are brought together in this chapter.

BEARINGS

18-1. Sleeve Bearings—Constructions.—Bearings are one of the most vital parts of the motor and, except for the starting switch, are the only wearing parts in many types of fractional horsepower motors. A large percentage of motor failures are due to bearing failures.

a. Elements of a Plain Sleeve Bearing.—Representative bearing constructions are shown in Fig. 18-1. The bearing itself is a hollow cylinder made of bronze, babbit-lined steel, or steel-backed bronze. The bearing has a window, or opening, through which oil is fed to the shaft journal, usually by means of wool wicking. The bearing is grooved to distribute the oil to the entire bearing surface. Oil enters through the window, is wiped from the grooves to the pressure areas, and comes out at both ends of the bearing, where it is collected and returned to the oil reservoir in the bearing housing. The bearing housing is provided with an overflow located at such a height that the oil level is always slightly below the bottom of the shaft.

Sometimes the oil grooves and the window of bronze bearings are filled with graphite; otherwise, the oil-circulating system and general arrangement are as described above.

b. Anti-end-bump Arrangements.—To minimize noise due to endwise bumping of the shaft shoulders against the bearing faces, numerous arrangements are used. In Figs. 18-1a and 18-3b, endwise bumping is cushioned by a steel diaphragm backed up by a neoprene washer. In Fig. 18-1b cork washers on the shaft absorb end bumps. Delco motors often use an end-play take-up plug of cork, as shown in Fig. 18-6. This plug is inserted in the front end shield; if the end play becomes excessive, the plug can be driven inward by tapping on it lightly, to take up the end play. (This adjustment should not be used after installation of a new switch; see Art. 18-6c.)

415

  c. Self-aligning Bearings.—In the smaller sizes of fractional horsepower motors (below $\frac{1}{20}$ hp), self-aligning bearings often are used.
A typical construction is shown in Fig. 18-2.   The bearing seats in a
spherical socket and is held in place by means of a phosphor-bronze
washer.   An "oilless bearing" of a porous bronze material is used.
Bearings of this type are oil-impregnated, but they are generally

(*a*)

FIG. 18-1.—For descriptive legend see opposite page.

surrounded by an oil-saturated wick so as to keep the bearing impregnated.   In Fig. 13-4, the bottom of this wick is in an oil reservoir;
oil seeps through the bearing and out along the shaft where it is caught
by the flingers and returned to the reservoir.   Likewise, the motor of
Fig. 13-6 makes use of porous self-aligning bearings.

  d. Bearing Construction for a Unit-heater Motor.—Motors used in
unit-heater service usually have a propeller fan mounted on the shaft.
This fan draws air over the motor, pushing it through the unit heater
(see Fig. 8-2).   The normal thrust of the propeller fan is, therefore,

toward the front bearing of the motor, and this front bearing must be capable of withstanding the thrust.   Larger motors of this type often use a construction such as illustrated in Fig. 18-3.   It is somewhat similar to the anti-end-bump construction used in the rear bearing, except that a countersunk cavity in the bearing housing is filled with a bearing specially molded from a porous bronze material.   There is a

(*b*)

FIG. 18-1.—Sleeve-bearing constructions.   (*a*) Waste-packed.   (*Courtesy of General Electric Company.*)   (*b*) Waste-packed.   (*Courtesy of Wagner Electric Corporation.*)

slight gap between the main sleeve bearing and the thrust bearing. Most of the oil that flows out of the sleeve bearing toward the inside of the motor is trapped in this gap.   Part of the oil so trapped seeps into the porous bronze material and lubricates the thrust surface. A hole through the bottom of the thrust bearing is provided so that excess oil may pass into the oil return and into the main oil reservoir.

In another form of construction, a steel ball is used to take the end thrust of the shaft.   This ball may be inspected by removing a plate from the bearing housing of the front end shield.

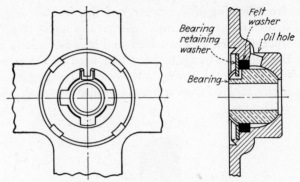

FIG. 18-2.—A self-aligning bearing.   (*Courtesy of Bodine Electric Company.*)

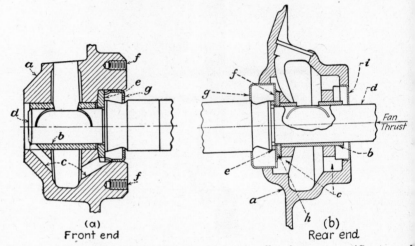

FIG. 18-3.—Sleeve-bearing construction for a propeller fan motor. (*Courtesy of Westinghouse Electric Corporation.*)

(*a*)	(*b*)
a. End-shield casting.	*a.* End-shield casting.
b. Bearing.	*b.* Bearing.
c. Oil returns.	*c.* Oil returns.
d. Shaft.	*d.* Shaft.
e. Thrust bearing, "oilless" type.	*e.* Fiber thrust washer.
f. Switch mounting holes.	*f.* Special spring washer.
g. Oil-retaining cup.	*g.* Oil-retaining cup.
	h. Neoprene washer.
	i. End cap.

e. Bearing Construction for a Vertical Motor.—Figure 18-4 illustrates a bearing construction used for a vertical-shaft sleeve-bearing motor. The guide bearing *d* differs from the usual sleeve bearing in that it has no oil grooves; the only oil groove is in the shaft journal, and this groove is spiral-shaped to form an oil pump to carry oil to the surfaces of the guide bearing and the thrust washer *c*. Oil is fed to the bearing through a window by means of a wick *f* held against the journal *e* by means of a spring.

18-2. Sleeve Bearings—Service and Maintenance.—As pointed out in the preceding article, all sleeve bearings—except oilless bearings —are provided with a window which usually is located at the top of the bearing. The motor should be so installed in service that the belt pull never comes against the window because of the reduced surface area of the bearing at that point. For example, if the bearing

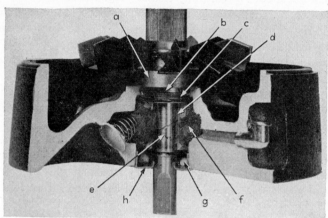

Fig. 18-4.—Sleeve-bearing construction for a vertical motor. (*Courtesy of Westinghouse Electric Corporation.*)

  a. Rotating shield to protect bearing assembly from dirt.
  b. Thrust runner of sintered porous iron (rotating member).
  c. Hardened-steel stationary thrust washer. Note that it is supported by a wavy steel spring.
  d. Guide bearing.
  e. Shaft journal with spiral oil groove to carry oil upward.
  f. Main oil wicking.
  g. Auxiliary wick to return oil from oil-retaining cup *h* to main oil reservoir.
  h. Oil-retaining cup.

window is at the top and the motor drives its appliance through a belt, the driven pulley ought not to be vertically above the motor.

It is important not to pull the belt up too tight or excessive bearing pressures will be developed causing abnormal wear, perhaps "seizing," and early failure of the bearing. In general, the belt should be made only tight enough to avoid slipping. It is much easier than commonly supposed to overload a motor severely and to cause early failure of the bearing by excessive belt tension. In this connection, a watt-meter measuring the input to the motor will often be most helpful. The belt tension should be reduced to the point where it begins slipping, and the minimum watts input noted; the belt can then be tightened until the watts input starts to increase noticeably.

When replacing a sleeve bearing in service, it is necessary to size and line up the two bearings. This operation usually is best done by means of a line reamer. The shaft journal should be trued and smoothed if necessary and then carefully measured for size. A line reamer should be chosen to give a bearing clearance in the order of 0.0005 to 0.0012 in. (These figures represent total clearance.) Porous oil-impregnated bearings require a slightly larger clearance. When the end shields are bolted onto the motor for line reaming, the end-shield fits should be carefully cleaned to make certain that there is no dirt in them. Otherwise the bearings will be reamed out of line.

Similarly, when reassembling a motor, it is also important that the end-shield fits be clean, as otherwise the bearing will be out of line and will bind. It is also important that there be a little free end play, as otherwise the bearings might bind and seize at the thrust surfaces. If end-bumping noise is to be held to a minimum, this free end play must be small—say 0.002 to 0.010 in. If the motor is provided with some form of anti-end-bump construction, the end play need not be held to such low values; $\frac{1}{32}$ in. will not allow bumping noise on ordinary applications. If the motor is of the anti-end-bump construction shown in Fig. 18-3b, the term **free end play** refers to the amount of possible free axial movement of the rotor without deflecting either of the spring thrust washers.

Sleeve bearings should be lubricated with a light grade of machine oil, lighter than the light auto oil designated as S. A. E. 10. Such oils are sold in repair shops as "dynamo oil" and in gasoline filling stations as "household oil." It is strongly recommended that only petroleum oils be used and that all lubricants containing any animal or vegetable oils be carefully avoided.

18-3. Ball Bearings—Construction.—Many kinds and types of ball bearings have been developed to fulfill the requirements of a wide variety of applications. For most fractional-horsepower-motor applications, the single-row radial bearing is adequate and, therefore, the most popular. Such bearings are capable of handling the radial and *axial-thrust* loads usually encountered. For operating speeds of 1725 rpm and below, grease-lubricated ball bearings are generally used. Bearings now commonly use either a shield or a felt seal to retain the lubricant inserted by the manufacturer, and to exclude dirt and other foreign matter. A *shield* is a thin steel disc affixed to the outer race and arranged to cover all of the space between the inner and outer races; it fits into a labyrinth or semilabyrinth on the inner race with very narrow clearances but no rubbing contact. Either one or both sides of the bearing may be shielded. A bearing with a single shield is illustrated in Fig. 18-5. Shielded bearings are the same length (along the shaft) as unshielded bearings and are generally interchangeable with plain bearings. *Sealed* bearings generally use a felt seal of some sort which retains the lubricant and excludes dirt better than shields do. Because of the space occupied by the felt seal, sealed bearings are usually longer than either plain or shielded bearings; hence, *sealed* bearings are not generally interchangeable with either *plain* or *shielded* bearings. The additional length required for the

Fig. 18-5.—Ball-bearing construction.
With self-sealed bearings. (*Courtesy of General Electric Company.*)

seal may be added only to the inner race, or it may be added to both races. Seals may be provided on one or both sides of the bearing.

Shaft journals are ground to such a diameter as to give a light press fit between the inner race and the shaft. *When pressing a bearing on the shaft, the pressure must always be applied to the inner race directly, never to the outer race, lest the balls or the races, or both, be damaged.* The outer race fits into the recess in the end shield snugly, but loosely enough that only light hand pressure is required to insert it. For general-purpose motors, an **opposed-mounting construction** is extensively used. With this construction, the inner races are secured to the shaft by light press fits, and the outer races are free to slide axially in the end shields; rearward end play is limited by a shoulder in the rear end shield, and forward end play by a similar shoulder $\frac{1}{16}$ in., in the front end shield. This end play is commonly of the order of $\frac{1}{16}$ in., but as a rule it is taken up by a steel finger spring inserted in the bearing cavity of the front end shield. This spring presses against the outer race and takes up all the end play in a rearward direction. In general, this spring is strong enough that it takes a force of several pounds to move the shaft against it. In Fig. 18-5, a sectional view of the rear end of a motor using opposed-mounting construction is illustrated. In this view, the inside of the bearing is sealed, and the outside left open; the outer race is shown seated against the shoulder of the end shield. With opposed mounting, the finger spring can be used in the rear end shield equally well.

If axial motion of the shaft cannot be permitted, a **locked-bearing construction** is used. Either the front or the rear bearing can be locked; but both must not be, because differential expansion between the rotor and the housing can set up destructive axial forces. The shaft is threaded and the inner race is locked in position by means of a thin nut and lock washer; the outer race then has to be clamped securely in the end shield by some suitable means. With *locked-bearing* construction, there is no endwise movement of the shaft except for the small movements due to thermal expansion, and the slight axial freedom in the bearing due to clearances between the balls and the races. *Tight fit-up* bearings have less of this freedom than *loose fit-up* bearings.

Ball-bearing motors are capable of withstanding considerable endwise thrusts and are generally suitable for operation in any position. How much thrust load a particular motor can handle safely should be obtained directly from the recommendations of the motor manufacturer, or from the ball-bearing manufacturer.

18-4. Ball Bearings—Service and Maintenance.—Lubrication of ball bearings is most important. If the bearings are open at one or both ends, they should be lubricated annually; moreover, it is a desirable practice to wash the bearing and bearing housings thoroughly approximately every two years, with alcohol or carbon tetrachloride. (If the motor has a commutator and brushes, take care that the tetrachloride does not come in contact with either.) The bearings themselves and all grease used in them must be scrupulously clean; it is even more important to keep all dirt and foreign matter out of ball bearings than it is to keep it out of sleeve bearings. For a general-purpose lubricant, a neutral soda-base soap grease is recommended in preference to other kinds. Ordinary cup greases are frequently compounded with a calcium soap and have a melting point too close to motor operating temperatures. Greases compounded from very heavy or very light oils should be avoided. Viscosities between 200 and 500 sec Saybolt at 100°F give good results. *Ball bearings should not be overgreased.*

Ball bearings that are sealed at both ends generally require less attention. The claim that these have enough lubricant sealed in them for the life of the bearing can be somewhat ambiguous, for obviously the bearing would not last long after all the oil had evaporated from the grease! *Operating temperature* is a major factor in the life of any ball bearing. At a bearing temperature of 40°C (104°F), the life of sealed ball bearings operating 24 hr per day may be from 3 to 5 years or more. However, the life halves for each 10-deg (centigrade) increase in operating temperature. Application of this rule indicates that if the bearing operates at a temperature of 80°C (176°F), the life on a 24-hr day basis may be reduced to as little as 2 or 3 months. Opinion is divided as to whether it is desirable to pack grease around the outside of a shielded bearing. But one rule is certain: The higher the operating temperature, the more frequent must be the attention to lubrication.

When removing ball bearings from a shaft, it is desirable to press against the inner race; if pressure is applied to the outer race to remove the bearing, the latter should not be used again in the motor because the races are likely to become ball-dented during their removal.

Some vertical motors, such as sump-pump motors, use one ball bearing and one sleeve bearing. When the ball bearing of such a motor is replaced, use of a tight fit-up bearing is recommended.

STARTING SWITCHES

Split-phase and capacitor-start motors can never be more reliable than the switches in them. Endless skill and ingenuity have been devoted to the design of starting switches, and an almost limitless number of designs have been used. To discuss all of them would fill a book in itself, but a brief summary of some general considerations, followed by a discussion of specific designs, is given in the following paragraphs.

18-5. Centrifugal Starting Switches—General.—From the standpoint of the electrical function they perform, there are at least three different kinds of starting switches:

a. Single-pole, Single-throw.—A single circuit is closed in the starting position and open in the running position. This type is by far the most common, being used in split-phase, capacitor-start, and two-value capacitor motors with two capacitors (Fig. 6-2).

  b. Transfer Switch—Single-pole, Double-throw.—Used in two-value capacitor motors with capacitor-transformer unit (Fig. 6-1) and certain other special applications.

  c. Special Switch for Pole-changing and Electrically Reversible Capacitor-start Motors.—This switch (Figs. 4-43 and 5-40) makes one circuit in the starting position; in the running position it connects one line to two isolated lines, as shown schematically in Fig. 4-43.

  Whenever a fractional horsepower motor is serviced for any reason whatsoever, the switch should always be examined carefully, even though it may not have been the cause of the complaint. When the motor is disassembled, the stator and rotor members may each be worked separately by hand to see that they work freely in a normal manner, and also to see that the contacts are not burned, pitted, or likely to stick. It is further very useful to assemble the rotor into the front end shield and to actuate the *rotor* weights by hand to see if the stator member opens and closes properly. It is also desirable to turn the rotor around slowly, observing the action. For a more thorough check, it is recommended that the motor be assembled and the actual total end play measured. Then, disassemble the motor, add a washer —equal in thickness to the total end play—to the switch end of the shaft, and again put the rotor into the front end shield, noting the action of the switch in order to determine whether it would work properly in the motor when the rotor is in this position. When the motor is reassembled (with the washer removed, of course), great care must be taken to see that no leads can possibly foul or interfere either with the stator or with the rotor member of the switch.

  Sometimes it is possible to observe the action of a switch through openings in the end shields when the motor is running. For this purpose, a stroboscopic source of light is desirable. If the stroboscopic source of light can be controlled by means of a make-and-break switch driven by the motor itself, it is easy to follow the action of the switch as the motor comes up to speed. The motor is allowed to come up to speed with reduced voltage on the windings in order to keep it from coming up to speed too rapidly. While the action of the switch is being observed, the rotor should be pushed manually to both extremes of the end play, and the switch action of opening and closing noted under all possible conditions. An examination of a switch carried out in this manner will usually show up any faulty action that may be present. Often it will be necessary to observe a great many operations of the switch, for they sometimes have the annoying characteristic of working perfectly for a large number of times, then suddenly failing to function properly for a single operation, after which they again function properly.

18-6. Delco Starting Switches.—These switches are illustrated in Figs. 18-6 and 18-7. The first shows the position of the switch parts

Fig. 18-6.—Delco starting switch with both members in the starting position. (*Courtesy of Delco Products.*)

A–B. Skillet contact pivot points.
C–D. Skillet contact points.
F. Governor spring.
G. Governor weight assembly.
J. Governor weight pin.
L. Skillet assembly.
O. Skillet mounting stud spring.
R. Switch plate assembly.
T. End-play take-up device.
V. Weight-assembly fan.

when the motor is not running. How the switch functions can best be understood by referring to both figures, ignoring for the moment the gauge shown in the second figure, which is used for checking the switch in a manner to be explained later. The starting winding is in the circuit by virtue of the fact that the skillet *L* short-circuits the contact points *C-D*. As the motor comes up to speed, the governor weight assembly *G* moves outward owing to centrifugal force, allowing the spring *O* to push the skillet *L* toward the rotor, pivoting about points

A-B until the contacts *C-D* open, opening the starting-winding circuit. When the motor stops, this cycle is repeated in inverse order. For two-value capacitor motors using a capacitor-transformer unit, pivot points *A-B* are replaced by two contacts which are then closed in the running position only.

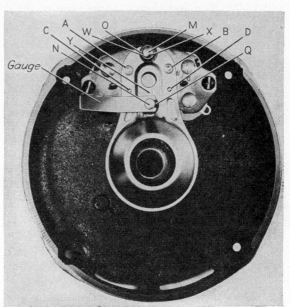

FIG. 18-7.—Stationary member of Delco starting switch mounted in end shield with gauge in position for determining proper depth location of skillet mounting stud *N*. (*Courtesy of Delco Products.*)

> *A-B.* Skillet contact pivot points.
> *C-D.* Skillet contact points.
> *M.* Skillet mounting stud (long).
> *N.* Skillet mounting stud (short).
> *O.* Skillet mounting stud spring.
> *Q.* Skillet mounting stud, rubber bushing.
> *W.* Top switch-plate hole.
> *X.* Top skillet hole.
> *Y.* Position of pressure on skillet *L*.

a. Servicing and Adjusting the Rotating Member.—The governor-weight assembly *G* consists of a governor weight which carries on a knurled pilot fit a felt washer sandwiched between two fiber washers; at its lower end it carries a cork bumper to cushion the noise of reclosing. This weight assembly slides on the governor weight pin *J*. Points to be checked are

1. Inspect cork bumper; if damaged, replace complete weight assembly.
2. Inspect felt washer; if it has flat spots, rounded edges, reduced diameter (correct diameter is $7/8$ in.), or other obvious defects, replace with new felt washer.

3. If hole in sliding weight shows excessive wear in the form of an oval-shaped hole, or looseness in excess of $\frac{1}{64}$ in., the weight assembly should be replaced.

Governor spring F, also both felt and fiber washers, can be removed without removing the weight pin J. To do this, use a pocket scale or similar instrument and pry the first coil of the governor spring F over the retainer on the end of the weight pin J; the governor spring can then be removed over the weight pin by turning it counterclockwise, using care not to stretch its free length or to bend the coils. The felt and fiber washers can then be removed, by pressing them off the knurled pilot fit with the fingers, and replaced with new ones. If either the governor weight assembly or pin J requires replacement, new parts and instructions for installing them should be obtained from the manufacturer.

When replacing the movable weight spring, be sure to choose a spring that is plated in the same way as the one taken off, to ensure the proper operating speed. Following are the identifying spring colors:

Standard frame diameter Weight pin length $1\frac{1}{4}$ in. from spring seat of pin head to rotor shaft		Small frame diameter Weight pin length $1\frac{1}{16}$ in. from spring seat of pin head to rotor shaft	
Type of plating	Frequency	Type of plating	Frequency
Cadmium..................	60 and 30	Zinc....................	.60 and 30
Brass.....................	50 and 25	Black enamel.............	50 and 25
None.....................	40	Blue enamel..............	40
Copper...................	50/60		

b. Servicing and Adjusting the Stationary Member.—With end shield removed from the motor and switch in position as shown in Fig. 18-7, the following check and adjustment should be made (gauge is not used for this):

Apply to the skillet at point Y just enough pressure to close pivot points A-B and contact points C-D. All four of these points must make contact with the phenolic switch plate at the same time; if the skillet rocks on diagonally opposite points—as A-D or B-C—correct by slight forming of the skillet.

Studs M and N, shown in Fig. 18-7 as round-head drive pins that have knurled fits, have since been changed to hex-head self-tapping screws. Experience showed that the knurled drive pins would sometimes loosen in their mounting holes, thereby failing to maintain proper switch-contact setting; in particular, this often happened when a Thermotron or skillet was replaced.   Whenever these drive pins are found to be loose or whenever a new skillet or Thermotron is installed, the knurled drive pins should be replaced by the new pins with self-tapping threads.   Pin M is replaced by screw No. 5387875, and N by No. 5387876.

When a new stationary member is installed, skillet and contact spring O are first assembled onto stud M (longer stud), which is then screwed into the end shield until it clamps the phenolic switch plate R firmly.   Now, insert stud N through rubber bushing Q and hold skillet in position by maintaining a pressure at Y to make contact at A-B and C-D; screw stud in to a depth determined by the thickness of the gauge which is inserted between bushing Q and the head of stud N as shown in Fig. 18-7.   Pins should be staked on end opposite head to maintain proper contact setting.   Correct gauge thickness is as follows:

1. 0.024 in. for all $\frac{1}{8}$-hp small-frame motors which have a $\frac{5}{8}$-in. rotor shaft and weight-pin height of $1\frac{1}{16}$ in.
2. 0.032 in. for all other motors.

This gauge can be obtained from any United Motors Service Branch.

c. *Final Adjustment of Switch Assembly.*—With governor weight assembly in standstill position, make the following checks and adjustments:

1. Set end shield in a suitable holding fixture and assemble rotor in position shown in Fig. 18-6, *except that the shaft must be vertical.*
2. Insert gauge of proper thickness (Art. 18-6b) between contacts A-B and phenolic switch-mounting plate.
3. Hold skillet in closed position by applying pressure at point Y (Fig. 18-7).
4. Adjust cork end-play take-up device T until felt washer on governor weight assembly *just* contacts skillet on its flat portion, as shown in Fig. 18-6.   Then remove gauge.   This adjustment will allow a slight wobble of the skillet if the rotor is turned one complete revolution.   However, no further adjustment should be made.
5. For motors having thrust washers instead of cork end-play take-up device, subtract or add thrust washers to obtain the same position of skillet relative to rotor as described in the preceding paragraph.

Now, block the governor weight in its extreme outward position where it would be in the running position, slowly rotate the rotor by hand, and check the following:

1. Felt washer on governor weight assembly must clear head of stud N; it must also clear the skillet in all positions.
2. Skillet must clear governor weight assembly, staked or nut end of stud J, fan V, and shaft.

When the motor is assembled, it may be necessary to insert some of the thrust washers on the rotor shaft on *end opposite switch* to remove rotor end play. CAUTION: *Do not adjust end-play take-up device after switch setting is obtained as this device must not be adjusted to remove rotor end play at this time.*

18-7. Ohio Starting Switches.—A starting switch used in Ohio motors is shown in Fig. 18-8.   The stationary contacts consist of two collector rings permanently secured to the end shield.   These two collector rings are connected in series with the starting winding and are short-circuited by a single carbon brush—attached to the rotor— which revolves about the collector rings.   The centrifugal force, at a definite predetermined speed, causes the brush to leave the rings, opening the circuit of the starting winding.   Detailed service instructions for assembling this switch are given in Fig. 18-9.

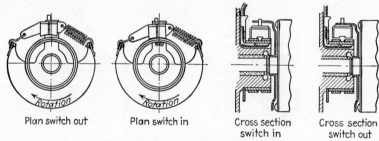

Plan switch out   Plan switch in   Cross section   Cross section
                                            switch in   switch out

FIG. 18-8.—An Ohio starting switch.

18-8. Reynolds Electric Company Switches.—Switch-setting instructions for Reynolds motors are given in Fig. 18-10.

18-9. Westinghouse Starting Switches.—A number of types of centrifugal switches are illustrated in Fig. 18-11.   In general, the type-letter designation of the switch indicates the first, but not the only, use of the switch.   For example, the type FJ switch is used in type FH motors as well as in type FJ motors; the type FT switch has been used in types FH, FJ, and FT motors.

a. Type CAH Switch.—This early form of centrifugal starting switch is shown in Fig. 18-11.   The stator member of this switch is snap-acting, owing to the toggle action of the two leaf springs which hold the switch in either one of two definite positions: open or closed. There are three weights on the rotor member interlocked so that they move out simultaneously under the action of centrifugal force. Starting from rest, the rotating member does not touch the stationary member of the switch; but as the rotor accelerates, the weights move

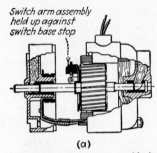

Switch arm assembly held up against switch base stop

(a)

Assemble switch-arm assembly in position as shown in diagrams (*d*) and (*e*). Lift switch-arm assembly up against switch base stop as shown above, and then slide shaft in cover. Be sure that wicking does not protrude through bearing and bind shaft. If shaft binds, remove oil cup or pipe plug and pull out wicking.

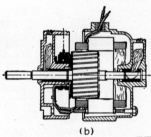

(b)

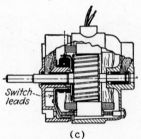

Switch leads

(c)

Hold switch-arm assembly up against stop on switch base and push armature shaft in cover as far as it will go. Release switch-arm assembly so that it rests on the switch rings. Check to see that switch arm is on center with the switch rings. If necessary, use end play washers to get the proper adjustment of switch arm and switch rings.

Push switch leads back of stator windings so that the switch base does not strike them. Check cover and frame counter-bores to see that they are clean and free from chips. Be careful not to pinch leads in counter-bore as cover will not seat properly and armature shaft will bind. Keep pressure of armature against cover to prevent switch-arm assembly from coming off of the switch rings and then slide armature and cover into the frame. Make sure cover is in correct position (oil wells and oil cups in line) before fastening cover to frame. After cover is fastened down, turn rotor shaft by hand to see if it turns freely.

NOTE: Make sure that the wicking has been put back if it had been taken out. Put oil cups and pipe plugs back in place. Oil motor.

FIG. 18-9.—For descriptive legend see opposite page.

out against the stator switch member, causing the latter to snap open. Owing to toggle action, the stator member overtravels, but the weights of the rotating member are restrained; thus, there is no rubbing during normal operation of the motor. In this type of switch, it can be seen

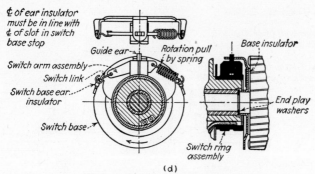

(d)

New-style starting-switch assembly

Hook spring and switch link to switch arm as shown. Hook spring to switch-arm insulator. Hook switch link to switch-arm insulator. Make sure switch-arm assembly and switch rings are on center and that the guide ear of the switch arm protrudes through the slot in the switch base stop. Use end play washers to get center line adjustment of switch-arm assembly and switch rings.

Use spring part 4020 for 860 rpm motor	Use switch-arm assembly part 5004 C for 860 rpm motor
Use spring part 4026 for 1150 rpm motor	Use switch-arm assembly part 5004 B for 1150 rpm motor
Use spring part 4020 for 1450 rpm motor	Use switch-arm assembly part 5004 B for 1450 rpm motor
Use spring part 4005 for 1725 rpm motor	Use switch-arm assembly part 5004 B for 1725 rpm motor
Use spring part 4136 for 1750 rpm motor	Use switch-arm assembly part 5004 B for 1750 rpm motor
Use spring part 4110 for 2900 rpm motor	Use switch-arm assembly part 5004 B for 2900 rpm motor
Use spring part 4017 for 3500 rpm motor	Use switch-arm assembly part 5004 B for 3500 rpm motor

NOTE: Assembly consists of a switch contact carbon and a switch arm only.

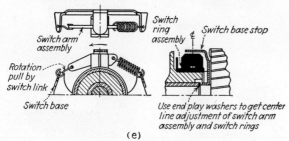

(e)

Old-style starting-switch assembly

NOTE: To use the new-style switch-arm assembly with this style of switch base, break guide ear off and file flat. Assemble same as new-style switch.

FIG. 18-9.—Assembling instructions for standard Ohio starting switch.

that the weights move radially. When a switch of this type is replaced, the rotor member usually can be located in the same position as the previous member. The rotor member must be located so that (1) the rotor core does not interfere with its action; (2) the rotor member cannot rub the stator member when the rotor is as near the switch-end end shield as possible; and likewise (3) the rotor member will engage the stator member when the rotor is hard against the rear end shield, *i.e.*, as far as possible from the front end shield.

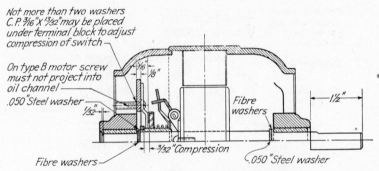

Not more than two washers
C.P. 3/16" X 13/32" may be placed
under terminal block to adjust
compression of switch

On type B motor screw
must not project into
oil channel

.050" Steel washer

3/16"
1/8"
1/32"

Fibre
washers

1½"

Fibre washers

3/32" Compression

.050" Steel washer

FIG. 18-10.—Switch-setting instructions for Reynolds Electric Company motors.

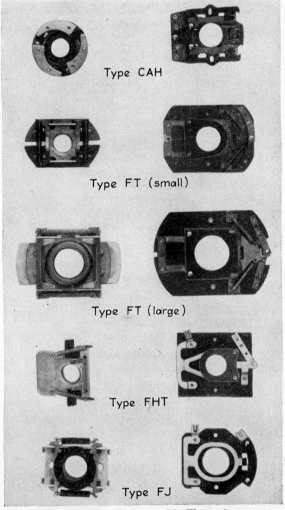

Type CAH

Type FT (small)

Type FT (large)

Type FHT

Type FJ

FIG. 18-11.—Starting switches used in Westinghouse motors.

b. Type FT *Switches.*—These switches, illustrated in Fig. 18-11, were developed principally for two-value capacitor motors; the large switch is used in 180-frame motors and the small in 140-frame motors. It has also been used in both split-phase and capacitor-start motors. In the CAH switch, described above, the movement of the weights against the stator member was in a radial direction but, in all other switches shown in Fig. 18-11, the stator members are actuated by

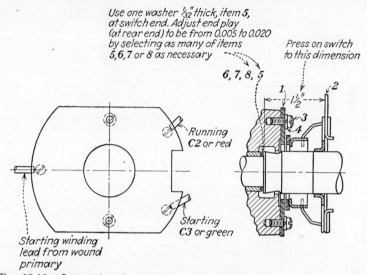

Use one washer $\frac{1}{32}$"thick, item 5, at switch end. Adjust end play (at rear end) to be from 0.005 to 0.020 by selecting as many of items 5, 6, 7 or 8 as necessary

Press on switch to this dimension

6, 7, 8, 5

$1\frac{1}{2}$"

Running C2 or red

Starting C3 or green

Starting winding lead from wound primary

Fig. 18-12.—Instructions for assembling type FT (large) switch of Fig. 18-11.

Item   Description and material
1. Starting switch (stationary part).
2. Starting switch (routing part).
3. 0.190-32 × $\frac{3}{8}$ in. long fillister-head iron machine screw.
4. 0.190 lock washer.
5. Washer ($\frac{1}{32}$ in. thick) (fiber).
6. Washer ($\frac{1}{64}$ in. thick) (fiber).
7. Washer ($\frac{1}{16}$ in. thick) (fiber).
8. Washer ($\frac{3}{64}$ in. thick) (fiber).

NOTE: For anti-end-bump motors use one washer $\frac{1}{16}$ in. thick, item 7, at switch end and one at rear end. Adjust free end play to be from 0.002 to 0.032 either by substituting $\frac{3}{64}$-in. thick washer for $\frac{1}{16}$-in. thick washer or by adding $\frac{1}{64}$-in. thick washer. Make adjustment at rear end of motor.

an axial movement. Stator members of both large and small FT switches are snap-acting because of their toggle mechanisms.

Instructions for assembling the large FT switch are given in Fig. 18-12.

Instructions for assembling the small FT switch are given in Fig. 18-13. In this figure a motor with anti-end-bump construction is shown and the permissible end play is given as 0.002 to 0.032; if the motor does not have anti-end-bump construction, the end·play should be held to about 0.002 to 0.010.

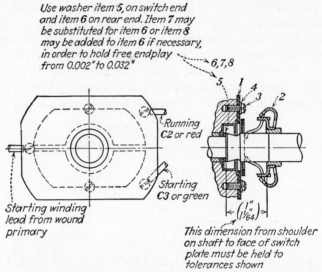

Use washer item 5, on switch end and item 6 on rear end. Item 7 may be substituted for item 6 or item 8 may be added to item 6 if necessary, in order to hold free endplay from 0.002" to 0.032"

Running C2 or red

Starting C3 or green

Starting winding lead from wound primary

This dimension from shoulder on shaft to face of switch plate must be held to tolerances shown

FIG. 18-13.—Instructions for assembling type FT (small) switch shown in FIG. 18-11.
(*Courtesy of Westinghouse Electric Corporation.*)

Item	Description and material
1.	Starting switch (stationary part).
2.	Starting switch (rotating part).
3.	0.138-32 $\times$ $\frac{3}{8}$ in.-long fillister-head iron machine screw.
4.	0.138 lock washer.
5.	Washer (fiber) ($\frac{1}{32}$ in. thick).
6.	Washer (fiber) ($\frac{1}{16}$ in. thick).
7.	Washer (fiber) ($\frac{3}{64}$ in. thick).
8.	Washer (fiber) ($\frac{1}{64}$ in. thick).

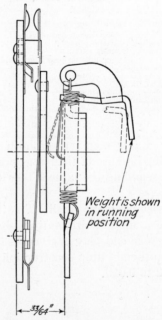

Weight is shown in running position

FIG. 18-14.—Instructions for assembling type FHT switch of FIG. 18-11.

c. Type FHT *Switch.*—This switch is used on high-torque split-phase motors and for certain other limited applications. It is illustrated in Fig. 18-11. This switch has but a single weight, and light steel cushioning springs for quietness of operation. Assembly instructions are given in Fig. 18-14.

d. Type FJ *Switch.*—This switch, shown in Fig. 18-11, is used in split-phase motors type FH, and in capacitor-start motors type FJ.

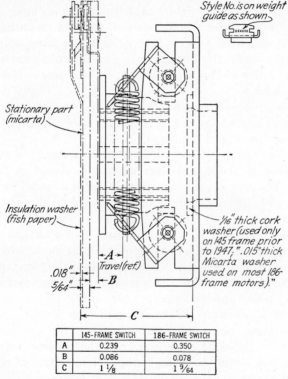

	145-FRAME SWITCH	186-FRAME SWITCH
A	0.239	0.350
B	0.086	0.078
C	1 1/8	1 9/64

Fig. 18-15.—Switch-setting dimensions for type FJ starting switch, shown in Fig. 18-11.

It is made in two sizes, for the 145 and 186 frames, respectively. Assembly instructions for both are given in Fig. 18-15. It is to be noted that a washer is shown between the micarta slider and the weight guide; it was used on 145-frame switches made prior to 1947. Use of this washer has since been eliminated on 145-frame motors by increasing the length of the micarta slider. Slider lengths, measured along the shaft, are

$2\frac{1}{32}$ in. for the 145-frame switch that uses the cork washer.
$4\frac{5}{64}$ in. for the 145-frame switch that does not use the washer.

RIGID AND RESILIENT MOUNTINGS AND COUPLINGS

Almost limitless is the number of different mounting and drive arrangements that have been used for fractional horsepower motors. Only a few of the most common variations are discussed in the following paragraphs.

18-10. Types of Mounting.—Common and still popular mounting arrangements are

a. Rigid-foot.—A foot rigidly attached to, or an integral part of, the motor frame is probably the earliest form of mounting arrangement. It is still widely used where noise is not a major factor.

b. Resilient-foot.—Resilient mounting arrangements are used extensively in the interests of quiet operation. These are discussed in Arts. 18-11 and 18-12.

c. Round-frame.—Round-frame motors, *i.e.*, motors without a foot, are often held in place by means of a band clamped around the body of the motor (see Fig. 8-2c and d).

d. Face-mounting.—(Also called *flange-mounting.**) One form of face-mounting, used for oil-burner motors, is shown in Figs. 18-16 and 20-3. The rear end shield is provided with a rabbet fit machined concentric with the shaft; the motor is bolted to the oil burner by means of bolts passing through the extended lugs in the rear end shield. In the other variation of face-mounting, shown in Fig. 20-4, the extended lugs are omitted, and the motor is held in place by means of bolts projecting from the driven apparatus into the four tapped holes shown in the rear end shield. This mounting arrangement is used for a number of pump applications.

e. Extended Through Bolts.—Round-frame motors are often mounted by means of extended through bolts. Such an arrangement does not center the shaft so accurately as the machined rabbet fit of a face-mounted motor, but this method of mounting is often satisfactory and convenient for fan applications.

18-11. Torque Pulsations in Single-phase Motors.—Polyphase induction motors supply a steady and smooth flow of power to the shaft. Torque developed by electromagnetic action of the windings is steady, like the torque developed by a turbine. Single-phase motors supply the torque in a series of pulses, just like a reciprocating

---

* The term *flange-mounting* is often used when the motor has extended lugs and machined rabbet fit as shown in Fig. 18-16, and the term *face-mounting* if there are no extended lugs. However, present Nema standards refer to both types of mounting as *face-mounting*.

engine. These torque pulsations, inherent in any single-phase motor, are a major source of noise in many applications, particularly when the motor is mounted rigidly to any sheet-metal cabinet or structure capable of radiating sound. Fortunately, the effect of this major source of noise can be virtually eliminated by use of an effective resilient mounting. In order to understand the source of these torque pulsations, it is first necessary to understand the pulsating nature of single-phase power.

Fig. 18-16.—A face-mounted split-phase motor used for oil-burner service. This motor is rated at ⅛ hp, 1750 rpm, and is equipped with a manual-reset thermal protective device. (*Courtesy of Ohio Electric Manufacturing Company.*)

a. Pulsating Nature of Single-phase Power.—In Art. 1-2 the nature of alternating current was pointed out; the current at any instant in time was shown to vary in accordance with the sine wave in Fig. 1-2. A similar curve of *instantaneous amperes* vs. time is given in Fig. 18-17. Likewise, a curve of *instantaneous volts* vs. time, also a sine wave, is shown. In this figure, the current wave is shown displaced 45 electrical degrees in time behind the voltage, such as is the case when the power factor is 70.7 per cent. The instantaneous power—or watts— in a single-phase circuit is equal to the product of the voltage at that instant by the current at that same instant. Therefore, to obtain the instantaneous watts at a number of points in time, we multiply the instantaneous volts by the instantaneous amperes, taking care to observe the plus and minus signs of both current and voltage. A curve obtained in this fashion is also shown in Fig. 18-17.   Studying this curve of *instantaneous watts*, it is interesting to note that

1. The instantaneous watts vary, the same as do the volts and amperes.
2. The frequency of this variation is *twice* the supply circuit frequency; *i.e.*, in a 60-cycle circuit, the power frequency is 120 cycles.
3. The power is not always positive but is negative at certain portions of the cycle; negative power indicates a reversal in direction of power flow; *e.g.*, if the power input to a motor is taken as positive, the power is said to be negative when the motor is feeding power back to the line.

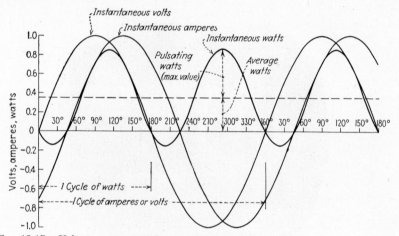

FIG. 18-17.—Voltage, current, and power relations in a single-phase circuit of 70.7 per cent lagging power factor.

4. It will be noted that the power can be thought of as consisting of two components; the first component is the steady power, or *average watts*, which remains constant in value, as in a d-c circuit; the second component is the *pulsating watts* which vary sinusoidally with time at a frequency double the frequency of the applied voltage; the *pulsating watts* are superimposed upon the *average watts*.
5. *Pulsating* power is greater than the *average* power, showing that the former is of major importance.

b. Pulsations in Torque.—In any single-phase motor, the torque produced by the electromagnetic forces consists of two components: (1) an *average torque* and (2) a *pulsating torque*, alternating at twice line frequency.   Since the power input to the motor, by the very nature of single-phase power, varies over a wide range, the torque developed by the electromagnetic forces must also vary over a wide range.   This point becomes obvious when the fundamental law of conservation of energy is considered; when the power input is zero or negative, there can be no power output, hence no torque.   Readers interested in pursuing the subject of torque pulsations are referred to an article on the subject by Kimball and Alger.[1]   Although the flywheel effect of the rotor smooths out variations in speed and permits the motor to carry the load steadily, it must be remembered that the torques due to electromagnetic forces contain a strong component of *pulsating* torque.   If the stator is rigidly attached to the driven device, this double-frequency torque pulsation and its harmonics are likely to be the principal source of noise and vibration caused by the motor.

Fig. 18-18.—A spring-mounted motor.   The leaf springs are to take out the double-frequency torque pulsations.   (*Courtesy of Holtzer-Cabot Electric Company.*)

This statement is particularly true if the motor is mounted on any structure capable of vibrating and radiating sound.   Dominant pitch, for 60-cycle motors, is 120 cycles, a note about one octave below middle C on the piano.   It is primarily to eliminate this 120-cycle hum that resilient mountings are used.   How this is done forms the subject of the following article.

18-12.   How Resilient Mounting Eliminates Noise Due to Torque Pulsations.—A resilient-mounting arrangement used to overcome the 120-cycle torque pulsation is shown in Fig. 18-18.   In this figure, it can be seen that the steel leaf springs, if extended, would pass through the center of the shaft and that consequently this stator is free to turn about the shaft but has relatively little freedom to move in any other

[1] For numbered references, see Bibliography at end of the chapter.

direction.   The whole motor is then free to vibrate in accordance with the forces set up by the pulsating torque of 120-cycle frequency; but, since the stator is free to oscillate, practically none of this torque vibration is transmitted to the mounting foot.   The effectiveness of this spring mounting can be felt by resting a fingernail lightly against the leaf springs near the bearing housing; a distinct vibration will be felt, but if the nail is slowly moved down the spring toward the base, the vibration will be felt to disappear.

Fig. 18-19.—A rubber-mounted, capacitor-start motor with built-in thermal protection. (*Courtesy of Westinghouse Electric Corporation.*)

In Fig. 18-19, another form of resilient mounting is shown.   In this construction, two rubber mounting rings are used, one on each end of the motor.   Each "rubber" ring consists of two concentric steel rings, between which the actual rubber ring is bonded.   The inner steel ring is pressed onto a machined fit on the end shield, and the outer ring is clamped in a mounting cradle.   A sectional view of this rubber-ring construction is shown in Fig. 5-2.   The stator is thus free to move, but the principal freedom of motion is about the center of the shaft; motion about the center of the shaft stresses the rubber in shear, the most effective way to use rubber to isolate noise and vibration. Since the whole motor is free to vibrate about the center of the shaft, the 120-cycle torque pulsation is not transmitted to the base. Interesting discussions of elastic mountings have been written by Morrill[2] and by Appleman.[3]

Polyphase and d-c motors do not have the same inherent double-frequency torque pulsation as single-phase motors, but they are frequently made rubber-mounted because the companion single-phase motor is rubber-mounted. Resilient mounting does help, though it is not so necessary as it is for the single-phase motor. A permanent-split capacitor motor tends to have less torque pulsation than a single-phase motor without the capacitor, but the capacitor does not dispense with the need for resilient mounting.

18-13. Flexible Couplings.—Flexible couplings may be used either to allow for misalignment between shafts or to provide torsional

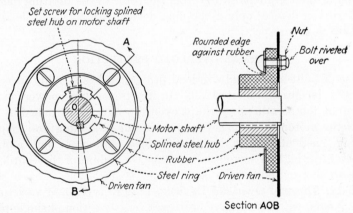

FIG. 18-20.—Construction for resiliently mounting a fan on a motor shaft. (*Courtesy of Carrier Corporation.*)

flexibility between the motor and its load. A coupling may take care of misalignment and still provide no torsional flexibility, but the latter feature is quite essential in many applications. It has been brought out that single-phase motors have very pronounced double-frequency torque pulsations set up by the electromagnetic forces in the motor. Resilient mounting isolates the effect of this pulsating force from being transmitted through the stator to the frame of the driven device. However, it must be remembered that the pulsating torque is exerted on the rotor as well as on the stator. Therefore, 60-cycle motors will have a 120-cycle vibration in the rotor as well as in the stator. If the motor is belted to the load, the belt will usually isolate this vibration from the driven load. However, if no torsional flexibility is provided, this 120-cycle vibration can be transmitted to the driven member of the load and is, in some cases, objectionable. One example is that of a large fan mounted directly on the motor shaft. When, on one application, it was found that a large fan rigidly mounted on the motor shaft emitted an objectionable 120-cycle hum, a special hub was designed to provide torsional flexibility; the construction used for this purpose is shown in Fig. 18-20.

Another interesting application is that of hot-water circulating pumps used for residences. Couplings used to connect the pump impeller to the motor are provided with torsional flexibility in order to prevent the 120-cycle hum from getting into the hot-water system and setting up objectionable noises in the radiators.

No amount of elastic suspension of the stator will prevent transmission of the torque pulsation from the rotor to the rotating member of the driven device; only a coupling device with torsional flexibility will help in this respect.

THERMAL OVERLOAD PROTECTION

Use of built-in thermal overload protection has steadily increased since its inception about 1930. In fractional horsepower motors dangerous temperatures—perhaps even fire—may be reached by failure of the motor to start; severe overloading or stalling; too frequent starting, particularly if a high-inertia load is started; high ambient temperature; high or low circuit voltage; or failure of the ventilation owing to obstructions of the openings.

18-14. Thermal Overload Devices.—Many types and varieties of thermal overload devices have been used for protection of single-phase fractional horsepower a-c motors. Generally speaking, they are all intended to open the motor circuit directly. Such devices should be serviced by complete replacement of a new unit obtained from the motor manufacturer. No adjustments should be attempted in the field.

a. Disc-type Thermostats.—The disc-type thermostat has as its single moving element a bimetallic disc invented by J. A. Spencer. The disc has a dished shape, with the high-expansive side of the bimetal on the concave side of the disc at normal temperature. As the disc is heated, the bimetal on the inside of the disc tries to expand but is restrained from doing so by the concave shape of the disc, for the outer side, being of nonexpansive metal, does not expand similarly; as the

FIG. 18-21.—A disc-type thermostat used for built-in thermal protection of a fractional horsepower motor. (*Courtesy of Westinghouse Electric Corporation.*)

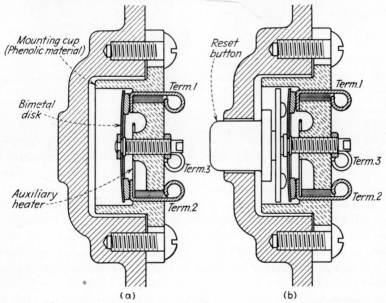

FIG. 18-22.—Other forms of the disc-type thermostat. (*Courtesy of Spencer Thermostat Company.*)

temperature of the disc is increased, stresses are set up in the disc tending to buckle the latter, and as soon as its temperature has reached a certain predetermined value, the disc snaps suddenly over to the other position. When the disc cools down to a definite temperature, it will snap back to its original shape.   It is to be noted that this disc operates when, and only when, it reaches a certain fixed temperature. This temperature may be attained by heat received from the motor, by heat generated in an auxiliary heater inside the thermostat, or by both.   A thermostat of this type is illustrated in Fig. 18-21.

In Fig. 18-22, other constructions of the disc-type thermostat are shown.   Of particular interest is Fig. 18-22b, a manual-reset thermostat.   The disc is arranged so that its automatic reclosing temperature is well below normal room temperatures; hence once the disc snaps open, it stays open until the button on the outside of the motor is pressed, resetting the disc.

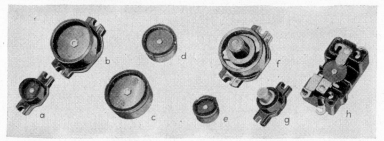

Fig. 18-23.—Types and sizes of motor-protection thermostats.   (*Courtesy of Spencer Thermostat Company.*)   (*a*) Ear-type, ½-in. disc, automatic-reset.   (*b*) Ear-type, 1-in. disc, automatic-reset.   (*c*) Round-base, 1-in. disc, automatic-reset.   (*d*) Round-base, ¾-in. disc, automatic-reset.   (*e*) Round-base, ½-in. disc, automatic-reset.   (*f*) Ear-type, 1-in. disc, manual-reset.   (*g*) Ear-type, ½-in. disc, manual-reset.   (*h*) Air-flo type, automatic-reset (used in repulsion-start motors).

A cutaway view of a disc-type thermostat mounted inside a motor is shown in Fig. 5-2.   Figure 18-23 shows a number of different forms of motor-protection thermostats.

b. Thermotector.—In Fig. 18-24 is shown another thermal protective device used in fractional horsepower motors.   The elements of the switch shown in Fig. 18-24a consist of a thermostatic bimetallic helix, a heater helix, a bowed spring, a contact arm, and terminals. The thermostatic helix is fixed at one end.   The opposite end carries a slotted fork which rotates about one support of the bowed spring. The low-resistance heater helix, which is connected in series with the motor winding and which carries the motor current, completely surrounds the bimetallic helix.   This heater element is welded in place securely.   The flat steel spring is mounted between two rigid supports in such a manner that it is slightly bowed.   This bowed spring carries a contact arm which makes contact when the spring is bowed in one direction but which opens the circuit when it is bowed in the other

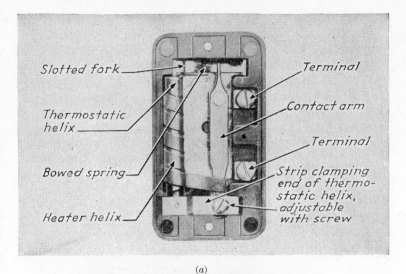

Slotted fork

Thermostatic helix

Bowed spring

Heater helix

Terminal

Contact arm

Terminal

Strip clamping end of thermostatic helix, adjustable with screw

(a)

(b)

Fig. 18-24.—The thermotector. (*Courtesy of General Electric Company.*) (a) With cover removed. (b) Mounted on the conduit box.

direction. When the bimetallic helix is heated to a temperature above normal, the free end rotates and reverses the bow of the spring. When the spring passes dead center, it also moves the contact arm and disconnects the motor from the line. With the line open, the current ceases to flow in the heater helix, the bimetallic helix turns in the opposite direction, and when the temperature is again normal, which may be from 2 to 5 min, the spring snaps to the "on" position.

A more recent form of Thermotector is simpler in construction. For an actuating element, it uses a simple bimetal strip carrying contacts at one end and anchored at the other. Since a simple strip thermostat of this type would inherently have a slow make and a slow break, a small alnico magnet is used to provide snap action, both opening and closing. This device is usually built into the front end shield.

c. Thermotrons.—An automatic-reset snap-acting strip-type thermal protective device is shown in Fig. 18-25. Contacts *A* and *F* are

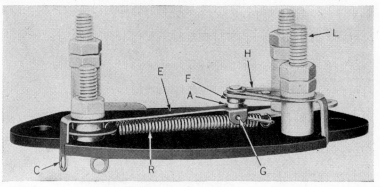

Fig. 18-25.—An automatic-reset Thermotron; see Art. 18-14c for description.   (*Courtesy of Delco Products.*)

closed by the load set up by the spring *R* and link assembly *G*. These contacts are connected in series with the common stator lead (terminal *C* to stator lead, terminal *L* to supply line). As the temperature in the motor windings increases, the bimetal element *E* will distort and will bend in the direction that tends to separate the contacts *A* and *F*. The contacts remain closed during the initial bending of the bimetal element until the force set up by the downward expansion of the bimetal is strong enough to overcome the upward force of the spring *R* and link assembly *G*, at which time the contacts open with a snap action. Snap action is effected by the toggle link *G*, the pivot point of which becomes displaced when the bimetal *E* bows upward owing to heating. The contact *F* is riveted to a light follow-up spring *H* which prevents fluttering and arcing as the contacts open, thus giving longer contact life. As the motor temperature decreases, the bimetal element contracts to its original position, thus allowing the upward force of the spring to be stronger than the downward force of the bimetal element, which closes the contacts with a snap action.

A manual-reset Thermotron of the solder-pot type is illustrated in Fig. 18-26. Contacts *A* are locked closed by a phosphorbronze spring strip *B* engaged in a ratchet and solder-pot assembly *S*. These contacts are connected in series with the common stator lead (terminal *C* to stator lead, terminal *L* to supply line). When the temperature of the solder pot becomes high enough, the alloy in the wheel *S* melts, thereby disengaging spring strip *B* and allowing spring *D* to open the contacts. The device can be manually reset after the temperature drops, by pushing in on the reset button. This button touches at point

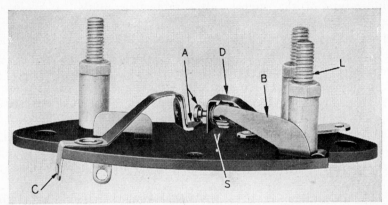

Fig. 18-26.—A manual-reset Thermotron; see Art. 18-14*c* for description. (*Courtesy of Delco Products.*)

D forcing the ratchet assembly over locking spring *B*. As the button is released, contacts *A* are again locked closed. The circuit will not be completed until the button pressure is released.

d. Fusetron.—Another very popular device, particularly for d-c motors, is the Fusetron, or Fustat. It is manufactured by the Bussman Manufacturing Company of St. Louis, Mo. The external appearance of this device very much resembles a household fuse. Actually, the Fusetron does have a fuse ribbon—visible inside the window—which can blow as can an ordinary fuse, but one end of this loop of fuse wire is anchored in a pot of solder. A spring exerts a continuous pressure to pull the loop out of the solder. Inside the fuse and around this solder pot is wrapped a heater wire, connected in series with the line. Heat from this heater can cause the Fusetron to open by the softening of the solder. There is a second solder pot inside the Fusetron which receives heat directly from the motor frame.

If the motor frame gets too hot, this solder softens, tripping the Fusetron.

18-15. Inherent Overheating Protection.—A device such as one of those described in the preceding article is known as an **inherent overheating device.** That is, the device operates on temperature alone, on current alone, or upon the combined effect of both.

The idea of a protective device is to protect the windings by limiting them to a certain definite maximum operating temperature, regardless of how they might arrive at this temperature. If it were possible to insert a protective device inside the winding so that the operating temperature of the device were always identical with the temperature of the copper, ideal protection would be obtained. Actually, it is impossible to make a commercial device that will follow all variations of the winding temperature if the device receives all of its heat solely from the windings. It is a practical necessity to provide an auxiliary heater, or its equivalent, inside the protective device. If no auxiliary heater were used, the actuating element of the protective device would be cooler than the windings. The auxiliary heater tends to compensate for this effect and to make the thermally responsive actuating element follow the winding temperature more closely, as can be demonstrated by a concrete discussion of a specific device. For this discussion, the disc-type thermostat will be used for illustrative purposes.

The actual temperature of the motor windings is found by adding together three factors:

1. Ambient temperature
2. Rise of iron parts above air
3. Rise of windings above iron parts

Factor 1 plus factor 2 is the actual temperature of the iron parts. The temperature of the disc would, if no current were flowing in the heater, be the same as the temperature of the iron parts (except for a relatively small lag of 1 or 2 deg). It would not make any difference what elevated the temperature of the iron parts; whether it were core loss, rotor copper loss, failure of ventilation, or high ambient temperature, the disc would still follow the temperature of the iron parts. Now, then, suppose that an auxiliary heater is placed in the thermostat in such a position that it can transmit heat directly to the disc. If this auxiliary heater is connected in series with the line, the losses generated in it will be directly proportional to the stator copper loss, for both are proportional to the square of the stator current. Therefore, the disc will get hotter than the iron parts by an amount proportional to the square of the stator current; likewise, the temperature rise of the windings above the iron parts is very nearly proportional to the stator copper loss. In other words, the temperature rise of the disc above iron parts will be proportional to the temperature rise of the winding above the iron parts.

Perhaps these relations can be better understood by referring to Fig. 18-27: *the temperature rise of the windings above the end shield* and the *temperature rise of the disc above the end shield* are plotted as proportional to the square of the stator current. The actual opening temperature of the disc is unaffected by variations in stator current and remains constant as shown. We subtract the *temperature rise of the disc above the end shield* from the *disc opening temperature* to obtain the curve of *end-shield temperature to trip the disc.* We add the *temperature rise of the winding above the end shield* to obtain the curve of *maximum winding temperature* vs. current. The temperature rises shown here were taken by thermometer on a ⅙-hp motor. It will be noted

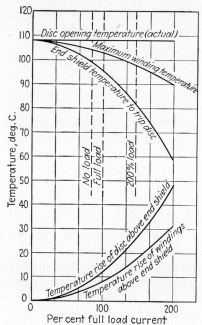

Fig. 18-27.—Temperatures in a motor protected by an inherent overheating device.

that under no-load conditions the protective device would allow the winding temperatures to creep up to 105°C; but on 200 per cent of full-load torque it would only allow the winding to reach a temperature of 98°C.

Thus, from no-load to full-load torque, this disc thermostat with an auxiliary heater limits the winding temperature to a very nearly constant value. At heavier loads, it limits the maximum temperature, as measured by thermometer, to a lower value than at light loads, as should be the case; for there is more difference between hot-spot temperature and thermometer temperature at high loads than there is at light loads.

Perhaps the true action of the inherent overheating device can be even better understood by comparing it with the more familiar external current-operated overload device. The externally mounted device is rated in terms of its ultimate tripping current, *i.e.*, the least current that will trip the device. Usually the ultimate tripping current of a device of this type is set to be 115 to 120 per cent of full-load current. This ultimate tripping current of the separately mounted device is, of course, unaffected by the actual temperature of the motor. The inherent overheating device discussed in the preceding paragraphs also has an ultimate tripping current, but this ultimate tripping current is definitely dependent upon the temperature of the iron parts of the motor. At different temperatures of the motor end shield, the ultimate tripping current is as follows:

End-shield Temperatures, Degrees	Ultimate Tripping Amperes, Per Cent
25	250
60	200
88	125
95	100
108	0

Thus, at 88 deg, the inherent overheating device affords the same protection as the external device; at higher temperatures, it provides better protection; and at lower temperatures, it allows more overload capacity than the current-operated external device.

18-16. Underwriters' Laboratories Standards for Inherent Overheating Protection.—Underwriters' standards specify three requirements:

1. Under no condition of running load shall the protective device allow the temperature of the motor windings, as measured by thermocouple, to exceed 125°C.

2. Under continuous locked-rotor condition, the temperature of the windings is not to exceed 150°C.

3. The motor must withstand having the rotor locked for a period of 15 days with full voltage applied, without burning up the windings.

There are other detailed requirements and test procedures outlined in their standards on this subject,[4] but those given above are the most essential. Lists of inherent overheating protective devices tested with specific motors are published by the Underwriters' Laboratories in their List of Inspected Electrical Equipment, issued annually, with monthly or bimonthly supplements.

GEAR MOTORS

Built-in speed reducers are popular in fractional horsepower sizes as well as in the integral ratings. Worm gears, spur gears, and even herringbone gears are used; one or more reduction stages may be employed.

18-17. Worm-gear Reducers.—Worm-gear reducers are used for all types of fractional horsepower motors. Figure 18-28 shows a typical motor with a double-reduction gear. Single-reduction gearing may be had for ratios from 6:1 to as high as 60:1; with a 1725-rpm

Bronze sleeve bearings on secondary and drive shafts

Worm on nitralloy steel shaft

Laminated Bakelite primary gear

Bronze secondary gear

Pre-lubricated sealed ball bearing

Oil seals

Fig. 18-28.—Fractional horsepower motor with double-reduction worm gear. May be used with universal, induction, or synchronous motors. (*Courtesy of Bodine Electric Co.*)

motor, this means output speeds from 300 to 30 rpm. Double-reduction gearing is used for ratios from 36:1 to 2880:1, giving, for 1725-rpm motors, output speeds from 50 to 0.6 rpm. Universal motors operate at somewhat higher speeds.

Most worm-gear reducers are irreversible; *i.e.*, the motor cannot be driven by turning the slow-speed shaft. Care must be taken not to connect high-inertia loads directly to the output shaft, because the momentum of the load during stopping or starting may damage the gears. Many of these motors, particularly double-reduction universal motors, can deliver more torque than the gears can handle continuously. Care should, therefore, be exercised to avoid applying these motors to drive devices that may become jammed—lest the gears be damaged. For such applications, a safety clutch or shear pin between the motor and the load is recommended.

18-18. Spur-gear Reducers.—Multi-stage spur gearing is often used for small motors when a high ratio is desired. Examples are illustrated in Figs. 15-3, 15-6, and 15-7.

18-19. Double-parallel Reduction Gear.—An interesting example of a built-in speed reducer is given in Fig. 18-29. It will be noted that this speed reducer is a double-reduction unit, uses herringbone gears, and has antifriction bearings. Ball bearings are used on the high-speed shaft and Timken roller bearings on the slowspeed countershafts.

Fig. 18-29.—A double-parallel geared-head motor. (*Courtesy of Master Electric Company.*)

A mechanical efficiency of 85 to 95 per cent is claimed by the manufacturer. Available reduction ratios range from 6:1 to 36:1. Sufficient lubricant is put into this motor at assembly to last for 500 hr of operation, which is equivalent to one year's service under average operating conditions. Directly under the gear case is a supporting bracket to take the stresses caused by the slow-speed drive and to avoid transmitting these stresses through the gear case and head to the field ring and feet of the motor. The supporting bracket is shorter than the center height of the motor to allow for shims under the supporting bracket. This geared-head support must be shimmed carefully at the time of installation.

Bibliography

1. KIMBALL, A. L., and ALGER, P. L.: Single-phase Motor Torque Pulsations, *A.I.E.E. Trans.*, June, 1924, p. 730.
2. MORRILL, W. J.: Elastic Mountings for Quieter Motors, *Elec. Manufacturing*, May, 1938, p. 76.
3. APPLEMAN, W. R.: Resilient Mountings for Motor Isolation, *Elec. Manufacturing*, December, 1944, p. 116.
4. "Standard for Industrial Control," Underwriters' Laboratories, Chicago, Ill.
5. BREMER, E. B., and VEINOTT, C. G.: Refrigerator Motors Need Thermal Protection, *Elec. Refrigeration News*, Oct. 11, 1933.
6. VEINOTT, C. G.: Some Problems in the Standardization of Temperature Ratings of Fractional Horsepower Motors, *A.I.E.E. Trans.*, 1940, p. 1055.
7. POTTER, C. P.: The Inherent Overheating Protection of Single-phase Motors, *A.I.E.E. Trans.*, vol. 60, 1941, pp. 993–996.
8. Because Bearings Affect Motor Performance, *Elec. Manufacturing*, August, 1939, p. 40.
9. SPAULDING, DAVID C.: Making the Most of Sleeve Bearings, *Elec. Manufacturing*. August, 1940, p. 62.

CHAPTER XIX

TESTING FRACTIONAL HORSEPOWER MOTORS

It is impossible to overestimate the importance of the role that testing plays in the development and manufacture of fractional horsepower motors. Service shops will also find it desirable to test motors

1. To aid in diagnosing defects in a motor sent in for repairs.
2. To check a motor that has been repaired.
3. To check a motor on its application to see if it is overloaded or to determine if the motor is suited to the job and, if not, what type and rating of motor will be required.

It will seldom be necessary to take on any one motor all of the tests described in this book. Sufficient tests are described in this chapter to make an extensive analysis of a motor, but it is not expected that it will often be found necessary to take the full number of tests described.

METERS AND EQUIPMENT

19-1. Power Source.—For accurate and reliable testing, it is absolutely essential that a source of variable voltage be provided. For a source of a-c power, an autotransformer is recommended. Many such transformers are available commercially, some of which are illustrated in Fig. 19-1. Four of the transformers shown consist of a laminated iron core built up of doughnut-shaped punchings. A single-layer winding, traversed by a moving contact, provides both the transformer effect and a convenient means of voltage adjustment. Each turn of the winding can be reached by the contact, and a continuous adjustment of voltage is obtained. For the moving contact, a carbon brush is used to limit the current in the short-circuited turn. On some models, any voltage between 0 and 135 volts can be obtained from a 115-volt 60-cycle line.

For testing d-c motors, a motor-generator set with field control of the generator is recommended. A possible alternate is a transformer-rectifier unit with adjustable autotransformer.

19-2. Measurement of Voltage.—Commercial voltmeters can be used for all ordinary voltage measurements. It is desirable to use low-loss voltmeters if possible. (A low-loss voltmeter has a high internal resistance.) Probably the most convenient and most useful a-c voltmeter will be one having two scales, a 0–150 and a 0–300. In testing polyphase motors, 440 or even 550 volts may be encountered, and for this purpose a 0–600 or 0–750 voltmeter is required. In testing two-value transformer types of capacitor motors (see Figs. 6-1 and

Fig. 19-1.—Autotransformers for controlling a-c voltage. (*Courtesy of General Radio Company.*)

6-6), 700 to 800 volts may be encountered. For these higher voltages, it is often possible to use a voltage multiplier in connection with the voltmeter to extend the scale reading of the latter. If a voltage multiplier is not available for the particular instrument, one can be made from a standard decade or resistance box, for the voltage multiplier consists only of an ohmic resistance of proper value connected in series with the voltmeter. To determine the proper value of resistance, it is necessary first to measure or determine the resistance of the voltmeter; sometimes this resistance will be printed on the meter itself, or it may be necessary to measure it. For a voltage multiplier to double the reading, use an external resistance equal in value to the internal resistance of the voltmeter. For a voltage multiplier to multiply the reading by three, the external resistance should be twice the resistance of the voltmeter. To multiply the voltmeter range by four, the external resistance must be equal to three times the resistance of the voltmeter, etc.

Often, it will be found more convenient to use potential transformers instead of voltage multipliers. Potential transformers ordinarily are satisfactory, but a direct-reading instrument is to be preferred to either a transformer or a multiplier for testing the element voltages of two-value transformer-type capacitor motors. It is often necessary to obtain voltmeters to indicate voltages lower than can readily be read on a 0–150 scale, and for this purpose it is necessary to obtain meters with a lower full-scale reading, since there is no practical way to increase the sensitivity of a commercial voltmeter.

For accurate measurement of d-c voltages, d-c meters should be used. However, a-c voltmeters will read approximately correctly on a d-c circuit, but a d-c meter should never be used on alternating current. The meter will give no reading, and it is likely to be injured by the application of alternating current.

A more extended discussion of measuring instruments is given in the "Standard Handbook for Electrical Engineers."[1]

19-3. Measurement of Current.—Commercial ammeters are generally satisfactory for measuring currents of fractional horsepower motors. For full-load readings, it will be necessary to provide instruments reading up to 15 amp, and for locked-rotor currents, up to 65 amp. Approximate values of full-load and locked-rotor currents on various sizes and ratings of fractional horsepower motors are given in Table XXVI, which will be of assistance in selecting meters of the right size.

Direct-current ammeters are often provided with external shunts; by use of the proper shunts, any range of currents can be covered with a single meter.

19-4. Measurement of Power Input (Watts).—Commercial watt-meters, preferably of the low-loss type, are quite satisfactory for testing fractional horsepower motors. Losses in these meters, even of the low-loss type, are always present, and corrections should be made for these losses; this point is discussed in Art. 19-11. The potential and

---

[1] For numbered references, see Bibliography at the end of this chapter.

current scales of a wattmeter should be so chosen as to match the voltage and current scales of the voltmeters and ammeters that are being used on the same test. For checking the power factor of electrolytic capacitors (see Art. 5-10), low-power-factor wattmeters are essential.

For measurement of polyphase power, polyphase wattmeters are available, although this power can be measured with two single-phase wattmeters. There is some advantage in using polyphase wattmeters on polyphase circuits; for thus a single reading is obtained, and there is never any question as to the sign of the smaller wattmeter reading, although there is a possibility of connecting the polyphase wattmeter incorrectly in the circuit.

Wattmeters are unnecessary in d-c measurements.

19-5. Measurement of Power Factor.—It is recommended that the power factor be computed from the readings of volts, amperes, and watts, rather than from a direct reading on a power-factor meter. In a single-phase circuit,

$$\text{Power factor} = \frac{\text{watts}}{\text{volts} \times \text{amperes}} \qquad (19\text{-}1)$$

In a two-phase circuit,

$$\text{Power factor} = \frac{\text{total watts}}{2 \times \text{volts} \times \text{amperes}} \qquad (19\text{-}2)$$

In a three-phase circuit,

$$\text{Power factor} = \frac{\text{total watts}}{\sqrt{3} \times \text{line-to-line volts} \times \text{line amperes}} \qquad (19\text{-}3)$$

19-6. Measurement of Frequency.—It is usually unnecessary to measure the frequency of a commercial 60-cycle circuit, particularly if electric clocks can be operated from it. When the measurement of frequency is necessary, a meter of the vibrating reed type should be satisfactory. For accurate results, however, the recommended type is an indicating instrument with a normal frequency point located in the middle of the scale, and calibrated to read in hundredths of a cycle.

An alternative method of frequency measurement is to measure the speed of a small synchronous motor operated on the same circuit.

19-7. Measurement of Speed.—Close and accurate measurement of speed is essential. There are two basically different methods available for measuring speed: *direct* and *visual.*

a. Direct Methods.—Probably the most convenient and direct way of measuring the speed is by means of a centrifugal tachometer, such as a Horn tachometer, or a liquid tachometer of the Veeder type, both of which read rpm directly. With this type of instrument, the reading is instantaneous. However, the tachometer should be checked often; if it is only infrequently used, it will probably be advisable to check the instrument each time it is used. An excellent way to check such a tachometer is by measuring the speed of a synchronous motor running from a 60-cycle circuit, the frequency of which is accurately controlled. (If a synchronous motor is not available, one can be made as described in Art. 15-8.) When the tachometer is checked, it should be checked at a speed as near to the speed to be measured as possible and also in the same position; *i.e.*, if the tachometer is to be held vertically when measuring an unknown speed, it should be calibrated in a vertical position, for the reading of these instruments sometimes is affected by the position in which they are held.

Another type of speed-measuring device is the integrating tachometer, which is probably more accurate, although not instantaneous in reading. Built into the device is a clockwork mechanism which, when a button is pushed, allows the tachometer to count the actual number of revolutions in a measured interval of time, usually from 3 to 5 sec. The instrument is calibrated to give the answer directly in rpm. For this type of speed measurement, from 3 to 5 sec is required for a reading.

Less elaborate, but still used to some extent, is the old familiar counter which counts revolutions in a given measured period of time.

When a tachometer with a rubber tip is used, the rubber must be kept free from oil or grease which would cause the point to slip and give an erroneously low reading; if the rubber tip is dipped in powdered chalk occasionally, this error can be avoided. Care must be taken to hold the tachometer shaft in line with the motor shaft and tight against it; if the tachometer is held at an angle or if it is not held in the center of the shaft, an erroneously high reading may be obtained.

b. Visual Methods.—Many small electric motors, below $\frac{1}{20}$ hp, do not have sufficient power to drive an ordinary tachometer without a serious reduction in speed because of the addition of the load of the tachometer. With such motors, some visual method of measuring the speed is an absolute necessity. Stroboscopic tachometers are recommended for this purpose. With a tachometer of this type, an intermittent, or stroboscopic, source of light is provided; the frequency of these flashes of light can be controlled. To measure the speed, the frequency of the flashes of light is adjusted so that the running device appears to stand still; the speed of the light flashes and rpm are indicated by a dial on the instrument.

A less elaborate but fully as accurate visual device for measuring speed can readily be made in a service shop. For this purpose, a disc 5 or 6 in. in diameter is secured to the shaft of a small universal motor, the speed of which can be controlled by means of an autotransformer or external resistance. A narrow slit, $\frac{1}{8}$ to $\frac{1}{4}$ in. wide and 1 in. long radially, is cut in the disc. An indicating tachometer is either belted to the motor or held against it by hand. To measure the speed of a rotating shaft, the latter is viewed through the slit in the disc with the motor running, and the speed of the motor driving the disc is increased from standstill up to the first speed at which the shaft of unknown speed appears to stand still. Under this condition, the speed of the device under measurement is the same as the speed of the slitted disc, which can then be measured. At double, triple, or quadruple speeds, the device under test will also appear to stand still, and care must be taken to avoid an error in this respect.

When induction motors are tested, if the speed is within 100 rpm of synchronous speed, the **slip** itself should be measured directly instead of the actual rpm.

19-8. Measurement of Slip.—The **slip** is the difference between the actual speed of an induction motor and the speed of the rotating field. (The term *slip* has no significance for motors other than those motors of the induction type.) The slip can be determined by measuring the actual speed and subtracting it from the known synchronous speed; but, for slips up to 100 rpm, it is more accurate and generally more satisfactory to measure the slip directly. For this purpose, it is necessary to mark the shaft in some manner with paint or chalk; or marking the keyway or flat on the shaft may be sufficient. In general, as many lines should be marked on the shaft as there are pairs of poles. It is then necessary to view the shaft extension with a stroboscopic source of light connected to the same source of power as the primary winding. For this purpose, neon lamps for operation on 115-volt circuits are available commercially in small bulbs, about the size of an English walnut. These lights are quite satisfactory in dark places, but the light is too dim to be of assistance in bright daylight. The lamps have two semicylindrical electrodes which light alternately on opposite halves of the cycle; the bulb should be held so that light from only one electrode strikes the marked shaft. Some of the neon bulbs now on the market have two electrodes about the size and shape of a quarter split through the center. It is almost impossible to use only the light from one electrode because of the shape, but a copper oxide rectifier connected in series with the lamp will cut off one-half the cycle, making one electrode dark. An arc light can be used, although it is intensely brilliant and rather hard on the eyes as well as somewhat awkward to handle. The commercial stroboscopic tachometers mentioned in the preceding article are sometimes arranged so that they can be connected directly to the power circuit to flash in synchronism with the line frequency; in such a case, they can be used in place of the neon or arc light.

It is possible to use for the measurement of slip the same sort of slitted disc described in the preceding article. In this case, the slitted disc is placed on the shaft of a synchronous motor which must be wound for the same number of poles as the motor being tested.

When the shaft of an induction motor is viewed either with a stroboscopic light such as has been already described or through the slit of a disc on a synchronous motor of the same number of poles, the shaft will appear to revolve backward, and this apparent backward revolution can be counted and timed, giving a direct measurement of the slip.

19-9. Measurement of Resistance.—For the measurement of resistances of 1 to 10,000 ohms, a Wheatstone bridge is recommended. The resistance of the leads from the bridge to the unknown resistance should be carefully measured—if not known—by short-circuiting the two leads together. When a measurement is made, the resistance of the leads should be subtracted from the observed value to obtain the true resistance. Kelvin double bridges are recommended for measurement of resistances below 1 ohm; these bridges are supplied with four leads—two for current, two for potential. This type of bridge does away with the necessity for accounting for the resistance of the leads and the contact drop. Ohmmeters provided with a self-contained battery are now commercially available; these instruments will read resistance in ohms directly and instantaneously. However, direct-reading ohmmeters are not so accurate as the Wheatstone bridge.

For the measurement of insulation resistance, a megger may be used. An alternative method is by the voltmeter-drop method, described as follows in the A.I.E.E. Test Code.[2]

A source of voltage, V, 500 if possible, is required together with a direct-current voltmeter having a known internal resistance, r, and a full scale slightly greater than V. The potential V should be applied between the insulated parts and the grounded parts with the voltmeter in series and the voltmeter reading, e, is taken. The insulation resistance R is then

$$R = \frac{(V - e)r}{e \times 1{,}000{,}000} \text{ megohms} \tag{19-4}$$

Another method of measuring resistance is by means of the voltmeter-ammeter method. A direct current of E volts is impressed across the unknown resistance, and the current I passing through it is measured. To obtain the true value of I, the current taken by the voltmeter should be subtracted from the measured value of current. The resistance R in ohms is

$$R = \frac{E}{I} \tag{19-5}$$

When this method is used, the value of current used should not be great enough, nor applied long enough, to cause appreciable heating of the winding.

Regardless of how the winding resistance was measured, the room temperature should be recorded, and the resistance corrected to 25°C, as explained in Art. 19-16a.

19-10. Measurement of Temperatures.—Three recognized and generally satisfactory methods of measuring the temperatures of fractional horsepower motors are by (1) thermometers, (2) thermocouples, and (3) rise of resistance. When thermometers are used, it is recommended that the mercury-type reading in degrees centigrade be used. These can be attached to the motor by means of a pad of thick felt glued to the motor or by means of modeling clay (modeling clay is to be preferred to putty as it does not become oily and sticky). When thermocouples are used, a potentiometer should be used to measure the thermal emf's. Some potentiometers are commercially available which read directly in degrees centigrade, in which case, only the one specified pair of metals can be used for the thermocouples. Other potentiometers read directly in millivolts, and the proper conversion charts are supplied by the manufacturer of the thermocouple wire. Whenever thermocouples are used, it is always necessary to correct for the "cold junction temperature," and there are numerous ways of making this compensation. Most potentiometers calibrated to read temperature directly now provide compensation for the cold junction temperature automatically without attention from the operator. The instructions accompanying the potentiometer should be studied carefully and followed implicitly.

The temperature rise by resistance is taken by measuring the cold resistance of the winding and then the hot resistance which is measured *immediately* after shutdown before the motor has time to cool sensibly. The temperature rise of copper windings is computed by the following formula:

$$T = \left(\frac{R_t}{r_t} - 1\right)(235 + t) \tag{19-6}$$

where T = total temperature rise of winding in degrees centigrade above temperature t.

R_t = hot resistance.

r_t = cold resistance, at room temperature.

t = temperature of winding, in degrees centigrade, when cold resistance r_t was measured.

For greater accuracy, several values of hot resistance should be measured at different time intervals following shutdown; a curve of the hot resistance vs. time can then be plotted and extrapolated back to the instant the power was shut off.

19-11. Meter Loss Corrections.—There are two methods of connecting a single-phase wattmeter in a single-phase circuit. These

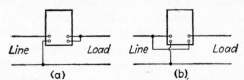

Line   Load   Line   Load

(a)   (b)

Fig. 19-2.—Two ways of connecting a wattmeter in a single-phase circuit.

methods are shown in Fig. 19-2. If the meter is connected as in Fig. 19-2a, the wattmeter will read the input to the load plus the loss in the potential coil of the meter. If the meter is connected as in Fig. 19-2b, the wattmeter will indicate the load plus the loss in the current coil of the wattmeter. Thus, it will be seen that regardless of which way the meter is connected, there will be losses in the wattmeter; and to obtain accurate readings it is essential that these losses be subtracted from the readings of the wattmeter to obtain the true power. This point is important in accurate testing of fractional horsepower motors, although it may be of no consequence when testing large motors. For general use, it is recommended that the circuit shown in Fig. 19-2a be used; when this circuit is used, the loss that must be subtracted from the wattmeter reading is always the loss in the potential coil, and, if all tests are taken at a single voltage, as is often the case, the same meter correction for losses will be applicable to all readings.

The loss in the potential coil may be expressed thus:

$$\text{Loss} = \frac{E^2}{R_v + R_m} \tag{19-7}$$

where E = actual voltage being measured.

    R_v = resistance of voltmeter.

    R_m = resistance of external multiplier.

It is possible to read the loss on the wattmeter itself by exciting *line* connections shown in Fig. 19-2a, leaving open the *load* connections. There are wattmeters that are provided with internal compensation for the loss in the potential coil; such wattmeters must be connected as in Fig. 19-2a and no correction made for the loss in its own potential coil.

19-12. Meter Connections for Single-phase Circuits.—Recommended meter connections for testing single-phase motors are shown in Fig. 19-3. A frequency meter—optional—is shown across the

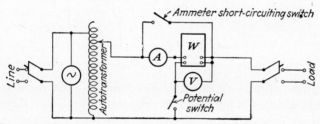

Fig. 19-3.—Instrument connections for metering single-phase power.

source of the power. Next in the circuit is the autotransformer for variable voltage control. It will be noted that the potential coil of the wattmeter, and also the voltmeter, are connected on the load side of the ammeter and wattmeter current coil. With this connection, it is necessary to subtract the loss in the potential coil of the wattmeter, also the loss in the voltmeter, from the actual wattmeter reading in order to obtain the true net watts. As suggested in the preceding paragraph, this loss can be read directly on the wattmeter in Fig. 19-3 by leaving the *load* and *ammeter short-circuiting* switches open and closing the *line* and *potential* switches. The *potential switch* shown is for the purpose of opening the potential circuit when the currents are being read. Also, the *ammeter short-circuiting switch* is provided to short-circuit the ammeter and current coil of the wattmeter; *it is*

*recommended that this switch be left closed at all times except when it is
desired to read either amperes or watts.* This precaution will save many
a meter! If much testing is done, it will be found desirable to make
all these connections permanently on some switchboard or in some
cabinet, leaving open and accessible only those connections necessary
for changing meters.

It will often be found convenient to determine the loss in the potential coil of the wattmeter, also the losses in the various voltmeters, at,
say 115 volts, and to mark each one of these values in some convenient
place or on a card in the meter case itself for future record.

19-13. Meter Connections for Polyphase Circuits. *a. Three-
phase Circuits.*—Three-phase circuits are usually metered by use of
two wattmeters which can be connected as shown in Fig. 19-4. In

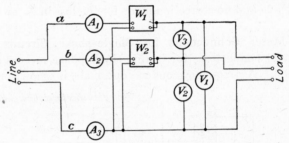

Fig. 19-4.—Instrument connections for metering three-phase circuits.

this diagram, two wattmeters, three voltmeters, and three ammeters
are shown, whereas in practice it is customary to use only three meters
altogether. In such a case, means for switching each meter to each
one of the various positions indicated in Fig. 19-4 have to be provided.
A polyphase wattmeter has two potential coils and two current coils,
and these are connected as if they were the two single meters in Fig.
19-4. Great care must be taken to connect these elements in corresponding positions in the circuit, instructions for which should be
given with the meter. If a polyphase wattmeter is used, it is a good
plan to open one line, as *a*, to give a single-phase load and then open
the other line, as *b*, to give a single-phase load again; in either case,
the wattmeter will give a positive reading if it is connected properly.

b. Determination of Sign of Smaller Wattmeter Reading.—On a
single-phase circuit, if a wattmeter reads backward when first connected, the connections to either the potential coil or the current coil
should be reversed, and the wattmeter will then read correctly. However, a backward deflection of one of the two meters of Fig. 19-4 does

not necessarily indicate that the meter was connected incorrectly. It may indicate only that the power factor of the load is less than 50 per cent; in such a case, one of the meters *should* read backward. At a load power factor of 50 per cent, one meter will read zero; at higher power factors, it will read positive, or forward. If a backward deflection is noted, the connections to either the potential or the current coil must be reversed in order to obtain a reading. It is usually preferable to reverse the connections to the potential coil, as this eliminates the necessity for opening the motor circuit. Now, if the load power factor is less than 50 per cent, the smaller wattmeter reading must be *subtracted* from the larger reading to obtain the total power; if the power factor is more than 50 per cent, the two readings must be *added*. It is always a problem, then, to determine whether to add or to subtract the two readings, since the power factor of the load is not always known. A simple test can be made by opening one line. For example, if W_2 in Fig. 19-4 reads less than W_1, we would open line *a* and allow the motor to run on single phase; under these conditions, a negative reading indicates that W_2 must be subtracted from W_1, whereas a positive reading would indicate that the two readings should be added. If W_1 is the smaller reading, line *b* should be opened. It is interesting to note that it is usually necessary to subtract the two wattmeter readings when taking the no-load input to a polyphase induction motor, and to add them when measuring full-load input. If a permanent or semipermanent test setup is made, the connections to the potential coil can be made through a reversing switch, the two positions of which can be marked + and −, respectively. This arrangement will save a lot of time and will help avoid mistakes.

If the test setup has been torn down and there is reason to doubt whether the smaller wattmeter reading is positive or negative, a simple test is afforded by the following relations:

$$\text{If } W_1 < 0.866EI, \ W_2 \text{ is } -$$
$$\text{If } W_1 > 0.866EI, \ W_2 \text{ is } +$$

This method affords a check on the sign of the smaller wattmeter reading except in cases where the smaller wattmeter reading is very small by comparison with the larger reading.

   c. Meter Losses in Three-phase Circuits.—If two wattmeters—or a single wattmeter used twice—are employed as shown in Fig. 19-4, it is recommended that the two readings be properly totaled, *i.e.*, added or subtracted as the case may be, before the correction is made for meter losses. If one voltmeter and one wattmeter are used twice, the total meter losses are

$$2 \times (\text{loss in potential coil} + \text{loss in voltmeter})$$

If separate meters are used, the losses in both wattmeter potential coils and in both voltmeters must be added to obtain total meter losses. The total meter losses are then subtracted from the total power indicated by the sum—or difference—of the wattmeter readings to obtain net power.

    d. Two-phase Three-wire Circuit.—Two-phase three-wire circuits can be metered by the same connections as those shown in Fig. 19-4. It is to be noted that the line *c* should be the common line of the circuit.

    e. Two-phase Four-wire Circuit.—For metering a two-phase four-wire circuit, the meters in each phase can be individually connected, as shown in Fig. 19-3. For total power, the net wattmeter readings should be added directly.

    19-14. Measurement of Mechanical Output.   *a. By Dynamometer.* —The best method for measuring the output of a fractional horse-

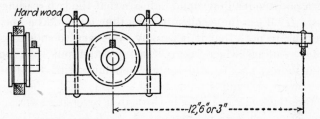

Fɪɢ. 19-5.—A prony brake for testing small motors.

power motor, particularly in the larger sizes, is by means of a dynamometer, for a brake arm heats too rapidly with motors of a ½- or ¾-hp rating. A dynamometer itself has no inherent limitations as to size, for they are built to test motors as low in rating as $\frac{1}{100}$ hp. Where dynamometers are not available, a prony brake, or a string or rope over a pulley, can be used.

    b. By Prony Brakes.—For most test purposes, a prony brake will be found convenient and generally quite satisfactory. A sketch of one is shown in Fig. 19-5. The diameter of the pulley wheel is not important, but the length of the brake arm *is*. Recommended standard lengths are 12, 6, and 3 in. The shorter brake arms are used for motors having low torques.

    The length of brake arm should be chosen, depending upon the scales available, so as to give an indication that can be read accurately.

Accurate scales, preferably of the gravity-balance type, should be used. It is sometimes helpful to make the pulley of the brake arm hollow so that it can be filled with water, the better to dissipate the heat generated. The brake arm can be provided with a balancing weight (not shown), or the tare can be measured and subtracted from the scale reading. When determining the tare, the thumb nuts should be loosened and it should be made certain that the brake arm is loose on the pulley. When brake-test readings are taken, no pressure should be exerted on the thumb nuts, for it may affect the reading; a recommended procedure is to set the load as nearly to the desired value as possible, adjusting the wing nuts by hand, and then to make the fine adjustment by tapping one nut with a bolt, screwdriver, or other small metal object.

c. By String or Cotton Sleeving.—Another method of testing the output of the smaller sizes of fractional horsepower motors is by means of a soft string. Cotton sleeving, such as is used for insulating armature leads, may be used. The string is looped one or more times around the pulley, leaving one end practically loose. The tension in the cord is adjusted by means of wrapping more or less turns around the pulley or by a very slight pull on the slack end of the cord. It is obvious that the pull on the slack end must be very small compared with the reading of the scales, as otherwise an error will be introduced into the reading. The method is illustrated in Fig. 19-6.

TESTS TO TAKE—SINGLE-PHASE INDUCTION MOTORS

19-15. A Commercial Test.—A commercial test on a motor is a simplified test that usually gives most of the desired information about the motor. It is a test such as is taken by manufacturers on each production motor before shipment. It is the sort of test that should be taken and recorded by repair shops. Such a test consists of the following:

a. No-load Readings.—Allow the motor to run at no load for a sufficient time for the bearings to warm up (10 min to $\frac{1}{2}$ hr or more will be satisfactory). Then measure the amperes, watts, and rpm at rated voltage. While the motor is running, it is advisable to check for unusual or abnormal noises, such as rubbing insulation, or dirt in the air gap; also it should be observed whether or not the rotor "floats" within the limits of the end play. That is, does the rotor seem to seek a position in the middle of the end play, or does it crowd excessively against one bearing or the other? This condition will indicate whether or not the rotor core is properly located with respect to the stator core.

Sometimes, however, the rotor core is offset intentionally (see Art. 8-16).

b. Full-load Readings.—Holding the output at rated full-load torque, measure the amperes and watts input, also the rpm. These readings can be compared with Table XXVI or with previous readings. Conversely, this table will serve as a guide in the selection of meters of the proper size.

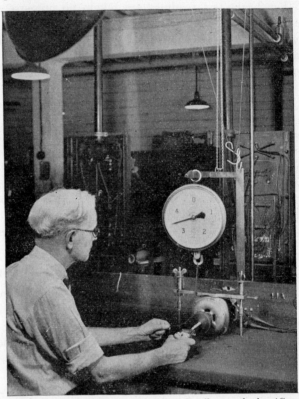

Fig. 19-6.—Loading a small motor by the cord-and-pulley method. (*Courtesy of Diehl Manufacturing Company.*)

c. Locked-rotor and Breakdown Torques.—The locked-rotor and breakdown torques should be taken. The method of taking these is described in more detail in Art. 19-16c, e. In the case of repulsion-start motors, the actual locked-rotor torque varies considerably with rotor position, and it may be desirable to take this torque at 50 rpm if a dynamometer is available; if a dynamometer is not available, only locked-rotor torque readings can be taken.

19-16. A Complete Engineering Test.—More complete information about a motor is often desired, and, for this reason, there are many other tests that may be taken, as described in the following paragraphs:

a. Cold Resistances.—The cold resistances of each of the windings should be carefully measured and the room temperature recorded. In the case of repulsion-start motors, the armature resistance should also be measured; for this purpose, the brushes should be lifted and pointed leads used, the points being pressed tightly against the commutator bars. The armature resistance is to be measured between bar 1 and bar $\left(\dfrac{\text{bars}}{\text{poles}} + 1\right)$. In many cases, it may be necessary to take a motor apart in order to measure the separate resistances of the several windings. For record purposes, the resistances so measured should all be corrected to a standard room temperature of 25°C by the following formula:

$$R_{25°C} = \frac{260}{235 + t}\, r_t \tag{19-8}$$

where $R_{25°C}$ = resistance at 25°C.

r_t = resistance at temperature t.

b. Locked-rotor Readings.—Locked-rotor readings on fractional horsepower motors can be taken at approximately rated voltage. The wattmeter, voltmeter, and ammeter, connected as shown in Fig. 19-3, should be read simultaneously, and the readings should be taken within 4 or 5 sec of the time of application of the voltage; for the windings heat rapidly and this heating affects the accuracy of the readings. It is not necessary that the line voltage be exactly rated voltage, but it should be set somewhere near the correct value, and all three meters must be read simultaneously as soon as the needles have settled down to a steady reading. Immediately after the reading, the primary resistance should be measured and recorded. With split-phase motors, a separate set of locked-rotor readings of both main and auxiliary windings should be taken; when the readings on one winding are being taken, the other winding need not be excited. When locked-rotor readings are taken on a motor of the repulsion type, the brushes should all be raised and the commutator bars short-circuited together; this can be done readily with the axial or cylindrical type of commutator by wrapping several turns of bare fine copper wire around the commutator. A similar procedure, though slightly more difficult of execution, can be followed with the radial type commutators. With straight repulsion, or repulsion-start induction motors (but not repulsion induction motors) a reading of locked watts and amperes should be taken with the brushes lifted but with the commutator on open circuit; under this condition, the current input will be only slightly more than half of the no-load amperes.

c. Breakdown Torques.—The breakdown torque of an induction motor is the maximum torque that the motor will develop at rated voltage and frequency, without an abrupt drop in speed. Breakdown torque is taken by increasing the torque load on the motor until the motor "pulls out," *i.e.*, drops off in speed sharply or stops entirely.

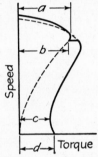 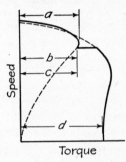

Fig. 19-7.—Typical speed-torque curves of single-phase motors illustrating definitions of the various kinds of torque.

a. Breakdown torque.
b. Switching torque.
c. Pull-up torque.
d. Locked-rotor torque.

Care must be taken to increase the load slowly enough so that inertia effects do not increase the apparent breakdown torque.

d. Switching and Pull-up Torques. **Switching torque** is a term used in recent A.S.A. and A.I.E.E. standards to denote the minimum external torque developed by a motor as it accelerates through the switch operating speed. This torque is an essential characteristic of any single-phase motor with an automatic switching mechanism such as a starting switch or short-circuiter. (In the first edition of this book, this was called "pull-in torque"—for want of any officially recognized name. Now, use of the term *pull-in torque* is restricted to synchronous motors.) **Pull-up torque** of an a-c motor is the minimum external torque developed by the motor during the acceleration of the motor from rest to the speed at which breakdown torque occurs.

Definitions of the various kinds of torque in single-phase motors are illustrated in Fig. 19-7. It will be noted that, in some cases, the switching and pull-up torques are identical; in other cases, they are not. Formal definitions of these torques are given in the Glossary.

The procedure for measuring the switching torque of a capacitor-start motor, where the switch operating speed is below the crossover point of the two speed-torque curves (Fig. 5-4), is different from the procedure to be followed in taking the switching torque of a repulsion-start motor, where the crossover point is usually below the operating speed of the short-circuiter (Fig. 10-1). For taking the switching torque of a capacitor-start motor, start with a light load, increasing the load gradually by means of the brake arm until the motor "breaks down," *i.e.*, falls off in speed abruptly onto the starting connection. Since the torque on the starting connection is greater than the torque on the running connection, the rotor will accelerate, and the switch will again operate; if the brake arm were adjusted for the breakdown torque of the motor, the motor would "pump," *i.e.*, would pass alternately from starting to running connections, and vice versa. If the torque of the brake arm is slowly reduced by loosening the wing nuts, the motor eventually will cease pumping and stay on the running connection. This highest value of torque at which the motor will cease pumping and stay on the running connection is the switching torque. The switching-torque test of a repulsion motor is begun with the motor on the starting connection; the brake-arm torque is adjusted to a very high value and then slowly decreased, allowing the motor to come up to speed; at a certain value of torque, *viz.*, at the switching torque, the short-circuiter will operate suddenly, and then the motor will come up to speed. The lesser of the two torques developed by the motor at the operating speed of the short-circuiter is the switching torque.

e. Locked-rotor Torque and Current.—The locked-rotor torque of a fractional horsepower motor varies with rotor position. One method of measuring this torque is to obtain seven or eight square pieces of wood, $\frac{3}{16}$ in. thick by approximately 2 in. square. The whole pile can be set on the scales and the brake arm set on top of the complete pile. The tare is determined with the blocks in position. The locked-rotor torque is measured with the complete set of blocks; then one block is removed *but left on the scales* and the locked-rotor torque measured in the second position; then the second block is removed from the pile *but left on the scales* and the torque again noted; and so on, repeating until the torque has been taken in all of the positions. When taking these tests, the voltage should be held at rated line voltage, and the current should be noted with an ammeter and recorded. The readings should be taken as quickly as possible to prevent overheating of the motor.   In the case of capacitor-start or two-value capacitor motors, the capacitor volts should also be measured.   Only the maximum and minimum values of locked-rotor torque need be recorded.   An alternative method of testing is to turn the motor over onto the round part of the frame, rolling the motor slowly through a small angle and noting the maximum and minimum values of the locked-rotor torque.   If this procedure is followed, the motor should be rolled away from the scales so that the bearing friction is subtracted from the developed torque, instead of added to it, as would be the case if the motor were rolled toward the scales.

f. Running Saturation.—The purpose of the running saturation test is to aid in the segregation of losses; this test permits the separate determination of the friction and windage, also the core losses of the motor.   With the motor running at no load, take a series of readings of volts, amperes, and watts, starting at 130 per cent of rated voltage and varying the voltage downward until the motor loses speed rapidly or until the current starts to increase.   If the motor is a repulsion-start motor and it is desired to measure the brush friction, two input readings should be taken at approximately half voltage, one with all brushes up and the other with all brushes down; the difference is the brush friction loss.   In the case of capacitor motors, only the main winding should be excited for this test.   Amperes and net watts should be plotted against voltage and the net watts curve extrapolated to zero volts to give the value of friction and windage (see Art. 19-24).

g. Brake Test.—The purpose of the brake test is to determine the variation of the power factor, efficiency, watts, amperes, and rpm with changes in load.   Starting at as near breakdown torque as possible, hold the load constant at one value of torque, and read the watts input, amperes, rpm, slip by stroboscopic means, and torque. Repeat these readings for different settings of torque down to no load. The horsepower output is computed by one of the formulas in Art. 20-23.   The readings may all be plotted against torque or against horsepower output.   Such a curve sheet is shown in Fig. 19-9.

If a capacitor motor (see Art. 5-1) is being tested, readings should be taken of the separate watts and current input to each of the two phases, also the total line amperes and watts.   For these tests, a slight modification of the connections shown in Fig. 19-4 may be used; lines *a* and *b* are connected to one side of the line, and *c* to the other side; the load side of line *a* is connected to the main phase, and the load side of line *b* to the auxiliary phase.   With these connections,

W_1 reads main-phase watts, W_2 reads auxiliary-phase watts, and A_3 reads line amperes. If the current coil of the wattmeter is connected at A_3 and the potential coil in place of V_1 or V_2, the total input watts will be measured. With this type of motor, the capacitor volts also should be measured. It is desirable, although not necessary, to measure the voltage across the auxiliary winding. The brake test may be plotted as described in the preceding paragraph, except that a second curve sheet is used to plot main-phase amperes, watts, auxiliary-phase amperes, watts, and capacitor volts; all of these quantities may be plotted vs. torque or vs. horsepower output.

h. Full-load Saturation.—The purpose of the full-load saturation test is to determine how the full-load performance of the motor varies with a change in line voltage. Holding the output torque of the motor constant at full load, vary the applied voltage; readings are to be taken at seven voltages, *viz.*, one reading at rated line voltage, three in steps of 10 per cent each above line voltage, and three more in steps of 10 per cent each below line voltage. These readings should be plotted against voltage.

i. Temperature Run.—Usually it is not practicable or feasible to take a temperature run at full load by means of a brake arm; for, if the motor is of any substantial horsepower rating, the brake arm will get too hot, and, even if it does not, continuous attention is required for 2 or 3 hr. If a dynamometer is available, the output torque can be held constant at rated value. If not, the motor can be belted up to a generator or some other load, and the load can be adjusted until the watts input shows that the motor is delivering full-load output. Thermometers (or thermocouples) should be placed on the hottest accessible parts of the frame and the primary copper, and read during the run; they should also be placed on the secondary copper and secondary iron after the run is shut down. Record volts, watts, amperes, slip, and temperature every 15 min throughout the test—unless the motor has an intermittent rating—until the temperatures become constant. The additional thermometers should be preheated to the expected rise before the motor is shut down and then immediately placed in position. The hot resistance of the winding should be recorded immediately after shutdown.

Unless it is known that the motor operates on iron, the temperature run should be taken with the motor mounted on wood. (An appreciable amount of heat can be conducted away by the feet if they are mounted directly on a steel base.) Also, care should be taken to shield the motor from drafts, particularly if it is an enclosed motor.

j. Speed-torque Tests.—Dynamometers are necessary for taking a complete speed-torque test of a single-phase induction motor; neither the prony-brake nor the cord-and-pulley method is satisfactory for obtaining points between the breakdown and zero speeds. For most satisfactory results, the field of the dynamometer should be connected to a fixed-voltage d-c bus in series with a field rheostat; the armature of the dynamometer should be connected to a separate d-c bus, the voltage of which is preferably adjustable. The procedure for obtaining a point on the speed-torque curve is as follows: the dynamometer is started as a motor with full field and at a low armature voltage to give a low operating speed; the a-c line voltage is adjusted to a value slightly above rated value, then the switch is closed to apply the voltage to the motor being tested; motor voltage is quickly adjusted to rated value; and the torque and speed are both simultaneously noted and recorded. Generally speaking, the less the speed changes when the a-c power is applied, the easier it is to obtain good readings. In order to avoid overheating the motor and thereby obtaining false readings, it is essential to apply the a-c voltage to the motor for not more than 4 or 5 sec for each reading and, further, the motor must be allowed to cool between readings.

k. Winding-ratio Test.—This test is necessary only in capacitor-type motors that employ a capacitor on the running connection; the purpose of it is to obtain data necessary to segregate the losses in this type of motor. Run the motor at rated voltage E_m, on the main winding only, and measure E_a', the auxiliary-winding voltage. Impress E_a, arbitrarily chosen as approximately 18 per cent more than E_a' (the underlying idea is to operate the motor at normal air-gap flux), upon the auxiliary winding, and run the motor on the auxiliary winding; then measure E_m', the voltage across the main winding. The winding ratio is

$$K = \sqrt{\frac{E_a'}{E_m} \times \frac{E_a}{E_m'}} \tag{19-9}$$

where
$$K = \frac{\text{effective conductors in auxiliary winding}}{\text{effective conductors in main winding}}$$

l. Test on Capacitor Units.—On the running connection of the capacitor unit, impress a voltage equal to the voltage measured during the brake test at full load, and record the watts and amperes input at this voltage. If the motor is a two-value capacitor motor, repeat this reading on the starting connection; this reading should be taken at the capacitor voltage observed on the locked-rotor test described in paragraph *e* (see also Arts. 6-8, 8-13).

TEST TO TAKE—OTHER TYPES

19-17. Adjustable Varying-speed Fan Motors.—Adjustable varying-speed fan motors of the type described in Chaps. VIII and IX should, in addition to the other usual tests, be checked for *minimum starting volts* on the low-speed connection. The controller should be set to give the lowest possible speed, and it should be determined what is the minimum line voltage required to start the fan in any position. It is to be noted that more voltage is required to start the fan in some positions than in others. *A minimum starting voltage* of 85 to 90 per cent of normal rated line voltage should be satisfactory.

Readings on any connection other than high speed should be taken with the motor driving its fan, since the speed depends to a large extent upon the load, as explained in Arts. 8-5 and 8-6.

19-18. Polyphase Induction Motors.—A commercial test on a polyphase induction motor comprises the same tests as a commercial test on a single-phase induction motor, which was described in Art. 19-15, except that it is necessary to measure polyphase power instead of single-phase power input.

Likewise, a complete engineering test can be taken on a polyphase induction motor, in general, in the same way as on a single-phase induction motor, as described in Art. 19-16, with these exceptions: When locked-rotor readings are taken on a three-phase motor, all phases must be excited simultaneously. With two-phase motors, it is not necessary, but it is permissible, to excite both phases at the same time. (When taking locked-rotor readings on single-phase motors, it is the usual practice to excite only one winding at a time.) The running saturation, brake test, full-load saturation, and temperature run should be taken on the polyphase induction motor in the same fashion as on the single-phase induction motor, except that the input is polyphase. There is, of course, no winding-ratio test for polyphase motors.

More elaborate and more detailed tests have been described by the A.I.E.E.[2] The A.I.E.E. Test Code was drafted more specifically for integral horsepower motors, but many helpful hints and suggestions will be found in it for testing fractional horsepower motors.

19-19. D-c Motors.—The testing methods for d-c motors generally resemble those for a-c motors, except that it is preferable to use d-c meters instead of a-c meters. Tests on d-c motors may likewise be divided into two classifications: commercial and engineering.

a. Commercial Tests.—A commercial test on a d-c motor should include the following:

1. Cold resistances of all windings separately. Measure and record the air temperature.

2. Mark the neutral setting on machines on which a brush-shifting device is provided, and set the brushes for the proper position.

3. *No-load readings.*—Record line volts, line amperes, field amperes, and rpm.

4. *Full-load readings.*—Record line volts, line amperes, rpm, and torque. Torque is to be held at full-load rated output.

b. Engineering Tests.

1. *Brake test.*—Warm the motor up to normal operating temperature, and take a series of readings starting at approximately double full-load torque; or if this is impossible, start as near breakdown torque as possible, and decrease the load, taking the last reading at no load. On series motors, the no-load reading may have to be omitted unless the preceding readings indicate that the speed will be within a safe limit. The resistance of the winding, and the air temperature, should be taken just before and after this series of readings. Read and record volts, line amperes, shunt-field amperes, rpm, and torque.

2. *Running light losses.*—Operate the motor at no load at rated speed, and measure separately the inputs to the field and to the armature. The armature input less armature copper loss and brush-contact I^2R losses will be equal to friction and windage, brush friction, and core loss.

3. *Locked-rotor torque.*—On motors rated at ½ hp or less, take the locked-rotor torque at rated voltage, in both directions of rotation (if possible), with the armature in several different positions over one slot pitch, in the same manner as described in Art. 19-16e. Record armature volts, armature amperes, field volts, field amperes, and torque. Also indicate whether the test was taken at full voltage or at double full-load current. If the motor is rated at more than ½ hp, it is desirable to excite the field separately and impress only enough voltage on the armature to obtain approximately two times full-load current, measuring the locked-rotor torque in different positions.

4. *Temperature run.*—A temperature run on a d-c motor is similar to the temperature run on an a-c motor described in Art. 19-16.

19-20. Universal Motors.—In general, the technique of testing universal motors will be the same as that of testing d-c series motors, as described in Art. 19-19. When taking a brake test on a universal motor, however, it will usually be found more satisfactory to take the series of readings at different speeds, holding the motor at a fixed speed rather than at a fixed torque.

A complete curve test on a universal motor should include a brake test at 60 cycles, another brake test at 25 cycles, and a third brake test on direct current.

19-21. Reluctance-type Synchronous Motors.—Reluctance-type synchronous motors may have several different types of stator windings, as discussed in Chap. XV, and they may generally be tested as if they were induction motors, except that the pull-in and pull-out torques should also be measured. **Pull-in torque** of a synchronous motor is defined by A.S.A. as "the maximum constant torque under which the motor will pull its connected load into synchronism, at rated voltage and frequency." By this definition, pull-in torque is greatly affected by the inertia of the connected load. A.S.A. get around this difficulty by simply stating that the pull-in torque cannot be determined without the WR^2 as well as the torque of the load. The A.I.E.E. Single-phase Test Code gets around the difficulty by stating that the pull-in torque shall be "measured with no appreciable external inertia." Pull-in torque so measured is of little significance if the load has high inertia. **Pull-out torque** of a synchronous motor is defined by A.S.A. as the "maximum sustained torque which the motor will develop at synchronous speed for one minute, with rated voltage applied at rated frequency . . . ." For fractional horsepower motors, the 1-min provision need not be considered as applying.

19-22. Dielectric Tests.—Dielectric tests are taken primarily to determine whether the windings are adequately insulated from ground. A.I.E.E.[4] suggests the following procedure for making dielectric tests:

The dielectric test should be applied between all electrical circuits and the frame of the motor. All leads (except ground leads) must be connected together during this test in order to prevent severe strains which might otherwise occur. Capacitors used in capacitor type motors must be left connected to the windings in the normal manner. In making this test care should be taken to impress only the desired value of voltage on the windings. A sudden application of the test voltage may result in surges of considerable overvoltage. One method of overcoming this difficulty is to use in the primary circuit of the transformer a variable resistor which is cut out after the potential has been applied. An alternative way is to use a suitable choke in the primary to limit surges. It is possible to obtain appreciable over-voltage on the machine through a resonant or partial resonant condition between the capacity of the windings to ground and the leakage reactance of the testing transformer. For most accurate results, the output voltage should be measured by a direct-reading electrostatic voltmeter or by an oscillograph. For more details reference may be had to A.I.E.E. Standard No. 4—June, 1940.

Specified voltages for dielectric tests have been established by Nema as given in Table XX.

TABLE XX.—DIELECTRIC TEST VOLTAGES FOR FRACTIONAL HORSEPOWER MOTORS

	Duration of application of test voltage	
	1 min	1 sec
Universal motors, all ratings..................	900	1,080
A-c and d-c motors:		
½ hp and larger, all voltages...............	2E + 1,000	2.4E + 1,200
Less than ½ hp, but rated more than 250 volts.	2E + 1,000	2.4E + 1,200
Less than ½ hp, 250 volts or less...........	900	1,080
Armatures or rotors of a-c motors with insulated windings not connected to the line (repulsion types):		
½ hp and larger..........................	1,000	1,200
Less than ½ hp, but rated more than 250 volts.	1,000	1,200
Less than ½ hp, 250 volts or less...........	900	900

NOTE: Voltages given in this table are for clean, dry, new machines tested at the factory. When testing machines that have been in service for some time, the author recommends reducing these voltages by at least 25 per cent.

SEGREGATION OF LOSSES

19-23. General—Polyphase Motors.—Segregation of losses means the breaking down of the total losses in a motor into their several components, each one of which can be separately measured and the whole added together to give the total losses. If the losses are known for any given input, the efficiency may be determined; the value so obtained is known as **conventional efficiency.** If both the input and output are measured, the total loss is the difference between these two values. Segregation of losses affords a convenient means for checking the accuracy of an input-output test. The methods for segregating the losses of polyphase induction motors are so generally well known—as well as being covered in detail in the A.I.E.E. Test Code[2]— that they will be mentioned only very briefly here. The components of loss are as follows:

1. *I²R loss in the primary windings.*
2. *Rotor copper loss*, which is equal to

$$\text{Slip} \times (\text{stator input} - \text{stator } I^2R \text{ loss})$$

3. *Core loss and friction*, which is equal to no-load watts input minus primary *I²R* losses. Friction loss can be separated from core loss by extrapolating the no-load saturation curve of watts down to zero voltage.

4. *Stray load losses.*—Opinion varies considerably as to the importance of stray load losses in fractional horsepower motors. In many cases, they can be omitted from calculations.

19-24. Single-phase Induction Motors.—The underlying theory of segregation of losses in single-phase motors has been developed in an article published in *Electrical Engineering*[5] and is somewhat too involved to be discussed in detail here. A practical form for recording and analyzing the necessary tests is given in Fig. 19-8, which is applicable both to motors employing a running capacitor and to straight single-phase induction motors. The use of the form is illustrated by an analysis of a test on a two-value capacitor motor, of the type shown in Fig. 6-1, tested without the running capacitor in the circuit and again with the running capacitor in the circuit. The numbers in this figure that are underlined with a dotted line represent values taken directly from test without computation, as follows:

E_m, I_m, W_m, and line 5 are taken from the locked reading on the main winding.

E (line 9) is the rated voltage.

I_o' is the current taken from the running saturation curve at E' volts.

Lines 17 and 19 are measured by bridge as indicated.

W_o' is the number of watts read from the running saturation curve at E' volts.

s, I_1 are from the brake test, at the full-load point, taken when the motor was operating as a single-phase induction motor with no capacity in the circuit.

How to fill out the rest of the form is more or less self-explanatory. In line 10, if the motor is not a capacitor motor, use

$$1.15 \times r_{1m} \times I_1 \times \text{power factor}$$

instead of the quantities shown. The friction (line 24) is determined from the running saturation curve which is extended to zero volts, and the watts input at zero volts is read from the curve; from this value is subtracted the

$$\text{"Min. Cu. loss"} = (\text{minimum current})^2 \times (\text{item 20})$$

The remainder of the analysis of losses is given in lines 32 to 47, inclusive, under "As 1-ϕ motor." It is to be noted that the scratch-work calculations for lines 35 and 36 are carried out at the right under "Note."

The foregoing method of analysis is directly applicable to split-phase motors, reactor-start motors, capacitor-start motors, or repulsion-start motors.

		WINDINGS ONLY		AUX.WDG. WITH CAP.	CAPACITOR UNIT ONLY	
		MAIN	AUXILIARY		STG.C.	RNG.C.
1	Locked volts	E_m 110	E_a 110	E_{ac} 110	E_c *120	**180
2	Locked amps., sec. shorted	I_m 16.6	I_a 8.3	I_{ac} 7.7	I_c 7.15	1.08
3	Locked watts, sec. shorted	W_m 1260	W_a 640	W_{ac} 710	W_c 147	10.1
4	Total res., $R=W/I^2$	R_m 4.57	R_a 9.28	R_{ac} 12.0	R_c 2.88	8.61
5	Pri. res. after locked rdg.	1.48	3.49	Z_{ac} 14.3	Z_c 16.8	166
6	④ - ⑤	3.09	5.79	X_{ac} 7.75	X_c 16.55	166
7	Impedance, $Z=E/I$	Z_m 6.62	Z_a 13.26	E_a 102	Mfd 160.1	16.0
8	Sh.ckt. reactance $X=\sqrt{Z^2-R^2}$	X_m 4.79	X_a 9.45	E_c 131	E_cI_c	

9	No load volts	E 110	Cap. element volts
10	$\dfrac{1.68}{1.15r_{1m}} \times \dfrac{1.36}{A}$ or $\dfrac{x}{1.15r_{1m}} \dfrac{x}{I_1} \dfrac{x}{P.F.}$	2.3	*Cap. volts locked ; ** Cap. volts @ F.L.
11	Induced volts @ F.L. ⑨ - ⑩	E' 107.7	
12	Mag. amps. @ E' volts	I'_o 2.73	
13	$X_o = 2E'/I'_o - X$	X_o 74.2	
14	$K_r = X_o - X/X_o$	K_r 0.935	Actual k from design data =

Wdg. ratio; $k=\sqrt{\dfrac{E'_a=122.5}{E_m=110} \times \dfrac{E_a=145}{E'_m=99}} = 1.274$

15	r_2 cold (⑥/K_r) × (⑰/⑤)	r_2 3.26		WATTS	AMPERES @ F.L.		
16	$0.5K_r r_2$	1.525	@ F.L.	TOTAL	REAL	REACTIVE	
17	r_1 cold @ 25°C.	r_1 1.463	Main ph.	W_{1m} 150	I_{1m} 2.31	A=1.362	B=-1.87
18	r_o cold = ⑯ + ⑰	r_o 2.988	Aux. ph.	W_{1a} 99	I_{1a} 1.09	g=0.90	h=0.61
19	Pri. res. after rng. sat.	1.64	Line	(246)249	(2.55)2.56	2.26	-1.26
20	r_o hot = r_o × ⑲/⑰	3.34	26 I_{1m}^2	5.33	A_h	0.831	
21	No load. Watts @ E' volts	W'_o 56.0	27 $(kI_{1a})^2$	1.93	Bg	-1.683	
22	$I^2R@E'volts = I'^2_o r_o$ hot	24.9	28 $I_{1m}^2+(kI_{1a})^2$	7.26	A_h-Bg	2.514	
23	Core loss+friction = ㉑ - ㉒	31.1	29 $2k(A_h-Bg)$	6.40	$A=W_{1m}/E$		
24	Friction [min.cu.loss = 1.9]	11.0	30 ㉘ + ㉙	13.66	$B=\pm\sqrt{I_{1m}^2-A^2}$		
25	Core loss @ F.L.	20.1	31 ㉘ - ㉙	0.86			

		AS 1-Φ MOTOR		AS CAP. MOTOR		Note:
32	r_2/X_o hot = 1.15r_2/X_o	r_2/X_o	0.0505	r_2/X_o	0.0505	
33	Slip @ full load	s	0.0417	s	0.0333	
34	Slip of backward field	2-s	1.958	2-s	1.967	
35	sR_f		0.711		0.531	
36	$(2-s)R_b$		1.753		1.753	
37	Amperes @ F.L.	I_1	3.75			
38	Sec. $I^2R(f)$	$I_1^2 \times$ ㉟	10.0	㉚×㉟	7.25	
39	Sec. $I^2R(b)$	$I_1^2 \times$ ㊱	24.6	㉛×㊱	1.51	
40	Main wdg.cu.loss; r_{1m} hot = 1.68	$I_1^2 r_{1m}$	23.6	$I_{1m}^2 r_{1m}$	9.0	
41	Aux. wdg. cu. loss; r_{1a} hot = 3.97			$I_{1a}^2 r_{1a}$	4.7	
42	Cap. unit loss			$I_{1a}^2 R_c$	10.2	
43	Core loss + friction	㉓	31.1	㉓	31.1	
44	Total losses @ F.L.		89.3		63.3	
45	Output		186.4		186.4	
46	Output + losses		275.7		249.7	
47	Efficiency by losses		67.6		74.7	

$sR_f = \dfrac{1.15 \times ⑯ = 1.753·}{1 + \left(\dfrac{㉜}{㉝}\right)^2}$

1+1.465=2.465
1+2.30=3.30

$(2-s)R_b = \dfrac{1.15 \times ⑯ = 1.753}{1 + \left(\dfrac{㉜}{㉞}\right)^2}$

TYPE *FT.*   FRAME *B145*   CALC. REF.____

HP *¼*   VOLTS *110*   CYCLES *60*   POLES *4*   R.P.M.____

D-SPEC.____   S.O.____   SIG.____

SERVICE____   DATE *2-5-38*   CAP. L.____   MOT. L.____

FIG. 19-8.—A form for analyzing the test results and segregating the losses of either a single-phase induction motor or a capacitor motor.

19-25. Capacitor Motors.—The test analysis form of Fig. 19-8 is applicable to motors employing a running capacitor, such as shown in Fig. 6-1, 6-2, 7-1, or 7-6, but does not apply directly to such motors as are shown in Fig. 7-2, 7-3, 8-5b, 8-5c, 9-1, or 9-2. In using the form, items 1 to 25, except for item 10 as previously noted, are determined and computed exactly as described in Art. 19-24, as if the motor had no running capacitor. The winding ratio K is determined from the winding-ratio test. W_{1m}, W_{1a}, I_{1m}, and I_{1a} are read from the brake test as a capacitor motor. The main-winding current I_{1m} is broken up into its real and reactive components A and B by the formulas given. The measured value of watts is 246, entered in () to compare with 249, which is the sum of the two wattmeter readings. The measured line amperes 2.55 is compared with the value 2.56, computed from

$$\text{Line amperes} = \sqrt{(A + g)^2 + (B + h)^2} \qquad (19\text{-}10)$$

The close agreement between the two figures of watts, also between the two figures of current, is a check on and an indication of the accuracy of the tests.

Items 26 to 31 are self-explanatory. The remainder of the analysis of losses is given in lines 32 to 47, under "As Cap. Motor." The scratchwork calculations for items 35 and 36 are shown in the blank space under "Note," together with the similar previous calculations.

The effect of a running capacitor on a single-phase induction motor is strikingly illustrated by a comparison of lines 32 to 47 in Fig. 19-8. The rotor and stator copper losses are greatly reduced, improving the efficiency and substantially reducing the slip. This comparison was noted in Art. 6-3.

APPLICATION TESTS

How to select the proper motor for any specific application has been made the principal subject of Chap. XX. After a preliminary choice has been made, it is advisable to obtain a motor of the type, horsepower, and speed rating selected, and run an application test in order to determine accurately the power and torque requirements of the appliance. When possible, it is desirable to run application tests on a new stiff machine and on a well-worn-in machine.

19-26. Determination of the Power Requirements.—The test motor should be set up on the device and wired to a source of power through meters, as shown in Fig. 19-3. The load on the motor should be varied, subjecting the appliance to all the possible and conceivable conditions likely to be encountered in service; for each different significant value of load, the motor voltage should be adjusted to rated value and readings taken of the watts and amperes input.

These readings of watts and amperes input can be interpreted *accurately* in terms of motor output watts—or horsepower—only by use of a *brake test on that particular motor.* For this reason, it is recommended that a brake test be taken on the particular motor used. If only one load point is significant, a complete brake test is unnecessary; instead, the motor can be set up with prony brake and scales, and the brake adjusted to give the same input *watts* as was read on the application test. The scales will then read directly the mechanical torque

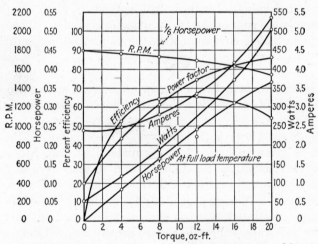

Fig. 19-9.—A brake test on a single-phase induction motor rated at ⅙ hp, 110 volts, 60 cycles, 1725 rpm.

required by the appliance. A brake test can generally be obtained from the manufacturer of the motor, but as this test was taken on a different motor—though of the same design—there is slightly more chance for error. Moreover, should the meters used on the application test be slightly off calibration, there will be no error in the output horsepower if the brake test on the motor is carefully taken *with the same meters,* for the meter errors will automatically cancel out. Sometimes it may not be possible to take or obtain a brake test because of a lack of suitable equipment or because the motor is built into the appliance—as in a hermetically sealed refrigerator. In such a case, it is usually possible to determine the losses as described in Arts. 19-23 to 19-25, for any desired input; the losses are then subtracted from the input to give the mechanical load. This procedure is somewhat more tedious and time-consuming than the direct measurement of the mechanical output.

A method often used to gauge the output is to measure simply the amperes input and compare it with the nameplate reading, assuming that the motor output is proportional to the amperes. This method is unsound, false, and absolutely unreliable in the case of single-phase induction motors, but it may be used for d-c motors. For example, in Fig. 19-9, the full-load current is 2.8 amp; if the load is adjusted to give 3.8 amp, this represents a 35 per cent increase in current, but the output torque is increased from 8 to 14.4 oz-ft, an 80 per cent increase. In this case, a 35 per cent increase in current means an 80 per cent increase in torque. From full load to no load, a 100 per cent decrease in output, the current decreases only 15 per cent. Moreover, the no-load current on different motors of the same design may vary as much as 10 per cent. *Thus a comparison of tested amperes with nameplate amperes is most unreliable as an indication of the motor load, and this method is subject to grave errors.*

19-27. Determination of the Torque Requirements.—Locked-rotor torque is almost never a problem where universal motors are used, and the terms **switching, pull-up,** and **breakdown torque** are of no significance. The discussion that follows applies to motors of the induction type and not to universal motors.

To measure the torque requirements, determine

1. Minimum voltage required to start the load, in any position.
2. Minimum voltage required to bring motor up to above half speed.
3. Minimum voltage required for motor to transfer from the starting connection to the running connection.
4. Minimum voltage at which motor will carry load without an abrupt drop in speed.

When these tests are being taken, the appliance should be adjusted or set to give the maximum load anticipated in service. If the locked-rotor, pull-up, switching, and breakdown torques of the test motor are known at rated voltage, the four readings given above can be interpreted on the assumption that each one of the torques varies as the square of the applied voltage. Tests 1, 2, 3, and 4 then give, respectively, locked-rotor torque, pull-up torque, switching torque, and breakdown torque required by the appliance.

In many cases, it may be desirable or necessary to consult a reliable motor manufacturer as doubtful points may crop up. Tests such as those just described are often sufficient for the user to select the proper motor himself; but, in any case, they will assist the manufacturer to make his recommendations.

Bibliography

1. "Standard Handbook for Electrical Engineers," 7th ed., McGraw-Hill Book Company, Inc., New York, 1941.
2. "Test Code for Polyphase Induction Machines," A.I.E.E. No. 500, August, 1937, American Institute of Electrical Engineers, New York.
3. "Test Code for Direct-current Machines," A.I.E.E. No. 501, American Institute of Electrical Engineers, New York.
4. "Test Code for Single-phase Motors," A.I.E.E. No. 502, American Institute of Electrical Engineers, New York.
5. VEINOTT, C. G.: Segregation of Losses in Single-phase Induction Motors, *Elec. Eng.*, December, 1935, pp. 1302–1306.

CHAPTER XX

SELECTING A MOTOR FOR THE JOB

Often the prospective user of a fractional horsepower motor wishes to start "from scratch" and determine what motor is best suited to his own particular requirements, even though common usage has made one particular type of motor standard for similar applications. This chapter is written primarily to assist this kind of user in determining the proper motor for his application. His task will become easier as the new Nema standards,[9] adopted in 1946, come into universal use; these standards make the horsepower rating on the nameplate tell more precisely what the motor will do (see Art. 20-4, last paragraph).

20-1. General-purpose and Special-purpose Motors.—Fractional horsepower electric motors fall into two broad classes: **general-purpose motors,** which are designed for a wide variety of applications; and **special-purpose motors,** which are built for particular applications. Requirements and specifications for general-purpose, and for a number of special-purpose, motors have been established by Nema. Although the use of a special motor is sometimes justified, first consideration should be given to the use of either a general-purpose motor or a standardized special-purpose motor.[1,5] By so doing, the user usually gains lower prices, greater ease in obtaining new motors, more sources of supply, greater ease in obtaining service, and more general all-round satisfaction.

GENERAL-PURPOSE MOTORS

20-2. Selection of the Type.—A comparison of the principal characteristics of 13 major types of motors is given in Table XXI. Each of the characteristics listed may be a factor in selecting the type of motor. The kind of *power supply* available necessarily narrows down the number of possible types to be considered. Single-phase motors can be used on polyphase circuits, but polyphase motors are not suitable for operation on single-phase circuits. *Horsepower* and *speed* ratings required are important because most types are not available in the whole range of ratings; however, by using a belted or a geared drive, almost any speed can be obtained from any type.

[9] For numbered references, see Bibliography at end of this chapter.

TABLE XXI.—CHARACTERISTICS OF FRACTIONAL

	Alternating				
	Single-phase				
	Split-phase types			Capacitor-start	Perm. split capacitor
	General-purpose	High-torque	Two-speed pole-changing		
Schematic diagram of connections. Arrangements shown are typical or representative; most of the types illustrated have numerous other arrangements which are also used.					
Characteristic speed-torque curves. Ordinates are speed; 1 division = for all a-c motors, 20% of syn. rpm; for universal motors, 1000 rpm; for d-c motors, 20% of full-load rpm. Each abscissa division = 100% of full-load torque.			HIGH LOW		FAN CURVE
Rotor construction..........................	Squirrel-cage	Squirrel-cage	Squirrel-cage	Squirrel-cage	Squirrel-cage
Built-in automatic starting mechanism..........	Centrifugal switch	Centrifugal switch	Centrifugal switch	Centrifugal switch	None required
Horsepower ratings commonly available.........	1/20–1/3	1/6–1/3	1/8–3/4	1/8–3/4	1/20–3/4
Usual rated full-load speeds (for 60-cycle a-c motors; also d-c motors)	3450, 1725, 1140, 865	1725	1725/1140 1725/865	3450, 1725, 1140, 865	1620, 1080, 820
Speed classification...........................	Constant	Constant	Two-speed	Constant	Constant, or adjustable varying
Means used for speed control..................	....	....	Two-speed switch	....	2-speed switch or autotransformer
Comparative torques { Locked-rotor.............	Moderate	High	Moderate	Very high	Low
Comparative torques { Breakdown..............	Moderate	High	Moderate	High	Moderate
Radio interference, running...................	None	None	None	None	None
During acceleration...........................	One click	One click	Two clicks	One click	None
Approximate comparative costs { Below 1/20 hp....	....	....	....	....	....
between types, for same { 1/20–1/4 hp.......	100	75	210	125	140
horsepower rating { 1/3–3/4 hp.......	80	54	150	100	100–110

General remarks

Standard motors are ordinarily designed to operate in ambient temperatures from 10 to 40°C (50 to 104°F). Variations in line voltage of plus or minus 10%, or variations in frequency of plus or minus 5% are allowable.

Locked-rotor currents for single-phase motors, except split-phase high-torque and synchronous types, usually do not exceed the following limits established by NEMA:

Rating, hp	Amperes at	
	115 volts	230 volts
1/6 and smaller..........	20	10
1/4..........................	23	11½
1/3..........................	31	15½
1/2..........................	45	22½
3/4..........................	61	30½

Fractional horsepower motors are built for across-the-line starting.

The standard direction of rotation is counterclockwise facing the end opposite the shaft extension.

For constant-speed operation, even under varying load conditions, where moderate torques are desirable or mandatory, this type is often used in preference to the more costly capacitor-start motor. Meets NEMA starting currents. Typical applications: blowers; centrifugal pumps; duplicating machines; refrigerators; oil burners; unit heaters.

High locked-rotor currents (in excess of NEMA) limit the use of this type on lighting circuits to applications where the motor starts only very infrequently, because of a tendency to cause flickering of the lights. Principal applications: washing and ironing machines; cellar-drainer pumps; tools for a home workshop.

Used where two definite speeds independent of load are required. Ratings above 1/4 hp usually made capacitor-start. Motor shown always starts on high-speed connection; transfer to low speed made by starting switch. Common applications: belted blowers for warm-air furnaces or for other purposes; attic ventilators; air-conditioning apparatus.

A general-purpose motor suitable for most applications requiring constant speed under varying loads, high starting and running torques, high overload capacity. Also available as two-speed pole-changing and air conditioning compressors; air compressors; stokers; gasoline pumps.

Primarily used for unit heaters, or for other shaft-mounted fans. Essentially a constant-speed motor, but by means of a two-speed switch, or by means of an autotransformer, other speeds can be obtained, with fan loads, if horsepower rating selected closely matches the fan load. Can also be used in intermittent ratings for plug-reversing service.

* From Knowlton, "Standard

ND SUBFRACTIONAL HORSEPOWER MOTORS*

current motors	1, 2, or 3 phase			Polyphase	D-c or a-c (60 cycles or less), universal types		Direct current	
	Repulsion-start	Shaded-pole	Nonexcited synchronous (reluctance)	Squirrel-cage induction	Without governor	With governor	Shunt or compound	Series
			Stator winding may be: split-phase, capacitor-start, capacitor, polyphase					
	Drum-wound; commutator	Squirrel-cage	Cage, with cutouts	Squirrel-cage	Drum-wound; commutator	Drum-wound; commutator	Drum-wound; commutator	Drum-wound; commutator
	Short-circuiter	None	Depends on stator winding	None	None	None	None	None
	1/8–3/4	1/2000–1/20	1/3000–1/3	1/6–3/4	1/150–1	1/50–1/20	1/20–3/4	1/125–1/30
	3450, 1725, 1140, 865	1450–3000	3600, 1800, 1200, 900	3450, 1725, 1140, 865	3000–11,000	2000–4000	3450, 1725, 1140, 865	900–2000
	Constant	Constant, or adjustable varying	Absolutely constant	Constant	Varying, or adjustable varying	Adjustable	Constant, or adjustable varying	Varying, or adjustable varying
	....	Choke or resistor	....	....	Choke or resistor	Adjustable governor	Armature resistance	Resistor
	Very high High	Low Low	Low Moderate	Very high Very high	Very high	Very high	Very high	Very high
	None Continuous	None None	None	None None	Continuous Continuous	Continuous Continuous	Continuous Continuous	Continuous Continuous
	.... 128 100	100	.... 200–400 275	.... 165–195 100	75 105–175	110 140–160	.... 175–225 120–140	185

Descriptions:

Repulsion-start: A constant-speed motor suited to general-purpose applications requiring high starting torque, such as pumps and compressors. An associated type, the repulsion induction (buried cage) is used for door openers and other plug-reversing applications. Has been displaced for many applications by the capacitor-start motor.

Shaded-pole: For ratings below 1/20 hp, this is a general-purpose motor. For fan applications, speed control is effected by use of a series choke or resistor. Applications: fans, unit heaters, humidifiers, hair driers, damper controllers.

Nonexcited synchronous (reluctance): Cutouts in rotor result in synchronous-speed characteristics. Curve shown is for split-phase stator. Pull-in ability is affected by inertia of connected load. Used for teleprinters, facsimile-picture transmitters, graphic instruments, etc. Clocks and timing devices usually use shaded-pole hysteresis motors rated at a few millionths of a horsepower.

Squirrel-cage induction: Companion motor to capacitor-start motor with comparable torques and generally suited to same applications if polyphase power is available. Inherently plug-reversible and suitable for door openers, hoists, etc. High-frequency motors used for high-speed applications, as for woodworking machinery, rayon spinning, and portable tools.

Without governor: Light weight for a given output, high speeds, varying-speed and universal characteristics make this type very popular for hand tools of all kinds, vacuum cleaners, etc. Ratings above 1/4 hp usually compensated. Some speed control can be effected by a resistor or by use of a tapped field. Used with reduction gear for slower speed applications.

With governor: By means of a centrifugal governor, a constant-speed motor having the advantages of the universal motor is obtained. Governor may be single speed or adjustable even while running. Speed is independent of applied voltage. Used in typewriters, calculating machines, food mixers, motion-picture cameras and projectors, etc.

Shunt or compound: A constant-speed companion motor for the capacitor-start or split-phase motor for use where only d-c power is available. For unit-heater service, armature resistance is used to obtain speed control. Not usually designed for field control.

Series: Principally used as the d-c companion motor to the shaded-pole motor for fan applications. Used in these small ratings in place of shunt motors to avoid using extremely small wire.

Handbook for Electrical Engineers."

What *speed classification* is required: constant-speed;* adjustable-speed;* varying-speed;* or adjustable varying-speed?* *Torques* required by the driven device are of obvious importance. *Cost* is usually of concern to the user. Other factors influencing selection of the best type are discussed in the table under General Remarks.

20-3. What Full-load Speed?—When 60-cycle single-phase motors are used, 1725-rpm motors cost less and are usually easier to obtain, than 3450-, 1140-, or 850-rpm motors; the same consideration applies to d-c motors in the fractional range ($\frac{1}{20}$ to $\frac{3}{4}$ hp). However, use of one of these four speeds and direct drive is usually to be preferred to use of a belted or geared drive. Universal motors may operate at almost any speed from 3500 rpm or less up to 10,000 or 15,000 rpm. Operating speeds of subfractional horsepower motors are discussed in Chaps. XIII and XV.

20-4. Choosing the Horsepower Rating.—First, the actual power requirements of the load under different conditions should be determined by means of an application test (see Art. 19-26). When taking this test, it is best to determine how much the load can be increased in service; for example, if a V-belt is used, the load can be increased considerably by tightening the belt, which an electrician or serviceman is likely to do; tightening the packing gland of a pump can increase the load considerably; on an air compressor, the load can sometimes be increased by tampering with the setting of the pressure-limiting switch. After the true horsepower requirements of the load have been determined, it is generally best to select a motor of the nearest standard horsepower rating. Although fractional horsepower motors are generally capable of carrying small overloads continuously, it is usually more satisfactory in the long run to select a motor large enough to handle the job under normal and adverse conditions. Some appliance manufacturers knowingly overload a motor so that they can use a motor of lower horsepower rating than required, partly to reduce cost and selling price, and partly to influence the ultimate customer to believe that the power consumption of the appliance is small because the motor carries a low horsepower rating. However, overloading a motor invariably means shortening the life, because the overload means higher operating temperatures. Hence, the appliance manufacturer who is concerned with establishing for his product a reputation for long and satisfactory life uses motors large enough for the job. Thermal protection, now available on most single-phase motors, offers additional assurance of trouble-free operation; however, thermal pro-

* See Glossary for definitions of these terms.

tection does not prevent prolonged overloading from shortening the life of the motor by deterioration of the insulation and lubricant.

Standard horsepower and speed ratings for both a-c and d-c fractional horsepower motors are given in Table XXIII. Formerly, the horsepower rating referred only to the full-load rating, but now horsepower is defined by Nema primarily on the basis of the break-down torque, *i.e.*, the *momentary* overload capacity, of the motor[2] (see Art. 1-5 and Table II). *Continuous* overload capacity, under favorable conditions, is the horsepower rating multiplied by the service factor (Art. 1-20). Approximate locked-rotor current is given by the horsepower rating and the code letter on the nameplate (Art. 1-14, Table XXIX). There are no standard horsepower and speed ratings for universal motors (see Art. 12-2), or for subfractional horsepower motors which are usually of the shaded-pole (Art. 13-6) or synchronous type (Chap. XV).

20-5. Constructional and Design Features.—*a. Mechanical Protection and System of Cooling.*—General-purpose motors are usually built as *open machines** and are often *drip-proof** as well. *Totally enclosed** motors are commonly available in most ratings; these cost more and are often larger and heavier than the corresponding open motors. Less common forms of construction are *protected machine** (semienclosed machine), *semiprotected machine,* splash-proof machine,* explosion-proof machine,* watertight machine,* dust-tight** machine,* and *submersible** machine. Motors are designated as *moisture-resistant,*† *fume-resistant,*† *acid-resistant,*† etc., when they are so constructed that they are not readily injured by moisture, fumes, acid, etc. Open machines are usually *self-ventilated;** they should be applied in such a way as to permit unobstructed flow of clean cooling air to and from the machine.

b. Bearing Construction.—Both sleeve and ball bearings are standard. Standard sleeve-bearing motors are usually designed for operation with shaft horizontal only, but ball-bearing motors can be operated with the shaft in any position. Specially constructed sleeve-bearing motors are made for vertical operation. Subfractional horsepower motors commonly use self-aligning porous bearings (see Figs. 13-4, 13-6, 18-2, Art. 18-1c).

c. Method of Mounting.—Rigid and resilient mountings are both standard, but the latter is to be preferred if quietness of operation is

---

* See Glossary for definitions of these terms.

† See Glossary for definition of "-resistant" used as a suffix.

an important consideration (Art. 18-11). *Floor mounting* is the standard arrangement for foot-mounted motors. Other arrangements of foot-mounted motors are *wall mounting* and *ceiling mounting*. Unless specifically stated otherwise, wall-mounted and ceiling-mounted motors are understood to be designed for operation with the shaft horizontal. *Right-hand wall mounting* means that, as the observer looks squarely at the front end shield, the mounting wall is at his right. Face mounting (flange mounting) is another form of attaching the motor to the driven device; also, extended end-shield clamp bolts are sometimes used to mount the motor (Art. 18-10). Sometimes a band may be clamped around the motor (Fig. 8-2).

d. *Thermal Overload Protection.*—Built-in thermal overload protection is now available on most single-phase motors (Arts. 18-14 to 18-16). Where there is danger of overloading or stalling, its use is to be recommended, both to protect the motor and to minimize danger from fires. Most such devices are now automatic resetting, which seems to be the preferred arrangement, particularly for automatically controlled devices. For some applications (*e.g.*, oil burners) manual resetting may be preferable.

e. *Reversibility.*—Most general-purpose motors are *externally reversible,** but few are *electrically reversible.** Capacitor-start motors can be made electrically reversible by use of a special arrangement such as described in Art. 5-30. Electrically reversible repulsion and repulsion induction motors are discussed in Arts. 11-5 to 11-7. Use of d-c motors for this service is discussed in Art. 17-14. Shaded-pole motors, as a rule, are not reversible at all, except for the types discussed in Art. 13-8.

20-6. Service Conditions.—General-purpose motors are designed to withstand all normal conditions. Some abnormal conditions requiring consideration and, possibly, special motors, are the following: exposure to chemical fumes, explosive vapors, dust, dirt (particularly if gritty, combustible, conducting, or explosive), lint, steam, oil vapor, or salt air; operation in ambient temperatures below 10°C (50°F) or above 40°C (104°F); altitudes of more than 3,300 ft; prolonged operation at excessive overloads; exposure to abnormal shock or vibration; operation of motor in an enclosure that hinders free dissipation of the heat from the motor; proximity of objects that block normal ventilation; dripping or splashing of liquids on the motor; variations in line voltage of more than 10 per cent; variations in frequency of more than 5 per cent.

20-7. Effects of Variation of Voltage and Frequency upon the Performance of Induction Motors.

a. Induction motors are at times operated on circuits of voltage or frequency other than those for which the motors are rated. Under such conditions, the performance of the motor will vary from the standard rating. The following is a brief statement of some operating results caused by small variations of voltage and frequency and is indicative of the general character of changes produced by such variations in operating conditions.

b. Voltage variations of 10 per cent on power circuits are allowed in most commission rules. However, changing the voltage applied to an induction motor has the effect of changing its proper rating as to power factor and efficiency in proportion to the square of the applied voltage. Thus a 5 hp motor, operated at 10 per cent above the rated voltage, would have characteristics proper for a 6 hp motor (6.05 hp to be exact), and at 10 per cent below the rated voltage, those of a 4 hp motor (more exactly, 4.05 hp). It is, of course, obvious that if the rating of a motor were greatly increased in this way, the safe heating would frequently be exceeded.

c. In a motor of normal characteristics at full rated horsepower load, a 10 per cent increase of voltage above that given on the name-plate would usually result in a slight improvement in efficiency and a decided lowering in power factor. A 10 per cent decrease of voltage below that given on the nameplate would usually give a slight decrease of efficiency and an increase in power factor.

d. The locked-rotor and breakdown torque will be proportional to the square of the voltage applied. With a 10 per cent increase or decrease in voltage from that given on the nameplate, the heating at rated horsepower load will not exceed safe limits when operating in ambient temperatures of 40°C or less, although the usual guaranteed rise may be exceeded.

e. An increase of 10 per cent in voltage will result in a decrease of slip of about 17 per cent, while a reduction of 10 per cent will increase the slip about 21 per cent. Thus, if the slip at rated voltage were 5 per cent, it would be increased to 6.05 per cent if the voltage were reduced 10 per cent.

f. A frequency higher than the rated frequency usually improves the power factor, but decreases locked-rotor torque and increases the speed, friction, and windage. At a frequency lower than the rated frequency, the speed is, of course, decreased; locked-rotor torque is increased; and power factor is slightly decreased. For certain kinds of motor load, such as in textile mills, close frequency regulation is essential.

g. If variations in both voltage and frequency occur simultaneously, the effects will be superimposed. Thus, if the voltage is high and the frequency low, the locked-rotor torque will be very greatly increased, but the power factor will be decreased and the temperature rise increased with normal load.

h. The foregoing facts apply particularly to general-purpose motors.

They may not always be true in connection with special motors, built for a particular purpose, or as applied to very small motors.—Authorized Engineering Information, 1-31-1925. Nema rule MG3-75.

20-8. Operation of 60-cycle Induction Motors on 50 Cycles.— Fractional horsepower polyphase induction motors are often rated 60/50 cycles and may be expected to perform satisfactorily on both frequencies; operating speeds on 50 cycles are approximately five-sixths of the speeds on 60 cycles; breakdown and locked-rotor torques

TABLE XXII.—SHAFT EXTENSIONS FOR CONSTANT-SPEED GENERAL-PURPOSE MOTORS

60 cycle				25 cycle	U	N-W	Usable length or flat or keyway	Flat	Keyway
Hp at 3600–3450 rpm	Hp at 1800–1725 rpm	Hp at 1200–1140 rpm	Hp at 900–860 rpm	Hp at 1500–1425 rpm					
$\frac{1}{20}$	...	...	...	...	$\frac{3}{8}$	$1\frac{1}{8}$	$\frac{3}{4}$	$\frac{3}{64}$	
$\frac{1}{12}$	$\frac{1}{20}$	...	...	$\frac{1}{20}$	$\frac{3}{8}$	$1\frac{1}{8}$	$\frac{3}{4}$	$\frac{3}{64}$	
$\frac{1}{8}$	$\frac{1}{12}$	$\frac{1}{20}$	...	$\frac{1}{12}$	$\frac{1}{2}$	$1\frac{1}{2}$	$1\frac{1}{8}$	$\frac{3}{64}$	
$\frac{1}{6}$	$\frac{1}{8}$	$\frac{1}{12}$	...	$\frac{1}{8}$	$\frac{1}{2}$	$1\frac{1}{2}$	$1\frac{1}{8}$	$\frac{3}{64}$	
$\frac{1}{4}$	$\frac{1}{6}$	$\frac{1}{8}$	$\frac{1}{20}$	$\frac{1}{6}$	$\frac{1}{2}$	$1\frac{1}{2}$	$1\frac{1}{8}$	$\frac{3}{64}$	
$\frac{1}{3}$	$\frac{1}{4}$	$\frac{1}{6}$	$\frac{1}{12}$	$\frac{1}{4}$	$\frac{5}{8}$	$1\frac{7}{8}$	$1\frac{3}{8}$	...	$\frac{3}{16} \times \frac{3}{32}$
$\frac{1}{2}$	$\frac{1}{3}$	$\frac{1}{4}$	$\frac{1}{8}$	$\frac{1}{3}$	$\frac{5}{8}$	$1\frac{7}{8}$	$1\frac{3}{8}$	...	$\frac{3}{16} \times \frac{3}{32}$
$\frac{3}{4}$	$\frac{1}{2}$	$\frac{1}{3}$	$\frac{1}{6}$	$\frac{1}{2}$	$\frac{3}{4}$	$2\frac{1}{4}$	$1\frac{7}{8}$	...	$\frac{3}{16} \times \frac{3}{32}$
1	$\frac{3}{4}$	$\frac{1}{2}$	$\frac{1}{4}$	$\frac{3}{4}$	$\frac{3}{4}$	$2\frac{1}{4}$	$1\frac{7}{8}$	...	$\frac{3}{16} \times \frac{3}{32}$
....	...	...	$\frac{1}{3}$	...	$\frac{3}{4}$	$2\frac{1}{4}$	$1\frac{7}{8}$	...	$\frac{3}{16} \times \frac{3}{32}$

NOTES: W = $\frac{1}{8}$ in. maximum.

N-W = usable length of shaft.

U = diameter of shaft extension.

Recommended standard, May 16, 1940. From "Motor and Generator Standards," National Electrical Manufacturers' Association, New York.

on 50 cycles, in terms of ounce-feet, are approximately one-third greater than on 60 cycles.

In general, 60-cycle split-phase and capacitor-start motors are not to be recommended for operation on 50 cycles. Speeds are approximately five-sixths of the 60-cycle speed, and breakdown torques, expressed in ounce-feet, are approximately one-third greater, as in the case of polyphase motors. Locked-rotor torques, expressed in ounce-feet, are of the order of one-fourth greater, but the switching torques may become disastrously low because the operating speed of the 60-cycle switch will usually be too high. If a 50-cycle switch is installed to replace the 60-cycle one, satisfactory switching torques may be obtained. However, in the case of capacitor-start motors, the starting duty on the capacitor will be appreciably greater, and some reduction in capacitor life is to be expected. However, another more important factor to be considered is that of temperature rise, which will be of the order of 40 to 50 per cent higher on 50 cycles than on 60 cycles if the motor is operated at the same horsepower output on both frequencies. If the temperature rise on 60 cycles happens to be only 30 to 35 deg, the 50-cycle rise may not be too great.

To summarize the situation as regards split-phase and capacitor-start motors: A 50-cycle switch should be installed; then if the motor has a conservative temperature rise of 35 deg or less when operating on 60 cycles, operation on 50 cycles will probably be satisfactory, although capacitors on capacitor-start motors may have a shorter than normal life, particularly if the starting duty is severe.

20-9. Shaft Extensions—Dimensions and Tolerances.—Standard dimensions for shaft extensions for constant-speed general-purpose a-c motors are as given in Table XXII. Shaft extensions for constant-speed general-purpose d-c motors are the same as for 60-cycle a-c motors of the same horsepower and speed ratings.

Tolerances established by Nema on shaft extension diameters for fractional horsepower motors are as follows:

a. *Diameter.*— +0.000 in., −0.0005 in.

b. *Width of Keyways.*— +0.000 in., −0.002 in.

c. *For Making Keyway Parallel to Shaft.*— 0.002 in. max.

d. *Depth of Keyway.*—Distance from bottom of keyseat to opposite side of the shaft to be within following limits:

$\frac{5}{8}$ diam. shaft with $\frac{3}{16} \times \frac{3}{16}$ key................. 0.517–0.502
$\frac{3}{4}$ diam. shaft with $\frac{3}{16} \times \frac{3}{16}$ key................. 0.644–0.629

Keys are normally supplied by the motor manufacturer as a part of the motor.

SPECIAL-PURPOSE MOTORS

Many important applications require certain special features not found in general-purpose motors, versatile as they are. Ten applications of this nature are listed in the heading of Table XXIII. In the past, it was the practice for each individual user in each of these 10 fields to write his own specifications for motors; often certain provisions in these specifications, necessary as they might be, made it more difficult and costly for the user to obtain motors. So that motor users in these fields might enjoy the benefits of using standardized motors,

TABLE XXIII.—APPLICATION CHARACTERISTICS OF GENERAL- AND SPECIAL-PURPOSE FRACTIONAL HORSEPOWER MOTORS
(Compiled from Nema Standards)

	General-purpose motors	Special-purpose motors for special applications									
		Hermetic motors	For belt-drive refrigeration compressors	For washing machines	For fans and blowers — Shaft-mounted	For fans and blowers — Belted	For stokers	For oil burners	For jet pumps	For cellar drainers and sump pumps	For gasoline-dispensing pumps
Standard types of motors											
A-c types:											
Split-phase, single-speed	X			X	X	X		X	X	X	
Split-phase, two-speed	X					X			X		X
Capacitor-start, single-speed	X	X	X			X					
Capacitor-start, two-speed	X					X					
Permanent-split capacitor	X	X			X						
Two-value capacitor	X	X			⅙ hp and larger				X		X
Repulsion-start induction	X	X	X			X	X	X	X		X
Polyphase, squirrel-cage	X	X	X			X	X		X	X	X
Universal types:											
Uncompensated, concentrated-pole	X										
Compensated, distributed-winding	X										
D-c types:											
Shunt-wound	X	X	X	X	e				X	X	X
Compound-wound	X	X	X	X	f		X		X	X	X
Standard voltage ratings											
Single-phase motors:											
115 (split-ph., cap.-start)	X	X	X	X	X	X	X	X	X	X	X
230 (split-ph., cap.-start)	X	X	X	X	X	X	X	X	X	X	X
115/230 (cap.-start above ¼ hp, rep.-start, permanent-split cap.)	X	X	X			X	X	X	X	X	X
Polyphase motors:											
110	X	X	X	X	X	X	X	X	X	X	X
208 (60-cycle motors only)	X	X	X	X	X	X	X	X	X	X	X
220	X	X	X	X	X	X	X	X	X	X	X
440	X										
D-c motors:											
32	X										
115	X	X		X	X	X	X	X	X	X	X
230	X	X		X	X	X	X	X	X	X	X
Standard frequency ratings											
60 cycles	X	X	X	X	X	X	X	X	X	X	X
50 cycles	X	X	X	X	X	X	X	X	X	X	X
25 cycles	X						X	X	X	X	X

e Up to approximately 6 in. frame, diameter.
f Approximately 6 in. frame diameter and larger.

Standard horsepower and speed ratings

(Columns grouped under repeated "No. of poles" headers: 2 | 4 | 6 | 8)

60-cycle induction motors:

	2	4	6	8
1 hp.		x	x	
3/4 hp.	x	x	x	x
1/2 hp.	x	x	x	x
1/3 hp.	x	x	x	x
1/4 hp.	x	x	x	x
1/5 hp.	x	x	x	
1/6 hp.	x	x	x	x
1/8 hp.	x	x	x	x
1/12 hp.	x	x	x	x
1/20 hp.	x	x	x	x

50-cycle induction motors...... Horsepower ratings and number of poles same as for 60-cycle motors, except that 8-pole ratings are not standard for general-purpose motors.

25-cycle induction motors...... Only 2-pole ratings are standard, in same horsepower ratings as 60-cycle 4-pole motors. In addition, 4-pole motors, in same horsepower ratings as 60-cycle 8-pole motors, are standard for motors for shaft-mounted fans and blowers.

D-c motors................... Horsepower and full-load speed ratings same as for 60-cycle 4-pole motors.

Miscellaneous performance specifications

Minimum torques:						
Split-phase motors	Tables IV, II	Table XXIV	Tables IV, II	Tables IV, II	Tables IV, II	Art. 20-18
Capacitor-start motors	Tables VI, II	Table XXIV	Tables VI, II	Tables VI, II		Art. 20-19
Two-value capacitor motors	Tables VI, II	Table XXIV	Tables VI, II			Art. 20-19
Repulsion-start induction motors	Tables VIII, II	Tables VIII, II	Tables VIII, II	Tables VIII, II		
Polyphase motors	Art. 14-2	Art. 14-2	Art. 14-2	Art. 14-2	Art. 20-12	
Maximum locked-rotor current:						
Single-phase motors	Table XXVI	Table XXVI	Table XXVI	Table XXVI	Table XXVI	Table XXVI
Dielectric tests	Table XX	Table XX	Table XX	Table XX	Table XX	Table XX
Allowable variation from rated:						
Voltage, in % of rated	±10	±10	±10	±10	±10	±10
Frequency, in % of rated	±5	±5	±5	±5	±5	±5
Voltage, in % of rated, univ. mtrs. only	±6					
Combined voltage and freq., in %	±10	±10	±10	±10	±10	±10
Direction of rotation, from front end	CCW or CW	CCW	CW	CCW or CW	CCW or CW	CW

a 60-cycle and d-c motors, only.
b 50-cycle motors, only.
e 25-cycle motors, only.
g Capacitor-start, and repulsion-start.
h Capacitor-start, repulsion-start, and split-phase.
i Split-phase only.
k Basis of 1/2 hr. intermittent duty.

TABLE XXIII.—APPLICATION CHARACTERISTICS OF GENERAL- AND SPECIAL-PURPOSE FRACTIONAL HORSEPOWER MOTORS.—(Concluded)

	General-purpose motors	Special-purpose motors for special applications									
		Hermetic motors	For belt-drive refrigeration compressors	For washing machines	For fans and blowers		For stokers	For oil burners	For jet pumps	For cellar drainers and sump pumps	For gasoline-dispensing pumps
					Shaft-mounted	Belted					
		General mechanical features									
Protection, enclosure:											
Open	x		x	x		x			x		x
Drip-proof	x		x	x		x	Optional		(In vert. pos.) x		x
Totally enclosed	x				x		Recommended	x			x
Parts only		x									
Explosion-proof											
Bearings:											
Sleeve, horizontal mounting	x		x	x	x	x	j	j	x	x	x
Ball, one ball, vert. mtg	x				x					x	x
Provision for light axial thrusts					x	x					
Mounting:											
Rigid, foot mtg	x		½ and ¾ hp				½ and ¾ hp, ⅙, ¼, ⅓ hp				x
Resilient, foot mtg	x		⅓ hp and smaller	d		x					
Round frame	x			x	x	x		x	(Art.20-17) x	x	x
Face-mounted	x			x	x						
Extended studs	x				x	x		x			x
Oiling arrangement:											
Spring cap oilers, front and rear					x	x	j	j		x	x
Rear oiler extended to motor diam					x	x		j		x	x
Thermal overload protection:											
Optional on single-phase motors	x		x			x	j	x	x	x	x
Standard on single-phase motors	x	x	x			x	x	x	x	x	x
Automatic reset	x						x				
Manual reset	x			j		j	x				
Miscellaneous:											
Capacitor on top of frame	x		x		x		x		x	x	
Capacitor may be on front end shield											
Built-in line switch											
Built-in voltage-selector switch											
Outline dimensions		Fig. 20-1		Fig. 20-2				Fig. 20-3	Fig. 20-4	Fig. 20-5	Fig. 20-6

d Ungrounded rings (see Art. 20-12).
j Usual practice. No Nema standard on this.

Nema has drawn up application standards for these 10 applications; these are a result of the pooling of the experience of many motor builders and motor users. These standards are presented in condensed form in Table XXIII and supplementary notes in Arts. 20-10 to 20-19. Users following these standards will generally find greater ease in procuring motors, greater economy, and greater ease in obtaining service and repair. These standards are all new (1946), and the advantages of using them appear to be destined to grow with time.

20-10. Hermetic Motors.—According to Nema, "A hermetic motor consists of a stator and rotor without shaft, end shields, or bearings for installation in refrigeration condensing units of the hermetically sealed type. . . . Single-phase units include a starting relay, capacitor, and automatic-reset thermal overload protector as required." Hermetic motor systems are discussed in Arts. 4-33 and 5-28. Characteristics of standard motors are summarized in Table XXIII. Standard lead markings are given in Fig. 5-38. Locked-rotor and breakdown torques specified by Nema are not less than the values in Table XXIV. These values are based on a motor temperature of approximately 25°C at the start of the test.

TABLE XXIV.—NEMA TORQUE REQUIREMENTS FOR 4-POLE 60-CYCLE HERMETIC MOTORS

Rated hp	Breakdown torque, oz-ft	Locked-rotor torque, oz-ft		
	All types	Type I	Type II	Type III
$\frac{1}{12}$	11.5	7	17	22
$\frac{1}{8}$	16.5	9	23	30
$\frac{1}{6}$	21.5	10.5	30	39
$\frac{1}{5}$	25.5	11	36	46
$\frac{1}{4}$	31.5	12	43	56
$\frac{1}{3}$	40.5	18	56	72
$\frac{1}{2}$	58	40	79	103
$\frac{3}{4}$	82.5	60	113	146

Major outline dimensions that have been standardized are given in Fig. 20-1.

20-11. Motors for Belt-drive Refrigeration Compressors.—Application characteristics for these motors are summarized in Table XXIII. Shaft extensions are given in Table XXII.

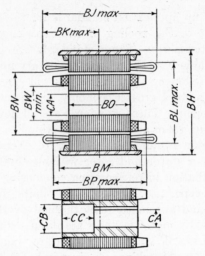

Rated Hp	BH*	BJ (max.)	CA†	CB (max.)
$\frac{1}{12}$	5.480	$3\frac{7}{8}$	0.500, 0.625, 0.750	1.062
$\frac{1}{8}$	5.480	$4\frac{1}{8}$	0.500, 0.625, 0.750	1.062
$\frac{1}{6}$	5.480	$4\frac{5}{8}$	0.500, 0.625, 0.750	1.062
$\frac{1}{12}$	6.292	$3\frac{7}{8}$	0.625, 0.750, 0.875, 1.000	1.437
$\frac{1}{8}$	6.292	$4\frac{1}{8}$	0.625, 0.750, 0.875, 1.000	1.437
$\frac{1}{6}$	6.292	$4\frac{3}{8}$	0.625, 0.750, 0.875, 1.000	1.437
$\frac{1}{5}$	6.292	$4\frac{5}{8}$	0.625, 0.750, 0.875, 1.000	1.437
$\frac{1}{4}$	6.292	5	0.625, 0.750, 0.875, 1.000	1.437
$\frac{1}{3}$	6.292	$5\frac{3}{8}$	0.625, 0.750, 0.875, 1.000	1.437
$\frac{1}{2}$	6.292	$5\frac{3}{4}$	0.625, 9.750, 0.875, 1.000	1.437
$\frac{3}{4}$	6.292	6	0.625, 0.750, 0.875, 1.000	1.437
$\frac{1}{3}$	7.480	5	0.875, 1.000, 1.125	2.000
$\frac{1}{2}$	7.480	$5\frac{1}{4}$	0.875, 1.000, 1.125	2.000
$\frac{3}{4}$	7.480	$5\frac{7}{8}$	0.875, 1.000, 1.125	2.000
1	7.480	$6\frac{1}{2}$	0.875, 1.000, 1.125	2.000

* Tolerance on this dimension, +0.000, −0.002.
Alternate dimensions; tolerance, +0.0005, −0.000.
All dimensions in inches.

Fɪɢ. 20-1.—Standard outline dimensions for hermetic motors.　(*From Nema.*)

20-12. Washing-machine Motors.—Application characteristics for washing-machine motors are given in Table XXIII. Following are the minimum torques specified by Nema:

Motors	Torques, oz-ft	
	Breakdown	Locked-rotor
60-cycle......................	33	24
50-cycle......................	37.6	27.5
25-cycle......................	36	26.1
Direct-current................	33*	24†

* Torque at not less than 900 rpm.
† Torque likely to be 1.5 to 3.0 times this value.

Outline dimensions are given in Fig. 20-2, which shows that three different ways of mounting are recognized as standard: round-frame, wing-type base (Sketch 3), and strap-type base (Sketch 4). So that through studs could be used for mounting the motor, stud spacing dimensions are standardized as shown in Sketch 5. Rubber rings are *ungrounded; i.e.,* the motor is electrically insulated from the cradle base in which it is mounted. This practice is contrary to that followed on general-purpose motors where the rubber rings are grounded so as

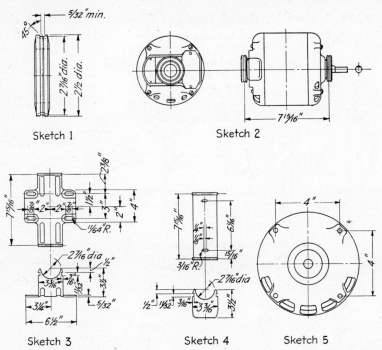

Fig. 20-2.—Standard outline dimensions for washing-machine motors. (*From Nema.*)

to provide an electrical connection between the motor and its mounting base.

20-13. Motors for Shaft-mounted Fans and Blowers.—These motors are designed for propeller or centrifugal fans mounted directly on the motor shaft; they are not suitable for belted drives (Art. 8-6). Some of these motors require air over the motor in order not to overheat. This fact may be indicated by the words "air over" on the nameplate following the temperature rise (Nema recommendation); but this practice may not yet be universally followed, so that it is best to consult the motor manufacturer on this point. Application characteristics of single-speed motors are given in Table XXIII. For two-speed and adjustable varying-speed service, the following is recommended by Nema:

1. *Single-phase.* Use permanent-split capacitor motors with two-speed switch or adjustable-speed controller, as described in Arts. 8-2 to 8-7.
2. *Polyphase.* Use single-phase permanent-split capacitor motors.
3. *Direct-current.* Use shunt- or compound-wound motors with armature-resistance control (Art. 17-15).

20-14. Motors for Belted Fans and Blowers.—Application characteristics for single-speed motors are given in Table XXIII. Two-

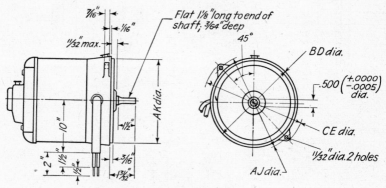

Dimensions and tolerances for face-mounted small power motors for oil burners shall be as follows:

A. Dimensions

AK	AJ	CE dia.	BD dia.
5½	6¾	7¾ max.	6¼ max.
6⅜	7¼	8¼ max.	7 max.

B. Tolerances

Max. face runout—   .006 in. indicator reading
Max. Pilot eccentricity - .006 in. indicator reading

Fig. 20-3.—Standard outline dimensions for face-mounted oil-burner motors. (*From Nema.*)

speed pole-changing motors are standard for this application. (For a description of two-speed split-phase motors, refer to Arts. 4-29 to 4-31; two-speed capacitor-start motors are discussed briefly in Art. 5-29.) Standard speed ratings for two-speed motors are

60-cycle motors.................................... 1725/1140
50-cycle motors. 1425/950

Standard horsepower ratings for two-speed motors are

Split-phase...................... ⅙ and ¼ at higher speed
Capacitor-start.................. ⅓, ½, and ¾ at higher speed

20-15. Stoker Motors.—Application characteristics of stoker motors are given in Table XXIII. It is to be noted that totally enclosed motors are recommended. To this recommendation Nema adds, "However, it is recognized that some stokers provide sufficient protection so that open motors may be used."

20-16. Oil-burner Motors.—Application characteristics of motors used to drive mechanical-draft oil burners for domestic service are listed in Table XXIII. Outline dimensions are given in Fig. 20-3. Note that these motors use a two-conductor rubber-covered flexible cord, type SJ (Underwriters' designation) or equivalent, brought out the back end of the motor.

20-17. Jet-pump Motors.—Application characteristics of these motors are given in Table XXIII, and outline dimensions in Fig. 20-4.

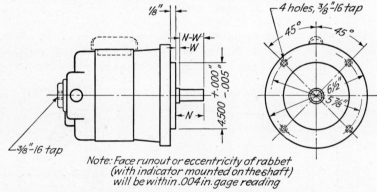

Fɪɢ. 20-4.—Standard outline dimensions for face-mounted motors for jet pumps. (*From Nema.*)

These motors are provided with a ⅜-16 tapped hole in the center of the bearing hub of the front end shield in order to accommodate a drip cover (not furnished as a part of the motor) when used as a vertical motor. Because this drip cover would conceal a nameplate mounted in the usual position on the front end shield, the nameplate is attached to the frame of the motor 180 deg from the leads.

20-18. Cellar-drainer and Sump-pump Motors.—Application characteristics are given in Table XXIII, and outline dimensions in Fig. 20-5. Motors are designed to be drip-proof with the shaft vertical. Bottom (rear) end shield is designed for direct mounting on a support pipe and contains a float-operated switch.   This switch will operate with a closing or upward force of 10 oz minimum, and an opening or downward force of 20 oz minimum.   These motors are

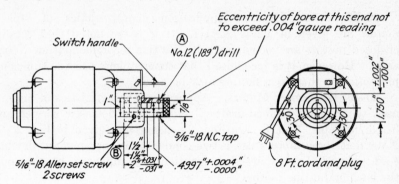

Note A: May be provided if necessary
Note B: This dimension may vary between ⅞" and 1½"

Fig. 20-5.—Standard outline dimensions for motors for cellar drainers and sump pumps.   (*From Nema.*)

provided with a rigid coupling, pinned to the motor shaft.   Sixty-cycle motors have a locked-rotor torque of not less than 20 oz-ft, and a breakdown torque of not less than 33 oz-ft, at rated voltage.

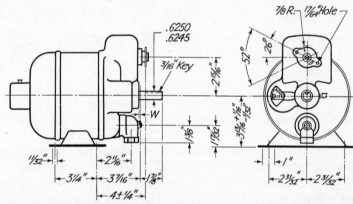

Fig. 20-6.—Standard outline dimensions for motors for gasoline-dispensing pumps. (*From Nema.*)

20-19. Gasoline-dispensing Pump Motors.—Motors for gasoline-dispensing pumps necessarily have to be of explosion-proof construction to meet Class I Group D requirements of the Underwriters' Laboratories.   Note that these motors carry a ½-hr intermittent

rating.   Sixty-cycle single-phase motors have a locked-rotor torque of not less than 48.8 oz-ft, and a breakdown torque of not less than 46 oz-ft, at rated voltage.   Application characteristics of these motors are given in Table XXIII, and outline dimensions in Fig. 20-6.   Note that this motor has a built-in voltage-selector switch, as well as a built-in line switch with operating lever.

MISCELLANEOUS

20-20. Performance Specifications for Single-phase Induction Motors.—Formerly, Nema gave specifications for minimum values of efficiencies, power factors, and apparent efficiencies of single-phase induction motors.   Although these are no longer in Nema standards, they are reproduced in part in Table XXV because they do give the uninitiated reader an approximate idea of the performance of fractional horsepower motors, particularly of those now in service which were built to these specifications.

TABLE XXV.—MINIMUM PERFORMANCE SPECIFICATIONS FOR SINGLE-PHASE INDUCTION MOTORS
(Two-, four-, six-, and eight-pole, 60-cycle motors)

Rating, hp	Efficiency, per cent				Power factor, per cent				Apparent efficiency, per cent			
	Speed, rpm				Speed, rpm				Speed, rpm			
	3600	1800	1200	900	3600	1800	1200	900	3600	1800	1200	900
General-purpose motors*												
1/8	45	53	45	38	57	52	43	36	28	30	21	15
1/6	49	58	49	42	62	56	46	38	34	36	25	18
1/4	53	62	53	45	66	60	49	40	39	42	29	20
1/3	54	63	54	46	67	61	50	41	41	44	31	22
1/2	55	65	55	47	69	63	52	43	44	47	33	23
3/4	57	67	57	49	72	65	53	44	46	49	34	24
High-torque Motors*												
1/6	..	46	..	..	..	52	..	..	..	27	..	..
1/4	..	51	..	..	..	56	..	..	..	32	..	..
1/3	..	54	..	..	..	58	..	..	..	35	..	..

NOTE: The power factor and efficiency must not be less than the values shown and such that their product is not less than the values given for apparent efficiency.
    * See Art. 4-5.

TABLE XXVI.—MAXIMUM INPUTS FOR 115-VOLT 60-CYCLE SINGLE-PHASE INDUCTION MOTORS
(Currents for 230-volt motors are half the values shown)

	Rating		Output		Input								
					General-purpose motors				Short-hour motors				
					No load		Full load		No load		Full load		Locked-rotor, amp
Horsepower	Poles	Rpm at full load	Watts	Torque, oz-ft	Amp	Watts	Amp	Watts	Amp	Watts	Amp	Watts	
1/20	2	3450	37.3	1.22	1.9	80	2.50	140					20
	4	1725	37.3	2.44	2.0	59	2.30	117					20
	6	1140	37.3	3.69	2.9	78	3.25	140					20
	8	860	37.3	4.89	4.2	97	4.40	166					20
1/12	2	3450	62.1	2.03	2.1	80	2.70	167					20
	4	1725	62.1	4.06	2.1	60	2.50	141					20
	6	1140	62.1	6.14	3.2	80	3.60	167					20
	8	860	62.1	8.14	4.4	100	4.93	198					20
1/8	2	3450	93.2	3.04	2.3	85	2.90	207					20
	4	1725	93.2	6.09	2.3	62	2.70	176					20
	6	1140	93.2	9.21	3.4	85	3.86	207					20
	8	860	93.2	12.21	4.9	110	5.40	245					20
1/6	2	3450	124.3	4.06	2.5	95	3.18	254					20
	4	1725	124.3	8.12	2.6	65	3.00	214					20
	6	1140	124.3	12.29	3.8	95	4.32	254	3.5	130	4.00	270	20
	8	860	124.3	16.29	5.4	125	6.00	296					20
1/4	2	3450	186.4	6.09	2.8	110	4.16	352					23
	4	1725	186.4	12.18	3.3	90	3.86	301					23
	6	1140	186.4	18.43	4.9	130	5.59	352	4.3	150	5.07	365	23
	8	860	186.4	24.42	7.3	175	8.10	414					23
1/3	2	3450	248.6	8.12	3.2	140	5.27	460					31
	4	1725	248.6	16.24	4.1	115	4.91	395					31
	6	1140	248.6	24.6	6.1	179	6.97	460	5.1	175	6.18	460	31
	8	860	248.6	32.6	8.8	235	9.83	540					31
1/2	2	3450	372.9	12.18	4.6	200	7.37	678					45
	4	1725	372.9	24.4	5.7	160	6.90	574					45
	6	1140	372.9	36.9	8.6	240	9.83	678					45
3/4	2	3450	559.3	18.27	7.1	280	10.57	981					61
	4	1725	559.3	36.6	8.3	220	9.93	835					61
1	2	3450	745.7	24.4	9.1	340	13.5	1265					

20-21. Maximum Inputs for Single-phase Induction Motors.—In Table XXVI the commonly recognized ratings of fractional horsepower induction motors are listed. Values of *output watts* correspond to the horsepower rating; values of *output torque* given represent the torque that has to be developed to develop rated horsepower at the speed shown. Full-load watts and amperes are maximum values to be expected; the figures given are the maximum values allowable accord-

TABLE XXVII.—WATTS AND AMPERES FOR THREE-PHASE MOTORS
(Data supplied by Westinghouse)

Horsepower	Poles	Rpm at full load	Output		No-load input			Full-load input		
			Watts	Torque	Amperes		Watts	Amperes		Watts
					220 volts	440 volts		220 volts	440 volts	
⅙	2	3,450	124.3	4.06	0.54	0.27	53	0.70	0.35	180
	4	1,725	124.3	8.12	0.48	0.24	37	0.62	0.31	173
	6	1,140	124.3	12.28	0.72	0.36	61	0.82	0.41	205
¼	2	3,450	186.4	6.09	0.54	0.27	53	0.86	0.43	259
	4	1,725	186.4	12.18	0.64	0.32	44	0.90	0.45	247
	6	1,140	186.4	18.42	0.76	0.38	62	1.04	0.52	260
	8	865	186.4	24.4	1.20	0.60	90	1.34	0.67	310
⅓	2	3,450	248.6	8.12	0.58	0.29	58	1.02	0.51	326
	4	1,725	248.6	16.24	0.80	0.40	55	1.16	0.58	326
	6	1,140	248.6	24.6	1.06	0.53	52	1.36	0.68	326
	8	865	248.6	32.6	1.50	0.75	90	1.68	0.84	364
½	2	3,450	372.9	12.18	0.70	0.35	63	1.48	0.74	465
	4	1,725	372.9	24.4	0.84	0.42	70	1.62	0.81	490
	6	1,140	372.9	36.9	1.28	0.64	57	1.78	0.89	465
¾	2	3,450	559.3	18.27	0.86	0.43	85	2.2	1.1	630
	4	1,725	559.3	36.6	1.24	0.62	70	2.4	1.2	680
1	2	3,450	745.7	24.4	1.60	0.80	150	3.0	1.5	880

For amperes at 550 volts, multiply 440-volt amperes by 0.80.
For amperes at 110 volts, multiply 220-volt amperes by 2.0.

ing to the now obsolete Nema performance specifications given in Table XXV, so far as the latter apply. All no-load inputs, also full-load inputs for ½₀-, ¹⁄₁₂-, and 1-hp motors, are estimated values, for which there are no standards in Table XXV.

Inputs for 50-cycle motors are of the order of 10 to 20 per cent higher than for 60-cycle motors of the same horsepower rating and same number of poles.

20-22. Inputs for Polyphase Induction Motors.—In table XXVII are given the *average* inputs of a line of motors on the market. It should be emphasized that these figures represent *average* and not maximum inputs of one line of motors, and variations either side of these figures are to be expected.

20-23. Relationships between Power, Torque, and Speed.

Let

$T_{\text{lb-ft}}$ = torque in lb-ft.
$T_{\text{lb-in.}}$ = torque in lb-in.
$T_{\text{oz-ft}}$ = torque in oz-ft.
$T_{\text{oz-in.}}$ = torque in oz-in.

Then

$$T_{\text{lb-ft}} = \frac{7.04 \times \text{watts}}{\text{rpm}} \tag{20-1}$$

$$T_{\text{lb-in.}} = \frac{84.5 \times \text{watts}}{\text{rpm}} \tag{20-2}$$

$$T_{\text{oz-ft}} = \frac{112.7 \times \text{watts}}{\text{rpm}} \tag{20-3}$$

$$T_{\text{oz-in.}} = \frac{1,352 \times \text{watts}}{\text{rpm}} \tag{20-4}$$

$$T_{\text{lb-ft}} = \frac{5,250 \times \text{hp}}{\text{rpm}} \tag{20-5}$$

$$T_{\text{lb-in.}} = \frac{63,000 \times \text{hp}}{\text{rpm}} \tag{20-6}$$

$$T_{\text{oz-ft}} = \frac{84,000 \times \text{hp}}{\text{rpm}} \tag{20-7}$$

$$T_{\text{oz-in.}} = \frac{1,008,000 \times \text{hp}}{\text{rpm}} \tag{20-8}$$

$$\text{Watts} = \frac{T_{\text{lb-ft}} \times \text{rpm}}{7.04} = \frac{T_{\text{lb-in.}} \times \text{rpm}}{84.5} \tag{20-9}$$

$$\text{Watts} = \frac{T_{\text{oz-ft}} \times \text{rpm}}{122.7} = \frac{T_{\text{oz-in}} \times \text{rpm}}{1,352} \tag{20-10}$$

$$\text{Horsepower} = \frac{T_{\text{lb-ft}} \times \text{rpm}}{5,250} = \frac{T_{\text{lb-in.}} \times \text{rpm}}{63,000} \tag{20-11}$$

$$\text{Horsepower} = \frac{T_{\text{oz-ft}} \times \text{rpm}}{84,000} = \frac{T_{\text{oz-in.}} \times \text{rpm}}{1,008,000} \tag{20-12}$$

Conversion factors for changing torque or power from one unit to another are given in Table XXX.

20-24. Radio Interference and Suppression Devices.—Commutator-type motors that require current commutation, or repeated interruption (*e.g.*, governor-controlled motors, Arts. 12-20 to 12-25), in order to perform their normal function may give trouble due to radio interference. This is because the commutation, or repeated interruption, of the currents produces components in the radio-frequency

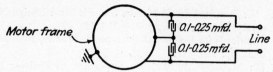

FIG. 20-7.—Circuit for suppressing radio noise from a small motor with solidly grounded frame.

ranges, which may interfere with reception. These interfering currents are conducted along the power wires from the motor, and the fields set up may affect the radio aerials in the vicinity. There may even be some radiation from the motor itself, though this is usually slight except within a few feet of the motor. The interference voltages exist across the power leads (symmetrical component), and from power leads jointly to the motor frame (asymmetrical component).

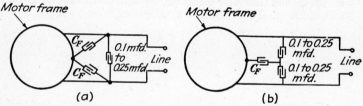

FIG. 20-8.—Circuits for suppressing radio noise from a small motor with a frame insulated from ground. For 115-volt motors, $C_F = 0.01$ mfd. For 230-volt motors, $C_F = 0.005$ mfd.

In order to suppress the interference it is necessary to use either one or both of the following methods:

1. Connect a capacitor from each motor lead to frame. This tends to put a short circuit on the motor for the high frequencies. (On motors that are operated with their frame insulated from ground, the microfarads of capacitance used is limited to approximately 0.0001 mfd per volt of motor rating; this limitation is because of danger of shock.)

2. Connect a choke coil in series with the power leads. This tends to open-circuit the motor for the high frequencies.

Capacitor methods generally used with quite satisfactory results are shown in Figs. 20-7 and 20-8. It is very important that the leads connecting the capacitors be as short as possible.   In most cases, it is practicable to wire a capacitor to a power lead with 2 to 3 in. of wire. Fuses are not commonly used in series with capacitors since they will reduce the effectiveness of a capacitor-type suppressor.   One should use capacitors with sufficient insulation strength.

Bibliography

1. VEINOTT, C. G.: Standard Small Motors Can Fit Most Design Needs, *Product Engineering*, April, May, 1946, pp. 313–318, 423–427.
2. New Nema Standards for Fractional-Horsepower Motors, *Elec. Manufacturing*, October, 1946, pp. 116, 117.
3. LLOYD, T. C.: Motor Parts Will Be Important to Postwar Designs, *Elec. Manufacturing*, December, 1943, p. 96.
4. RALL, C. A.: Mechanical Forms of Motors Are Important to the Specifier, *Elec. Manufacturing*, November, 1941, p. 72.
5. KENNEDY, C. L.: Standard or Special Motors, *Elec. Manufacturing*, June, 1940, p. 60.
6. PACKER, L. C., JOHNS, F. J., and CODLING, E. P.: Electrical Equipment for Hermetically Sealed Refrigerators, *Refrigerating Engineering*, June, 1945.
7. "Refrigerating Data Book," Chap. 22, American Society of Refrigerating Engineers, New York, 1942.
8. PACKER, L. C.: Design Factors Involved in the Design of Domestic Appliances, *A.I.E.E. Trans.*, vol. 60, 1941, pp. 500–507.
9. "Nema Motor and Generator Standards," Nema Publication No. 45-102, 1946, National Electrical Manufacturer's Association, New York.

APPENDIX

Table XXVIII.—Trouble Diagnosis Chart for Fractional Horsepower Motors

Problem	Probable causes	Test and remedy
A. Failure to start	1. Blowing of fuses	1. Check capacity of fuses; they should be rated at not less than 125 per cent of full-load current. Disconnect motor from line, replace fuses, and reconnect motor to line. If fuses blow, investigate and remedy cause.
	2. Overload device open-circuited. (Applies to manual-reset devices)	2. Reset overload device. If it trips out repeatedly, investigate further to find out why.
	3. Improper current supply, incorrect voltage or frequency	3. Make certain that voltage, frequency, and number of phases of supply circuit agree with the motor nameplate stamping. Correction involves getting the proper motor. Single-phase motors can be operated on polyphase circuits, but not vice versa. Alternating-current motors—except universal motors—will not operate on direct current, and vice versa.
	4. No voltage, or low voltage	4. Measure volts at motor terminals with line switch closed. It should be within 10 per cent of rating on nameplate; if not, larger feeder circuits, or shorter connections to motor, may be required.
	5. Improper line connections	5. See that connections are exactly in accordance with the connection diagram or connection instructions furnished with the motor; if no wiring diagram is available, a suitable one may be found in this book. However, terminal markings of the motor at hand may be different from the mark-

509

TABLE XXVIII.—TROUBLE DIAGNOSIS CHART FOR FRACTIONAL HORSEPOWER MOTORS.—(*Continued*)

Problem	Probable causes	Test and remedy
A. Failure to start (*Continued*)		ings on the wiring diagram given for a motor of the type concerned. If a wiring diagram that apparently fits is found, the first step should be a systematic check to see how the terminal markings differ, if at all, from those of the diagram selected.
	6. Mechanical failure in load	6. Check the driven appliance to see that it is not jammed and that it turns freely. Disconnect motor from the load, and determine if it will start idle. Watch out for excessive belt tension.
	7. Motor bearings tight, or seized	7. When bearings seize in a motor having high torques, such as a capacitor-start or repulsion-start motor, new bearings are usually required. In a motor having low torques, such as a shaded-pole motor, it is often sufficient to clean and relubricate the bearing. The bearing can be cleaned with a clean cloth soaked in gasoline or kerosene.
	8. Excessively worn or eccentric bearings	8. Motor shaft turns freely by hand when motor is not energized, but locks when power is applied so that it cannot be turned by hand. Remedy is to install new bearings.
	9. Dirt or foreign matter in air gap	9. Remove the obstruction.
	10. Excessive load	10. If motor starts idle and has no apparent defect, it may not have enough locked-rotor torque for the application, or may otherwise be misapplied. Refer to Chap. XX for guidance in selecting the right motor.
	11. Open circuit in starting phase, main phase, or both	11. This condition is often indicated by a humming sound when the line switch is closed. It may be due to a broken lead, improper or poorly soldered connection, defective starting switch (see Arts. 18-5 to 18-9), burned-out starting winding, defective capacitor, loose connection on thermal overload device.

TABLE XXVIII.—TROUBLE DIAGNOSIS CHART FOR FRACTIONAL HORSEPOWER
MOTORS.—(*Continued*)

Problem	Probable causes	Test and remedy
A. Failure to start (*Continued*)	12. Short-circuited stator	12. Likely to blow fuses; rewinding required. Similar condition can be caused by a grounded winding if motor is operated on a grounded circuit.
	13. Defective capacitor	13. If an electrolytic capacitor is used, disconnect it from the windings and test it as explained in Art. 5-10; if it is defective, it should be replaced (see Art. 5-9). Instructions for testing capacitor-transformer units are given in Arts. 6-8, 6-9, and 7-6.
	14. Defective controller	14. If motor uses an external controller, the latter should be checked for defects. Controllers are discussed as follows: *a.* Adj.-sp. cap. motors—Arts. 8-7, 8-8 *b.* Three-sp. cap. motors—Art. 8-13 *c.* Two-sp. cap. motors—Art. 8-15, Chap. IX
	15. Faulty starting switch	15. See Arts. 18-5 to 18-9.

Items applying especially to repulsion-type motors

	16. Worn or sticking brushes	16. Brushes may be worn so that they do not touch commutator, or only very lightly, in which case new brushes are required. If the brushes are sticking in the holders, clean brushes and brush holders so that brushes move freely. Brush springs may be weak and require replacing.
	17. Incorrect setting of brushes	17. Check to see that brushes are set the proper distance off neutral (see Art. 10-37).
	18. Defective short-circuiter, defective brush lifter	18. See if mechanism works freely, if commutator is clean opposite short-circuiter. Repair or replace the defective mechanism.
	19. Short-circuited armature	19. Remove brushes from commutator, impress full voltage on the stator winding, and turn armature by hand. If

Table XXVIII.—Trouble Diagnosis Chart for Fractional Horsepower Motors.—(*Continued*)

Problem	Probable causes	Test and remedy
A. Failure to start (*Continued*)		there are one or more points at which the rotor "hangs," the armature is short-circuited. By forcing the rotor to the position where it is most difficult to hold, the short circuit can be located, for the short-circuited coil will become hot. Sometimes the short circuit can be located, and repaired; frequently, rewinding the armature is required.
	Items applying especially to universal motors	
	20. Worn or sticking brushes	20. See Item 16, above.
	21. Defective speed governor	21. Inspect governor contacts, which may require cleaning. If contacts are badly burned, test capacitor for opens or shorts. Also inspect governor mechanism. Replace defective parts.
	22. Too much exterternal resistance	22 See Art. 12-29.
B. Excessive bearing wear	1. Belt tension too great; misalignment of belt, coupling or drive gears; unbalanced coupling; eccentric or too closely meshed gears; excessively heavy fan, flywheel, or other load hung on motor shaft	1. Correct the faulty mechanical condition. Belts, whether flat or V-shaped, should have only enough tension to prevent slipping.
	2. Dirty bearings, particularly if dirt is abrasive	2. If condition is bad, provide means for shielding motor from the dirt, or consult motor manufacturer and obtain a specially designed motor for the application.
	3. Insufficient or inadequate lubrication	3. Sleeve bearings should be lubricated with a good grade of light machine oil about once every 6 months for normal applications, and more frequently if the motor runs continuously (see Art. 18-2). For care of ball bearings, refer to Art. 18-4. See also *A*7, above.

TABLE XXVIII.—TROUBLE DIAGNOSIS CHART FOR FRACTIONAL HORSEPOWER MOTORS.—(*Continued*)

Problem	Probable causes	Test and remedy
B. Excessive bearing wear. (*Continued*)	4. Excessive thrust load	4. Reduce the thrust load or obtain a motor designed to handle the required thrust.
	5. Bent shaft (sleeve-bearing motors)	5. Remove rotor and check with a dial indicator; straighten as required.
C. Motor runs hot. *Don't judge motor temperature by hand.* Measure the temperature by thermometer, thermocouple, or rise of resistance (see Arts. 19-10, and 19-16*i*)	1. Improper line connections	1. See *A*5.
	2. Excessive load	2. Inspect the driven device and the belt, coupling, or other mechanical connection between the motor and its load. Run an application test, as explained in Art. 19-26, and determine if a motor of the right horsepower rating is used (see Art. 20-4); if not, it may be necessary to obtain a motor of larger rating. Continuous overloading shortens the life of a motor.
	3. Improper circuit voltage	3. Measure voltage at motor terminals with motor driving its load. If voltage differs more than 10 per cent from nameplate voltage, take full-load saturation test as described in Art. 19-16*h*. If watts input at operating voltage is materially greater than at rated voltage, this is the probable cause of the difficulty, but if there is little difference in inputs at these two voltages, a further search for the trouble should be made. See also Art. 20-7 for further discussion of this subject.
	4. Wrong frequency	4. Compare circuit frequency with nameplate frequency. See Art. 20-8 for a discussion of this subject.
	5. Too frequent starting	5. This condition may occur if motor is automatically controlled. Adjust the control to lengthen the cycle, if possible; reduce the WR^2 of the connected load; or, obtain manufacturer's recommendation for a new motor.
	6. Failure of ventilation	6. Clean motor, especially the ventilating passages. If motor has air-flow baffles to direct the air for effective

TABLE XXVIII.—TROUBLE DIAGNOSIS CHART FOR FRACTIONAL HORSEPOWER
MOTORS.—(*Continued*)

Problem	Probable causes	Test and remedy
C. Motor runs hot. (*Continued*)		cooling, make certain that these are correctly placed. Allow nothing to prevent free flow of necessary cooling air to and from motor.
	7. Ambient temperature too high	7. An ambient temperature above 40°C (104°F) is too high for standard motors. If motor is operated within an enclosure or restricted space, the temperature of this space may often rise several degrees above the room temperature. It is the temperature of the *immediate surroundings* of the motor that govern, not the room temperature. Sometimes this restricted space can be opened up or otherwise ventilated. If not, it may be necessary to obtain a special motor.
	8. Bearing trouble	8. See *A*7, *A*8, *B*1 to *B*5.
	9. Short-circuited coils	9. Condition may be indicated by abnormal magnetic noise, or excessive no-load watts. Rewind motor.
	10. Grounded winding or grounded switch	10. If the ground cannot be located and repaired, rewinding is required.
	11. Starting switch fails to open	11. Applies to split-phase and capacitor-start motors. Repair or replace faulty switch member (Arts. 18-5 to 18-9). This condition is apt to burn out the windings, particularly the starting winding.
	12. Poor soldering to commutator necks	12. Applies to d-c and universal motors. Resolder connections and check armature (see Arts. 12-17 to 12-19).
	13. Short-circuiter fails to function correctly	13. Applies to repulsion-start motors. Clean and repair or replace the mechanism (see Sec. *G*).
	14. Rotor rubbing stator	14. Best method of diagnosis is to dismantle motor and inspect stator bore and rotor surface for visual evidences of rubbing. If in doubt, apply Prussian blue to these surfaces, reassemble, run motor, dismantle, and reexamine. Remedy is to install new bearings (see *A*8).

Table XXVIII.—Trouble Diagnosis Chart for Fractional Horsepower
Motors.—(*Continued*)

Problem	Probable causes	Test and remedy
D. Motor burns out	1. Frozen bearings, misapplication, or any of the causes listed in Sec. *C*	1. Any of the bad conditions listed in Sec. *C*, if prolonged, may lead to motor burnout. After the motor has actually burned out, the real source of the trouble is often very difficult to trace. Recondition the motor, run an application test as described in Arts. 19-26 and 19-27, and investigate possibilities discussed in Sec. *C*.
E. Motor is noisy	1. Unbalanced rotor	1. An unbalanced rotor will set up a vibration that can be easily felt; the cure is to rebalance the rotor, dynamically, if equipment is available. Also, the shaft may be sprung slightly and may need straightening.
	2. Worn bearings	2. In single-phase induction motors, worn or dry bearings give rise to a characteristic noise; the noise is modulated at slip frequency and, at no load, is not unlike the sound of a purring cat. Sometimes oil will quiet the motor; at other times the bearings may have to be replaced (see Art. 18-2). If trouble is unduly frequent, see Sec. *B*.
	3. Switch rattles or rubs	3. Check switch for correct location and operation. Replace if necessary (see Arts. 18-5 to 18-9).
	4. Excessive end play	4. Dismantle motor and add thrust washers to take up end play (Art. 18-2); add these to the side opposite the switch so as not to disturb the location of the latter with respect to the stator. Some motors are provided with end-play take-up plug as shown in Fig. 18-6; take up end play on these motors by tapping in the end-play take-up device, being careful not to increase the input to the motor by more than 10 watts.
	5. Motor not properly aligned with driven machine	5. Correct mechanical condition.

TABLE XXVIII.—TROUBLE DIAGNOSIS CHART FOR FRACTIONAL HORSEPOWER
MOTORS.—(*Continued*)

Problem	Probable causes	Test and remedy
E. Motor is noisy (*Continued*)	6. Motor not fastened firmly to mounting base	6. Correct mechanical condition.
	7. Loose accessories on motor	7. Such parts as oil-well covers, capacitor box or cover, oil pipe, conduit boxes or covers, and guards should be carefully checked and tightened so that they cannot rattle.
	8. Air gap not uniform	8. Bent shaft may cause this condition (see *E*1). For extreme quietness, it may be necessary, after the shaft is straightened, to grind the rotor true. Only the barest minimum of material should be removed, as this increases the power and current consumption of the motor.
	9. Dirt in air gap	9. Noise is irregular, intermittent, and scratchy; dismantle and clean motor.
	10. Amplified motor noises	10. If this condition is suspected, uncouple motor from load and allow it to run idle; if noise persists, loosen the mounting bolts and lift the motor— while it is still running—off the mounting bolts. If motor is quiet, the mounting was acting as an amplifier. Use of resilient mounting will usually eliminate noise from this source (Art. 18-12). In some cases, it may be necessary to provide torsional flexibility in the coupling that connects the motor to the load (see Art. 18-13).
	11. Burrs on shaft shoulders, nicks on journals	11. Determine by inspection. Correct mechanical condition.
	12. Rough commutator	12. True up. See Art. 12-18.
F. Motor noisy when stopping	1. Regeneration (Cap-start motors)	1. Motor becomes noisy while coasting to a stop. See Art. 5-36.
Repulsion-start motors		
G. Motor runs but governor does	1. Dirty commutator	1. Clean with fine sandpaper, never with emery.

TABLE XXVIII.—TROUBLE DIAGNOSIS CHART FOR FRACTIONAL HORSEPOWER MOTORS.—(*Continued*)

Problem	Probable causes	Test and remedy
not operate in a few seconds (see Arts. 10-30 to 10-39)	2. Governor mechanism sticking	2. Work governor mechanism by hand. Clean and install new parts or new governor as required.
	3. Worn or sticking brushes	3. See *A*16.
	4. Frequency of supply circuit low	4. Check frequency of supply circuit. Get motor of proper frequency rating.
	5. Low line voltage	5. See *A*4.
	6. Wrong connections	6. See *A*5.
	7. Incorrect brush setting	7. See Art. 10-37.
	8. Excessive load	8. See *A*10.
	9. Short-circuited stator	9. See *A*12.
	10. Incorrect spring tension	10. Springs may lose temper or get out of adjustment; governor may not be of the proper speed rating.
Commutator-type motors		
H. Excessive brush wear	1. Dirty or oily commutator	1. Clean with fine sandpaper, never with emery.
	2. Any of the troubles in Sec. *G*	2. See Sec. *G*.
	3. High mica, rough commutator	3. True up. See Art. 12-18.
	4. Excessive spring tension	4. Adjust to correct tension.
	5. Loose-fitting brushes	5. Get brushes or brush-holder boxes of the correct size.
I. Radio interference	1. Any of the causes in Sec. *H*	1. Correct mechanical condition. If necessary add suppression filter, as explained in Art. 20-24.

TABLE XXIX.—LOCKED-ROTOR AMPERES FROM CODE-LETTER MARKINGS

| Rating | | | Code-letter marking | | | | | | | | | | | | | | | |
Hp	Volts	Ph	A	B	C	D	E	F	G	H	J	K	L	M	N	P	R
1/20	115*	1	0	1.37	1.54	1.74	1.96	2.17	2.44	2.74	3.09	3.48	3.91	4.35	4.87	5.44	6.09
1/12	115*	1	0	2.28	2.57	2.90	3.26	3.62	4.06	4.56	5.14	5.80	6.52	7.25	8.12	9.06	10.14
1/8	115*	1	0	3.42	3.86	4.35	4.89	5.44	6.09	6.85	7.72	8.70	9.78	10.87	12.17	13.59	15.22
1/6	115*	1	0	4.56	5.14	5.78	6.52	7.25	8.12	9.13	10.29	11.59	13.04	14.49	16.23	18.12	20.29
1/4	115*	1	0	6.85	7.72	8.70	9.78	10.87	12.17	13.70	15.43	17.39	19.57	21.74	24.35	27.17	30.43
1/3	115*	1	0	9.13	10.29	11.59	13.04	14.49	16.23	18.26	20.58	23.19	26.09	28.99	32.46	36.23	40.58
1/2	115*	1	0	13.70	15.43	17.39	19.57	21.74	24.35	27.39	30.87	34.78	39.13	43.48	48.70	54.38	60.87
3/4	115*	1	0	20.54	23.15	26.09	29.35	32.61	36.52	41.09	46.30	52.17	58.70	65.22	73.04	81.52	91.30
1	115*	1	0	27.39	30.87	34.78	39.13	43.48	48.70	54.78	61.74	69.57	78.26	86.96	97.39	108.7	121.7
1/8	220†	2	0	0.90	1.01	1.14	1.28	1.42	1.59	1.79	2.02	2.27	2.56	2.84	3.18	3.55	4.00
1/6	220†	2	0	1.19	1.35	1.52	1.70	1.89	2.12	2.39	2.69	3.03	3.41	3.79	4.24	4.74	5.30
1/4	220†	2	0	1.79	2.02	2.27	2.56	2.84	3.18	3.58	4.03	4.54	5.11	5.68	6.36	7.10	7.96
1/3	220†	2	0	2.39	2.69	3.03	3.41	3.79	4.24	4.77	5.38	6.06	6.82	7.58	8.48	9.47	10.61
1/2	220†	2	0	3.58	4.03	4.55	5.11	5.68	6.36	7.16	8.07	9.09	10.23	11.36	12.73	14.20	15.91
3/4	220†	2	0	5.37	6.05	6.82	7.67	8.52	9.55	10.74	12.10	13.64	15.34	17.05	19.09	21.31	23.86
1	220†	2	0	7.16	8.07	9.09	10.23	11.36	12.72	14.32	16.14	18.18	20.45	22.72	25.45	28.41	31.82
1/8	208	3	0	1.09	1.23	1.39	1.56	1.73	1.94	2.19	2.46	2.78	3.12	3.47	3.89	4.38	4.86
1/6	208	3	0	1.46	1.64	1.85	2.08	2.31	2.59	2.91	3.28	3.70	4.16	4.63	5.18	5.78	6.48
1/4	208	3	0	2.18	2.46	2.77	3.12	3.46	3.88	4.37	4.93	5.55	6.25	6.94	7.77	8.67	9.72
1/3	208	3	0	2.91	3.28	3.70	4.16	4.63	5.18	5.83	6.57	7.40	8.33	9.25	10.36	11.57	12.95
1/2	208	3	0	4.37	4.93	5.55	6.25	6.93	7.77	8.74	9.85	11.10	12.49	13.88	15.54	17.35	19.43
3/4	208	3	0	6.56	7.39	8.33	9.37	10.40	11.66	13.11	14.78	16.65	18.74	20.82	23.32	26.02	29.15
1	208	3	0	8.74	9.85	11.10	12.49	13.88	15.54	17.49	19.71	22.21	24.98	27.76	31.09	34.70	38.86
1/8	220†	3	0	1.03	1.16	1.31	1.48	1.64	1.83	2.07	2.33	2.62	2.95	3.28	3.67	4.10	4.59
1/6	220†	3	0	1.38	1.55	1.75	1.97	2.19	2.45	2.76	3.11	3.50	3.94	4.37	4.90	5.47	6.19
1/4	220†	3	0	2.07	2.33	2.62	2.95	3.28	3.67	4.13	4.66	5.25	5.90	6.56	7.35	8.20	9.19
1/3	220†	3	0	2.76	3.11	3.50	3.94	4.37	4.90	5.51	6.21	7.00	7.87	8.75	9.80	10.93	12.25
1/2	220†	3	0	4.13	4.66	5.25	5.90	6.56	7.35	8.27	9.32	10.50	11.81	13.12	14.70	16.40	18.37
3/4	220†	3	0	6.20	6.99	7.87	8.86	9.84	11.02	12.40	13.97	15.75	17.71	19.68	22.04	24.60	27.56
1	220†	3	0	8.27	9.32	10.50	11.81	13.12	14.70	16.53	18.63	20.99	23.62	26.24	29.39	32.80	36.74

* For locked-rotor currents at 230 volts, multiply values in table by 0.5.
† For locked-rotor currents at 110 volts, multiply values in table by 2.
‡ For locked-rotor currents at 440 volts, multiply values in table by 0.5.
Example: Code letter K on a ½-hp 115-volt single-phase motor means a locked-rotor current equal to or more than 34.78 amp but less than 39.13 amp.

TABLE XXX.—CONVERSION TABLE FOR UNITS OF POWER, TORQUE

Units of torque

Multiply	By	To obtain
Pound-feet....................	12	Pound-inches
Pound-feet....................	16	Ounce-feet
Pound-feet....................	192	Ounce-inches
Pound-feet....................	0.1383	Meter-kilograms
Pound-feet....................	13,830	Centimeter-grams
Pound-inches.................	1.333	Ounce-feet
Pound-inches.................	16.00	Ounce-inches
Pound-inches.................	0.01152	Meter-kilograms
Pound-inches.................	1,152	Centimeter-grams
Ounce-feet....................	12	Ounce-inches
Ounce-feet....................	0.00864	Meter-kilograms
Ounce-feet....................	864	Centimeter-grams
Ounce-inches.................	0.000720	Meter-kilograms
Ounce-inches.................	72	Centimeter-grams
Meter-kilograms..............	100,000	Centimeter-grams

Units of power

Multiply	By	To obtain
Kilowatts....................	1.341	Horsepower
Kilowatts....................	1,000	Watts
Kilowatts....................	737.6	Foot-pounds per second
Kilowatts....................	44,250	Foot-pounds per minute
Kilowatts....................	6,119	Kilogram-meters per minute
Kilowatts....................	10,200,000	Gram-centimeters per second
Horsepower...................	745.7	Watts
Horsepower...................	550	Foot-pounds per second
Horsepower...................	33,000	Foot-pounds per minute
Horsepower...................	4,564	Kilogram-meters per minute
Horsepower...................	7,600,000	Gram-centimeters per second
Watts........................	0.7376	Foot-pounds per second
Watts........................	44.26	Foot-pounds per minute
Watts........................	6.119	Kilogram-meters per minute
Watts........................	10,200	Gram-centimeters per second
Foot-pounds per second........	60	Foot-pounds per minute
Foot-pounds per second........	8.296	Kilogram-meters per minute
Foot-pounds per second........	13,830	Gram-centimeters per second
Foot-pounds per minute........	0.1383	Kilogram-meters per minute
Foot-pounds per minute........	230.5	Gram-centimeters per second
Kilogram-meters per minute.....	1,667	Gram-centimeters per second

Conversions can be made in the inverse order by dividing by the conversion factor instead of multiplying by it. For example: Divide centimeter-grams by 72.0 to obtain ounce-inches.

TABLE XXXI.—TABLE FOR CONVERTING DEGREES FAHRENHEIT TO DEGREES CENTIGRADE

	0	1	2	3	4	5	6	7	8	9
−100	−73.3	−73.9	−74.4	−75	−75.6	−76.1	−76.7	−77.2	−77.8	−78.3
− 90	−67.8	−68.3	−68.9	−69.4	−70	−70.6	−71.1	−71.7	−72.2	−72.8
− 80	−62.2	−62.8	−63.3	−63.9	−64.4	−65	−65.6	−66.1	−66.7	−67.2
− 70	−56.7	−57.2	−57.8	−58.3	−58.9	−59.4	−60	−60.6	−61.1	−61.7
− 60	−51.1	−51.7	−52.2	−52.8	−53.3	−53.9	−54.4	−55	−55.6	−56.1
− 50	−45.6	−46.1	−46.7	−47.2	−47.8	−48.3	−48.9	−49.4	−50	−50.6
− 40	−40	−40.6	−41.1	−41.7	−42.2	−42.8	−43.3	−43.9	−44.4	−45
− 30	−34.4	−35	−35.6	−36.1	−36.7	−37.2	−37.8	−38.3	−38.9	−39.4
− 20	−28.9	−29.4	−30	−30.6	−31.1	−31.7	−32.2	−32.8	−33.3	−33.9
− 10	−23.3	−23.9	−24.4	−25	−25.6	−26.1	−26.7	−27.2	−27.8	−28.3
− 0	−17.8	−18.3	−18.9	−19.4	−20	−20.6	−21.1	−21.7	−22.2	−22.8
0	−17.8	−17.2	−16.7	−16.1	−15.6	−15	−14.4	−13.9	−13.3	−12.8
10	−12.2	−11.7	−11.1	−10.6	−10	− 9.4	− 8.9	− 8.3	− 7.8	− 7.2
20	− 6.7	− 6.1	− 5.6	− 5	− 4.4	− 3.9	− 3.3	− 2.8	− 2.2	− 1.7
30	− 1.1	− 0.6	0	0.6	1.1	1.7	2.2	2.8	3.3	3.9
40	4.4	5	5.6	6.1	6.7	7.2	7.8	8.3	8.9	9.4
50	10	10.6	11.1	11.7	12.2	12.8	13.3	13.9	14.4	15
60	15.6	16.1	16.7	17.2	17.8	18.3	18.9	19.4	20	20.6
70	21.1	21.7	22.2	22.8	23.3	23.9	24.4	25	25.6	26.1
80	26.7	27.2	27.8	28.3	28.9	29.4	30	30.6	31.1	31.7
90	32.2	32.8	33.3	33.9	34.4	35	35.6	36.1	36.7	37.2
100	37.8	38.3	38.9	39.4	40	40.6	41.1	41.7	42.2	42.8
110	43.3	43.9	44.4	45	45.6	46.1	46.7	47.2	47.8	48.3
120	48.9	49.4	50	50.6	51.1	51.7	52.2	52.8	53.3	53.9
130	54.4	55	55.6	56.1	56.7	57.2	57.8	58.3	58.9	59.4
140	60	60.6	61.1	61.7	62.2	62.8	63.3	63.9	64.4	65
150	65.6	66.1	66.7	67.2	67.8	68.3	68.9	69.4	70	70.6
160	71.1	71.7	72.2	72.8	73.3	73.9	74.4	75	75.6	76.1
170	76.7	77.2	77.8	78.3	78.9	79.4	80	80.6	81.1	81.7
180	82.2	82.8	83.3	83.9	84.4	85	85.6	86.1	86.7	87.2
190	87.8	88.3	88.9	89.4	90	90.6	91.1	91.7	92.2	92.8
200	93.3	93.9	94.4	95	95.6	96.1	96.7	97.2	97.8	98.3
210	98.9	99.4	100	100.6	101.1	101.7	102.2	102.8	103.3	103.9
220	104.4	105	105.6	106.1	106.7	107.2	107.8	108.3	108.9	109.4
230	110	110.6	111.1	111.7	112.2	112.8	113.3	113.9	114.4	115
240	115.6	116.1	116.7	117.2	117.8	118.3	118.9	119.4	120	120.6
250	121.1	121.7	122.2	122.8	123.3	123.9	124.4	125	125.6	126.1
260	126.7	127.2	127.8	128.3	128.9	129.4	130	130.6	131.1	131.7
270	132.2	132.8	133.3	133.9	134.4	135	135.6	136.1	136.7	137.2
280	137.8	138.3	138.9	139.4	140	140.6	141.1	141.7	142.2	142.8
290	143.3	143.9	144.4	145	145.6	146.1	146.7	147.2	147.8	148.3
300	148.9	149.4	150	150.6	151.1	151.7	152.2	152.8	153.3	153.9
310	154.4	155	155.6	156.1	156.7	157.2	157.8	158.3	158.9	159.4
320	160	160.6	161.1	161.7	162.2	162.8	163.3	163.9	164.4	165
330	165.6	166.1	166.7	167.2	167.8	168.3	168.9	169.4	170	170.6
340	171.1	171.7	172.2	172.8	173.3	173.9	174.4	175	175.6	176.1
350	176.7	177.2	177.8	178.3	178.9	179.4	180	180.6	181.1	181.7
360	182.2	182.8	183.3	183.9	184.4	185	185.6	186.1	186.7	187.2
370	187.8	188.3	188.9	189.4	190	190.6	191.1	191.7	192.2	192.8
380	193.3	193.9	194.4	195	195.6	196.1	196.7	197.2	197.8	198.3
390	198.9	199.4	200	200.6	201.1	201.7	202.2	202.8	203.3	203.9
400	204.4	205	205.6	206.1	206.7	207.2	207.8	208.3	208.9	209.4

Example: 53°F = 11.7°C.

TABLE XXXII.—WIRE TABLE

(Compiled from Phelps-Dodge, General Electric, and Westinghouse sources)

Gauge No.	Diameter, bare	Diameter over insulation								Weight, pounds per 1,000 feet				Area in circular mils	Resistance in ohms per 1,000 feet at 25°C
		Enam. or single formvar	Double formvar	Quadruple formvar	Single paper enam.	Single cotton enam.	Single silk (or Nylon) enam.	Double glass bare	Single glass heavy formvar	Bare	Double formvar	Single cotton enam.	Double glass bare		
13	0.072	0.0738	0.0753	0.0779	0.077	0.0786	......	0.0795	0.0803	15.68	15.9	16.0	16.3	5178	2.043
14	0.064	0.0659	0.0673	0.0699	0.0691	0.0707	......	0.0716	0.0723	12.43	12.6	12.7	13.0	4107	2.575
15	0.057	0.0588	0.0602	0.0628	0.062	0.0637	0.0604	0.0646	0.0652	9.858	10.05	10.1	10.3	3257	3.247
16	0.051	0.0525	0.0539	0.0563	0.0557	0.0571	0.0541	0.0583	0.0589	7.818	7.96	8.06	8.24	2583	4.094
17	0.045	0.0469	0.0482	0.0506	0.0501	0.0515	0.0485	0.0528	0.0532	6.20	6.34	6.41	6.56	2048	5.163
18	0.040	0.0418	0.0432	0.0456	0.045	0.0466	0.0434	0.0478	0.0482	4.917	5.02	5.10	5.23	1624	6.51
19	0.036	0.0374	0.0386	0.0409	0.0406	0.0421	0.039	0.0434	0.0436	3.899	4.00	4.06	4.18	1288	8.21
20	0.032	0.0334	0.0346	0.0368	0.0366	0.038	0.035	0.0395	0.0396	3.092	3.17	3.24	3.34	1022	10.35
21	0.0285	0.0299	0.031	0.0331	0.0331	0.0345	0.0315	0.036	0.0360	2.452	2.51	2.57	2.67	810.1	13.05
22	0.0254	0.0267	0.0278	0.0298	0.0299	0.0313	0.0283	0.0328	0.0328	1.945	1.99	2.05	2.14	642.4	16.46
23	0.0226	0.0239	0.0249	0.0269	0.027	0.0284	0.0254	0.0301	0.0299	1.542	1.58	1.63	1.72	509.5	20.76
24	0.0201	0.0213	0.0224	0.0243	0.0245	0.0259	0.0229	0.0276	0.0274	1.223	1.26	1.31	1.39	404.0	26.17
25	0.0179	0.0191	0.0201	0.022	0.0215	0.0233	0.0207	0.0232	0.0233	0.9699	0.998	1.04	1.12	320.4	33.00
26	0.0159	0.0170	0.018	0.0198	0.0194	0.021	0.0186	0.0212	0.0213	0.7692	0.793	0.837	0.900	254.1	41.62
27	0.0142	0.0153	0.0161	0.0178	0.0177	0.0193	0.0169	0.0195	0.0194	0.610	0.630	0.662	0.727	201.5	52.48
28	0.0126	0.0136	0.0145	0.016	0.016	0.0178	0.0152	0.0179	0.0177	0.4837	0.501	0.532	0.588	159.8	66.17
29	0.0113	0.0122	0.013	0.0145	0.0146	0.0164	0.0138	0.0166	0.0162	0.3836	0.396	0.427	0.477	126.7	83.44
30	0.0100	0.0109	0.0116	0.0131	0.0133	0.0151	0.0125	0.0153	0.0149	0.3042	0.316	0.344	0.387	100.5	105.2
31	0.0089	0.0098	0.0105	......	......	0.0139	0.0113	0.0142	0.0137	0.2413	0.251	0.278	0.314	79.7	132.7
32	0.0080	0.0088	0.0094	......	......	0.013	0.0104	0.0133	0.0126	0.1913	0.198	0.224	0.255	63.71	167.3
33	0.0071	0.0079	0.0085	......	......	0.0119	0.0094	0.0124	0.0117	0.1517	0.158	0.182	0.208	50.13	211.0
34	0.0063	0.0071	0.0075	......	......	0.0111	0.0086	0.0116	0.0108	0.1203	0.126	0.148	0.169	39.75	266.0
35	0.0056	0.0063	0.0067	......	......	0.0103	0.0078	0.0109	0.0100	0.0954	0.0996	0.120	0.138	31.52	335.5
36	0.0050	0.0057	0.0060	......	......	0.0093	0.0072	0.0103	0.0093	0.0757	0.0791	0.100	0.113	25.00	423.0
37	0.0045	0.0051	0.0055	......	......	0.0087	0.0066	0.0098	0.0087	0.060	0.0628	0.080	......	19.83	533.4
38	0.0040	0.0045	0.0049	......	......	0.0082	0.0061	0.0093	0.0081	0.0476	0.0498	0.068	......	15.72	672.6
39	0.0035	0.0040	0.0043	......	......	......	0.0055	0.0088	0.0075	0.0377	0.0397	0.060	......	12.47	848.1

TABLE XXXIII.—NATURAL SINES AND COSINES

(0 to 90° by tenths, to four decimal places)

NOTE.—For cosines use right-hand column of degrees and lower line of tenths.

Deg	°0.0	°0.1	°0.2	°0.3	°0.4	°0.5	°0.6	°0.7	°0.8	°0.9	
0°	0.0000	0.0017	0.0035	0.0052	0.0070	0.0087	0.0105	0.0122	0.0140	0.0157	89
1	0.0175	0.0192	0.0209	0.0227	0.0244	0.0262	0.0279	0.0297	0.0314	0.0332	88
2	0.0349	0.0366	0.0384	0.0401	0.0419	0.0436	0.0454	0.0471	0.0488	0.0506	87
3	0.0523	0.0541	0.0558	0.0576	0.0593	0.0610	0.0628	0.0645	0.0663	0.0680	86
4	0.0698	0.0715	0.0732	0.0750	0.0767	0.0785	0.0802	0.0819	0.0837	0.0854	85
5	0.0872	0.0889	0.0906	0.0924	0.0941	0.0958	0.0976	0.0993	0.1011	0.1028	84
6	0.1045	0.1063	0.1080	0.1097	0.1115	0.1132	0.1149	0.1167	0.1184	0.1201	83
7	0.1219	0.1236	0.1253	0.1271	0.1288	0.1305	0.1323	0.1340	0.1357	0.1374	82
8	0.1392	0.1409	0.1426	0.1444	0.1461	0.1478	0.1495	0.1513	0.1530	0.1547	81
9	0.1564	0.1582	0.1599	0.1616	0.1633	0.1650	0.1668	0.1685	0.1702	0.1719	80°
10°	0.1736	0.1754	0.1771	0.1788	0.1805	0.1822	0.1840	0.1857	0.1874	0.1891	79
11	0.1908	0.1925	0.1942	0.1959	0.1977	0.1994	0.2011	0.2028	0.2045	0.2062	78
12	0.2079	0.2096	0.2113	0.2130	0.2147	0.2164	0.2181	0.2198	0.2215	0.2232	77
13	0.2250	0.2267	0.2284	0.2300	0.2317	0.2334	0.2351	0.2368	0.2385	0.2402	76
14	0.2419	0.2436	0.2453	0.2470	0.2487	0.2504	0.2521	0.2538	0.2554	0.2571	75
15	0.2588	0.2605	0.2622	0.2639	0.2656	0.2672	0.2689	0.2706	0.2723	0.2740	74
16	0.2756	0.2773	0.2790	0.2807	0.2823	0.2840	0.2857	0.2874	0.2890	0.2907	73
17	0.2924	0.2940	0.2957	0.2974	0.2990	0.3007	0.3024	0.3040	0.3057	0.3074	72
18	0.3090	0.3107	0.3123	0.3140	0.3156	0.3173	0.3190	0.3206	0.3223	0.3239	71
19	0.3256	0.3272	0.3289	0.3305	0.3322	0.3338	0.3355	0.3371	0.3387	0.3404	70°
20°	0.3420	0.3437	0.3453	0.3469	0.3486	0.3502	0.3518	0.3535	0.3551	0.3567	69
21	0.3584	0.3600	0.3616	0.3633	0.3649	0.3665	0.3681	0.3697	0.3714	0.3730	68
22	0.3746	0.3762	0.3778	0.3795	0.3811	0.3827	0.3843	0.3859	0.3875	0.3891	67
23	0.3907	0.3923	0.3939	0.3955	0.3971	0.3987	0.4003	0.4019	0.4035	0.4051	66
24	0.4067	0.4083	0.4099	0.4115	0.4131	0.4147	0.4163	0.4179	0.4195	0.4210	65
25	0.4226	0.4242	0.4258	0.4274	0.4289	0.4305	0.4321	0.4337	0.4352	0.4368	64
26	0.4384	0.4399	0.4415	0.4431	0.4446	0.4462	0.4478	0.4493	0.4509	0.4524	63
27	0.4540	0.4555	0.4571	0.4586	0.4602	0.4617	0.4633	0.4648	0.4664	0.4679	62
28	0.4695	0.4710	0.4726	0.4741	0.4756	0.4772	0.4787	0.4802	0.4818	0.4833	61
29	0.4848	0.4863	0.4879	0.4894	0.4909	0.4924	0.4939	0.4955	0.4970	0.4985	60°
30°	0.5000	0.5015	0.5030	0.5045	0.5060	0.5075	0.5090	0.5105	0.5120	0.5135	59
31	0.5150	0.5165	0.5180	0.5195	0.5210	0.5225	0.5240	0.5255	0.5270	0.5284	58
32	0.5299	0.5314	0.5329	0.5344	0.5358	0.5373	0.5388	0.5402	0.5417	0.5432	57
33	0.5446	0.5461	0.5476	0.5490	0.5505	0.5519	0.5534	0.5548	0.5563	0.5577	56
34	0.5592	0.5606	0.5621	0.5635	0.5650	0.5664	0.5678	0.5693	0.5707	0.5721	55
35	0.5736	0.5750	0.5764	0.5779	0.5793	0.5807	0.5821	0.5835	0.5850	0.5864	54
36	0.5878	0.5892	0.5906	0.5920	0.5934	0.5948	0.5962	0.5976	0.5990	0.6004	53
37	0.6018	0.6032	0.6046	0.6060	0.6074	0.6088	0.6101	0.6115	0.6129	0.6143	52
38	0.6157	0.6170	0.6184	0.6198	0.6211	0.6225	0.6239	0.6252	0.6266	0.6280	51
39	0.6293	0.6307	0.6320	0.6334	0.6347	0.6361	0.6374	0.6388	0.6401	0.6414	50°
40°	0.6428	0.6441	0.6455	0.6468	0.6481	0.6494	0.6508	0.6521	0.6534	0.6547	49
41	0.6561	0.6574	0.6587	0.6600	0.6613	0.6626	0.6639	0.6652	0.6665	0.6678	48
42	0.6691	0.6704	0.6717	0.6730	0.6743	0.6756	0.6769	0.6782	0.6794	0.6807	47
43	0.6820	0.6833	0.6845	0.6858	0.6871	0.6884	0.6896	0.6909	0.6921	0.6934	46
44	0.6947	0.6959	0.6972	0.6984	0.6997	0.7009	0.7022	0.7034	0.7046	0.7059	45
	°1.0	°0.9	°0.8	°0.7	°0.6	°0.5	°0.4	°0.3	°0.2	°0.1	Deg.

TABLE XXXIII.—NATURAL SINES AND COSINES.—(*Continued*)

Deg	°0.0	°0.1	°0.2	°0.3	°0.4	°0.5	°0.6	°0.7	°0.8	°0.9	
45	0.7071	0.7083	0.7096	0.7108	0.7120	0.7133	0.7145	0.7157	0.7169	0.7181	44
46	0.7193	0.7206	0.7218	0.7230	0.7242	0.7254	0.7266	0.7278	0.7290	0.7302	43
47	0.7314	0.7325	0.7337	0.7349	0.7361	0.7373	0.7385	0.7396	0.7408	0.7420	42
48	0.7431	0.7443	0.7455	0.7466	0.7478	0.7490	0.7501	0.7513	0.7524	0.7536	41
49	0.7547	0.7559	0.7570	0.7581	0.7593	0.7604	0.7615	0.7627	0.7638	0.7649	40°
50°	0.7660	0.7672	0.7683	0.7694	0.7705	0.7716	0.7727	0.7738	0.7749	0.7760	39
51	0.7771	0.7782	0.7793	0.7804	0.7815	0.7826	0.7837	0.7848	0.7859	0.7869	38
52	0.7880	0.7891	0.7902	0.7912	0.7923	0.7934	0.7944	0.7955	0.7965	0.7976	37
53	0.7986	0.7997	0.8007	0.8018	0.8028	0.8039	0.8049	0.8059	0.8070	0.8080	36
54	0.8090	0.8100	0.8111	0.8121	0.8131	0.8141	0.8151	0.8161	0.8171	0.8181	35
55	0.8192	0.8202	0.8211	0.8221	0.8231	0.8241	0.8251	0.8261	0.8271	0.8281	34
56	0.8290	0.8300	0.8310	0.8320	0.8329	0.8339	0.8348	0.8358	0.8368	0.8377	33
57	0.8387	0.8396	0.8406	0.8415	0.8425	0.8434	0.8443	0.8453	0.8462	0.8471	32
58	0.8480	0.8490	0.8499	0.8508	0.8517	0.8526	0.8536	0.8545	0.8554	0.8563	31
59	0.8572	0.8581	0.8590	0.8599	0.8607	0.8616	0.8625	0.8634	0.8643	0.8652	30°
60°	0.8660	0.8669	0.8678	0.8686	0.8695	0.8704	0.8712	0.8721	0.8729	0.8738	29
61	0.8746	0.8755	0.8763	0.8771	0.8780	0.8788	0.8796	0.8805	0.8813	0.8821	28
62	0.8829	0.8838	0.8846	0.8854	0.8862	0.8870	0.8878	0.8886	0.8894	0.8902	27
63	0.8910	0.8918	0.8926	0.8934	0.8942	0.8949	0.8957	0.8965	0.8973	0.8980	26
64	0.8988	0.8996	0.9003	0.9011	0.9018	0.9026	0.9033	0.9041	0.9048	0.9056	25
65	0.9063	0.9070	0.9078	0.9085	0.9092	0.9100	0.9107	0.9114	0.9121	0.9128	24
66	0.9135	0.9143	0.9150	0.9157	0.9164	0.9171	0.9178	0.9184	0.9191	0.9198	23
67	0.9205	0.9212	0.9219	0.9225	0.9232	0.9239	0.9245	0.9252	0.9259	0.9265	22
68	0.9272	0.9278	0.9285	0.9291	0.9298	0.9304	0.9311	0.9317	0.9323	0.9330	21
69	0.9336	0.9342	0.9348	0.9354	0.9361	0.9367	0.9373	0.9379	0.9385	0.9391	20°
70°	0.9397	0.9403	0.9409	0.9415	0.9421	0.9426	0.9432	0.9438	0.9444	0.9449	19
71	0.9455	0.9461	0.9466	0.9472	0.9478	0.9483	0.9489	0.9494	0.9500	0.9505	18
72	0.9511	0.9516	0.9521	0.9527	0.9532	0.9537	0.9542	0.9548	0.9553	0.9558	17
73	0.9563	0.9568	0.9573	0.9578	0.9583	0.9588	0.9593	0.9598	0.9603	0.9608	16
74	0.9613	0.9617	0.9622	0.9627	0.9632	0.9636	0.9641	0.9646	0.9650	0.9655	15
75	0.9659	0.9664	0.9668	0.9673	0.9677	0.9681	0.9686	0.9690	0.9694	0.9699	14
76	0.9703	0.9707	0.9711	0.9715	0.9720	0.9724	0.9728	0.9732	0.9736	0.9740	13
77	0.9744	0.9748	0.9751	0.9755	0.9759	0.9763	0.9767	0.9770	0.9774	0.9778	12
78	0.9781	0.9785	0.9789	0.9792	0.9796	0.9799	0.9803	0.9806	0.9810	0.9813	11
79	0.9816	0.9820	0.9823	0.9826	0.9829	0.9833	0.9836	0.9839	0.9842	0.9845	10°
80°	0.9848	0.9851	0.9854	0.9857	0.9860	0.9863	0.9866	0.9869	0.9871	0.9874	9
81	0.9877	0.9880	0.9882	0.9885	0.9888	0.9890	0.9893	0.9895	0.9898	0.9900	8
82	0.9903	0.9905	0.9907	0.9910	0.9912	0.9914	0.9917	0.9919	0.9921	0.9923	7
83	0.9925	0.9928	0.9930	0.9932	0.9934	0.9936	0.9938	0.9940	0.9942	0.9943	6
84	0.9945	0.9947	0.9949	0.9951	0.9952	0.9954	0.9956	0.9957	0.9959	0.9960	5
85	0.9962	0.9963	0.9965	0.9966	0.9968	0.9969	0.9971	0.9972	0.9973	0.9974	4
86	0.9976	0.9977	0.9978	0.9979	0.9980	0.9981	0.9982	0.9983	0.9984	0.9985	3
87	0.9986	0.9987	0.9988	0.9989	0.9990	0.9990	0.9991	0.9992	0.9993	0.9993	2
88	0.9994	0.9995	0.9995	0.9996	0.9996	0.9997	0.9997	0.9997	0.9998	0.9998	1
89	0.9998	0.9999	0.9999	0.9999	0.9999	1.000	1.000	1.000	1.000	1.000	0°
	°1.0	°0.9	°0.8	°0.7	°0.6	°0.5	°0.4	°0.3	°0.2	°0.1	Deg.

TABLE XXXIV.—DECIMAL EQUIVALENTS OF COMMON FRACTIONS

1/64				0.015625	33/64				0.515625
	1/32			0.03125		17/32			0.53125
3/64				0.046875	35/64				0.546875
		1/16		0.0625			9/16		0.5625
5/64				0.078125	37/64				0.578125
	3/32			0.09375		19/32			0.59375
7/64				0.109375	39/64				0.609375
			1/8	0.125				5/8	0.625
9/64				0.140625	41/64				0.640625
	5/32			0.15625		21/32			0.65625
11/64				0.171875	43/64				0.671875
		3/16		0.1875			11/16		0.6875
13/64				0.203125	45/64				0.703125
	7/32			0.21875		23/32			0.71875
15/64				0.234375	47/64				0.734375
			1/4	0.25				3/4	0.75
17/64				0.265625	49/64				0.765625
	9/32			0.28125		25/32			0.78125
19/64				0.296875	51/64				0.796875
		5/16		0.3125			13/16		0.8125
21/64				0.328125	53/64				0.828125
	11/32			0.34375		27/32			0.84375
23/64				0.359375	55/64				0.859385
			3/8	0.375				7/8	0.875
25/64				0.390625	57/64				0.890625
	13/32			0.40625		29/32			0.90625
27/64				0.421875	59/64				0.921875
		7/16		0.4375			15/16		0.9375
29/64				0.453125	61/64				0.953125
	15/32			0.46875		31/32			0.96875
31/64				0.484375	63/64				0.984375
			1/2	0.5				1	1

GLOSSARY

NOTE: Many terms, defined elsewhere in the book, are omitted from this Glossary. References to all definitions are given in the Index. Most of the following definitions are taken from ASA Standard C42—1941.

Adjustable-speed Motor.—An adjustable-speed motor is one the speed of which can be varied gradually over a considerable range, but when once adjusted remains practically unaffected by the load, such as a shunt motor with field resistance control designed for a considerable range of speed adjustment.—*From ASA.*

Adjustable-speed Motor, Base Speed of.—The base speed of an adjustable-speed motor is the lowest speed obtained at rated load and rated voltage at the temperature rise specified in the rating.—*From ASA.*

Adjustable Varying-speed Motor.—An adjustable varying-speed motor is one the speed of which can be adjusted gradually, but when once adjusted for a given load will vary in considerable degree with change in load; such as a compound-wound direct-current motor adjusted by field control or a slip-ring induction motor with rheostatic speed control.—*From ASA.*

Armature.—The armature is the part of a machine which includes the main current-carrying winding. In direct-current machines and in alternating-current commutator machines, the armature winding is connected to the commutator and the armature is the rotating member. In alternating-current machines without commutators the armature may be either the rotating member or the stationary member.

  NOTE: In some types of alternating-current machines the use of the term "armature" is apt to be misleading and should be avoided.—*From ASA.*

Armature Core.—An armature core consists of the assembled armature laminations without the slot insulation or windings.—*From ASA.*

Asynchronous Machine.—An asynchronous machine is one in which the speed of operation is not proportional to the frequency of the system to which it is connected.—*From ASA.*

Back (of a Motor or Generator).—The back of a normal motor or generator is the end which carries the coupling or driving pulley.—*From ASA.*

Bracket.—This name is sometimes used in place of *end shield*.

Breakdown Torque.—The breakdown torque of a motor is the maximum torque which it will develop with rated voltage applied at rated frequency, without an abrupt drop in speed.—*From ASA.*

  See also Fig. 19-7.

Brush.—A brush is a conductor serving to maintain electric contact between stationary and moving parts of a machine or other apparatus.—*From ASA.*

Brush Holder.—A brush holder is a device which holds the brush in position.—*From ASA.*

Brush Yoke.—A brush yoke is a rocker arm, ring, quadrant, or other adjustable support for maintaining the brush holders or brush-holder studs in their relative positions.—*From ASA.*

Capacitance.—(**Capacity**) Capacitance is that property of a system of conductors and dielectrics which permits the storage of electricity when potential differences exist between the conductors.

Its value is expressed as the ratio of a quantity of electricity to a potential difference. A capacitance value is always positive.—*From ASA*.

Capacitor (Condenser)*—A capacitor is a device, the primary purpose of which is to introduce capacitance into an electric circuit.

Capacitors are usually classified, according to their dielectrics, as air capacitors, mica capacitors, paper capacitors, etc.—*From ASA*.

Capacity.—(*a*) The capacity of a machine, apparatus, or device is the rated load.

(*b*) The capacity of a machine, apparatus, or device is the maximum load of which it is capable under existing service conditions.—*From ASA*.

Sometimes erroneously used to denote *capacitance*.

Centrifugal Starting Switch.—See Starting Switch, Centrifugal.

Collector Rings (Slip Rings).—Collector rings are metal rings suitably mounted on an electric machine serving, through stationary brushes bearing thereon, to conduct current into or out of the rotating member.—*From ASA*.

Commutating Pole (Interpole).—A commutating pole is an auxiliary pole placed between the main poles of a commutating machine. Its exciting winding carries a current proportional to the load current and produces a flux in such a direction and phase as to assist the reversal of the current in the short-circuited coil.—*From ASA*.

Commutator.—A commutator is a cylindrical ring or disc assembly of conducting members, individually insulated in a supporting structure with an exposed surface for contact with current-collecting brushes and ready for mounting on an armature shaft, quill or spider. The end opposite to the armature core is known as the front end.—*From ASA*.

Commutator Bars.—(**Commutator Segments**) Commutator bars are the metal current-carrying members of a commutator which make contact with the brushes.—*From ASA*.

Commutator Insulating Rings (Also called **V-rings**).—Commutator insulating rings are rings which constitute all the insulation between the ends of the assembled commutator bars and the supporting structure.—*From ASA*.

Commutator Insulating Strips.—(**Commutator Insulating Segments**)* Commutator insulating strips are the insulating members between adjacent commutator bars.—*From ASA*.

Compensated Repulsion Motor.—A compensated repulsion motor is a repulsion motor with an added winding to improve the power factor. This type of motor may have constant or varying-speed characteristics.—*From ASA*.

Compound-wound Motor.—A compound-wound motor is a direct-current motor which has two separate field windings—one, usually the predominating field, connected in parallel with the armature circuit, and the other connected in series with the armature circuit.—*From ASA*.

See also Art. 17-1c.

Condenser.—See Capacitor.

Conductor.—A conductor is a body so constructed from conducting material that it may be used as a carrier of electric current.—*From ASA*.

*Deprecated.

Constant-speed Motor.—A constant-speed motor is one the speed of normal operation of which is constant or practically constant. For example, a synchronous motor, an induction motor with small slip, or an ordinary direct-current shunt-wound motor.—*From ASA.*

Drip-proof Machine.—A drip-proof machine is one in which the ventilating openings are so constructed that drops of liquid or solid particles falling on the machine at any angle not greater than 15 degrees from the vertical cannot enter the machine either directly or by striking and running along a horizontal or inwardly inclined surface.—*From ASA.*

Dust-tight.—Dust-tight means so constructed that dust will not enter the enclosing case.—*From ASA.*

Duty.—Duty is a requirement of service which defines the degree of regularity of the load.—*From ASA.*

Heavy duty is often used popularly to denote an application requiring high locked-rotor torque and having high intermittent overloads. Similarly, *light duty* is often used to describe an application requiring very little locked-rotor torque and little overload capacity.

Duty, Continuous.—Continuous duty is a requirement of service that demands operation at a substantially constant load for an indefinitely long time.—*From ASA.*

Duty, Intermittent.—Intermittent duty is a requirement of service that demands operation for alternate intervals of (1) load and no-load; or (2) load and rest; or (3) load, no-load, and rest; such alternate intervals being definitely specified. —*From ASA.*

Duty, Periodic.—Periodic duty is a type of intermittent duty in which the load conditions are regularly recurrent.—*From ASA.*

Duty, Short-time.—Short-time duty is a requirement of service that demands operation at a substantially constant load for a short and definitely specified time.—*From ASA.*

Duty, Varying.—Varying duty is a requirement of service that demands operation at loads, and for intervals of time, both of which may be subject to wide variation.—*From ASA.*

Dynamotor.—A dynamotor is a machine which combines both motor and generator action in one magnetic field, either with two armatures or with one armature having two separate windings.—*From ASA.*

Efficiency.—The ratio of useful power output to the power input, *expressed in the same units.*

Efficiency, Apparent.—The ratio of the power output in watts to the total input in volt-amperes. Used in connection with a-c motors only.

Electric.†—Electric means containing, producing, arising from, actuated by, or carrying electricity, or designed to carry electricity and capable of so doing.

Examples: Electric eel, energy, motor, vehicle, wave.—*From ASA.*

Electric Motor.—An electric motor is a machine which transforms electric energy into mechanical energy.—*From ASA.*

† Some dictionaries indicate these terms as synonymous but usage in the electrical engineering field has in general been restricted to the meaning given in the definitions above. It is recognized that there are borderline cases wherein the usage determines the selection.

Electrical.†—Electrical means related to, pertaining to, or associated with electricity, but not having its properties or characteristics.

Examples: Electrical engineer, handbook, insulator, rating, school, unit.—*From ASA.*

Electrically Reversible Motor.—A motor which can be reversed by changing the external connections, even while the motor is running. If, while the motor is running at full speed in one direction, the connections are suddenly changed for the opposite direction of rotation, the motor will stop, reverse, and come up to full speed in the opposite direction. A class of service where the motor is called upon to perform this duty is often known as **plugging service.**

See also Externally Reversible Motor.   .

End Bell.—See End Shield.

End Shield.—An end shield is a shield secured to the frame and adapted to protect the windings and to support the bearing, but including no part thereof.—*From ASA.*

End-shield Assembly.—An end-shield assembly is an end shield together with its bearing sleeve and all parts associated therewith.—*From ASA.*

Explosion-proof Machine.—An explosion-proof machine is one in an enclosing case which is designed and constructed to withstand an explosion of a specified gas or dust which may occur within it, and to prevent the ignition of the specified gas or dust surrounding the machine by sparks, flashes, or explosions of the specified gas or dust, which may occur within the machine casing.—*From ASA.*

Externally Reversible Motor.—A motor so arranged that it can be connected for either direction of rotation without dismantling the motor. (Dismantling the motor means the removal of one or both end shields and/or more parts; removal of a small cover to expose the connections does not mean *dismantling*.) When connected for a definite direction of rotation, the motor must be capable of starting from rest in the desired direction of rotation; however, if the connections are suddenly changed to give the opposite direction of rotation while the motor is running, the latter will not come to a stop and then start in the opposite direction.

See also Electrically Reversible Motor.

Field Coil.—A field coil is a suitably insulated winding to be mounted on a field pole to magnetize it.—*From ASA.*

Frame.—A frame is the supporting structure for the stator parts.

In a direct-current machine the frame usually forms a part of the magnetic circuit; it includes the poles only when they form an integral part of it.—*From ASA.*

Front (of a Motor or Generator).—The front of a normal motor or generator is the end opposite the coupling or driving pulley.—*From ASA.*

General-purpose Motor.—A general-purpose motor is any motor of 200 hp or less and 450 rpm or more, having a continuous rating, and designed, listed, or offered in standard ratings for use without restriction to a particular application.—*From ASA.*

† Some dictionaries indicate these terms as synonymous but usage in the electrical engineering field has in general been restricted to the meaning given in the definitions above. It is recognized that there are borderline cases wherein the usage determines the selection.

Induction Generator.—An induction generator is an induction machine, driven above synchronous speed by an external source of mechanical power.—*From ASA.*

Induction Machine.—An induction machine is an asynchronous alternating-current machine which comprises a magnetic circuit interlinked with two electric circuits, or sets of circuits, rotating with respect to each other and in which power is transferred from one circuit to another by electro-magnetic induction. Examples of induction machines are induction motors, induction generators, and certain types of frequency converters and phase converters.—*From ASA.*

Induction Motor.—An induction motor is an induction machine which converts electric power delivered to the primary circuit into mechanical power. The secondary circuit is short-circuited or closed through a suitable circuit.—*From ASA.*

Integral Horsepower Motor.—Same as Large Power Motor (*q.v.*).

Interpole.—See Commutating Pole.

Large Power Motor.—A large power motor is a motor built in a frame having a continuous rating of 1 hp, open type, at 1700–1800 rpm, or in a larger frame.—*From ASA.*

Locked-rotor Torque (**Static Torque**).—The locked-rotor torque of a motor is the minimum torque which it will develop at rest for all angular positions of the rotor, with rated voltage applied at rated frequency.—*From ASA.*

Also called, **Starting Torque, Breakaway Torque.** See also Fig. 19-7.

Motor-generator Set.—A motor-generator set is a machine which consists of one or more motors mechanically coupled to one or more generators.—*From ASA.*

Motor Reduction Unit.—A motor reduction unit is a motor with an integral mechanical means of obtaining a speed differing from the speed of the motor.

NOTE: Motor reduction units are usually designed to obtain a speed lower than that of the motor, but may also be built to obtain a speed higher than that of the motor.—*From ASA.*

Multispeed Motor.—A multispeed motor is one which can be operated at any one of two or more definite speeds, each being practically independent of the load. For example, a direct-current motor with two armature windings, or an induction motor with windings capable of various pole groupings.—*From ASA.*

Multispeed Motor, Single-winding.—A single-winding multispeed motor is a type of multispeed motor having a single winding capable of reconnection in two or more pole groupings.—*From ASA.*

Example: consequent-pole windings (see Art. 4-30).

Open Machine.—An open machine is a self-ventilated machine having no restriction to ventilation other than that necessitated by mechanical construction.

NOTE: In the sense of this definition an open machine, when the term is used without qualification, is understood not to be splashproof or drip-proof.—*From ASA.*

Pole Shoe.—A pole shoe is the portion of a field pole facing the armature of the machine. It may be separable from the body of the pole.—*From ASA.*

-proof (used as a suffix).—Apparatus is designated as splashproof, dustproof, etc., when so constructed, protected, or treated that its successful operation is not interfered with when subjected to the specified material or condition.—*From ASA.*

Protected Machine.—(Formerly called semienclosed machine.) A protected machine is one in which all ventilating openings in the frame are protected with wire screen, expanded metal or perforated covers.

NOTE: A common form of specification for "protected machine" is "The openings shall not exceed ½ square inch (323 sq mm) in area and shall be of such shape as not to permit the passage of a rod larger than ½ inch (12.7 mm) in diameter, except where the distance of exposed live parts from the guard is more than 4 inches (101.7 mm) the openings may be ¾ square inch (484 sq mm) in area and must be of such shape as not to permit the passage of a rod larger than ¾ inch (19 mm) in diameter."—*From ASA.*

Pull-in Torque.—The pull-in torque of a synchronous motor is the maximum constant torque under which the motor will pull its connected inertia load into synchronism, at rated voltage and frequency, when its field excitation is applied.

The speed to which a motor will bring its load depends on the power required to drive it and whether the motor can pull the load into step from this speed depends on the inertia of the revolving parts, so that the pull-in torque cannot be determined without having the WR^2 as well as the torque of the load.—*From ASA.*

The term "pull-in torque" was at one time widely used in connection with single-phase induction motors to denote the maximum torque that the motor would pull through switch-operating speed. This is now called **switching torque,** and the term "pull-in torque" should be used only in connection with synchronous motors.

Pull-out Torque.—The pull-out torque of a synchronous motor is the maximum sustained torque which the motor will develop at synchronous speed for one minute, with rated voltage applied at rated frequency and with normal excitation.—*From ASA.*

Pull-out torque is often used erroneously to denote the breakdown torque of an induction motor.

Pull-up Torque.—The pull-up torque of an alternating-current motor is the minimum external torque developed by the motor during the period of acceleration from rest to the speed at which breakdown torque occurs. For motors which do not have a definite breakdown torque, the pull-up torque is the minimum torque developed up to rated speed.—*From ASA.*

See also Fig. 19-7.

Rating.—A rating of a machine, apparatus, or device is a designated limit of operating characteristics based on definite conditions.

NOTE: Such operating characteristics as load, voltage, frequency, etc., may be given in the rating.—*From ASA.*

Rating, Continuous.—Continuous rating is the rating that defines the load which can be carried for an indefinitely long time.—*From ASA.*

Rating, Short-time.—The short-time rating is the rating that defines the load which can be carried for a short and definitely specified time, the machine, apparatus, or device being at approximately room temperature at the time the load is applied.—*From ASA.*

Reactor (Reactance).*—A reactor is a device, the primary purpose of which is to introduce reactance into a circuit.—*From ASA.*

* Deprecated.

Resistance.—Resistance is the (scalar) property of an electric circuit or of any body that may be used as part of an electric circuit which determines for a given current the rate at which electric energy is converted into heat or radiant energy and which has a value such that the product of the resistance and the square of the current gives the rate of conversion of energy.

In the general case, resistance is a function of the current, but the term is most commonly used in connection with circuits where the resistance is independent of the current.—*From ASA.*

Resistance Box.—A resistance box is a rheostat consisting of an assembly of resistors of definite values so arranged that the resistance of the circuit in which it is connected may be changed by known amounts.—*From ASA.*

-resistant (used as a suffix).—Apparatus is designated as moisture-resistant, fume-resistant, etc., when so constructed, protected, or treated that it will not be injured readily when subjected to the specified material or condition.—*From ASA.*

Resistor (Resistance).*—A resistor is a device, the primary purpose of which is to introduce resistance into an electric circuit.—*From ASA.*

Resistor, Adjustable.—An adjustable resistor is a resistor so constructed that its resistance can be readily changed.—*From ASA.*

Reversible Motor.—A motor capable of being operated in either direction of rotation.

See also Externally Reversible Motor, Electrically Reversible Motor.

Rheostat.—A rheostat is an adjustable resistor so constructed that its resistance may be changed without opening the circuit in which it may be connected.—*From ASA.*

Rotor.—A rotor is the rotating member of a machine.—*From ASA.*

Salient Pole.—A salient pole is that type of field pole which projects toward the armature.—*From ASA.*

Self-ventilated Machine.—A self-ventilated machine is one which has its ventilating air circulated by means integral with the machine.—*From ASA.*

Semiprotected Machine.—A semiprotected machine is one in which part of the ventilating openings in the frame, usually in the top half, are protected as in the case of a "protected machine" but the others are left open.—*From ASA.*

Separately Ventilated Machine.—A separately ventilated machine is one which has its ventilating air supplied by an independent fan or blower external to the machine.—*From ASA.*

Series-wound Motor.—A series-wound motor is a commutator motor in which the field circuit and armature circuit are connected in series.—*From ASA.*

See also Art. 17-1*b*.

Shell-type Motor.—A shell-type motor consists of a stator and rotor without shaft, end shields, bearings, or conventional frame. Separate fans or fans larger than the rotor are not included.—*From ASA.*

Short-circuiter, Automatic.—An automatic short-circuiter is a device designed to automatically short-circuit the commutator bars in some forms of single-phase commutator motors.—*From ASA.*

Shunt-wound Motor.—A shunt-wound motor is a direct-current motor in which the field circuit and armature circuit are connected in parallel.—*From ASA.*

See also Art. 17-1*a*.

* Deprecated.

Slip Rings.—See Collector Rings.

Special-purpose Motor.—A special-purpose motor is an industrial power motor specifically designated and listed for a particular power application where the load requirements and duty cycle are definitely known.—*From ASA.*

Splashproof Machine.—A splashproof machine is one in which the ventilating openings are so constructed that drops of liquid or solid particles falling on the machine or coming toward it in a straight line at any angle not greater than 100 degrees from the verticle cannot enter the machine either directly or by striking and running along a surface.—*From ASA.*

Squirrel-cage Induction Motor.—A squirrel-cage induction motor is one in which the secondary circuit consists of a squirrel-cage winding suitably disposed in slots in the secondary core.—*From ASA.*

Squirrel-cage Winding.—A squirrel-cage winding is a permanently short-circuited winding, usually uninsulated (chiefly used in induction machines), having its conductors uniformly distributed around the periphery of the machine and joined by continuous end rings.—*From ASA.*

Stabilized Shunt-wound Motor.—A stabilized shunt-wound motor is a shunt-wound motor having a light series winding added to prevent a rise in speed or to obtain a slight reduction in speed, with increase of load.—*From ASA.*

Starting Switch, Centrifugal.—A centrifugal starting switch is a centrifugally operated automatic mechanism usually used in connection with split-phase induction motors to open or disconnect the starting winding after the rotor has attained a predetermined speed, and to close or reconnect it prior to the time the rotor comes to rest.—*From ASA.*

Starting Torque.—See Locked-rotor torque.

Stator.—The stator is the portion of a machine which contains the stationary parts of the magnetic circuit with their associated windings.—*From ASA.*

Submersible.—Submersible means so constructed that it will operate successfully when submerged in water under specified conditions of pressure and time.—*From ASA.*

Switching Torque.—The switching torque of a motor having an automatic connection change during the starting period is the minimum external torque developed by the motor as it accelerates through switch operating speed.

NOTE: It should be noted that if the torque on the starting connection is never less than the switching torque, the pull-up torque is identical with the switching torque; however, if the torque on the starting connection falls below the switching torque at some speed below switch operating speed, the pull-up and switching torques are not identical.—*From ASA.*

See also Fig. 19-7.

Synchronous Induction Motor.—A synchronous induction motor is a wound-rotor induction motor to which direct-current excitation is supplied when it approaches rated speed, enabling it to start as an induction motor and operate as a synchronous motor.—*From ASA.*

Synchronous Machine.—A synchronous machine is one in which the average speed of normal operation is exactly proportional to the frequency of the system to which it is connected.—*From ASA.*

Synchronous Motor.—A synchronous motor is a synchronous machine which transforms electric power from an alternating-current system into mechanical power. Synchronous motors usually have direct-current field excitation.—*From ASA.*

Small synchronous motors rarely use d-c excitation (see Art. 15-2).

Thermocouple Thermometer (Thermocouple).—A thermocouple thermometer is a device for measuring temperature which depends upon the variation of the contact electromotive force between two different metals or alloys with temperature.

A thermocouple consists of a conductor of one metal or alloy which has attached to each end a conductor of a second metal or alloy for connecting to a measuring instrument, the arrangement being such that one of the junctions between the metals can be placed at the point where the temperature is to be measured and the second junction kept at a known temperature.—*From ASA,*

-tight (used as a suffix).—Apparatus is designated as watertight, dust-tight, etc., when so constructed that the enclosing case will exclude the specified material.—*From ASA.*

Torque.—A force which produces, or tends to produce, rotation. Common units of measurement of torque are pound-feet, pound-inches, ounce-feet, and ounce-inches. A force of one pound applied to the handle of a crank, the center of which is displaced one foot from the center of the shaft, produces a torque of one pound-foot on the shaft, provided the force is applied perpendicular to, and not along, the crank.

Totally Enclosed Machine.—A totally enclosed machine is one so enclosed as to prevent exchange of air between the inside and the outside of the case, but not sufficiently enclosed to be termed "airtight."—*From ASA.*

Varying-speed Motor.—A varying-speed motor is one the speed of which varies with the load, ordinarily decreasing when the load increases; such as a series motor or an induction motor with large slip.—*From ASA.*

See also Adjustable Varying-speed Motor.

V-rings.—See Commutator Insulating Rings.

Watertight Machine.—A watertight machine is a totally enclosed machine so constructed that it will exclude water applied in the form of a stream from a hose.

NOTE: A common form of specification for a totally enclosed machine is "A stream of water from a hose (not less than 1 inch in diameter) under a head of 35 feet and from a distance of about 10 feet can be played on the machine without leakage, except that leakage which may occur around the shaft may be considered permissible, provided it is prevented from entering the oil reservoir and provision is made for automatically draining the machine."

The machine may be provided with a check valve for drainage or a tapped hole at the lowest part of the frame which will serve for application of drain pipe or drain plug.—*From ASA.*

Wound-rotor Induction Motor.—A wound rotor induction motor is an induction motor in which the secondary circuit consists of a polyphase winding or coils whose terminals are either short-circuited or closed through suitable circuits.—*From ASA.*

LIST OF VISUAL AIDS

The following list of visual materials may be used to supplement some of the material in this book. It is suggested that each film and filmstrip be previewed before it is used.

These films and filmstrips may be obtained from the producer or distributor listed with each title. (The addresses of these producers and distributors are given at the end of this listing.) In many cases these materials may be obtained from your local film library or local film distributor; also, many universities have large film libraries from which they may be borrowed.

The running time (min), whether it is silent (si) or sound (sd), and whether it is a motion picture (MP) or filmstrip (FS) are listed with each title. All of the motion pictures are 16mm; filmstrips are 35mm.

Each film and filmstrip has been listed only once in connection with the chapter to which it is most applicable. However, in many cases these materials may be used advantageously in connection with other chapters.

Chapter I—The Story Behind the Nameplate

Electricity (SVE FS). Illustrates electrical principles and operations; covers condensers, dry cells, storage cells, electrical units, Ohm's Law, resistance, fuses, and generators.

Magnetic Effects of Electricity (EBF 15min si MP). Presents the electromagnet, the electric bell, the ammeter, the theory of permanent magnetism; uses the voltmeter to explain magnetism and magnetic induction.

Elements of Electric Circuits (EBF 11min sd MP). Depicts the flow of electrons, resistance and the ohm, current and ampere, electromotive force, Ohm's Law.

Alternating Current (Army FS). An introduction to the principles of alternating current; demonstrates and explains Lenz's law, simple wave alternator; discusses frequency, effective value, voltage-current time relationship, and power.

Single-phase and Polyphase Circuits (USOE 17min sd MP). Explains a single-phase synchronous generator, the use of sine curves to illustrate flow changes, a two-phase system and three-phase system; ways to simplify wiring in the two-phase and three-phase systems.

Alternating Current (JH FS).   Illustrates inductance, capacitance, and impedance in a circuit—transformers and rectifiers.

Chapter II—What Makes an Induction Motor Run?

Magnetism (JH FS).   Describes the general properties and laws of magnets; magnetic effects; natural and artificial magnets; polarity and laws of magnetic attraction; magnetic fields; the compass; magnetic induction; theory of magnetism; magnetic materials.

Magnetism (SVE FS).   Explains magnetism, furnishing historical background; presents the theory of magnetism; defines lines of force and magnetic fields.

Rotating Magnetic Fields (USOE 10min sd MP).   Explains a rotating magnetic field pattern; traces the three-phase winding in a demonstration stator; shows the factors that cause rotation of the magnetic field; construction of polyphase motors.

Squirrel-cage Rotor Principles (USOE 10min sd MP).   Explains the fundamental law of magnetism; fundamental law of induced emf; electron flow in squirrel-cage rotor setting up magnetic poles which create torque, and construction of squirrel-cage rotors.

Chapter III—Single-phase Motor Windings and Connections

Small Split-phase Motor Stator Winding with Enameled Wire (Westinghouse 12min si MP).   Shows operation in detail.

Stator Coil Winding by Machine (Westinghouse 8min si MP). Describes five methods of high speed stator coil winding by machine.

Chapter IV—Split-phase Motors

Split-phase Motor Principles (USOE 17min ds MP).   Explains the construction of stator and rotor; comparison of winding resistances and inductive reactances; use of capacitor to produce phase displacement.

Split-phase Motor : Rewinding (USOE 28min sd MP).   Shows how to test a split-phase motor for electrical and mechanical faults; how to record data necessary for accurate rewinding; how to dismantle a split-phase motor and strip the stator; how to rewind the stator by hand or by using a winding gun; how to form and install skein windings; how to insulate, lace, dip, and bake the stator; how to assemble, lubricate, and test the stator.

Assembly of Small Split-phase Motors (Westinghouse 12min si MP).   Shows complete assembly of small split-phase type of motor.

Chapter V—Capacitor-start Motors

Capacitance (Navy 31min sd MP).   Demonstrates the flow of electrons through a circuit; shows the charging and discharging of condensers; variations of charge on a condenser in relation to time and behavior of capacitance with alternating current.

Chapters X and XI—Repulsion-type Motors

Repulsion Motor Principles (USOE 18min sd MP). Explains construction of repulsion motor; rotor circuits and brush position; short-circuiting and brush-lifting mechanisms; applications of repulsion motors.

Repulsion Motors Type SCR (GE FS). Explains characteristics of the type SCR which is used in single-phase circuits.

Repulsion Induction Motor—General Overhaul (USOE 25min sd MP). Shows how to check a repulsion induction motor for electrical and mechanical faults; dismantle a repulsion induction motor; remove a damaged coil, wind and insulate new coil; assemble and lubricate repulsion induction motor.

Chapter XIV—Polyphase Induction Motors

Three-phase Motor, Part I: Preparing to Rewind (USOE 17min sd MP). Shows how to interpret and record nameplate data of a three-phase motor; identify the line leads and finish leads; remove coils and determine coil span; use a coil winding machine; end-tape machine-wound coils.

Three-phase Motor, Part II: Rewinding (USOE 17min sd MP). Shows how to insert mush coils; insert separators or "willies"; fold, trim, and wedge slot insulation; insert phase insulation; and make a delta connection.

Three-phase Stator Winding (Westinghouse 16min si MP). Describes three-phase motor stator winding operations.

Underground Raindrops (US Electrical Motors 40min sd MP). Shows the latest manufacturing methods related to production of electric motors; includes machine winding and treatment of motors.

Chapter XVII—Direct-current Motors

Direct-current Controllers (USOE 15min sd MP). Shows shunt motors and d-c controllers in operation; a d-c faceplate controller connected to a shunt motor.

D.C. Motor, Part I: Mechanical Overhaul (USOE 20min sd MP). Shows how to test for electrical and mechanical faults; dismantle d-c motor; turn the commutator; repair and replace field coils; assemble the motor; and adjust and make final tests.

D.C. Motor, Part II: Rewinding (USOE 37min sd MP). Shows how to dismantle and clean an armature core; determine commutator pitch; reinsulate the core; how to insert coils; band and armature; shape coil ends; lay in and solder leads; balance the armature; impregnate the armature; and turn a commutator.

Electric Motors (JH FS). Portrays principles of the motor; d-c and a-c motors; universal motors.

Chapter XIX—Testing Fractional Horsepower Motors

Electrical Measurement (DeVry 60min si MP). Describes the construction and operation of electrical instruments; needs of different measuring quantities.

Electric Meters (JH FS). Construction and operation of various types of meter for electrical use.

Alternating-current Voltmeters and Ammeters (SVE FS). Demonstrates principles on which a-c meters work; principles of ammeters and voltmeters and their parts; other types of a-c meters including the oscilloscope.

Principles of Electrical Measurement (DeVry 22min sd MP) Construction and operation of electrical instruments; explains operation of number of electrical measuring devices.

SOURCES OF FILMS LISTED ABOVE

Army—U. S. Army (Obtainable from Castle Films)

Castle Films, 30 Rockefeller Plaza, New York 20

DeVry Films, 1111 Armitage Ave., Chicago 14

EBF—Encyclopaedia Britannica Films, Inc., 20 N. Wacker Dr Chicago 6

GE—General Electric Co., Visual Instruction Section, 1 River Rd. Schenectady, N. Y.

JH—Jam Handy Organization, 2821 S. Grand Blvd., Detroit 11, Mich

Navy—U. S. Navy (Obtainable from Castle Films)

SVE—Society for Visual Education, 100 E. Ohio St., Chicago 11

U. S. Electrical Motors, 1500 S. Western Ave., Chicago

USOE—U. S. Office of Education (Obtainable from Castle Films)

Westinghouse Electric Corp., 306 Fourth Ave., Pittsburgh 30, Pa.

INDEX

A

Adjustable speed motor, base speed of, 525
definition of, 525
Adjustable-varying-speed motor, definition of, 525
Advance Electric Co., 4
"Air over," on nameplate, 23, 25
Alger, P. L., 43, 453
All-purpose capacitor motor for unit heaters, 191
Alliance Mfg. Co., 4
Alternating current (a-c), 2
nature of, 2
Alternating current systems, 20
A-c wave, effective value of, 20
peak value of, 20
Alternation, 2
Alternations per minute, 17
American Institute of Electrical Engineers (A.I.E.E.) Test Codes, 484
A.I.E.E. Transactions, 42, 43, 115, 164, 183, 223, 255, 265, 296, 314, 371, 389, 453, 508
American Society of Refrigerating Engineers, 508
American Standards Association, 69, 105, 115, 232, 354, 356, 361, 397, 414, 525–533
Ampere-conductors, 45
Amperes, 19
a-c, definition of, 19
maximum, or peak, value, 20
root-mean-square value, 20
d-c, definition of, 19
measurement of, 456
values of, at full load, for polyphase motors, 505
for single-phase induction motors, 504

Appleman, W. R., 453
Application tests, 481
for determination of power requirements, 481, 488
for determination of torque requirements, 483
Armature, definition of, 525
Armature connection diagrams, 235
(*See also* Armature windings)
Armature core, definition of, 525
Armature reaction, 395
Armature windings, 234, 284, 409
back-lead, 286, 287
with three bars per slot, 410
checking the rewound armature, 244
commutator refinishing, 288
d-c motors, 409
duplex, 243
front-lead, 284, 285
with three bars per slot, 286
lap, 234, 409
brush arms, number of, 237
coil connections to commutator, 235
how to lay out, 236
cross-connected, 237
position of brushes at neutral, 235
points to note before stripping armature, 244
in repulsion-type motors, 234
resistances, of measurement of, 469
reversed coils, checking for, 245
simplex, 234, 238
in universal motors, 284
wave, 238, 411
brush arms, number of, 242
circuits, number of, 242
coil connections to commutator, 240
how to lay out, 241
commutator throw, 239